Hydrological applications of remote sensing and remote data transmission

TITLES RECENTLY PUBLISHED BY IAHS

Erosion and Sediment Transport Measurement. Proceedings of the Florence Symposium, June 1981
Publ. no. 133 (1981), price $20

Proceedings of the symposia held during the First IAHS Scientific General Assembly, Exeter, July 1982

Advances in Hydrometry
Publ. no. 134, price $30

Optimal Allocation of Water Resources
Publ. no. 135, price $35

Improvement of Methods of Long Term Prediction of Variations in Groundwater Resources and Regimes Due to Human Activity
Publ. no. 136, price $30

Recent Developments in the Explanation and Prediction of Erosion and Sediment Yield
Publ. no. 137, price $35

Hydrological Aspects of Alpine and High-Mountain Areas
Publ. no. 138, price $30

Effect of Waste Disposal on Groundwater and Surface Water
Publ. no. 139, price $30

Hydrology of Humid Tropical Regions. Proceedings of the Hamburg Symposium, August 1983
Publ. no. 140 (1983), price $37

Dissolved Loads of Rivers and Surface Water Quantity/Quality Relationships. Proceedings of the Hamburg Symposium, August 1983
Publ. no. 141 (1983), price $37

Ground Water in Water Resources Planning, volumes I and II. Proceedings of the Koblenz Symposium, August–September 1983
Publ. no. 142 (1983), price $22

World Catalogue of Maximum Observed Floods
Publ. no. 143 (1984), price $30

Challenges in African Hydrology and Water Resources. Proceedings of the Harare Symposium, July 1984
Publ. no. 144 (1984), price $48

Hydrological Applications of Remote Sensing and Remote Data Transmission. Proceedings of the Hamburg Symposium, August 1983
Publ. no. 145 (1985), price $48

Relation of Groundwater Quantity and Quality. Proceedings of the Hamburg Symposium, August 1983
Publ. no. 146 (1985), price $30

Scientific Procedures Applied to the Planning, Design and Management of Water Resources Systems. Proceedings of the Hamburg Symposium, August 1983
Publ. no. 147 (1985), price $48

New Approaches in Water Balance Computations. Proceedings of the Hamburg Workshop, August 1983
Publ. no. 148 (1985), price $20

Techniques for Prediction of Runoff from Glacierized Areas
Publ. no. 149 (1985), price $18

Hydrochemical Balances of Fresh Water Systems. Proceedings of the Uppsala Symposium
Publ. no. 150 (1984), price $44

Scientific Basis for Water Resources Management. Proceedings of the Jerusalem Symposium, September 1985
Publ. no. 153 (1985), price $42

Hydrogeology in the Service of Man, volumes 1-4. Proceedings of the IAH/IAHS Cambridge Symposium, September 1985
Publ. no. 154 (1985), price $40 the set

PLEASE SEND ORDERS TO:

Office of the Treasurer IAHS
2000 Florida Avenue, NW
Washington, DC 20009, USA

IUGG Publications Office
39 ter Rue Gay Lussac
75005 Paris, France

IAHS Editorial Office
Institute of Hydrology
Wallingford, Oxon OX10 8BB, UK

HYDROLOGICAL APPLICATIONS OF REMOTE SENSING AND REMOTE DATA TRANSMISSION

Edited by
B. E. Goodison
Atmospheric Environment Service,
4905 Dufferin Street, Downsview,
Ontario, Canada M3H 5T4

Proceedings of a symposium held during the XVIIIth General Assembly of the International Union of Geodesy and Geophysics at Hamburg, FR Germany, August 1983. This symposium was organized by the IAHS International Committee on Remote Sensing and Data Transmission, and cosponsored by WMO and UNESCO

IAHS Publication No. 145

Published by the International Association of Hydrological Sciences 1985.
IAHS Press, Institute of Hydrology, Wallingford, Oxfordshire OX10 8BB, UK.
IAHS Publication No. 145.
ISBN ~~0-947571-20-5.~~
0947571205

ACKNOWLEDGEMENTS
The success of the Symposium and of the Proceedings is the result of dedicated efforts by many people. The efforts of the Programme Organizing Committee, consisting of all officers of ICRSDT and Arthur Askew of WMO is greatly appreciated. All papers were reviewed by several reviewers for scientific and technical merit, and their assistance is especially appreciated. The cooperating organizations - WMO, UNESCO, the International Association of Hydrogeologists and the International Society of Photogrammetry and Remote Sensing - were helpful in many ways and their assistance is gratefully acknowledged. Finally the Proceedings would not have been possible without the assistance of the IAHS Editorial Office, particularly Penny Kisby and her assistants - Sandra Smith, Jo Roberts and Sue Beresford; and in many cases the French would have been far from perfect without the tremendous help given by Dr J.A.Rodier in checking/translating the titles, abstracts and Preface.

The camera-ready copy for this publication was produced at the IAHS Press, Institute of Hydrology, Wallingford, Oxfordshire OX10 8BB, UK.

Preface

The papers presented in this publication were prepared originally for presentation at the Symposium on Hydrological Applications of Remote Sensing and Remote Data Transmission, convened during 18-25 August 1983 at Hamburg, FR Germany. Held as part of the XVIIIth General Assembly of the International Union of Geodesy and Geophysics, the Symposium was organized by the International Committee on Remote Sensing and Data Transmission (ICRSDT) of the International Association of Hydrological Sciences (IAHS). The United Nations Educational, Scientific, and Cultural Organization (UNESCO), the World Meteorological Organization (WMO), the International Association of Hydrogeologists, and the International Society of Photogrammetry and Remote Sensing were cooperating organizations.

A total of 106 papers were accepted for presentation in 19 oral and three poster paper sessions. Authors from 22 countries were represented on the programme which covered descriptions of instrumentation and applications of remote data transmission and applications of many different remote sensing techniques as related to all phases of the hydrological cycle. After review, approximately 60% of the papers were accepted for publication in this Proceedings.

The highlights of the opening day of the Symposium are provided in papers on existing and future satellite systems. Organized by WMO and chaired by their representative, J.Němec of Geneva, the papers were selected to identify the basic facilities to be available for hydrological purposes in the next decade or two. Both the space and ground segments of the satellite systems are covered in these papers. Details of the facilities are presented on behalf of the satellite operators in the USA, USSR, Europe, Japan, India, France and Canada.

The United States' systems with hydrological applications will continue to use both polar-orbiting satellites (meteorological and earth observing) and geostationary satellites. The main new development will focus on the microwave remote sensing of soil moisture, snow depth, snow water equivalent and rainfall. The importance of having a functioning Landsat satellite with its thematic mapper was emphasized by the attendees during the Symposium. The USSR reported the use of the satellite system "Meteor-Priroda" (Meteor-Nature) for remote sensing of regimes of water bodies and large-scale surveys of basins. These will use microwave measurements in what are basically research-oriented programmes. The French satellite systems will continue to include the Argos data transmission system on the TIROS-N satellite. A new French satellite system, very useful for hydrological applications, will be SPOT. Belgium and Sweden will cooperate in this programme. Four satellites are planned for an 8-10 year period starting in 1985. Their resolution will be 10 and 20 m in panchromatic and multispectral modes, respectively.

Japan intends to develop, in addition to its geostationary satellite GMS 2 (HIMAWARI-2), marine and land observation satellites using microwave measurement instruments such as microwave altimeters, scatterometers and synthetic aperture radar (SAR). India reported the launch of INSAT 1B to be used for very high resolution radiometer measurements and for data transmission from data collection platforms. The planned Canadian satellite systems with hydrological applications are RADARSAT, a polar-orbiting satellite with a synthetic aperture steerable radar, and MSAT (Mobile Satellite), a proposed system to provide data transmission to and from mobile (or fixed) ground stations.

An interesting discussion during the Symposium provided a consensus that the most promising future developments will be the launching of the French system SPOT and the use of microwave observational facilities. It was also agreed that one problem yet to be solved is how to ensure that remotely-sensed data are more readily accessible. The need for continuity of programmes was recognized as the one basic requirement for the application of satellite remote sensing and data transmission to operational hydrology.

The session on remote data transmission provided an excellent overview of various systems being used worldwide. A discussion of the data collection systems of the US National Oceanic and Atmospheric Administration, of the hydrological data collection and processing system of the US Geological Survey and recent efforts in the Amazon basin focus on the GOES system. Canadian efforts to specify and document their particular requirements for a variety of hydrometeorological parameters (including ranges and response times) telemetered by the GOES satellite are discussed. Experience on using Argos in Africa, Europe, North and South America, Sweden and Greenland is outlined in three separate papers. The basic elements of the METEOSAT system are discussed including the cost-benefits of retransmitting data via WEFAX from Darmstadt, FR Germany, to the UK. In many countries, other methods are in use. Radio telemetry is described in India, China and the Southern Hemisphere. Use of meteor-burst telemetry in the USA was shown to be effective. For the interchange of data from auto-stations the use of the Standard Hydrologic Exchange Format (SHEF) is described. Finally, at the international level, the HOMS system, which is the WMO-sponsored programme is discussed in relation to data retransmission.

An extensive overview of remote sensing applications related to precipitation, snow and ice, surface water, soil moisture, groundwater, wetlands and hydrological modelling, and water planning and management complements the discussion of the data transmission papers. For precipitation, considerable progress is shown to have been achieved during recent years, yet there is still a lot of research to be done. In particular, the potential for the use of combined information of satellite data from different channels is not yet well enough explored, as are the theoretical possibilities for the development of mathematical models transforming remote sensing data into precipitation data. Other papers deal with the use of ARAMIS, the French weather radar network, use of radar data for flood forecasting and satellite data for precipitation estimation. Geostationary satellites (e.g. GOES, METEOSAT) are used in this field as well as polar-orbiting satellites (e.g. NOAA, TIROS-N). During the Symposium, the session chairman, G.Schultz, mentioned several critical points related to precipitation estimation. Colleagues were urged not to raise unfounded expectations about such techniques. Since it became clear from discussions that no satellites can be expected in the near future to produce much better information for hydrometeorological purposes, it becomes necessary to exploit the available information to the maximum degree. This implies a more intense use of the available data and the development of better and more efficient mathematical models.

An overview of progress in snow and ice applications is provided by A.Rango. He shows that satellite-derived data on snow cover, when used as input to hydrological forecasting models, has proved to increase the accuracy of predictions of streamflow. It was noted that some techniques for snow-mapping based on digital satellite data are ready for operational applications. A paper on the potential for monitoring snowpack characteristics using active and passive microwave sensors reports that areal extent of snow cover can be mapped with passive microwave data from the NIMBUS-7 satellite with an accuracy of less than 3% on large-scale mapping and that a spatial resolution of 5-10 km may be realistic. Papers on the use of airborne gamma-ray spectrometry for snow surveying discuss the operational use in the USSR and Sweden. Use of remote sensing for snow and ice applications seems to be the most extensive and one of the more successful applications in hydrology. Reports on studies in China, USSR, Japan, India, Greenland and the USA support this view.

V.V.Kuprianov provides an overview of surface water applications and M.Vauclin introduces the session on soil moisture, groundwater and wetlands. Applications vary from studying flood plain inundations (USSR), variations in lake level regimes (China), to monitoring sedimentation in the Aswan High Dam Reservoir. The use of passive microwave sensors for determining soil moisture is the focus of two papers.

The last section of remote sensing papers is on more general applications which relate to hydrological modelling, water planning and management. Hydrological research within the US AgRISTARS programme, particularly that relating to soil moisture and snow cover studies is described. Use of remote sensing in hydrological models was discussed in several papers which review experiences in the USA, Canada and France. This subject is one which is critical for future developments in hydrology and it was decided that it should be the subject of a separate workshop which would be sponsored by IAHS and WMO.

The International Committee on Remote Sensing and Data Transmission of IAHS is pleased to have organized this Symposium. It is hoped that these papers will provide hydrologists, water resource managers and others with basic information on the potential application of remote sensing and remote data transmission in their work.

A.IVAN JOHNSON
7474 Upham Court, Arvada, Colorado 80003, USA
Symposium Convenor and President ICRSDT

F.GUNNEBERG
Bundesanstalt für Gewasserkunde, Pf 509, D-5400 Koblenz, FR Germany
Symposium Co-convenor

Préface

Les communications que l'on trouvera dans cette publication ont été préparées à l'origine pour être présentées au Colloque sur les Applications Hydrologiques de la Télédétection et de la Télétransmission, qui a eu lieu du 18 au 25 août 1983 à Hambourg, Allemagne fédérale. Il a été tenu comme une des manifestations de la XVIIIe Assemblée Générale de l'Union Internationale de Géodésie et de Géophysique et a été organisé par le Comité International sur la Télédétection et la Télétransmission (CITT) de l'Association Internationale des Sciences Hydrologiques (AISH), l'Organisation des Nations Unies pour l'Education, la Science et la Culture (UNESCO), l'Organisation Météorologique Mondiale (OMM), l'Association Internationale des Hydrogéologues et la Société Internationale de Photogrammétrie et de Télédétection ont coopéré à la préparation de cette réunion.

Au total 106 communications ont été acceptées pour être présentées soit oralement dans 19 sessions ordinaires, soit dans trois sessions de posters. Les auteurs de 22 pays ont été représentés dans le programme qui couvrait la description des instruments et des applications de la télétransmission et les applications d'un bon nombre de techniques de télédétection relatives à toutes les phases du cycle hydrologique. Après avoir passé en revue toutes les communications, on a accepté environs 60% d'entre elles pour être publiées dans ces comptes rendus.

Le point culminant du jour d'ouverture du colloque a été la présentation de communications sur les systèmes de satellites actuels et futurs. A cette session organisée par l'OMM et présidée par son représentant J.Němec, de Genève, les communications avaient été choisies pour identifier les moyens de base qui seraient disponibles à des fins hydrologiques dans la prochaine ou les deux prochaines décennies. Ces communications couvraient à la fois les parties des activités spatiales et au sol des systèmes de satellites. Des détails sur ces équipements sont présentés au nom des responsables de ces satellites aux Etats Unis, en URSS, en Europe, au Japon, dans l'Inde, en France et au Canada.

Les systèmes de Etats Unis pour applications hydrologiques continueront à utiliser à la fois des satellites à orbite polaire (météorologiques et pour observations terrestres) et des satellites géostationnaires. Les principaux progrès seront centrés sur la télédétection par micro-ondes de l'humidité du sol, de l'épaisseur de la neige, de l'équivalent en eau de la neige et des précipitations. L'importance qu'il y a à disposer d'un satellite Landsat avec cartographie thématique a été soulignée par les participants à ce colloque. L'URSS a présenté un rapport sur le système de satellite "Météor-Priroda" (Météor-Nature) pour la télédétection des régimes des cours d'eau et des lacs et l'étude sur une grande échelle des bassins. Ce système utilisera des mesures par micro-ondes dans des programmes qui seront fondamentalement orientés vers la recherche. Les systèmes de satellites français comprendront, comme actuellement, le système de transmission de données Argos à partir des observations du satellite Tiros N. Un nouveau système de satellite français très utile pour les applications hydrologiques sera SPOT, la Belgique et la Suède, coopèreront à ce programme. Quatre satellites sont prévus pour une période de 8 à 10 ans commençant en 1985. Leur pouvoir de résolution sera respectivement de 10 m et de 20 m dans les analyses panchromatiques et multispectrales.

Le Japon a l'intention de mettre au point, en plus de son satellite géostationnaire GMS 2 (HIMAWARI-2) des satellites d'observations marines et terrestres utilisant des instruments de mesure à micro-ondes tels que les altimètres à micro-ondes, des scatteromètres et un radar à ouverture synthétique (SAR). L'Inde a présenté un rapport sur le lancement de INSAT 1B qui sera utilisé pour des mesures par radiomètre à très haut pouvoir de résolution et pour la télétransmission de données provenant de plate formes de collectes de données. Le Canada a projeté des systèmes de satellites avec applications à l'hydrologie: RADARSAT satellite à orbite polaire avec radar à ouverture synthétique dirigée et MSAT (Satellite Mobile), un système que l'on propose pour la télétransmission vers et à partir de stations au sol, mobiles (ou stationnaires).

Au cours d'une intéressante discussion pendant ce colloque, on est arrivé à un consensus sur le fait que les progrès futurs les plus prometteurs seront: le lancement du système français SPOT et l'utilisation des dispositifs d'observations par micro-ondes. On a été également d'accord pour reconnaître qu'un problème encore à résoudre est le moyen d'assurer un accès plus facile aux données obtenues par télédétection. On a reconnu également la nécessité de la continuité des programmes pour faire face aux besoins fondamentaux de l'application de la télédétection par satellite et de la télétransmission à l'hydrologie opérationnelle.

La session sur la télétransmission a fourni une excellente série des divers systèmes utilisés à travers le monde. Une discussion sur les systèmes de collectes de données de l'Administration Nationale Océanique et Atmosphérique des Etats Unis (NOAA), du système de collecte et de traitement des données hydrologiques du Geological Survey des Etats Unis et les récents travaux dans le bassin de l'Amazone, s'est concentrée sur le système GOES. Les discussions ont également porté sur les efforts du Canada en vue de spécifier et de préciser leurs besoins particuliers pour un ensemble très varié de paramètres hydrologiques (y compris les ordres de grandeur et les temps de réponse) faisant l'objet de télémesures par le satellite GOES. L'expérience obtenue avec l'utilisation d'Argos en Afrique, en Europe, en Amérique du Nord et du Sud, en Suède et au Groenland est présentée brièvement dans trois communications. On a étudié les éléments de base du système METEOSAT y compris le bilan coût-bénéfice de la retransmission des données par WEFAX à partir de Darmstadt, République d'Allemagne Fédérale, vers le Royaume Uni. Dans de nombreux pays, on utilise d'autres méthodes. La radiotélémesure est décrite en Inde, en Chine et dans l'hemisphère austral. On a montré que l'utilisation de la "meteor burst" télémétrie était efficace aux Etats Unis. On a décrit également l'utilisation du "Standard Hydrologic Exchange Formats" (SHEF) pour l'échange de données provenant de stations automatiques. Enfin on a discuté, au niveau international et en relation avec la télétransmission du système

SHOFM, programme qui à l'appui de l'OMM.

Une revue extensive des applications de la télédétection aux précipitations, aux neiges et glaces, aux eaux de surface, à l'humidité du sol, aux eaux souterraines, à la mise en modèle des phénomènes hydrologiques, et de ceux qu'on observe dans les régions humides et à la planification et la gestion des ressources en eau, a complété la discussion des communications sur la télétransmission. Pour les précipitations on a montré que des progrès très importants avaient été accomplis au cours des derrières années, cependant il reste encore beaucoup de recherches à faire. En particulier on n'a pas encore bien exploré les potentialités de l'utilisation d'informations combinées des données de satellites provenant de différents canaux, de même que les possibilités théoriques de mise au point de modèles mathématiques transformant les données de la télédétection en chiffres de hauteurs de précipitations. D'autres communications traitent de l'emploi de ARAMIS, le réseau de radars météorologiques français, l'utilisation des données des radars pour la prévision des crues et des données des satellites pour l'estimation des précipitations. Les satellites géostationnaires (à savoir GOES, METEOSAT) sont utilisés dans ce domaine aussi bien que les satellites à orbite polaire (à savoir NOAA, TIROS-N). Au cours de ce colloque le président de session, G.Schultz, a mentionné plusieurs points critiques relatifs à l'estimation des précipitations. Il a insisté auprès des participants pour éviter des espoirs non fondés sur de telles techniques. Puisque la discussion a montré clairement qu'on ne pouvait s'attendre dans le proche futur à trouver un satellite qui produise des informations à des fins hydrologiques très supérieures à celles que l'on obtient actuellement, il devient nécessaire d'exploiter au maximum les informations disponibles. Ceci implique un usage plus intense des données disponibles et la mise au point de modèles mathématiques meilleurs et plus efficaces.

A.Rango a fourni une revue des progrès effectués dans les applications aux neiges et glaces. Il montre que les données sur la couverture neigeuse provenant des satellites, lorsqu'elles sont utilisées comme entrées dans les modèles hydrologiques de prévision augmentent l'exactitude des prévisions des débits. On a noté que certaines méthodes pour la cartographie de la neige basées sur les données digitales des satellites sont maintenant prêtes pour les applications opérationnelles. Une communication sur les potentialités de surveillance des caractéristiques de la couverture neigeuse par l'emploi de senseurs à micro-ondes actives et passives montre que l'extension spatiale de cette couverture neigeuse peut être cartographiée avec les données des micro-ondes passives provenant du satellite NIMBUS 7 avec une précision de moins de 3% pour les cartes à petite échelle et qu'une résolution partielle de 5 à 10 km est réaliste. D'autres communications sur l'emploi de la spectrométrie à rayons gamma à partir d'avions pour la surveillance de la neige discutent des applications opérationnelles en URSS et en Suède. l'utilisation de la télédétection pour les applications concernant les neiges et glaces semble être la plus répandue et l'une des plus réussies en hydrologie. Ceci est confirmé par des rapports sur les études en Chine, en URSS, au Japon, en Inde, au Groenland et aux Etats Unis.

V.V.Kuprianov a présenté une revue des applications aux eaux de surface et M.Vauclin a fait l'introduction de la session sur l'humidité du sol, les eaux souterraines et les terres humides. Les applications varient de l'étude du régime des eaux dans les plaines d'inondation (URSS) et du régime des variations du niveau des lacs (Chine) à la surveillance et au contrôle de la sédimentation dans le réservoir du Grande Barrage d'Asswan. Deux papiers portent sur l'emploi de senseurs à micro-ondes passives pour déterminer l'humidité du sol.

La dernière section des communications concernant la télédétection est relative à des applications d'ordre plus général relatives à la mise au point et l'emploi de modèles hydrologiques et à la planification et la gestion des ressources en eau. On décrit les recherches hydrologiques effectuées dans le cadre du programme américain AgRISTARS, et particulièrement celles qui concernent l'humidité du sol et la couverture neigeuse. L'utilisation de la télédétection dans les modèles hydrologiques a été discutée dans plusieurs communications qui passent en revue l'expérience acquise par les Etats Unis, le Canada et la France. Ce sujet est un point critique pour les progrès futurs en hydrologie et il a été convenu qu'il devrait être le thème d'un atelier séparé qui devrait bénéficier de l'appui de l'AISH et de l'OMM.

Le Comité International de la Télédétection et de la Télétransmission de l'AISH est heureux d'avoir organisé ce colloque. On espère que ces communications fourniront aux hydrologues, aux responsables de l'aménagement et de la gestion des ressources en eau et à d'autres utilisateurs des informations de base sur les applications potentielles de la télédétection et de la télétransmission à leurs travaux.

A. IVAN JOHNSON
7474 Upham Court, Arvada,
Colorado 80003, USA
Responsable de la Convocation
du Colloque et Président du CITT

F.GUNNEBERG
Bundesanstalt für Gewasserkunde,
Pf 509, D-5400 Koblenz,
RF d'Allemagne
Co-Responsable

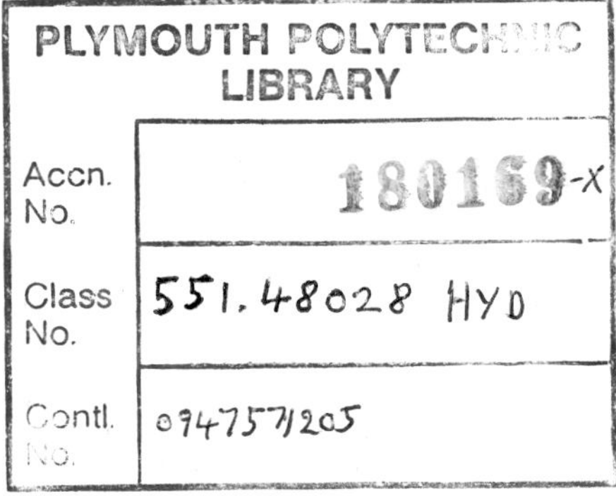

INTERNATIONAL HYDROLOGY PRIZE

The General Assembly of IAHS held at Canberra in 1979 endorsed the principle of an International Hydrology Prize awarded annually on an individual basis in recognition of an outstanding contribution to the science. Nominations for the Prize are made by National Committees and forwarded to the Secretary General for consideration by the Nomination Committee which consists of the President, the First and Second Vice Presidents and representatives of UNESCO and WMO according to the following criteria:

- The International Prize in Hydrology shall be awarded to a person who has made an outstanding contribution to hydrology such as confers on the candidate universal recognition of his international stature.
- The contribution should have an identifiable international dimension extending beyond both the country of normal work and the specific field of interest of the candidate.
- The contribution may have been made through scientific work, as evidenced by the publication in international journals of scientific literature of a high standard, and/or through practical work, as evidenced by reports of the projects concerned. Preference should be given to candidates who have contributed through both scientific and practical work.
- The Prize may be awarded to hydrologists of long international standing or to those who, while having gained such standing only recently, exhibit the qualities of international leadership in the science and practice of hydrology.
- An active involvement in the work of IAHS and other international organizations in the field of hydrology should be counted as an advantage.

LIST OF PRIZE WINNERS

1981 Prof. L.J. Tison (Belgium)
1982 Mr. W.B. Langbein (USA) and Dr. V.I. Korzun (USSR)
1983 Prof. J.C.I. Dooge (Ireland)
1984 Prof. A. Volker (Netherlands)
1985 Dr. J.A. Rodier (France)

Contents

Preface } A.Ivan Johnson & F.Gunneberg v
Préface } viii

International Hydrology Prize xii

Tison Award xviii

1 WMO SPECIAL SESSION ON EXISTING AND FUTURE SATELLITE SYSTEMS

Existing and future satellite systems for hydrological applications *H.W.Yates, M.Matson, D.F.McGinnis Jr, S.R.Schneider & G.Ohring* 3

"Meteor" type space vehicles for solving hydrological problems *V.V.Kuprianov* 17

The METEOSAT Operational Programme *L.Pera & D.Hoge* 25

Data collection and location by satellite: the Argos system *Michel Taillade* 33

Development of satellite remote sensing systems in Japan *National Space Development Agency of Japan* 45

Details of the INSAT meteorological applications programme of India *India Meteorological Department* 61

The SPOT programme: a new tool for the management of earth's resources *Gérard Brachet* 65

RADARSAT and MSAT: proposed Canadian satellite systems with hydrological applications *B.E.Goodison, E.J.Langham & D.Athanassiadis* 75

2 DATA TRANSMISSION

Operational satellite data collection systems operated by the National Oceanic and Atmospheric Administration (invited paper) *Douglas H.MacCallum* 89

Development of a distributive system for handling real time hydrological data collected by the US Geological Survey *William G.Shope Jr & Richard W.Paulson* 99

Collection of data using the METEOSAT DCP retransmission system *R.W.Herschy* 109

Hydrological data collection and transmission in Sweden *Gunlög Wennerberg* 119

Hydrological study in Greenland using the Argos system *Thorkild Thomsen* 125

Emploi des satellites à orbite polaire pour la collecte des mesures effectuées aux stations hydrométéorologiques: bilan de quatre années d'utilisation *Jacques Callède* 135

Hydrology and climatology of the River Amazon: GOES telemetry network *Manuel B.Dengo & Evaldo G.M.Cesar* 143

Hydrometeorological network for real time data collection in a Southern Hemisphere arid area
J.Amorocho, P.C.Fernandez, H.Roby & J.M.Fernandez 151

Water resources sensor characteristics for GOES retransmission in Canada *J.M.Whiting* 159

Technology transfer and satellite data collection
Allen F.Flanders & Susan F.Zevin 171

The Standard Hydrologic Exchange Format (SHEF) for operational hydrological data
Vernon C.Bissell, Phillip A.Pasteris & David G.Bennett 181

The use of random adaptive sub-telemetry systems for satellite and meteor-burst applications
J.A.Kleppe & L.G.Yori 189

Real time remote sensing in the Mt St Helens drainage basin
Charles E.Orwig 197

Preliminary application of the hydrological data telemetering and flood forecasting system on the Puyang River basin *Zhang Wenyao, Ren Keren & Feng Zhiling* 207

Planning for a remote sensing and data transmission network in a hilly region for flood forecasting and warning
Jagendra Singh & S.D.Chopra 217

The development and construction of an adaptable limnological measuring system based on a microprocessor
G.Michler & B.Wuschansky 229

Remote biosensing employing fish as real time monitors of water quality events *Eric L.Morgan & Kenneth W.Eagleson* 235

3 REMOTE SENSING: PRECIPITATION

Rainfall evaluation by remote sensing: problems and prospects (invited paper) *Eric C.Barrett* 247

Satellite-derived precipitation estimates for hydrological application *Roderick A.Scofield* 259

Estimation of convective rainfall volumes with the aid of satellite data *L.-R.Kruger, R.Harboe & G.A.Schultz* 273

Real time inference of convective rainfall from satellite data
Ceçilia Girz Griffith, John A.Augustine & William L.Woodley 281

Spatial transfer of precipitation data using Landsat imagery *A.K.Bagchi* 289

Projet Aramis: le réseau français de radars météorologiques
Marc Gilet, Monique Ciccione, Claude Gaillard & Jean Tardieu 295

Flood forecasting on the basis of radar rainfall measurement and rainfall forecasting
P.Klatt & G.A.Schultz 307

SARAH: outil de traitement des images météorologiques
Jean Tardieu 317

Rainfronts, fractals and rainfall simulations
S.Lovejoy & D.Schertzer 323

Quantitative measurements of snowfall using unattended mountain top radar *J.A.Kleppe & S.L.Liu* 335

4 REMOTE SENSING: SNOW AND ICE

A survey of progress in remote sensing of snow and ice (invited paper) *A.Rango* 347

Remote sensing of snow cover with passive and active microwave sensors *H.Rott & K.F.Künzi* 361

Resolution in operational remote sensing of snow cover
A.Rango, J.Martinec, J.Foster & D.Marks 371

Snow mapping in Greenland based on multi-temporal satellite data *Henrik Søgaard* 383

Snow cover on the Stanovoe Upland determined by satellite imagery *V.G.Prokacheva* 395

Studies of Himalayan snow cover area from satellites
M.S.Dhanju 401

The use of aerial gamma surveys of snowpack for spring snowmelt runoff forecasts *L.K.Vershinina* 411

Snow mapping and hydrological forecasting by airborne γ-ray spectrometry in northern Sweden
Sten Bergström & Maja Brandt 421

Field experiments on propagation of 10 and 30 GHz waves through a snow cover *Tadashi Matsumoto, Masahiro Suzuki, Daisuke Kuroiwa, Kazuo Fujino & Gorow Wakahama* 429

Studying aufeis by aerial and satellite survey imagery
A.E.Abakoumenko & V.F.Usachev 439

Studying lake ice regimes by remote sensing methods
V.V.Borodulin & V.G.Prokacheva 445

A study of spectral reflection characteristics for snow, ice and water in the north of China *Zeng Qunzhu, Cao Meisheng, Feng Xuezhi, Liang Fengxian, Chen Xianzhang & Sheng Wenkun* 451

5 REMOTE SENSING: SURFACE WATER

Satellite information for surface water research (invited paper) *V.V.Kuprianov* 465

Evaluation of flood plain inundations by remote sensing methods *V.F.Usachev* 475

The application of Landsat imagery in the surveying of water resources of Dongting Lake
Liu Xia, Zhang Shulin & Li Xianglian 483

Estimation of monthly river runoff data on the basis of satellite imagery *G.Strübing & G.A.Schultz* 491

Assessment and monitoring of sedimentation in the Aswan High Dam Reservoir using Landsat imagery
Scot E.Smith, K.H.Mancy, A.F.A.Latif & E.A.Fosnight 499

6 REMOTE SENSING: SOIL MOISTURE, GROUNDWATER, WETLANDS

L'humidité des sols en hydrologie: intérêt et limites de la télédétection (invited paper) *Michel Vauclin* 511

Remote sensing of soil moisture from an aircraft platform using passive microwave sensors
T.J.Jackson, T.J.Schmugge & P.O'Neill 529

Détermination de la teneur en eau des sols par radiométrie passive en hyperfréquences
R.Caloz, J.P.Antille & P.Meylan 541

Validation of a soil-plant-atmosphere model for soybeans and an approach to inferring root-zone soil water potential from the canopy temperature *Bhaskar J.Choudhury* 551

Photographic detection of groundwater pollution
J.Švoma & A.Pyšek 561

Water volume estimates by Landsat data
Aaron L.Higer & Daniel G.Anderson 569

7 REMOTE SENSING: HYDROLOGICAL MODELLING, WATER PLANNING AND MANAGEMENT

Hydrological research in the AgRISTARS programme
A.Rango, E.T.Engman, T.J.Jackson, J.C.Ritchie & R.F.Paetzold 579

Combining measurement of hydrological variables of various sampling geometries and measurement accuracies
E.L.Peck, E.R.Johnson, T.N.Keefer & A.Rango 591

Development and testing of a remote sensing based hydrological model *J.R.Groves, R.M.Ragan & R.B.Clapp* 601

Utilisation de la télédétection pour améliorer la précision des crues de fonte de neige simulées par le modèle CEQUEAU *J.P.Fortin, G.Morin, W.Sochanska & L.Potvin* 613

Télédétection et modélisation hydrologique
Marc Lointier & Serge Pieyns 625

Application of remote sensing for seasonal runoff prediction in the Indus basin, Pakistan
B.Dey & D.C.Goswami 637

Operational requirements for water resources remote sensing in Canada: now and in the future
B.E.Goodison, J.M.Whiting, K.Wiebe & J.Cihlar 647

Study of the impact of man's activity in Middle Asia using remote sensing data *V.A.Sumarokova* 659

Estimation of percent imperviousness of urban basins using remote sensing data *Srinivas G.Rao & Stephen E.Draper* 667

Landsat image interpretation of dune sand movement in the Yellow River valley *Niu Zhan* 677

TISON AWARD

Following the presentation by the Exeter Assembly Organizing Committee of the sum of $13 000 to the Association and the acceptance of the idea of an annual prize to recognize the scientific contributions of young hydrologists to IAHS, the Bureau established the Tison Fund. Investment income from the Fund will be used to provide an annual prize of $750 according to the terms of the Award set out below:

TISON AWARD – RULES

1. The IAHS Tison Award aims to promote excellence in research by young hydrologists. The award will be announced annually and will be presented in a public ceremony during either an IUGG/IAHS General Assembly or an IAHS Scientific Assembly.
2. The Tison Award will be granted for an outstanding paper published by IAHS in a period of two years previous to the deadline for nominations. Nominations should be received by the Secretary General of IAHS not later than 31 December each year. The award will be announced by 31 May of the following year.
3. Candidates for the award must be under 41 years of age at the time their paper was published.
4. The Award will consist of a citation in the name of L.J. Tison and an amount of US$750. (If the successful paper is jointly authored, the monetary award will be divided equally between the authors.)
5. Nominations for the Tison Award may be submitted by the National Committees of IAHS and also by any individual or group of persons. They should be sent directly to the Secretary General of IAHS and should contain a reasoned argumentation.
6. The award decision will be made by a committee of seven members, one from each of the IAHS Commissions and Committee. The members of the Award Committee will be hydrologists of outstanding research reputation. The IAHS Bureau will appoint the members of the Award Committee, membership lasting for a period of two years. The Chairman of the Award Committee will be rotated among the different representatives of the IAHS Commissions and Committee.
7. The Award Committee may not recommend an award in any one year if none of the papers submitted is of sufficiently high standard.

ADDRESS FOR NOMINATIONS: Dr. J.C. Rodda, Secretary General IAHS, Institute of Hydrology, Wallingford, Oxfordshire OX10 8BB, UK.

1 WMO special session on existing and future satellite systems

Hydrological Applications of Remote Sensing and Remote Data Transmission
(Proceedings of the Hamburg Symposium, August 1983). IAHS Publ. no. 145.

Existing and future satellite systems for hydrological applications

H. W. YATES, M. MATSON, D. F. MCGINNIS, JR, S. R. SCHNEIDER & G. OHRING
NOAA/National Environmental Satellite, Data, and Information Service, Washington, DC 20233, USA

ABSTRACT Many parameters of hydrological interest can currently be monitored and studied using satellite remote sensing platforms. This paper reviews the satellite systems, the techniques, and the hydrological parameters derivable from the observations. Sequential thermal infrared and visible geostationary (GOES) satellite images are used in a technique that provides real time rainfall estimates from convective systems. These estimates are particularly useful for flash flood forecasting. Snow cover data, based mainly on interactive processing of GOES visible images, provide input to run-off models, dam and reservoir release decisions, and water supply forecasts. High resolution Landsat images and GOES data can be used for ice jam detection and polar orbiting thermal infrared imagery can be used to map flood extent. Water quality monitoring has been demonstrated by GOES and Landsat detection of calcium carbonate "whitings", seiches, algal blooms, and suspended sediment. Satellite data archives now exist for long-term monitoring of the hydrological cycle, specifically of Northern Hemisphere snow cover, based on analysis of the visible observations from the GOES and polar orbiters, and of global vegetation index, based on the difference between the near infrared and visible radiance observations of the polar orbiters. The latter may prove particularly useful for detecting drought areas. In addition to current hydrological applications of visible and thermal infrared satellite data, future microwave equipped satellites may be able to measure soil moisture, snow depth, snow water equivalent, and rainfall.

Systèmes actuels et futurs de satellites en vue d'applications hydrologiques

RESUME On peut actuellement contrôler et étudier de nombreux paramètres présentant un intérêt en hydrologie en utilisant les plates-formes de télédétection des satellites. Le présent document passe en revue les systèmes satellitaires, les techniques et les paramètres hydrologiques que l'on peut tirer des observations. Il est courant d'évaluer les précipitations provenant de systèmes convectifs à partir d'images de satellites géostationnaires pour l'étude de l'environnement (GOES) qui fournissent d'utiles données pour la prévision des crues-éclair. Les données relatives à la couverture de neige, fondées principalement sur le traitement interactif des images prises dans le spectre visible par GOES, fournissent des entrées pour les modèles d'écoulement et les prévisions relatives à l'approvisionnement en eau. Les images à haute résolution de Landsat peuvent être utilisées pour la détection des embâcles de glace et les images thermiques prises dans l'ingrarouge par les satellites à défilement peuvent être utilisées pour établir la carte de l'étendue des crues. Le contrôle de la qualité de l'eau a été démontré par la détection, à l'aide de GOES et de Landsat, de "dépôts blancs" de carbonate de calcium, de seiches, d'efflorescences, d'algues et de sédiments en suspension. Il existe maintenant des archives de données satellitaires pour la couverture de neige de l'hémisphère Nord, établies d'après l'analyse des observations effectuées dans le visible à l'aide de GOES et de satellites à défilement, et de l'index de la végétation mondiale, fondées sur la différence entre les observations faites à l'aide de satellites à défilement et portant sur la luminence énergétique dans le proche infrarouge et dans le visible. Les satellites futurs équipés d'instruments de mesure d'hyperfréquence pourront peut-être mesurer l'humidité du sol, l'épaisseur de la neige, l'équivalent en eau de la neige et les précipitations.

EXISTING SYSTEMS

Introduction

Polar-orbiting and geostationary satellite data are used to monitor many parameters of hydrological interest, including rainfall, snow cover, ice jams, floods, water quality, and desertification. Currently the National Environmental Satellite, Data, and Information Service (NESDIS) operates two polar-orbiting satellite systems (Landsat and NOAA series) and one geostationary system (GOES series). Some specifications for these systems are listed in Table 1. The polar-orbiting satellites are useful for hydrological applications because of their multispectral capability, their global coverage, and, in the case of Landsat, the high spatial resolution. The GOES satellites are useful because they provide continuous observation of the earth with images every 30 minutes in normal operation or, for special purposes, as frequently as every 7½ minutes for a selected portion of the earth. Case studies which document the use of these satellite systems for studying selected hydrological parameters are given below.

Precipitation - flash flood warnings

Scofield & Oliver (1977) have developed a technique which gives half-hourly or hourly rainfall estimates from convective systems by using GOES thermal infrared and visible images. The technique was

TABLE 1 Selected specifications of current NESDIS satellite systems

Satellite	*Spectral range (microns)*	*Resolution (m)*
Landsat-D	*Multispectral scanner (MSS)*	
	0.50-0.60	*80*
	0.60-0.70	*80*
	0.70-0.80	*80*
	0.80-0.10	*80*
	Thematic mapper (TM)	
	0.45-0.52	*30*
	0.52-0.60	*30*
	0.63-0.69	*30*
	0.76-0.90	*30*
	1.55-1.75	*30*
	2.08-2.35	*30*
	10.40-12.50	*120*
NOAA series	*Advanced very high resolution radiometer (AVHRR)*	
	0.58-0.68	*1100*
	0.725-1.10	*1100*
	3.55-3.93	*1100*
	10.30-11.30	*1100*
	11.50-12.50	*1100*
GOES series	*Visible and infrared spin scan radiometer (VISSR)*	
	0.55-0.75	*1000*
	10.50-12.50	*8000*

designed for deep convective systems which occur in tropical air masses with high tropopauses. Estimates of convective rainfall are made by quantitative observation of the changes between two consecutive images, using both the thermal infrared and the visible channels. The technique is divided into three main parts: (a) the active portion of the convective system is identified, (b) an initial estimate of expected average rainfall is made using cloud top temperatures derived from enhanced thermal infrared imagery alone, and (c) successive pairs of visible and thermal infrared images are examined to find additional clues which indicate heavier than average rainfall. These clues include overshooting tops, merging thunderstorms, merging convective cloud lines, and rapidly expanding anvils. The total rainfall prediction is computed by summing these two estimates.

Currently NESDIS meteorologists compute precipitation estimates using the Scofield & Oliver technique. The estimates are then passed on to the appropriate National Weather Service Forecast Office whenever these estimates are expected to exceed threshold values for flooding as determined by the National Weather Service River Forecast Centers. Following are the results of using the Scofield &

Oliver technique in real time on a convective system.

During 1 April 1981, rains of up to five inches (127 mm) fell on portions of Georgia and Alabama in the southern United States. Estimated isohyets were computed, drawn every ½ h and graphically added. In this case the satellite signatures of cloud-top temperature/cloud growth and stationary storms were the principal contributors to the estimates. The results of 5½ h of estimates are shown in Fig.1(a). In the area of 4-5 inch estimates (102-127 mm), flash flood guidance values indicated that only 1-2 inches (25-50 mm) of rain were required in 3 h to produce a flash flood. The complete 24-h rainfall observations for this area are shown in Fig.1(b) and agree quite well with the satellite estimates.

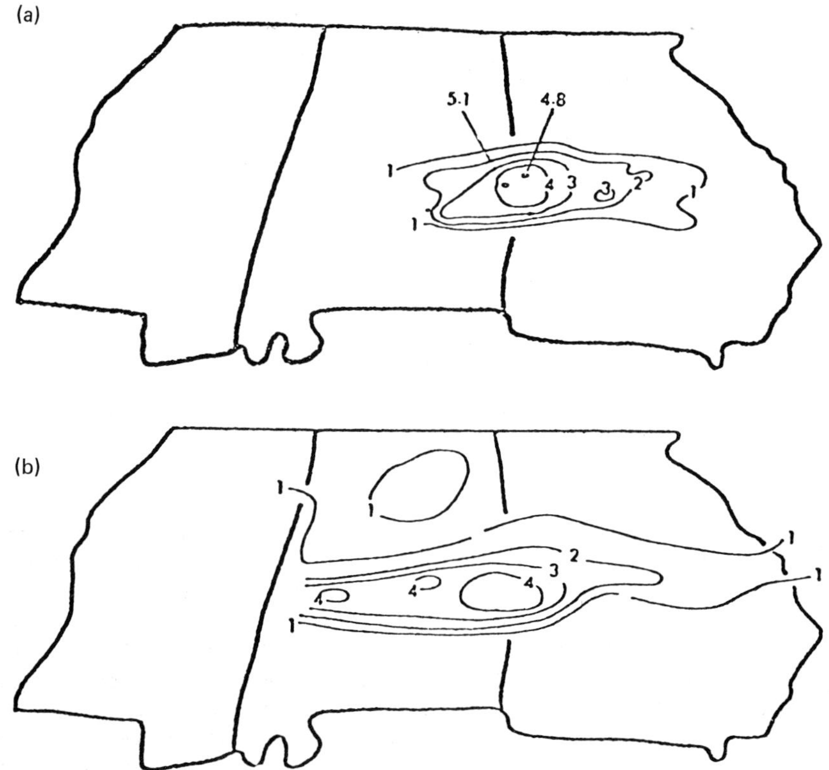

FIG.1(a) Estimated rainfall amounts (in inches) in Alabama and Georgia on 1 April 1981 as determined from GOES satellite data over a 5½-h period. (b) Isopleths of the 24-h observed rainfall amounts (in inches) in Alabama and Georgia on 1 April 1981. Most of the heavy 24-h rainfall fell between 0600 and 1200 GMT.

Snow cover

GOES satellite data are being used operationally to monitor river basin snow cover for selected basins throughout the western United States and Canada (Schneider, 1981). Twenty eight basins, varying in size from 3400 to 65 000 km^2 and shown on the map in Fig.2, were

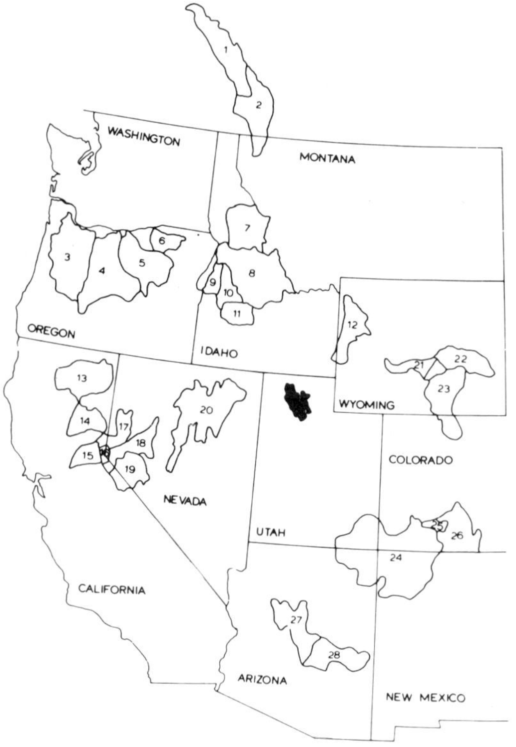

FIG.2 River basin for NESDIS operational snow mapping programme.

monitored at NESDIS headquarters in Suitland, Maryland, from 1973 to 1980. Since 1980 the programme has been decentralized and transferred to regional NESDIS offices as well as to primary users. Basins in the Rocky Mountains and Nevada (12, 16-26, 29) are being mapped from the NESDIS office in Kansas City; basins in the Pacific Northwest (1-11) are monitored from the NESDIS office in San Francisco. Responsibility for monitoring basins in Arizona, California, and New Brunswick, Canada has been taken over by the Salt River Project, Sierra Hydrotech, Inc., and the Canadian Atmospheric Environment Service, respectively.

River basin snow maps are used by numerous federal, state, and local governmental agencies as well as public power utilities. The data are used in Arizona and Wyoming to aid in dam and reservoir operations. In the Pacific Northwest and New Brunswick the snow cover data are used to calibrate runoff models. In California, Nevada, and Montana the data are used for preparing seasonal water supply forecasts. There are several analysis methods available when using GOES satellite imagery/data for snow mapping. The simplest is photo interpretation. In this method, and optical transfer device, such as the Bausch & Lomb zoom transfer scope, is used to magnify and rectify the GOES image until it overlays a standard hydrological basin map. The snow line can then be transferred from image to map. The second method involves use of computer interactive systems to display the image data on a video screen. A joystick cursor or data tablet is then used to trace the snow line onto the image data. The final method involves use of large main frame computer systems such as the IBM 360/370 to determine snow cover on a pixel basis. This involves thresholding each individual pixel according to terrain type and solar illumination angles. All three of the techniques mentioned may be used at NESDIS depending upon basin characteristics and equipment availability.

River ice

The dynamics of river ice are important because of the problems the ice creates for hydropower stations, bridge piers, and ship navigation. In addition, when the ice breaks up it forms a dam causing the water to rise behind it, thus posing a flood threat to nearby communities. McGinnis & Schneider (1978) have used Landsat and GOES imagery to detect and monitor ice jams in the Ottawa River in Canada. Fourteen distinct ice-covered reaches on the Ottawa River were located and identified on GOES imagery on 4 April 1976 (Fig.3). Manmade dams are partly responsible for the persistence of ice in five of the reaches. Sharp river bends account for two ice-covered segments and branching of the main channel by islands contributes to the presence of ice in four other reaches. The profusion of ice in the downstream portion of the river may be attributable to the reduced slope of the river bottom as it approaches its confluence with the St Lawrence River. In contrast, the presence of rapids may explain the large ice-free stretch between the two most upstream reaches. As can be seen on the GOES image of 14 April (Fig.3), only three of the original ice reaches remained at the end of the 10-day study period.

This case study demonstrates that daily monitoring of changes in river ice can be effectively accomplished from geostationary satellites. The distortion observed in GOES imagery limits its usefulness to latitudes between 50°N and 50°S, and to rivers at least 2 km wide. This precludes monitoring many subarctic rivers where ice is a problem, but polar-orbiting satellites could be used for these areas.

Surface water - flood extent mapping

Floods have resulted in death and destruction throughout history, although construction of flood-preventing structures helps to protect lives and reduce losses. Annual flood losses in the United States often exceed $1 billion. Economics dictate that engineers and government officials be given improved information on the location of flood hazard areas and the assessment of areas of inundation when floods occur. Operational satellites are a source of this information and have been used in research studies for the 1973 Mississippi River floods (Wiesnet *et al.*, 1974), the 1978 Kentucky River floods (Berg & McGinnis, 1980), and the Red River of the North floods (Fig.4) of the same year (Berg *et al.*, 1981a). In each case the flooded areas showed up best on the night-time thermal infrared imagery owing to high land/water temperature contrasts. Recently, operational monitoring of flood extent using NESDIS satellite data was done in support of National Weather Service

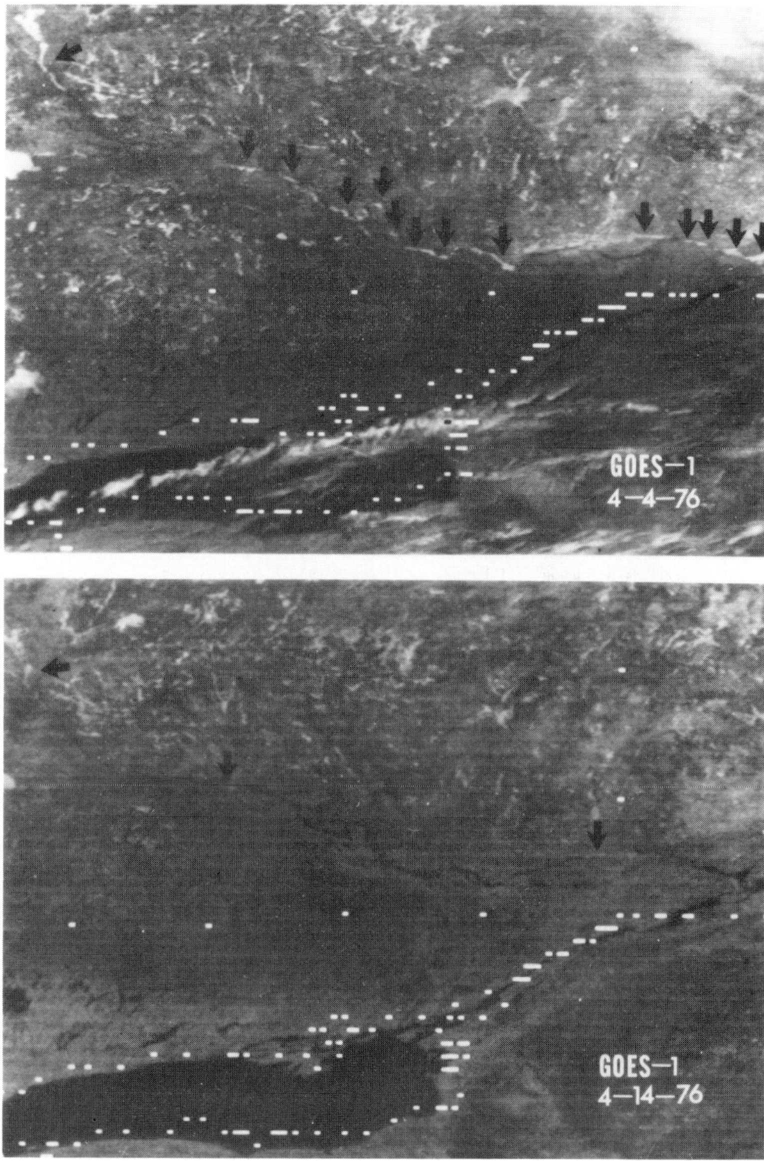

FIG.3 Ottawa River basin as viewed from the GOES satellite on 4 April 1976 and 14 April 1976. Arrows indicate areas of river ice.

River Forecast Centers during the Illinois River flood of December 1982 and the Pearl River floods of April 1983.

Water quality

Satellite detection of water quality is possible because eutrophication and pollutants give rise to changes in water colour, temperature, or surface characteristics. In some cases the nutrient loadings that lead to eutrophication result in algal blooms. Strong

(1974) documented such a case using Landsat multispectral imagery for a massive, highly variable bloom of *Aphanizomenon flos-aguae* on Utah Lake, Utah. This highly eutrophic lake (PO 0.5mg l^{-1}) is known for its high turbidity and summer algae blooms. Munday *et al.* (1981) used Landsat multispectral data to measure suspended sediment concentration, chlorophyll, Secchi disc depth, and turbidity for the Bay of Fundy, Canada. Matson & Berg (1981) used the increased brightness due to suspended sediment to monitor seiche activity in Great Salt Lake, Utah. Turbulence and mixing associated with lake seiches are important to the ecology of lakes because they affect the dispersal and transport of heat, dissolved oxygen and nutrients.

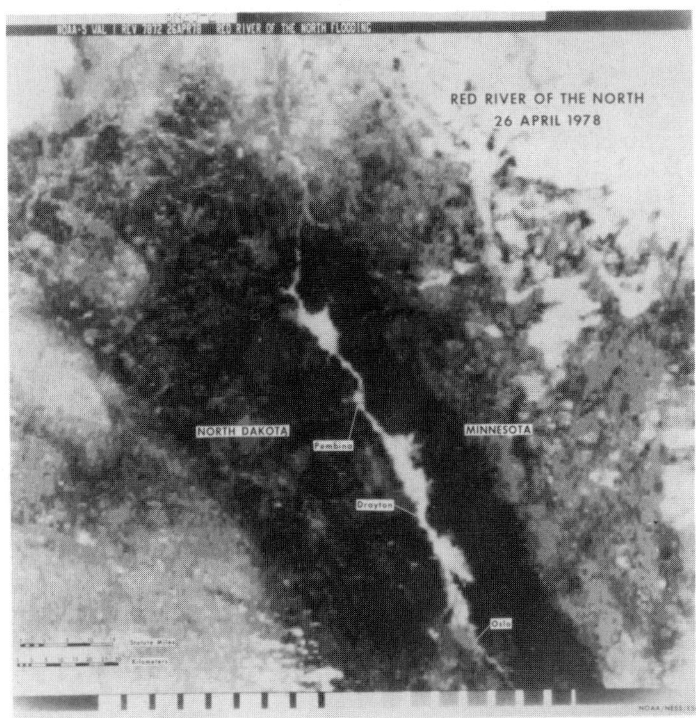

FIG.4 Thermal infrared NOAA-5 image of the Red River of the North for 26 April 1978. The area inundated by the cold flood waters appears grey, contrasting sharply with the warm dry land (dark).

Berg *et al.* (1981b) monitored massive precipitations of calcium carbonate "whitings" in Pyramid Lake, Nevada (Fig.5) using Landsat and GOES visible band data. When compared to available ground truth, it was found that the satellite data had detected brightness differences attributable to very small amounts of particulate calcium in near-surface waters, in this case 0.2mg l^{-1}.

FIG.5 Landsat image taken on 30 July 1978 showing a calcium carbonate "whiting" beginning in the south end of Pyramid Lake.

Long term monitoring of the hydrological cycle - snow cover and vegetation index

Since November 1966 NESDIS has prepared the Northern Hemisphere Weekly Snow and Ice Cover Chart (Matson & Wiesnet, 1981). These charts show the areal extent and brightness of continental snow cover, but do not indicate snow depth. The analysis is based on NESDIS satellite imagery and the snow line represents the latest cloud-free image of that particular area of the world. The Northern Hemisphere snow cover charts have been digitized and stored on computer tape (Dewey & Heim, 1981). From the digitized data monthly, anomaly, and climatological snow cover maps can be created. In addition, continental or regional snow cover area can be calculated over a long time series as shown in Fig.6 for Eurasian winter snow.

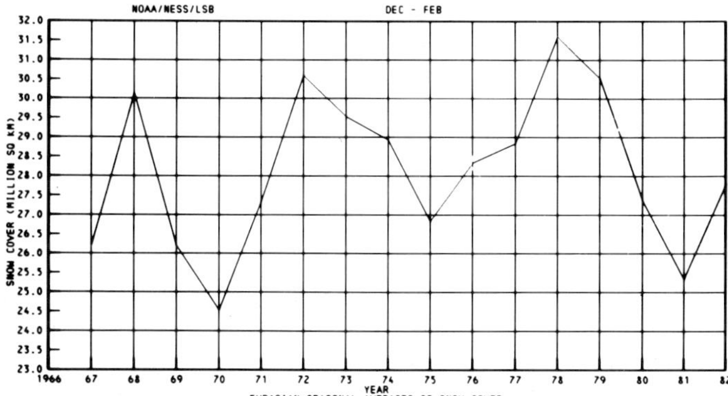

FIG.6 Eurasian satellite derived winter snow cover area from 1967 to 1982.

Channels 1 (0.58-0.68 μm) and 2 (0.725-1.1 μm) of the AVHRR are in the visible and near infrared portions of the spectrum. These channels are sensitive to the presence of chlorophyll in a target scene and can be used together to determine vegetation extent and vigor. Various mathematical combinations of Channel 1 and 2 data have been found to be indicators of the presence of green vegetation, and these are referred to as vegetation indices (Tucker, 1979). The most commonly used vegetation indices are (a) the Channel 2-Channel 1 difference and (b) the normalized vegetation index, NVI, computed as follows: NVI = (CH2 - CH1)/(CH2 + CH1).

Applications of the 1 km AVHRR data in the form of vegetation indices are being reported on by a rapidly expanding community of investigators. Gray & McCrary (1981) favourably compared the NOAA AVHRR and Landsat MSS data for a study area along the Brazil-Argentina border. Greegor & Norwine (1981) developed a gradient model of vegetation and climate using the NOAA AVHRR satellite data together with ground truth collected over 12 sites in Texas. Tucker *et al.* (1984) studied vegetation growth in Egypt's Nile Delta during the May-October 1981 growing season. Schneider & McGinnis (1982) showed how these data could be used to monitor the impact of climate changes on Africa's Lake Chad basin. Use of a reduced

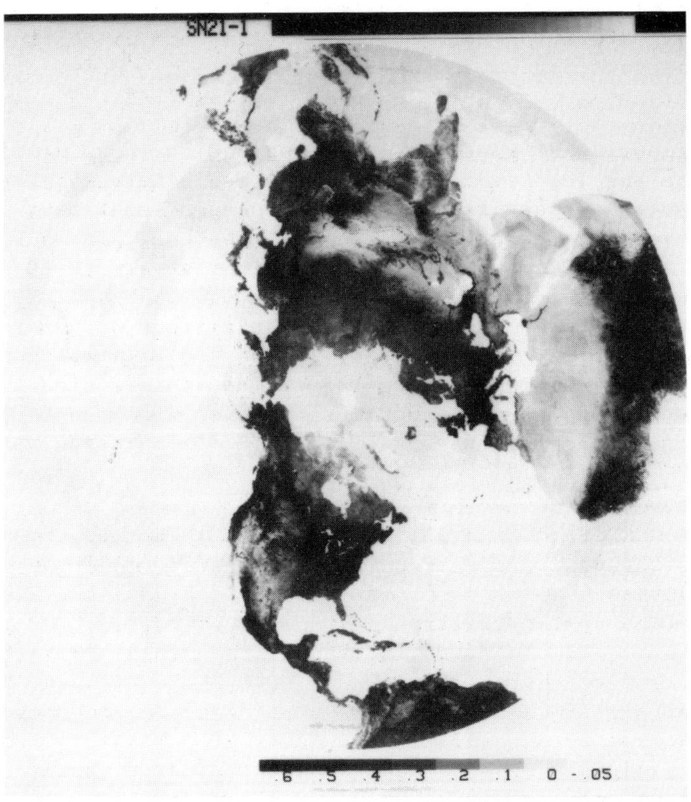

FIG.7 A Northern Hemisphere vegetation index map composited over a 7-day period. The darker the area on the image, the greener it is on the ground.

resolution AVHRR vegetation index to monitor land cover on a global basis (Fig.7) is reported by Tarpley *et al.* (1983).

The vegetation indices are also being used operationally by government agencies. The United States Department of Agriculture uses the data to monitor primary grain producing regions. The United States Bureau of Land Management and Bureau of Reclamation use the data respectively to assess fire danger ratings and monitor the effects of irrigation. The United Nations Food and Agriculture Organization uses the data to (a) monitor the spread of deserts, (b) search for desert locust breeding grounds, and (c) monitor vegetation available for grazing herds in third world nations (Schneider & McGinnis, 1982).

FUTURE SYSTEMS

Introduction

Visible, near infrared, and thermal infrared satellite sensors are restricted in their hydrological applications by cloud cover and the inability to provide subsurface information. Microwave radiometers, which are only slightly affected by even dense clouds and which provides some penetration of soils, offer a promise on future operational satellite systems of determinations of rainfall rates, various snowpack parameters, and soil moisture. Model studies have already been performed by Fowler *et al.* (1981) that show that it is possible to estimate rain rates over land using spaceborne passive microwave sensors near 35 and 85 GHz. Chang *et al.* (1981) have demonstrated that a multispectral passive microwave approach is useful for determining snow depth, snow state, snow volume, and snow water equivalent. Burke & Burke (1981) used airborne 21 cm and 1.67 cm microwave radiometers to assess the feasibility of monitoring soil moisture content. They have shown that the near surface moisture can be determined quite accurately at 1.67 cm. A combination of the two channels was required for determining subsurface moisture content.

Advanced microwave sounding unit

In early 1990 the advanced microwave sounding unit (AMSU) will be flown on a NESDIS polar-orbiting satellite. The AMSU is a 20-channel passive microwave radiometer divided into two components - a 15-channel unit to be provided by the United States and a 5-channel unit to be provided by the British Meteorological Office. Of particular interest to hydrologists are the three channels at 23.8, 31.4, and 89 GHz; the five channels at 89 GHz, 166 GHz, and three frequencies near the strong 183 GHz water vapour resonance. The channels at 23.8, 31.4, and 89 GHz will have a horizontal resolution of 40 km and will be capable of sensing tropospheric water vapour, ocean precipitation, sea-ice type and coverage, snow cover and depth, and soil moisture. The 89 GHz, 166 GHz, and 183 GHz channels sense water vapour profiles and precipitation over land and ocean. These channels are particularly sensitive to convective cells with ice crystals aloft. Resolution in these channels will be 15 km.

REFERENCES

Berg, C.P. & McGinnis, D.F. (1980) Mapping of the 1978 Kentucky River flood from NOAA 5 satellite thermal infrared data. *Proc. 46th Annual Meeting of the American Society of Photogrammetry* (March 1983, St Louis, Missouri, USA), 106-111.

Berg, C.P. Wiesnet, D.R. & Matson, M. (1981a) Assessing the Red River of the North 1978 flooding from NOAA satellite data. In: *Satellite Hydrology* (ed. by M.Deutsch, D.R.Wiesnet & A.Rango), 309-315. American Water Resources Association, Minneapolis, Minnesota, USA.

Berg, C.P., Schneider, S.R. & Galat, D.L. (1981b) Calcium carbonate precipitation in Pyramid Lake, Nevada as monitored by satellite: 1978 and 1980. In: *Proc. 14th International Symposium on Remote Sensing of Environment* (Ann Arbor, Michigan, USA), 721-731.

Burke, K. & Burke, W.J. (1981) Requirements of space-borne microwave radiometers for detecting soil moisture contents. In: *Satellite Hydrology* (ed. by M.Deutsch, D.R.Wiesnet & A.Rango), 377-384. American Water Resources Association, Minneapolis, Minnesota, USA.

Chang, A.T.C., Hall, D.K., Foster, J.L., Rango, A., & Shine, J.C. (1981) Passive microwave sensing of snow characteristics over land. In: *Satellite Hydrology* (ed. by M.Deutsch, D.R.Wiesnet & A.Rango), 213-217. American Water Resources Association, Minneapolis, Minnesota, USA.

Dewey, K.F. & Heim, R., Jr (1981) Satellite observations of variations in Northern Hemisphere seasonal snow cover. *NOAA Tech. Report NESS 87*. US Dept of Commerce, Washington, DC.

Fowler, M.G., Burke, H.K., Hardy, K.R., & Tripp, N.K. (1981) The estimation of rain rate over land from spaceborne passive microwave sensors. In: *Satellite Hydrology* (ed. by M.Deutsch, D.R.Wiesnet & A.Rango), 101-108. American Water Resources Association, Minneapolis, Minnesota, USA.

Gray, T.I. & McCrary, D.C. (1981) Meteorological satellite data - a tool to describe the health of the world's agriculture. *AgRISTARS Report EW-NI-040, NASA, Houston, Texas, USA*.

Greegor, D.H. & Norwine, J. (1981) A gradient model of vegetation and climate utilizing NOAA satellite imagery, phase 1: Texas transect. *AgRISTARS Report FC-JI-04176, NASA, Houston, Texas, USA*.

Matson, M. & Berg, C.P. (1981) Satellite detection of seiches in Great Salt Lake, Utah. *Wat. Resour. Bull.* 17 (1), 122-128.

Matson, M. & Wiesnet, D.R. (1981) New data base for climate studies. *Nature* 289 (5797), 451-456.

McGinnis, D.F. & Schneider, S.R. (1978) Monitoring river ice breakup from space. *Photogramm. Engng and Remote Sensing* 44 (1), 57-68.

Munday, J.C., Jr, Alfoldi, T.T. & Amos, C.L. (1981) Bay of Fundy verification of a system for multidate Landsat measurement of suspended sediment. In: *Satellite Hydrology* (ed. by M.Deutsch, D.R. Wiesnet & A.Rango), 622-640. American Water Resources Association, Minneapolis, Minnesota, USA.

Schneider, S.R. (1981) Operational applications of satellite snow-cover observations - NOAA/NESS support study. *NASA Tech. Paper 1827*. NASA, Washington, DC, USA.

Schneider, S.R. & McGinnis, D.F. (1982) The NOAA/AVHRR: A new satellite sensor for monitoring crop growth. In: *Purdue Symp. on Machine Processing of Remotely Sensed Data* (West LaFayette, Indiana, USA), 281-290.

Scofield, R.A. & Oliver, V.J. (1977) A scheme for estimating convective rainfall from satellite imagery. *NOAA Tech. Memorandum NESS 86*. US Dept of Commerce, Washington, DC.

Strong, A.E. (1974) Remote sensing of algal blooms by aircraft and satellite in Lake Erie and Utah Lake. *Remote Sens. Environ.* 3, 99-107.

Tarpley, J.D., Schneider, S.R., and Money, R.L. (1983) Global vegetation indices from the NOAA-7 meteorological satellite. *Bull. Am. Met. Soc.* (in press).

Tucker, C.J. (1979) Red and photographic infrared linear combinations for monitoring vegetation. *Remote Sens. Environ.* 8, 127-150.

Tucker, C.J., Gatlin, J.A. & Schneider, S.R. (1984) Monitoring vegetation in the Mile Delta with NOAA-6 and NOAA-7 AVHRR imagery. *Photogramm. Engng and Remote Sensing* L (1), 53-61.

Wiesnet, D.R., McGinnis, D.F. & Pritchard, J.A. (1974) Mapping of the 1973 Mississippi River floods by the NOAA-2 satellite. *Wat. Resour. Bull.* 10 (5), 1040-1049.

Hydrological Applications of Remote Sensing and Remote Data Transmission
(Proceedings of the Hamburg Symposium, August 1983). IAHS Publ. no. 145.

"Meteor" type space vehicles for solving hydrological problems

V. V. KUPRIANOV
State Hydrological Institute, 2 Linija 23, Leningrad 199053, USSR

ABSTRACT The Soviet Union has established the "Meteor" satellite system to provide information on the state of the atmosphere, cloud cover, land and ocean surfaces. The system consists of operational and experimental satellites. The operational satellites are polar orbiting, cover 70-80% of the total surface of the earth twice a day and collect and transmit data in the visible and infrared portion of the spectrum. They provide global information on such elements as cloud, ice and snow cover, temperature fields and cloud-top heights, and water surface temperatures which are used in snowmelt runoff prediction, assessing the dynamics of snow cover, determining the ice cover on large lakes and rivers, and estimating the extent of flooding. The experimental satellite programme involves analysis of potential remote sensing sensors and techniques in the visible, infrared and microwave spectrum. The types, characteristics and applications of the experimental instruments carried by satellites are outlined in the paper. Various multiband scanners with various resolutions and different microwave radiometers have been assessed for hydrometeorological and hydrological applications.

Vaisseaux spatiaux du type "Météor" pour résoudre les problèmes hydrologiques

RESUME L'URSS a mis au point le système de satellites "Météor" pour fournir des informations sur l'état de l'atmosphère, la couverture nuageuse, les surfaces des continents et des océans. Le système comporte des satellites opérationnels et expérimentaux. Les satellites opérationnels ont un orbite polaire, couvrent 70 à 80% de la surface totale de la terre deux fois par jour, collectent et transmettent des données dans les parties visibles et infra-rouge du spectre. Ils fournissent une information globale sur des éléments tels que les nuages, la glace et la couverture neigeuse, les champs de températures et les hauteurs des sommets des nuages, et les températures superficielles de l'eau qui sont utilisés dans la prévision de l'écoulement dû à la fonte des neiges, pour déterminer la dynamique de la couverture neigeuse, déterminer la couverture de glace sur les grands lacs et les fleuves et évaluer l'étendue des zones inondées. Le programme des satellites expérimentaux comporte l'analyse de senseurs et de techniques potentiels dans les parties du spectre visibles, infra-rouges et les micro-ondes. Les types, les caractéristiques et les applications des instruments expérimentaux transportés par les satellites sont décrits dans cette communication. Des scanners variés à multibandes avec différents pouvoirs de resolution et différents radiomètres pour micro-ondes ont été évalués pour leurs possibilités d'applications hydrométéorologiques et hydrologiques.

INTRODUCTION

In the Soviet Union during recent years, intensive research into the use of satellites as a source of information on the state of the atmosphere, cloud cover, land and ocean surfaces for the benefit of hydrometeorology has been in progress. The "Meteor" satellite system was created to meet these purposes. Considerable progress has been made because of this system, which has become an essential part of the whole system of hydrometeorological observations during the last 16 years.

The "Meteor" space system, intended for obtaining environmental information for hydrometeorology, consists of both operational and experimental satellites. Operational satellites are equipped with similar types of instruments and are launched on quasi-polar near-circular orbits 900 km above the earth with an inclination of 81°. Operational satellites are used to obtain information for the forecasting service of the USSR State Committee for Hydrometeorology and Control of the Natural Environment which supplies various branches of the economy with hydrometeorological information and forecasts. Experimental satellites are used to test the results of research and engineering developments intended to increase the number of types of hydrometeorological observations and to improve techniques of obtaining, processing and interpreting satellite data. Experimental satellites carry various types of instruments and are placed on quasi-polar near sunsynchronous orbits at an altitude of 600-650 km.

Two or three operational satellites and one experimental "Meteor" satellite are placed simultaneously in an orbit. The Regional Data Reception and Processing Centres in Khabarovsk and Novosibirsk and the Principal Data Reception and Processing Centre in Moscow provide numerous users with operational information. Similar techniques, methods, algorithms and processing programmes have made it possible to receive, record and interpret satellite data at these centres. The main purpose of interpretation is to reduce initial satellite data to a convenient form for use in operational work and scientific research as well as for dissemination via communication links.

Information from satellites is intended for use in many branches of the economy. Such information has improved the accuracy of different kinds of maps: geographical, topographical, geological, vegetation, hydrological, agricultural, forest and other small-scale and meso-scale maps which are used in the study of the environment and its resources. Accordingly, the experimental "Meteor" satellites are called "Meteor-Nature".

OPERATIONAL SATELLITES

At present, improved second generation "Meteor-2" satellites are used to obtain operational information; their operating and design characteristics and the volume and quality of the observational data are better than those of the first generation. Second generation "Meteor-2" satellites, using scanning sensors, collect not only global data by means of a recorder, but also transmit visible images in real time to all users and also to other countries. Orbital data from operational "Meteor-2" satellites are transmitted over the WMO Global Telecommunication System. There are more than 60 stations in the USSR providing direct readout of images.

The "Meteor-2" system provides the following:

(a) twice a day information on the distribution of clouds and ice and snow cover over the earth as images in the visible and infrared bands;

(b) twice a day global data on temperature fields and cloud-top heights, as well as on water surface temperatures;

(c) twice a day global information on the radiation budget in near space;

(d) two or three times a day TV-images of cloud, ice and snow cover from areas of 6-7 million km^2 each, being received in any region of the earth at self-contained receiving points. This information is received all over the world since the radiolink frequency is international and image formats are similar to those transmitted by United States satellites.

Hydrometeorological information obtained from satellite data is new in form and it requires construction of special processing and interpretation systems. At the same time, these data permitted the development of new methods for the analysis of hydrometeorological events and processes which greatly influenced all aspects of the information and forecasting activities of the hydrometeorological service.

Considerable progress has been made in the interpretation of visible and infrared satellite imagery. These results have greatly contributed to conventional hydrometeorological observations. Satellite pictures have become an important source of information for providing services to aviation, fisheries, agriculture, forestry, water management and other segments of the economy. In addition to weather analysis and forecasting, satellite data have found application in hydrology, oceanography, and other fields of hydrometeorology.

Research using satellites within the framework of various experimental programmes during recent years has shown the possibility of increasing the volume and the types of satellite data for hydrometeorological purposes. Table 1 shows the types and basic characteristics of the hydrometeorological instruments on board the operational "Meteor-2" satellites, as well as the forms of presentation of processed observational data.

Operational satellites cover 70-80% of the total surface of the globe twice a day. The scanning 8-channel infrared radiometer for vertical thermal atmospheric sensing is not yet considered among the sensors providing operational data.

Trends in future development of the medium altitude orbiting

TABLE 1 Instrumentation on board operational "Meteor-2" satellites and forms of presentation of observational data

Instrument and characteristics	*Observational output*
Scanning telephotometer for direct transmission of imagery (APT system) in the visible portion of the spectrum (0.5-0.7 μm). Field of view: 2100 km; resolution: 2 km at nadir	*Single pictures and photomosaics from two-three orbits for the receiving stations area of up to 200 km in radius (2-3 times a day)*
TV-type scanning instrument with storage capacity for imagery in the visible portion of the spectrum (0.5-0.7 μm). Field of view: 2200 km; resolution: 1 km at nadir	*Single pictures and photomosaics for different areas of the globe (2-3 times a day); photomosaics for Arctic and Antarctic seas from ice cover pictures when free of clouds (once in five days)*
Scanning infrared radiometer (8-12 μm) with image storage capability. Field of view: 2600 km; resolution: 8 km at nadir	*Global photomosaics for the northern hemisphere, southern hemisphere and tropical zone; separately, single pictures, radiation temperature charts and charts of cloud tops for different areas of the globe (twice a day); coordinates of tropical storms and data of cloud amount at the regular grid points for the whole globe (twice a day using visible imagery)*
Scanning 8-channel infrared radiometer (11.10; 13.33; 13.70; 14.24; 14.43; 14.75; 15.02 and 18.70 μm). Field of view: 1000 km; angular resolution: 2°	*Global thermal atmospheric sensing data*

meteorological system "Meteor-2" envisage the following:

(a) increase in orbital altitude of the vehicle to ensure complete coverage of the earth's surface in the equatorial zone;

(b) introduction of torque-motors to synchronize the three vehicle system and to increase the system's efficiency;

(c) introduction of improved, higher-resolution infrared-equipment, with direct transmission capability;

(d) execution of experiments and the introduction of microwave sensors into the sensor complex to perform all-weather observations of ice and snow cover and to determine cloud moisture content.

Possibilities for using information from operational "Meteor" satellites for solving fundamental and operational problems in hydrology are discussed more fully in Kuprianov (1985) and in other papers in this proceedings volume. Here it is appropriate to mention that, at present, the satellite information is widely applied to solve the following basic problems:

(a) development of models for the computation and prediction of snowmelt runoff in different time and space scales;

(b) obtaining operational information on the dynamics of snow cover, and ice situation in large rivers, lakes and reservoirs;

(c) estimation of flooding and its dynamics over large areas of river systems;

(d) obtaining qualitative assessments of pollution in large water bodies.

EXPERIMENTAL SATELLITES

Within the framework of the experimental "Meteor" satellite programme, possibilities of using remote-sensing techniques have been investigated in different parts of the visible, infrared and microwave ranges of the spectrum. Experiments aimed at refining techniques for obtaining new types of satellite information have been based on a comprehensive analysis of satellite, aircraft and land observations. The types, characteristics and applications of the experimental instruments carried by satellites are given in Table 2.

A large number of microwave measurements was obtained using the microwave 0.8 cm radiometer. Analysis of these measurements enabled rainfall areas to be identified, water content of clouds and intensity of precipitation to be estimated quantitatively (three graduations) and cloud phase composition to be determined. It was also possible to determine cloud phase composition from measurements by the scanning infrared polarimeter (1.5-1.9 μm and 2.1-2.5 μm). Ice crystal and water droplet clouds were distinguished by this method with 86% probability.

Measurements from the three-channel microwave radiometer (0.8, 1.35, 8.5 cm wavelengths) made it possible to determine the total atmospheric vapour content and water content of clouds, to detect areas of heavy and moderate precipitation, to see ice cover boundaries and to estimate ice concentration.

One of the most important parts of the "Meteor" programme is the feasibility study of a technique for a multi-band visible and near-infrared survey, using scanning TV-type instruments. In selecting the instrument's parameters, the purpose was to produce multi-band imagery of the earth's surface with different degrees of generalization, but with a relatively wide field of view, so that the state of large natural features could be studied, and short-term seasonal phenomena over vast areas could be monitored. Very high resolution imagery is less suitable for these purposes, because of the narrow field of view and the long period between the repeated passes over the same area.

The TV-type instrumentation, including a 4-channel scanner of low resolution and a 2-channel scanner of medium resolution, has been designed to study the possibilities of such imagery. These scanners are constructed on the basis of single-line mechanical scanning across the satellite track. The first experimental

TABLE 2 Experimental instrumentation on board "Meteor" satellites

Instruments and characteristics	*Applications*
Spectrometric infrared instruments; 10-17 μm range; angular resolution 6 x 1.5°	*Determination of vertical atmospheric temperature profiles*
Spectrometer-interferometer developed in the German Democratic Republic, 6.25-25 μm range; angular resolution 2°	*Determination of vertical atmospheric temperature profiles and atmospheric water vapour and ozone content*
Microwave 0.8 cm radiometer; two orthogonal polarizations; angular resolution: 2.5°	*Tracking of falling precipitation areas, determination of cloud water content and phase composition*
Three-channel microwave radiometer (scanning in 1000 km band) at 0.8, 1.35 and 8.5 cm wavelengths; resolution (with orbit at altitude of 900 km) 24 x 30 km, 90 x 90 km and 100 x 100 km on the ground, respectively	*Determination of the total atmospheric water content, cloud water content, sea-surface temperature, tracking of falling precipitation areas and ice-cover boundaries*
Scanning infrared polarimeter 1.5-1.9 and 2.1-2.5 μm range; field of view (with orbit at altitude of 900 km) - 2200 km; angular resolution 3°	*Determination of cloud phase composition*
Instruments for studying sun-atmosphere relationships, including: *- 4 channel corpuscular spectrometer 0.3-30 KeV range* *- scanning infrared slant sounding radiometer (0.3-30 μm)*	*Obtaining information on corpuscular radiation affecting the upper atmosphere intensity of thermal infrared radiation in the upper atmosphere, which is one of the agents of energy transfer from the upper to the lower atmosphere*
Scanning TV-type unit including scanners: *- of low resolution (0.5-0.6; 0.6-0.7; 0.7-0.8; 0.8-1.0 μm); field of view 2000 km; resolution 1 km at nadir (with orbit at altitude of 650 km)* *- of medium resolution (0.5-0.7; 0.7-1.0 μm); field of view: 1400 km; resolution 240 m*	*Obtaining overlapping images in various ranges of visible and near infrared spectrum with various resolutions on the ground aimed at refining techniques for obtaining, processing and interpreting multi-band video information*

TABLE 2 continued

Instruments and characteristics	*Applications*
Informative unit of instrumentation (experimental) including multi-band scanners: *- of medium resolution with conic scanning (0.5-0.6; 0.6-0.7; 0.7-0.8; 0.8-1.0 µm); field of view: 600 km; resolution: 170 m at nadir (with orbit at altitude of 650 km)* *- of high resolution with electronic scanning (0.5-0.7; 0.6-0.8; 0.8-1.0 µm); field of view; 30 km, resolution: about 60 m (projection of aperture on the ground: 30 m)*	*Obtaining overlapping images in various ranges of visible and near infrared spectrum with various resolutions on the ground aimed at refining techniques for obtaining, processing and interpreting multi-band video information*
Multispectral instrumentation of high resolution Fragment" (0.4-0.8; 0.5-0.6; 0.6-0.7; 0.7-0.8; 0.8-1.1; 1.2-1.3; 1.5-1.8; 2.1-2.4 µm); field of view: 85 km, resolution at nadir: 80 m (with orbit at altitude of 650 km)	*Obtaining overlapping images in various ranges of visible and near infrared spectrum with various resolutions on the ground aimed at refining techniques for obtaining, processing and interpreting multi-band video information*

satellite with these instruments on board was launched on 9 June 1974. Others were launched on 15 May 1976, 29 June 1977, 25 January 1978 and 18 June 1980. Beginning with the third launch, the experimental satellites have been placed on a sunsynchronous orbit at a height of 600-650 km.

Analysis of the multi-band imagery obtained has shown that it has a higher information capacity than single-band imagery, in particular for studying surface features. Its higher information content is due to the possibility of using the known reflectivity-wavelength relationship for natural features to identify them on the imagery.

The wider field of view with selected generalization of small details in the multi-band imagery enabled identification of flood plains with persistent high moisture content and denser vegetation, dry valleys of intermittent and ephemeral streams, pollutant discharges near river mouths, sand and dust storms, irrigated land and reservoirs, shelves, underwater vegetation in shallows, surface currents in some areas, surface water pollution near sea ports and pollution of snow around industrial cities.

Information on hydrometeorological processes and phenomena occurring on the land and sea surfaces derived from multi-band imagery is more complete, detailed and accurate than that derived from the analysis of single-band visible imagery obtained from operational "Meteor" satellites. This is because of the higher resolution of multi-band imagery and the possibility in its interpretation, as mentioned above, of using spectral differences caused by the reflectivity variation of natural objects depending on wavelength.

In hydrological applications, ice boundaries and ice concentrations in rivers, lakes and reservoirs are more accurately estimated; ice freezing and drift, the dynamics of ice melting and flooding of valley bottoms can be monitored in greater detail, especially on medium-resolution imagery which allows estimation of the flood area. Multi-band imagery also provides more complete and accurate information for hydrological forecasts of lowland and mountain river runoff and calculation of the intensity of floods. In particular, better information is provided on the boundaries and areal distribution of snow cover in river basins. It is also possible to determine more precisely the area, boundaries, and duration of simultaneous snowmelt.

Information from experimental satellites is of extreme importance for solving the following three hydrological problems:

(a) discovery of laws and the quantitative evaluation of water transfer determining the regimes of the water bodies and areas;

(b) obtaining large-scale images of individual water bodies during specific water regime phases;

(c) development of methods for interpretation of large-scale surveys from operational satellites.

For hydrological investigations evaluating the areal water extent and the prediction of changes in the water content it is very important to have information obtained from different instruments in the field of microwave measurements.

Experience gained in the development and application of satellites and the results of satellite experiments show that the role of satellites in the system of hydrometeorological observations will undoubtedly increase. Likewise, satellites will be used more intensively in providing radio communication for data collection, transmission and distribution.

REFERENCE

Kuprianov, V.V. (1985) Satellite information for surface water research. In: *Hydrological Applications of Remote Sensing and Remote Data Transmission* (Proc. Hamburg Symp., August 1983), 465-474. IAHS Publ. no. 145.

Hydrological Applications of Remote Sensing and Remote Data Transmission (Proceedings of the Hamburg Symposium, August 1983). IAHS Publ. no. 145.

The METEOSAT Operational Programme

L. PERA & D. HOGE
ESA/Toulouse, 18 Avenue E.Belin, F-31055 Toulouse, France

ABSTRACT As a follow-on to the METEOSAT Programme of the European Space Agency (ESA), a new programme called METEOSAT Operational Programme has recently been approved. This programme will be conducted by a new international organization called EUMETSAT, and will be carried out by ESA. The programme will comprise three satellites derived from current METEOSAT satellites. The overall schedule for the programme as well as differences in the legal framework and technical content compared with the previous programme are presented.

Le programme METEOSAT Opérationnel
Pour faire suite au Programme METEOSAT de l'Agence Spatiale Européenne (ASE), un nouveau programme appelé Programme METEOSAT Opérationnel vient d'être décidé. Il sera conduit par une nouvelle organisation internationale appelée EUMETSAT et exécuté par l'ASE. Il mettra en oeuvre trois satellites dérivés des METEOSATs actuels. Le calendrier général de ce programme ainsi que les différences de cadre juridique et de contenu technique avec le programme précédent sont présentés.

INTRODUCTION

In summer 1980, the European Space Agency (ESA) made a proposal for the continuation of the pre-operational programme of the meteorological satellites that it had undertaken in 1972. In January 1981, the first session of the Intergovernmental Conference on a METEOSAT Operational system was held in Paris to examine the desirability and the means of carrying out, under the responsibility of the Meteorological Services, the METEOSAT Operational Programme.

During this session, the Conference, convinced of the need to maintain European participation in the global observing system of the World Weather Watch, impressed by the quality of the results achieved in the course of the pre-operational programme and by their success with the users, and firmly believing that maximum advantage needed to be taken of the experience gained, declared itself in favour of the project. It set up the METEOSAT Operational Programme Working Group (MOPWG) and intrusted it with the preparation of the second session of the Conference, to which a detailed plan would be submitted, covering both the technical and institutional aspects of the programme.

After examining these aspects, the Working Group in 1982 concluded that the execution of the programme in question should be entrusted to ESA which would accordingly have to submit an updated version of its initial proposal. Under the revised proposal, ESA would undertake to carry out the operational programme on behalf of an international organization called EUMETSAT which would be set up for the purpose.

The political will to institute an operational European meteorological programme was fully illustrated when, at the Conference of Plenipotentiaries in Geneva on 24 May 1983, representatives of Belgium, France, Germany, Italy, the Netherlands, Norway, Portugal, Spain, Sweden, Switzerland, Turkey and the United Kingdom signed the EUMETSAT Convention. In addition, three other countries - Finland, Greece and the Republic of Ireland - attended the conference as observers and could well decide, in the near future, to participate in the programme and to sign the Convention.

The delegates decided that the programme should get underway without delay and therefore accepted that the METEOSAT Operational Programme should be conducted as an ESA optional programme until the Convention entered into force. The operational programme will consist of exploiting the data from three satellites representing improved versions of those produced for the pre-operational programme. The launch of the first satellite is planned for May 1987. The programme will terminate in November 1995, at the end of the exploitation of the last of these satellites (see Fig.1).

THE OPERATIONAL METEOSAT SPACECRAFT CONCEPT

The design concept of METEOSAT is based on studies performed by CNES in the late sixties. The europeanization of the programme took place in 1972 and, after a competition phase, the contract to develop and manufacture the METEOSAT satellite was awarded to the COSMOS Consortium at the end of 1973. The kickoff meetings for the operational satellite were held in June and July of 1983. Between 1972 and the present time, two satellites have been launched: METEOSAT-F1 in November 1977 and METEOSAT-F2 in June 1981.

The operational satellite programme is well-supported by:

(a) the early system studies,
(b) the development and manufacturing experience,
(c) the operational experience and orbital performance,
(d) the technical proposals and their evaluation.

However, due to the long interval between these programme phases, the change in personnel, companies, responsibilities, the use of this knowledge often requires a special effort.

The operational satellite is a re-build of the METEOSAT-F2 satellite with two major improvements for the mission capability:

(a) the mission performance transponder provides an additional channel for meteorological data dissemination; and,

(b) the water vapour channel is available in parallel with visible and infrared channels.

A number of other modifications based on F1 and F2 experience are also included.

Figure 2 gives a view of the main modifications and Table 1 summarizes the reasons for these changes.

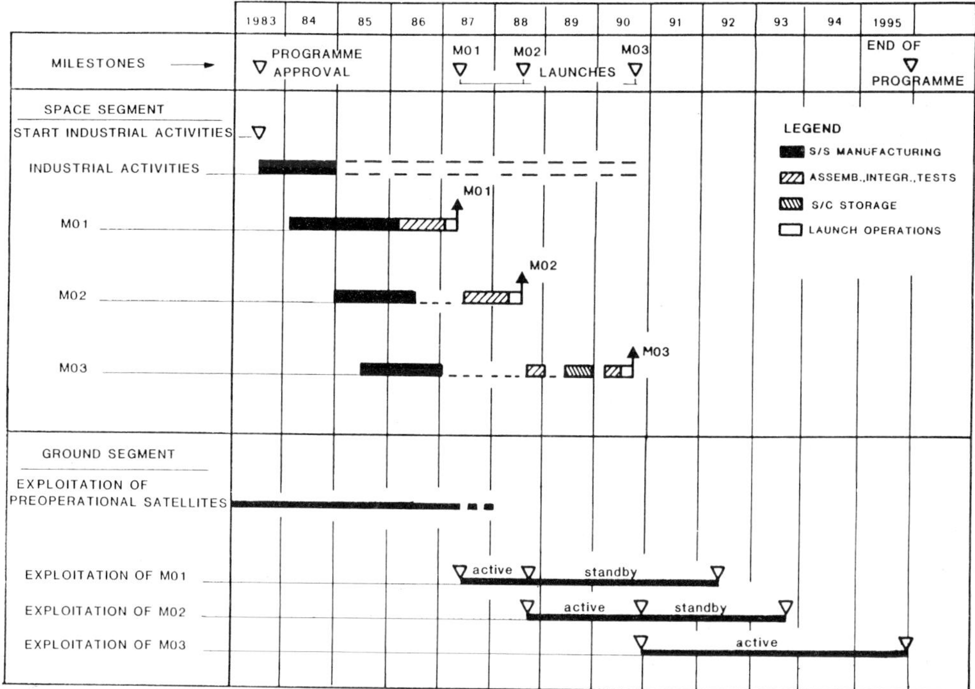

FIG.1 Planning of the METEOSAT Operational Programme.

MISSIONS

The METEOSAT Operational Programme satellites are designed to fulfil three missions: imaging; data dissemination; and data collection. Since the launch of the first operational spacecraft is planned to take place by mid-1987, it is foreseen, in order to ensure continuity of service, that in a bridging phase beginning at the end of 1983 the Customer will take over the exploitation of the pre-operational satellites which are, or will be, in orbit before that launch date. Figure 3 gives a view of the overall METEOSAT system.

Mission 1: earth imaging

The radiance of the earth's surface and of its cloud cover are simultaneously detected in three spectral bands. The details of each image are:

(a) The visible (VIS) image in the 0.5 to 0.9 μm region of the spectrum is made up of 5000 lines, each containing 5000 picture elements. The resolution at the sub-satellite point is 2.5 km. The signal-to-noise ratio will be greater than 200 for 80% albedo.

(b) The thermal infrared (IR) image covers the 10.5-12.5 μm region in the spectrum. It comprises 2500 lines, each containing 2500 picture elements. The resolution at the sub-satellite point is 5 km. The performance, given as NEΔT, will be better than 0.65 K for a black-body at 290 K.

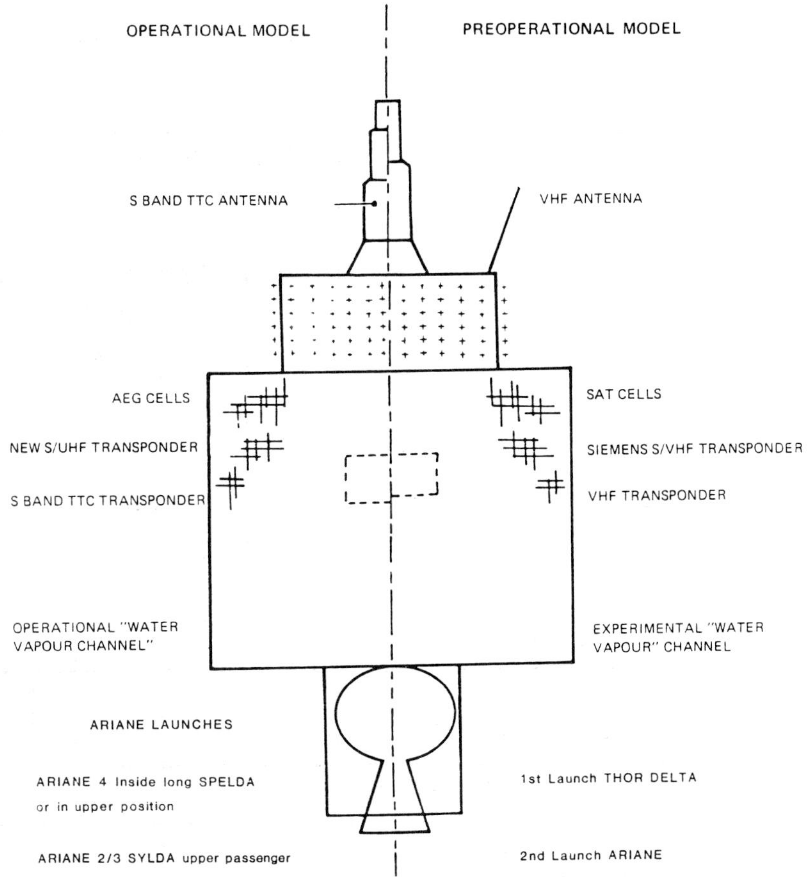

FIG.2 Main modifications between pre-operational and operational satellites.

(c) the water vapour (WV) absorption band image is in the 5.7-7.1 μm region of the spectrum. It consists of 2500 lines, each containing 2500 picture elements. The resolution at the sub-satellite point is 5 km. The performance given as NEΔT will be better than 1 K for a black-body at 260 K.
For each spectral channel the radiometric information is encoded into 256 grey levels.

Mission 2: dissemination

Pre-processed images and other meteorological data are relayed to user stations using dedicated dissemination channels. The transmissions are made in both digital and analogue formats. Transmitted digital data include high resolution images, data collection platform (DCP) messages and meteorological data. Dissemination of meteorological data (MDD) will be possible via the new satellites.

Mission 3: data collection

Environmental data gathered by various types of data collection

TABLE 1 METEOSAT-F2/Operational - reasons for changes per subsystem

Subsystem	additional mission performance	change of launcher	ground system changes	change of manufacturer	change of components	rationalisation of manufacturer	new interfaces
Structure		O				X	O
Thermal control							X
ABM Adapter		O		X		O	
Solar generator	O			X			
Attitude measurement		X				O	
Attitude, orbit control		O			X		
Synchronisation, image control					X		O
Telemetry, telecommand			X			O	
Antennas			X		O		
Power conditioning			O	O	O	O	X
Radiometer	X			O			
Mission transponder	O			X			
Harness				X			O
EGSE				X	O		

X Major O Additional reason

platform (DCPs) are collected by up to 66 channels provided for this purpose. This mission supports platforms which transmit messages according to an agreed schedule (known as selftimed platforms) as well as platforms which only transmit in response to specific environmental criteria (the alert platforms). The channels conform to an internationally agreed specification. The system can be used by both fixed and mobile platforms.

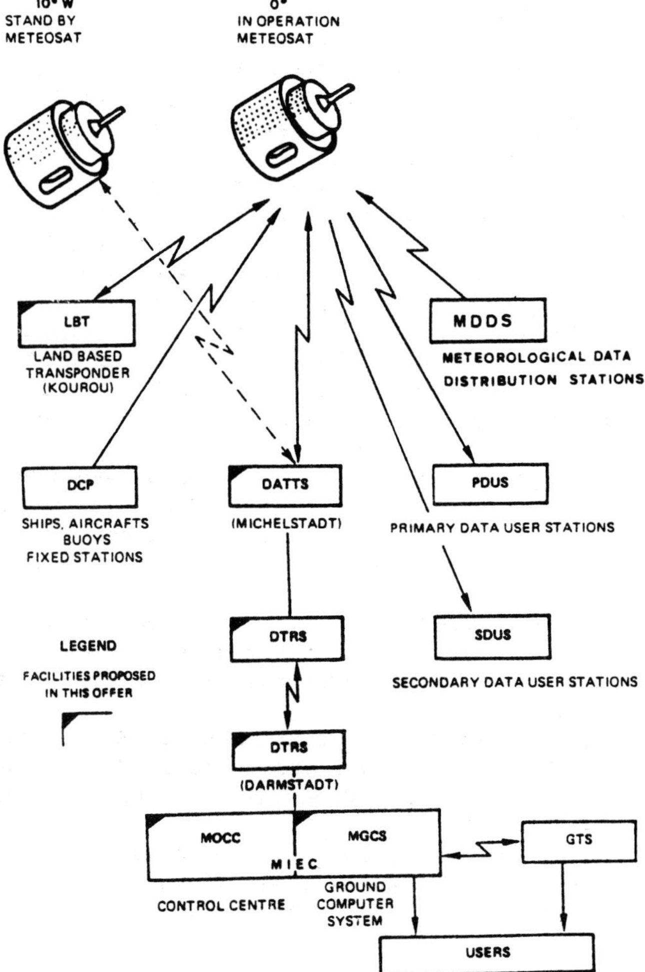

FIG.3 The overall METEOSAT system.

METEOROLOGICAL PRODUCTS

The extraction and distribution of quantitative meteorological data from processed images will be performed by the Meteorological Information Extraction Centre (MIEC) in ESOC.

The actual extraction of products will be performed automatically for the region within at least 50° great circle arc from the sub-satellite point. Before data are distributed, they will be quality-controlled by experienced meteorologists. The availability of all products will be 95% on a monthly basis within the quoted delivery deadline. Products have a 32 x 32 infrared pixel resolution, except for cloud-top-height charts which have a 4 x 4 infrared pixel resolution.

(a) *Cloud motion vectors (CMV):* extracted twice per day at 0000 UT and 1200 UT and distributed to GTS by 0230 UT and 1430 UT. Around 600 vectors per run will be produced with a target accuracy ranging from 5 m s^{-1} RMS for low level to 10 m s^{-1} for high level CMVs. Validation will be against rawindsonde data.

(b) *Sea surface temperatures (SST):* extracted daily at 1200 UT and based on a three-hourly composite, distributed to GTS by 1430 UT. Eight hundred data per day with a target accuracy of $\Delta T < 1.5°C$ RMS. Validation will be against ship and buoy SSTs.

(c) *Cloud analysis (CA):* provides cloud cover in up to three layers together with cloud top temperature. Extraction at 0000 UT and 1200 UT and distributed to GTS by 0230 UT and 1430 UT. Validation will be done by comparison with image data.

(d) *Upper tropospheric humidity (UTH):* provides average relative humidity between 700 and 300 mb in line with the WV channel contribution function. Extraction at 0000 UT and 1200 UT and distributed to GTS by 0230 UT and 1430 UT. Target accuracy $\Delta R < 20\%$ RMS relative humidity. Validation will be done against radiosonde data.

(e) *Cloud top height (CTH):* provides in image form a WEFAX map of cloud tops in 1500 m intervals between 4.5 and 12 km. Extraction will be done at 0300, 0900, 1500, 2100 UT and disseminated within an hour via METEOSAT. Validation will be done by comparison with image data.

(f) *Climate data set (CDS):* several statistical parameters (to be defined by customer) per 32 x 32 infrared pixel segments. Extraction will take place at three-hourly intervals with data being archived for non-real time distribution.

CMV, SST, CA and UTH will be encoded into WMO SATOB Bulletins and injected into the GTS via the Offenbach Regional Telecommunications Hub (DWD). CTH maps will be broadcast as WEFAX pictures via the satellite.

All MIEC products except CTH maps will be archived in digital form in the METEOSAT Archive and will be available as a retrievable standard product from the METEOSAT Data Service.

CONCLUSION

The services which can be offered during the execution of the METEOSAT Operational Programme will satisfy the needs expressed by the Working Group (MOPWG) set up by the Intergovernmental Conference on an Operational METEOSAT System.

The experience of ESA in the production of space systems and their exploitation is a guarantee that the programme will be successful and will meet the requirements of the customer.

Hydrological Applications of Remote Sensing and Remote Data Transmission
(Proceedings of the Hamburg Symposium, August 1983). IAHS Publ. no. 145.

Data collection and location by satellite: the Argos system

MICHEL TAILLADE
Service Argos - Centre National d'Etudes Spatiales, 18 avenue Edouard Belin, 31055 Toulouse Cédex, France

ABSTRACT The French Argos system onboard meteorological NOAA satellites deals with the data collection and the platform location of environmental programmes (meteorology, oceanography, offshore, hydrology, biology, vulcanology, seismology). The Argos system is composed of the user platforms (buoys, balloons, fixed or offshore stations, animals, etc.), the onboard satellite equipment, the data processing centre and the data distribution system for Argos users. Platforms data are available in Toulouse (France) a few hours after their acquisition by satellite and are easily accessible, via usual telephone or telex networks, from anywhere in the world. After three years of operational use, it can be said this unique system has proved its efficiency and reliability and will continue to be used by dozens of countries during the next decade.

Collecte des données et localisation par satellites: le système Argos
RESUME L'équipement français Argos est embarqué à bord des satellites de la NOAA; il permet la collecte de données et la localisation de plates-formes dans différents domaines (météorologie, océanographie, offshore, hydrologie, biologie, vulcanologie, séismologie). Le système Argos comprend dans son ensemble: les plates-formes des utilisateurs dont le type diffère selon le domaine d'activité (bouées, ballons, plates-formes fixes ou mobiles, etc.), l'équipement embarqué à bord des satellites, le Centre Informatique de Toulouse (France), le système de distribution des données. La mise à disposition des résultats a lieu au Centre de Calcul de Toulouse. Les données sont disponibles quelques heures après le passage du satellite dans une région donnée. Elles peuvent être prélevées par téléphone ou par télex suivant une procédure bien définie. Après trois ans de service opérationnel, on peut affirmer que le système Argos a fait ses preuves et qu'il sera utilisé dans la prochaine décennie par des dizaines de pays.

INTRODUCTION

The Argos system is primarily intended to locate fixed or mobile platforms and to collect environmental data from these platforms.

This system is the result of a cooperative programme between the Centre National d'Etudes Spatiales (CNES, France), the National Aeronautics and Space Administration (NASA, USA), and the National Oceanic and Atmospheric Administration (NOAA, USA).

CNES, NASA and NOAA are bound by a Memorandum of Agreement signed in December 1974. The main mission has been to provide an operational service for the entire duration of the TIROS N/NOAA programme, that is from 1979 until at least 1990.

The responsibilities of each agency (Fig.1) can be summarized as follows:

(a) NASA manages the design of TIROS-N (RCA is subcontractor) and the construction of TIROS-N and NOAA-A through NOAA-I spacecraft;

(b) NOAA develops mission requirements, operates the spacecrafts and the ground system;

(c) CNES supplies the Argos data collection system (DCS) for integration into the spacecrafts and the Argos data processing centre (DPC), and manages the Argos DPC and distributes the data.

Service Argos operates the system under the supervision of the Argos Operations Committee (NASA, NOAA, CNES). Its duties include attending to user's interests, coordinating system utilization and promotion, and supervising the system in general.

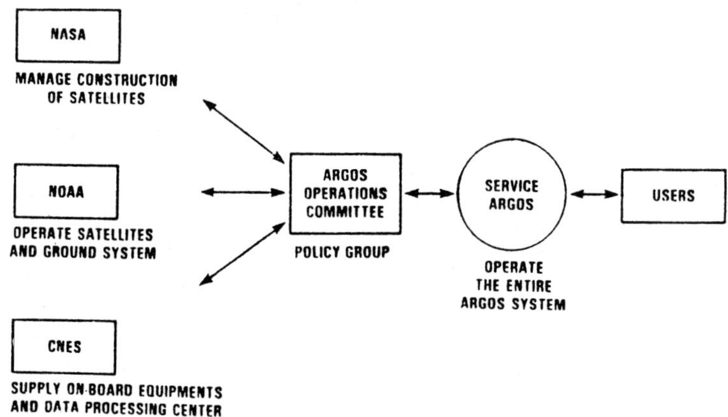

FIG.1 Responsibilities of each agency.

USER PLATFORMS

The electronics package to equip a platform of the user's choice is termed a Platform Transmitter Terminal or PTT. Argos PTTs may be mounted on fixed platforms (meteorological, hydrological stations, etc.) and moving platforms (buoys, balloons, icebergs, animals, etc.). However, all include as a minimum: ultrastable oscillator (severity or stability requirement depends on whether the platform's location is required), antenna, digital message generation logic, power supply, interfaces with sensors (Fig.2).

The transmitted standard message comprises an unmodulated part, for satellite receiver lock-on and a modulated one which includes synchronization signals, PTT identification code and sensor data.

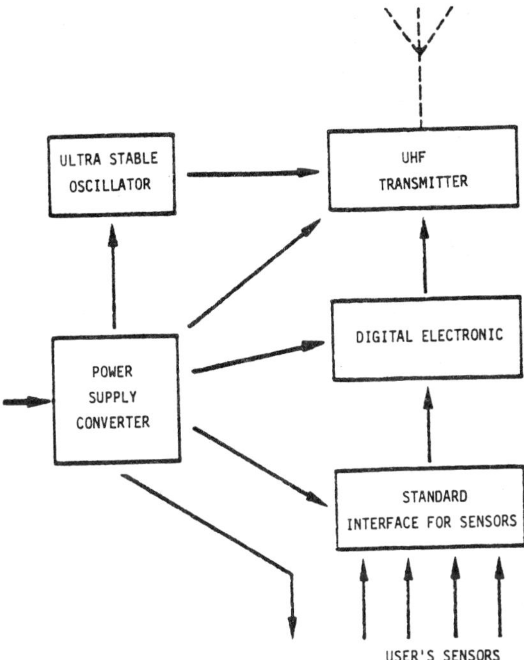

FIG.2 The user platform.

The main characteristics of Argos PTTs can be summarized as follows:

(a) Transmission frequency is 401.650 MHz at regular intervals, i.e. 40-60 s in the case of platforms to be positioned, every 100-200 s for a data-collection-only-type platform. Message duration depends on the number of sensor output values to be transmitted, but it is always less than 1 s.

(b) Radiated power of 3 W with a low power consumption of just 200 mW which allows power sources such as dry cells, conventional batteries and even solar cells.

(c) Message capacity for sensor data is 32 to 256 bits; this length can be adapted to user requirements, in the case of standard processing (see Argos DPC description), by fields of 32 bits each. Each of 32 possible sensors can then be generated between 0 and 16 bits, inclusive.

(d) Ease of implementation, since all Argos PTTs operate on the same frequency and are of moderate price. The equipment for an individual up-link with the satellite can be purchased for US $2000.

THE ONBOARD EQUIPMENT

The input to the Argos onboard DCS "sees" a composite signal comprising a mixture of messages generated by a number of different PTTs within the satellite's coverage.

As each message is acquired, the DCS records the time and date, measures the carrier frequency and demodulates the platform identification number and sensor data (Fig.3). These data are then

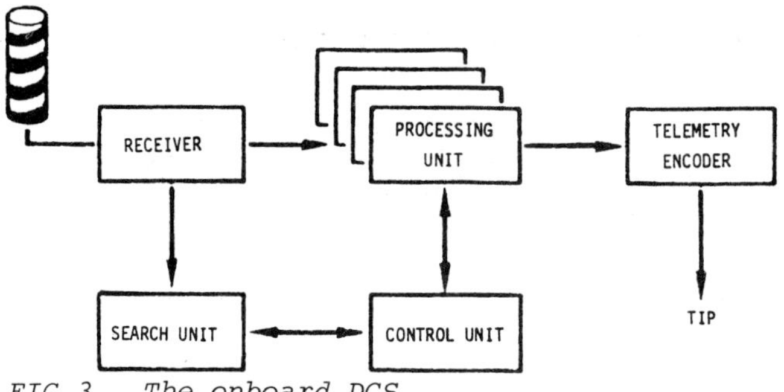

FIG.3 The onboard DCS.

formatted and stored onboard magnetic tape recorders. Each time one of the two satellites passes over one of the three telemetry stations (Wallops Island, Virginia, USA; Gilmore Creek, Alaska, USA; Lannion, France), the data recorded on tape are read-out and transmitted to the ground stations. Once a satellite has completed telemetry data transmission for a particular pass, the received data are transmitted to NESDIS (National Environmental Satellite, Data and Information Service) Center at Suitland, Maryland, USA. Data concerning the Argos system are separated from those concerning other satellite experiments and transmitted to the Argos DPC located in the Toulouse Space Centre in France (Fig.4).

The instantaneous coverage on the ground corresponds to a circle with a radius of 2600 km for a minimum receiving angle of 5°. From one day to the next the "contact" passes for a given platform come nearly at the same time within a satellite's coverage (sunsynchronous satellites).

The indicated number of contact passes per day (Table 1) corresponds to the mean number of passes during which the potential contact time is at least 10 minutes.

The problem of how to select messages for acquisition is

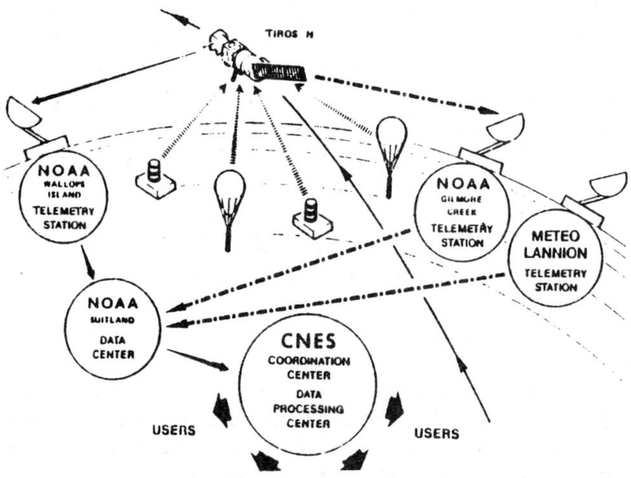

FIG.4 The Argos data flow.

TABLE 1 Number of "contact" passes per day

Latitude	*Number of contacts:* *Minimum*	*Mean*	*Maximum*
0	*6*	*7*	*8*
±15	*8*	*8*	*9*
±30	*8*	*9*	*12*
±45	*10*	*11*	*12*
±55	*16*	*16*	*18*
±65	*21*	*22*	*23*
±75	*28*	*28*	*28*
±90	*28*	*28*	*28*

essentially the "random access" problem. The satellite must acquire the largest possible number of messages, yet the number of message processing channels is obviously limited. The key design concepts can be summarized as follows: messages from platforms within the satellite coverage appear at the input of the onboard receiver in a random fashion; message separation in time is obtained through the asynchronization of the transmissions and the use of different repetition periods; message separation in frequency is achieved as a result of the different Doppler shifts in the carrier frequency transmitted by the various platforms. Up to four simultaneous messages can be aquired providing they are separated in frequency. The onboard DCS performs within instrument specification, i.e. the probability of acquiring a message during one pass of a satellite, providing all messages transmitted during this pass are identical, is over 0.99.

Direct readout capabilities

PTT messages received by the Argos DCS are mixed onboard the satellite with data from other experiments. The combined data streams are handled in two ways: stored onboard tape recorders and transmitted to the ground in real time by a 136.77 or 137.77 MHz transmitter. Thus, the satellite acts like a relay that continuously transmits to the ground a signal containing data from PTTs within the satellite's coverage at that time. By using a suitable receiving station, the telemetry signal can be picked up (within 2000 km radius around the station) and the data extracted each time the satellites pass overhead (Fig.5).

These local user terminals (LUT) are designed mostly to handle data-collection-only platforms. The main advantages of a LUT are the real-time data availability and thus the alarm capabilities of this system. The drawbacks compared to a centralized system such as the Argos DPC include: the duplication of equipment and permanent manpower to ensure operational use; the satellite coverage limitations, and the non-availability of data at a single place (for example the decision centre).

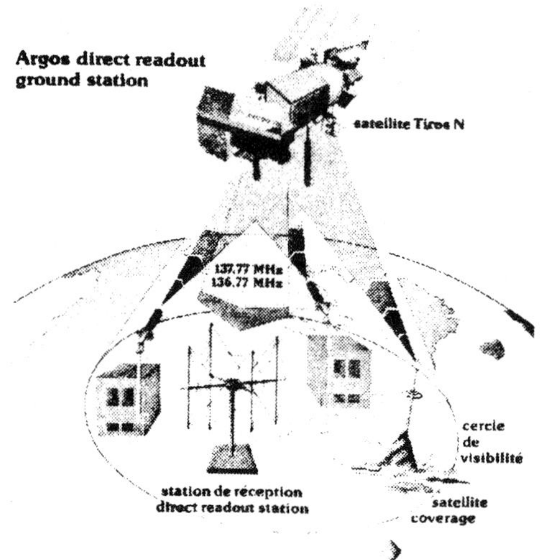

FIG.5 The local user terminal.

THE DATA PROCESSING CENTRE

System configuration

The Argos data processing system was designed for a reliability of 99%. This is achieved by providing redundant facilities at all critical points. All telemetry data are transmitted from the telemetry receiving stations to the NOAA-NESDIS processing centre at Suitland, Maryland, where the Argos data are extracted for retransmission to the Argos DPC over a dedicated 7200 bps communications link. In Toulouse, the incoming Argos data are received and stored by a French-built Télémécanique T1600 acquisition computer. A second modem is on standby for the NOAA-CNES link. The computers, including a standby T1600, are linked to the main data processing facility via a high-bit-rate (4800 baud) link. The main facility is an Iris 80 bi-processor manufactured by Cii Honeywell-Bull.

Results are distributed in real time by a third T1600 computer which, through the intermediary of a microprocessor-based system, manages the dissemination of information to all system users. Backup is provided by the standby T1600 computer. All components of the system can be readily and quickly reconfigured so that operational services can be performed with minimum degradation under virtually all conditions (Fig.6).

Preprocessing

The real time preprocessing performed can be summarized as follows: management of telemetry data streams; elimination of redundant data and arrangement of telemetry data in chronological order; separation of users telemetry data and satellite housekeeping telemetry data;

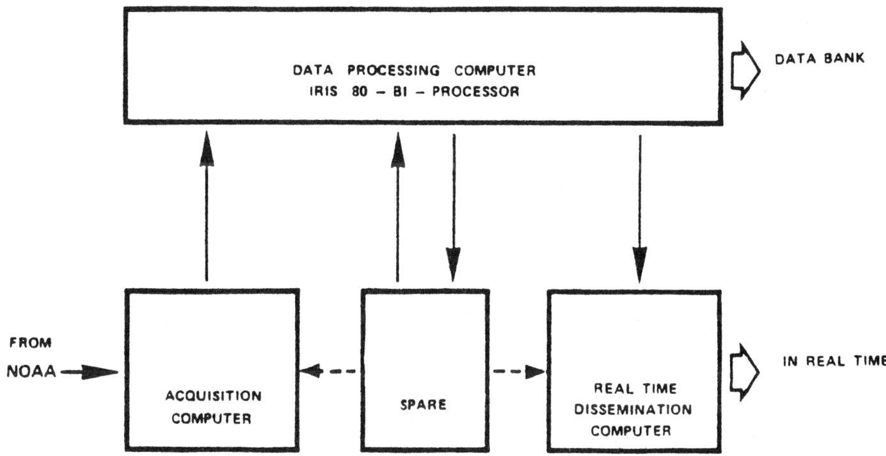

FIG.6 The Argos data processing centre flow chart.

processing of housekeeping telemetry data; processing of users telemetry data - message restitution and verification of content, and time coding of each message in universal time (UT); determination of incoming signal level (in decibels) and Doppler frequency (in hertz); and, finally, message classification by PTT (Fig.7).

Platform location and accuracy

The platform location is determined solely by measuring the Doppler effect on the carrier frequency of incoming messages. As the satellite's orbit is accurately known, five Doppler measurements during a given pass are sufficient to attempt a location calculation.
The number of location calculations per day as a function of

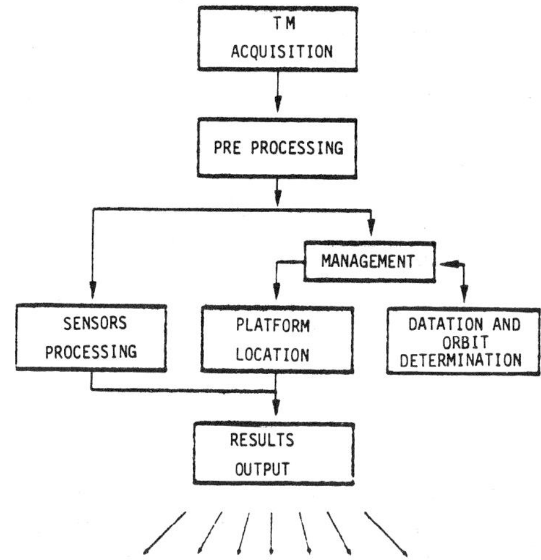

FIG.7 Software flow chart.

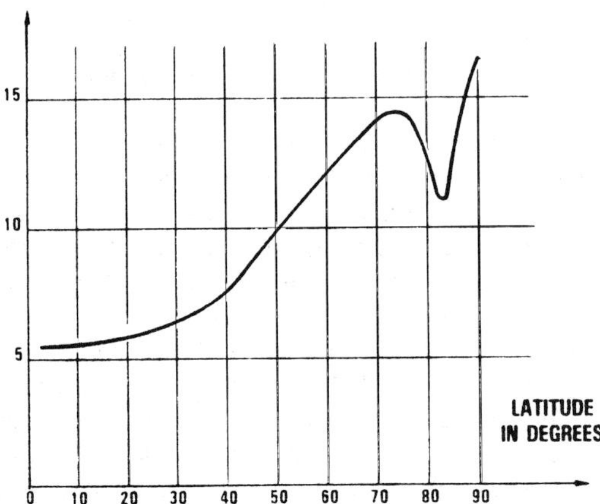

FIG.8 Number of location calculations per day.

latitude is shown in Fig.8.

The location accuracy of the Argos system is affected by numerous factors. In so far as the PTTs are concerned, the most important parameter remains the medium-term (20-minute) stability of the oscillator, irrespective of the cause of frequency drift.

Table 2 summarizes the results on location accuracy both at 1σ and at 3σ, given as a function of oscillator medium-term stability.

Two important conclusions can be drawn. First, even if the required accuracy is only very low, it is not advisable to use oscillators for which the medium-term stability is less than 10^{-7}. At 2 x 10^{-7} the error is several tens of kilometres while the system does not operate at all for greater errors. Secondly, with very stable oscillators (10^{-9}) the location accuracy may reach 150 m at 1σ and 500 m at 3σ. Since the system is apparently free from systematic errors, by averaging the positions obtained for fixed platforms over several days it is possible to reduce the error to less than 100 m.

TABLE 2 Location accuracy of the Argos system as a function of oscillator stability

Oscillator stability	*Accuracy (m): At 1σ 66°*	*At 3σ 99°*
2×10^{-9}	150	500
5×10^{-9}	500	1300
10^{-8}	1100	2000
2×10^{-8}	2100	3600
5×10^{-8}	4000	6000
10^{-7}	5500	9000

Sensor data processing

Sensor data processing is also performed in real time. The data gathered by platform sensors can be processed in several different ways. Data from each platform sensor are processed independently so that a different processing option can be selected for each.

With respect to data code conversion, in the case of sensors that generate data in pure binary code, the code conversion program can supply data in octal, decimal or hexadecimal. For data received in BCD (binary coded decimal) form, the only available conversion is into decimal. For data encoded directly in ASCII, there is no code conversion, i.e. the output data will be in the same code.

Standard processing corresponds to the conversion of sensor data into engineering parameters. This is performed using a calibration curve, defined by a maximum of 20 points, provided by the user for each platform sensor. The points may be chosen so as to optimize the accuracy of the encoded data. Each sensor calibration curve must be independent of all others.

At the request of various users, a number of special sensor data processing options have been developed and integrated into the online processing system. The definition of such processing options is subject to negotiations between the user and Service Argos so that the complexity of the processing programs to be developed can be determined prior to their integration with the system software.

DATA DISTRIBUTION SYSTEM

It is important for a system of this type, which is primarily intended to provide user services, to offer data distribution options compatible with modern data transmission techniques. The data distribution system was designed to supply results the moment that they became available, that is, immediately after the corresponding data flow has been processed.

On-line distribution

On-line data distribution may be via:

(a) The Global Telecommunications System (GTS): the Argos DPC is linked to the main GTS hub in Paris; this means that results can be available in Canada or the USA in 20 minutes. The results are disseminated either as soon as the processing is completed or at synoptic hours, but in any case all data are converted into meteorological codes (special processing option), i.e. COLBA for position and scientific measurement from tropospheric balloons, DRIBU for the same type of data concerning drifting buoys, HYDRA for hydrological data, etc.

(b) Switched networks: telephone and telex lines are available at Service Argos to all system users. The dial-in and dialogue procedures are rather simple and the user requires a telephone and an acoustic coupler terminal or a standard telex.

(c) Dedicated links or networks: a permanent dedicated link has been developed for the Toulouse-Suitland connection. It is possible to gain direct access to the results of North American experiments through a terminal concentrator at Suitland by dialling one of the two telephone numbers of this remote "Argos computer". A connection to the French TRANSPAC dedicated network is working allowing the possibility of access on other dedicated networks, such as EURONET and TIMENET, because of their mutual interconnection (Fig.9).

When accessing the computer, users can choose between three files:

(a) AJOUR: for all platforms belonging to a given experiment, this file contains the most recent platform location data and the last sensor message selected according to predetermined quality criteria.

(b) TELEX: for all platforms belonging to an experiment, this file contains, in chronological order, one sensor message and the corresponding position data for each of the satellites.

(c) DISPOSE: for all platforms belonging to a given experiment, this file contains, in chronological order, all sensor messages and all location data for all orbits.

In the last two files, data that are more than 12-h old are eliminated and replaced by more recent data.

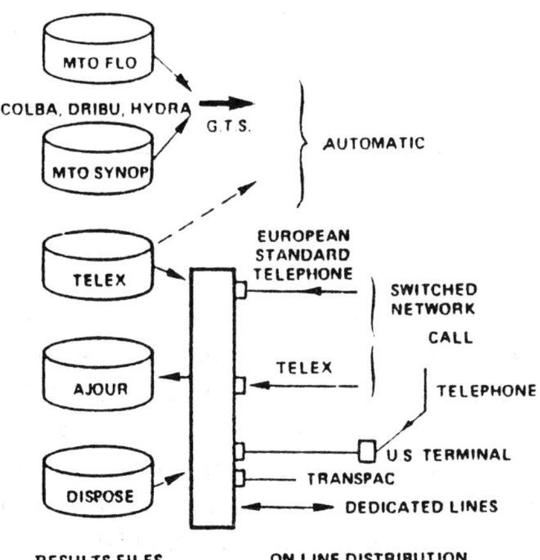

FIG.9 Argos data distribution.

Off-line distribution

Results for off-line distribution are obtained from the data bank which itself is supplied in real time. Data stored in the data bank are read out once a week for all current experiments. These data, in the form of computer printouts or magnetic tapes, are forwarded once a fortnight or once a month, as requested by the user, by the fastest postal means available. Magnetic tapes containing data from several experiments are also available.

Data availability

The critical parameter for an operational data distribution system is the overall response time. This corresponds to the interval

TABLE 3 Number of users of the Argos system

	1980: Number	*%*	*1981: Number*	*%*	*1982: Number*	*%*
USA	*30*	*29*	*38*	*29*	*45*	*30*
France	*28*	*27*	*33*	*25*	*35*	*23*
Canada	*17*	*16*	*22*	*17*	*19*	*12.5*
Norway	*6*	*6*	*8*	*6*	*11*	*7*
United Kingdom	*5*	*5*	*7*	*5.5*	*12*	*8*
Japan	*5*	*5*	*5*	*4*	*11*	*7*
Australia	*3*	*3*	*3*	*2*	*4*	*3*
Sweden	*2*	*2*	*2*	*1.5*	*3*	*2*
Denmark	*1*	*1*	*2*	*1.5*	*2*	*1*
New Zealand	*2*	*2*	*2*	*1.5*	*1*	*0.7*
South Africa	*1*	*1*	*1*	*1*	*2*	*1*
Portugal	*1*	*1*	*1*	*1*	*1*	*0.7*
Finland	*1*	*1*	*1*	*1*	*0*	*0*
Germany	*1*	*1*	*1*	*1*	*3*	*2*
India	*1*	*1*	*1*	*1*	*2*	*1*
New Guinea	*1*	*1*	*1*	*1*	*0*	*0*
Brazil	*1*	*1*	*1*	*1*	*1*	*0.7*
17	*106*		*129*		*152*	

between the time when a given platform message is acquired by the satellite and the time when the data are made available to the user following processing at the Argos DPC in Toulouse. The breakdown of this interval depends on the orbit interval (up to 100 m), the time for data transmission from the telemetry stations to NOAA-NESS facility, the transmission over the dedicated Suitland-Toulouse link and the processing time for data generated by a single orbit. The statistics corresponding to 31 months of observation are as follows:

56% of all data were made available in less than 2 h 30 min;
66% of all data in less than 3 h;
87.5% of all data in less than 6 h.

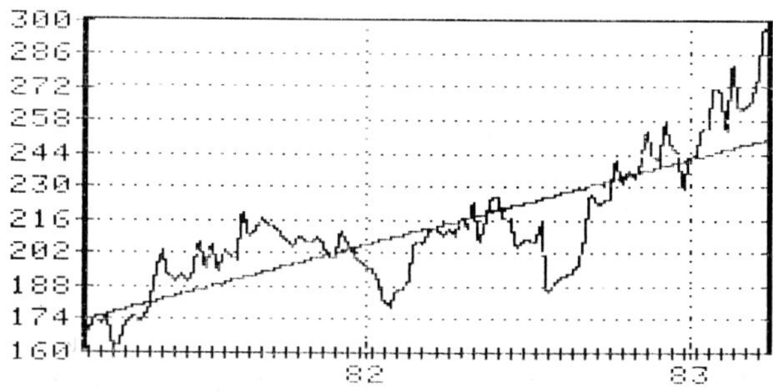

FIG.10 Number of platforms using Argos.

SYSTEM UTILIZATION

Platform number

Figure 10 indicates the evolution of the number of platforms in operation from the beginning of 1981.

Number of users

Table 3 indicates the evolution of the number of the users admitted to the system to the end of 1982. This corresponds to programs under preparation for implementation and those already operating in the system.

Hydrological Applications of Remote Sensing and Remote Data Transmission
(Proceedings of the Hamburg Symposium, August 1983). IAHS Publ. no. 145.

Development of satellite remote sensing systems in Japan

NATIONAL SPACE DEVELOPMENT AGENCY OF JAPAN
(Yasushi Horikawa, 2-4-1 Hamamatsu-cho, Minatoku, Tokyo, Japan)

ABSTRACT In 1978, the Space Activities Commission of Japan, the policy making body of the Japanese space programme, produced an "Outline of Japan's Space Development Policy", which proposed that a marine and land observation satellite series should be developed in order to establish an earth observation operational system. The National Space Development Agency of Japan (NASDA) is carrying out the research and development of the satellite remote sensing system including satellites, sensors and ground facilities. Marine Observation Satellite-1, which is the first satellite of the series, is now under development with a launch targeted for 1986. The development of Earth Resources Satellite-1, which will carry a synthetic aperture radar, has been in progress since 1980. The research and development of active microwave sensors, which will be mounted on the follow-up satellite of the marine observation satellite series, are being carried out. This paper outlines the present status of development of satellite sensing systems in Japan.

Le développement des systèmes de télédétection par satellites au Japon

RESUME En 1978 la Commission des Activités Spatiales du Japon, l'organisme responsable de la politique du programme spatial japonais a mis au point un "Résumé de la Politique de Développement Spatial du Japon" qui proposait qu'une série de satellites d'observations marines et terrestres soit mise au point pour réaliser un système opérationnel d'observations terrestres. L'Agence Nationale de Développement Spatial du Japon (NASDA) éxécute les recherches et la réalisation d'un système de télédétection par satellites comportant les satellites, les senseurs et les aménagements au sol. Le Satellite-1 d'Observations marines, qui est le premier satellite de la série est actuellement en cours de réalisation, son lancement est programmé pour 1986. La mise au point du Satellite-1 de Resources terrestres, qui portera un radar à ouverture synthétique a progressé depuis 1980. Les recherches et la mise au point de senseurs actifs à micro-ondes qui seront montés sur le prochain satellite de la série des satellites d'observations marines, sont en cours. Cette communication donne un aperçu sur l'état actuel de développement du système de télédétection par satellites au Japon.

MARINE OBSERVATION SATELLITE-1

Marine Observation Satellite-1 (MOS-1), Japan's first earth observation satellite, is an experimental satellite to establish the fundamental technologies which are common to both marine and land observation satellites and to collect information on the earth's surface.

The conceptual design and the preliminary design of MOS-1 were carried out in 1978 and 1979 respectively, and the basic design was completed at the end of July 1981. The detailed design was completed at the end of June 1983 and a prototype satellite is now being manufactured. MOS-1 will be launched by a N-II launch vehicle from the Tanegashima Space Centre in 1986.

MOS-1 system and objectives

The mission objectives of the MOS-1 programme are as follows;

(a) Establishment of fundamental technologies which are common to both the marine and land observation satellite.

(b) Observation of the state of the sea surface and atmosphere using visible, infrared and microwave radiometers, and verification of the performance of these sensors. In order to accomplish these objectives, MOS-1 carries three types of sensors: multispectral electronic self scanning radiometer (MESSR); visible and thermal-infrared radiometer (VTIR) and microwave scanning radiometer (MSR). Selected orbital parameters are as follows:

Altitude	about 909 km
Inclination	about 99.1 degrees
Recurrent period	17 days
Local time of decending node	10-11 a.m.

The orbit will be adjusted during the two years after launch by an orbit control system to keep the cross track drift from the nominal orbit of ground track at the equator within 20 km. Satellite control will be made by using NASDA's satellite tracking and control system and data acquisition facilities will be installed at the Earth Observation Centre (EOC) located about 50 km northwest of Tokyo, presently receiving the Landsat data. The total MOS-1 system is illustrated in Fig.1.

Sensors

As noted, MOS-1 will mount three types of sensors to observe visible, near infrared, infrared and microwave regions. A brief overview of each sensor follows.

Multispectral electronic self-scanning radiometer (MESSR)

A unique feature of this radiometer is that CCD is selected as the image detector to eliminate the moving portion in the sensor. The CCD is composed of 2048 photo-sensitive elements, and the size of one photosensitive element is about 14 μrad x 14 μrad, which corresponds to a measuring area of 50 m x 50 m on the ground. One CCD detector produces an earth image 100 km wide, such that a pair of sensors is required to cover the 180 km width which is the distance between adjacent orbits of MOS-1.

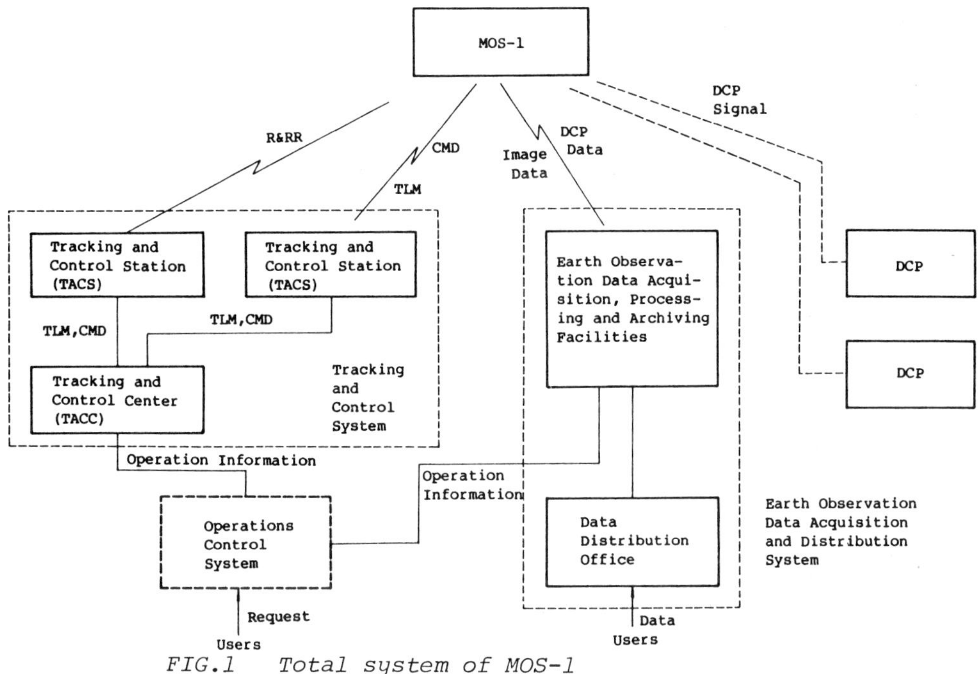

FIG.1 Total system of MOS-1

Figure 2 indicates the image producing concept of MESSR. Separate or simultaneous operation of sensors can be made by ground command. Major characteristics of MESSR are shown in Table 1.

Each sensor is composed of two optical systems which provide an earth surface image of four bands in the visible and near infrared region given in Table 1. Image signals generated by CCD are fed to

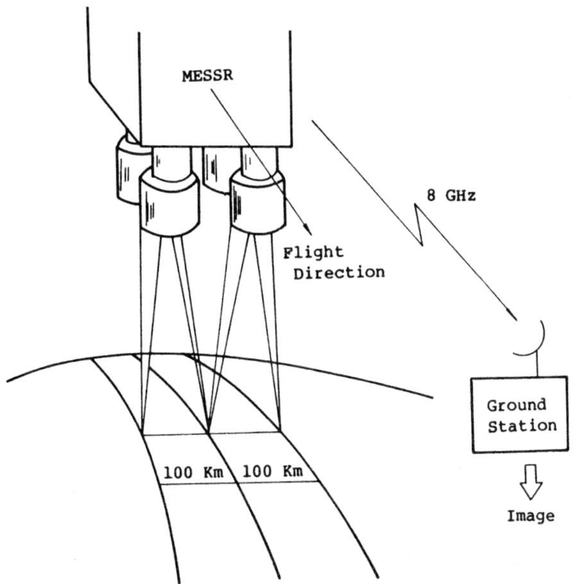

FIG.2 Image producing concept of MESSR.

TABLE 1 Characteristics of the MESSR

Item	*MESSR characteristics*
Wavelength	*0.51-0.59 μm* *0.61-0.69 μm* *0.72-0.80 μm* *0.80-1.10 μm*
IFOV	*54.7 ± 5 μrad*
Swath width (one optical element)	*100 km*
Scanning method	*electrical*
Optics	*Gauss type*
Detector	*2048 elements CCD*
S/N	*39-15 dB*
Quantization levels	*7.6 ms*
Data rate	*8.78 Mbits s^{-1} (including VTIR data)*
Power	*69 W*
Weight	*64 kg*

signal processing unit and converted to six bit digital signals. Signal produced by the VTIR is also combined in the MESSR data stream, and these combined data are sent to the modulator.

A solid state transmitter on 8 GHz band is newly developed to transmit the high speed image data. Satisfactory data have been obtained during BBM phase and design efforts will be continued to meet temperature conditions and environmental conditions required in orbit.

Visible and thermal infrared radiometer (VTIR) The VTIR has one visible band and three infrared bands. Scanning of the earth surface is made by a rotating mirror which has an aperture diameter of about 15 cm. Si-PIN diode and H_gCdT_e are selected for the visible and infrared detectors, respectively. IFOV of this radiometer is 1 mrad for visible band and 3 mrad for infrared bands which correspond to about 1 km x 1 km and 3 km x 3 km on the ground, respectively. Arrangement of IFOV is illustrated in Fig.3. Characteristics of the VTIR are tabulated in Table 2.

Each detector developed for this radiometer has two photo-electric converting elements on the focal plane to increase reliability. Generated image signals are A/D converted and fed to the MESSR signal processing unit as previously mentioned.

Development effort is also continued on this VTIR, and radiation cooling characteristics for infrared detectors is being carefully examined.

Microwave scanning radiometer (MSR) The MSR is composed of two Dicke type radiometers with frequencies of 23.8 GHz and 31.4 GHz band to observe sea surface temperature and liquid water/water vapour in the atmosphere. Characteristics of MSR are given in Table 3.

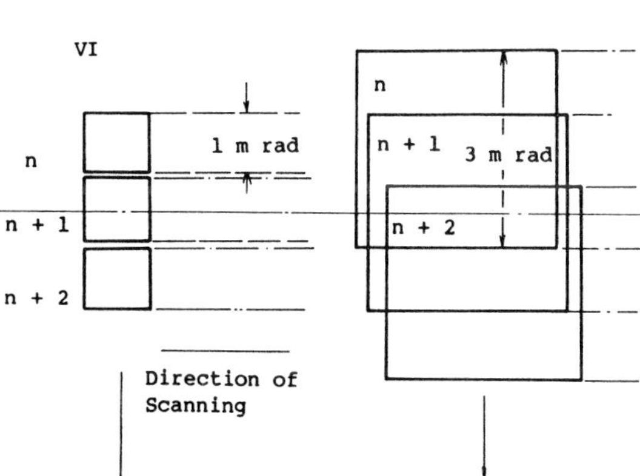

FIG.3 Arrangement of IFOV of VTIR.

TABLE 2 Characteristics of the VTIR

Item	*VTIR characteristics: Visible*	*Thermal infrared*
Wavelength	*0.5-0.7 μm*	*6.0-7.0 μm* *10.5-11.5 μm* *11.5-12.5 μm*
IFOV	*1 mrad*	*3 mrad*
Swath width (km)	*500 km*	*500 km*
Scanning method	*Mechanical*	*Mechanical*
Scan period	*1/7.3 s*	*1/7.3 s*
Detector	*Si-PIN Diode*	H_g *Cd Te*
Optics	*Ritchey-Chretien*	*Ritchey-Chretien*
S/N	*55 dB (Alb. = 80%)*	-
NEΔT	-	*0.5 K (at 300K)*
Quantization level	*256 (8 bits)*	*256 (8 bits)*
Total power	*35 W*	
Total weight	*20 kg*	

EARTH RESOURCE SATELLITE-1

System requirements and configuration

The total system of the ERS-1 programme is shown in Fig.4. This ERS-1 programme is under study. Image data from the synthetic aperture radar (SAR) and visible and near infrared radiometer (VNR) will be transmitted to data receiving stations of the earth observation station in Japan and foreign data receiving stations. ERS-1 tracking will be done by NASDA tracking stations and the TDRS net-

TABLE 3 Characteristics of MSR

Item	MSR characteristics	
Frequency	23.8 ± 0.2 GHz	31.4 ± 0.25 GHz
Beam width	1.99°	1.45°
Integration time	10, 47 ms	10, 47 ms
Swath width	317 km	317 km
Scanning method	Mechanical (conical scan)	Mechanical (conical scan)
Dynamic range	30 K-330 K	30 K-330 K
Antenna type	Offset casegrain	Offset casegrain
Receiver type	Dicke	Dicke
Accuracy	1.5 K (at 300 K)	1.5 K (at 300 K)
Scan period	3.2 s	
Quantization level	1024 (10 bits)	1024 (10 bits)
Data rate	2 K bits s^{-1}	2 K bits s^{-1}
Total power	60 W	
Total weight	54 kg	

work of the United States. ERS-1 will be launched by an H-I launch vehicle (two stages) of NASDA from Tanegashima Space Centre in Japan. Launch capability of H-I is approximately 1400 kg with about 570 km altitude circular orbit and about 98° inclination.

ERS-1 system design was performed based on the following criteria. System design is conducted with such technologies as design, test and integration techniques developed in the past space programme.

Since each subsystem will be developed separately as a module from the procurement policy, system requirements and interface conditions must be cleared. Some components will be, however, imported from foreign suppliers.

Each subsystem utilizes existing technology as much as possible. However, if new technology is needed, this must be started in an

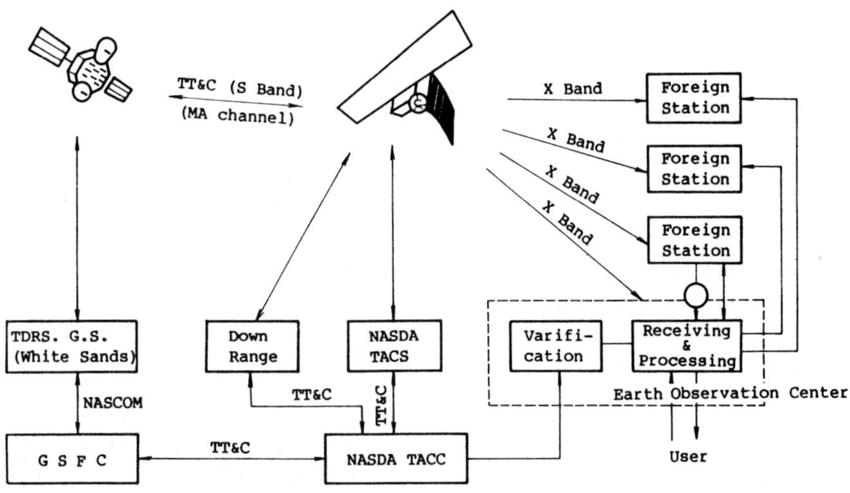

FIG.4 Total system of ERS-1.

early phase. SAR, VNR and bus equipment will be designed by domestic technology from this standpoint. Spacecraft bus equipment will achieve high reliability, weight reduction and low power consumption. System and subsystem design of ERS-1 will take into account the expansion of following operational and large scaled satellites. Also the design must consider the test facility and test method.

Design of mission equipment

Mission equipment of ERS-1 will be described for SAR, VNR, MDR and MDT.

Synthetic aperture radar (SAR) SAR is a main observation equipment to establish the technology of an active sensing satellite. L-band radar frequency was selected from the developing feasibility of antenna flatness and high power transmitter. Off nadir angle of 33° of antenna was selected from the point of view feasibility of pulse repetition frequency, signal to noise ratio and signal to ambiguity ratio. SAR characteristics are shown in Table 4.

TABLE 4 SAR characteristics

Item	*Characteristics*
Swath width	*74 km*
Spatial resolution	*25 m x 25 m*
Off nadir angle	*33 degrees*
Transmitting frequency	*1275 MHz*
Polarization	*H-H linear*
RF band width	*12 MHz*
S/N	*7 dB*
S/A	*20 dB*
Data rate	*60 MHz*
Transmitting power	*1 kW peak*
Pulse width	*35 μs*
Pulse compression ratio	*450*
Pulse repetition frequency	*1550-1690 pps*
Antenna size	*2.4 m x 12 m*
Weight antenna	*134 kg*
Weight electronics	*120 kg*

Visible and near infrared radiometer (VNR) VNR is an improvement of MESSR in the area of resolution and swath width installed in MOS-1 which was the first remote sensing satellite in Japan. VNR data will be used not only for optical observation but also complement SAR data. Characteristics of VNR are shown in Table 5.

Mission data recorder (MDR) Observation of ERS-1 will be done mainly by the existing Landsat station. However, as a backup to the Landsat station and for the area where the Landsat station is not available, a high density data recorder, called Mission Data Recorder

TABLE 5 VNR characteristics

Item	*Characteristics*
Swath width	*150 km*
Spatial resolution	*25 x 25 m*
Wavelength (1)	*0.45-0.52 μm*
(2)	*0.52-0.60 μm*
(3)	*0.63-0.69 μm*
(4)	*0.76-0.95 μm*
IFOV	*44 μrad*
FOV	*15.4°*
Image acquisition time	*3.6 ms*
Weight	*40 kg*

(MDR), is installed in ERS-1. This data recorder will be procured from the USA.

Characteristics of MDR are shown in Table 6.

TABLE 6 MDR characteristics

Item	*Characteristics*
Capacity	*272 Gbits*
Data rate (input/output)	*30 M pbs x 2 ch*
Recording/reproducing time	*20 min*
Weight	*approx. 80 kg*

Mission data transmitter (MDT) Observation data will be transmitted through the Mission Data Transmitter (MDT). In order to receive the ERS-1 data at the Landsat station, a 20 W TWTA transmitter will be used. A difficult problem with this transmitter is the on/off cycle of the transmitter. Reliability in this field will be studied further.

Characteristics of MDT are shown in Table 7.

GMS-2 SYSTEM

Mission objectives

As a member of WMO, Japan responded to the needs of the Global Atmospheric Research Programme (GARP) and WWW by developing a Geostationary Meteorological Satellite, known as GMS. In July 1977, GMS was launched into geosynchronous orbit, approximately 36 000 km above the equator at 140°E longitude. Epitomizing the spirit of international cooperation manifested by the Global Observing System, Japan's GMS is joined in its celestial watch by the United States'

TABLE 7 MDT characteristics

Item	*Characteristics*
Frequency	*8025-8400, 2 frequencies*
Data rate	*60 M bps/1 frequency*
Modulation	*QPSK*
EIRP	*EL 90° 2 dBW*
	EL 5° 17 dBW
Radiation pattern	*Shaped broad beam*
Polarization	*RHCL*
RF band width	*60 MHz/1 frequency*
Weight	*40 kg*

GOES satellites positioned at 75° and 135°W; Europe's METEOSAT at 0°; and Russia's GOMS at 70°E (GOMS replaced by GOES at 57°E during the First GARP Global Experiment (FGGE)).

GMS-2 (see Fig.5), the successor of GMS, was developed to continue

FIG.5 Geostationary Meteorological Satellite "GMS-2".

this meteorological satellite service.

The GMS-2 was launched by Japanese N-II rocket from Tanegashima Space Centre. Mission objectives of GMS-2 are fundamentally the same as GMS: weather watch by VISSR; collection of weather data; distribution of weather data; monitoring of solar particles.

Progress of GMS-2 programme

As shown in Fig.6, the basic and detailed design of GMS-2 was performed in 1978. During 1979 and 1980, two spacecraft (protoflight model and flight model) were assembled, integrated and tested by Hughes Aircraft Company. After the system integration test, two spacecraft were shipped to Japan. The protoflight model was stored at the Tsukuba Space Centre as a back-up. The flight model spacecraft was checked out and prepared for launch at Tanegashima Space Centre of NASDA. After launch, an in-orbit check of GMS-2 was performed.

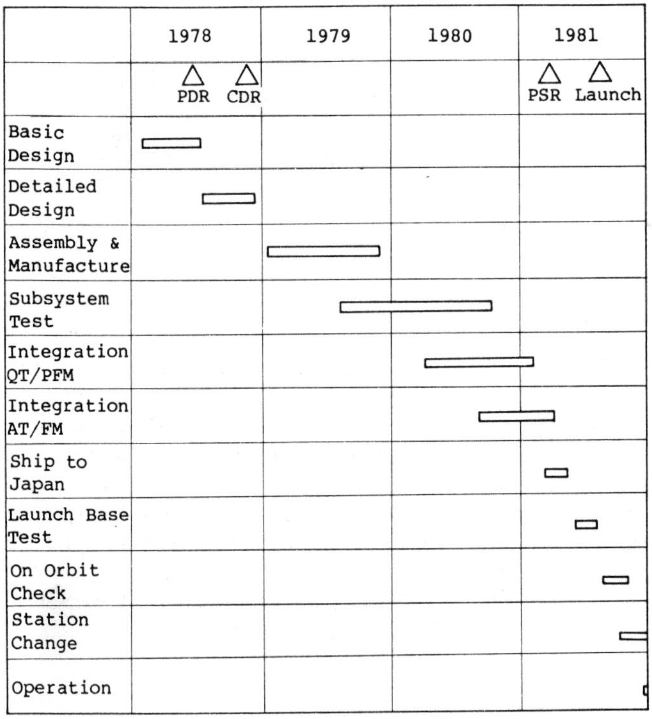

	1978	1979	1980	1981
	△ PDR △ CDR			△ PSR △ Launch
Basic Design				
Detailed Design				
Assembly & Manufacture				
Subsystem Test				
Integration QT/PFM				
Integration AT/FM				
Ship to Japan				
Launch Base Test				
On Orbit Check				
Station Change				
Operation				

FIG.6 Progress of the "GMS-2" programme.

GMS-2 configuration

The GMS-2 is a spin-stabilized geostationary meteorological satellite with mechanical despun antennas. The configuration and characteristics of the spacecraft are improved over those of the predecessor, GMS and most subsystems are flight-proven. The configuration is shown in Fig.7.

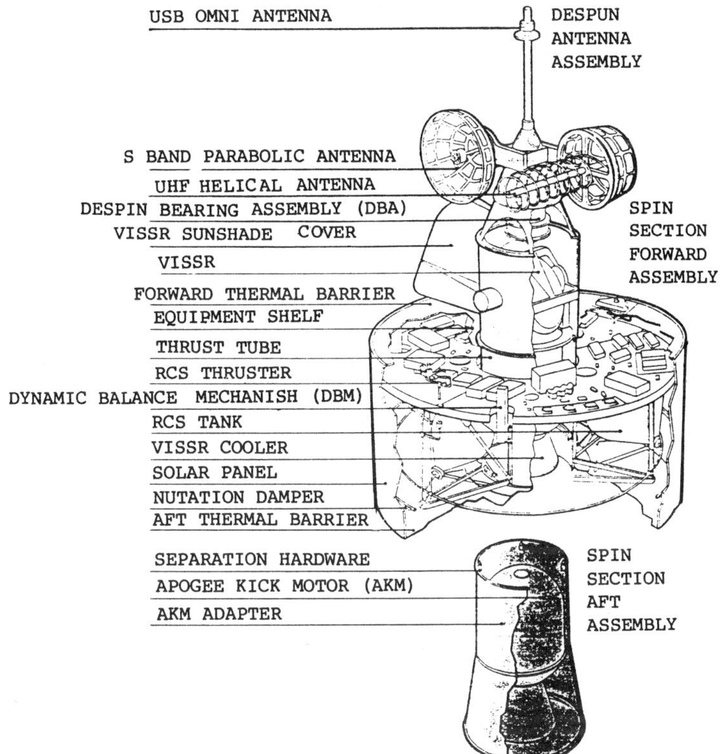

FIG.7 Overall view of GMS-2.

Overall size, weight and shape of the spacecraft are designed to be compatible with the N-II launch vehicles. The spacecraft length is 444 cm at launch and 345 cm on station, and the diameter is 215 cm. The weight when GMS-2 is separated from N-II third stage is 653 kg, and the spacecraft end of life (EOL) weight is 285 kg.

The satellite mission life is three years due to the limited amount of on-board hydrazine fuel; however, the design life is five years. Redundancy of mission-critical functions is provided to ensure electronic lifetimes significantly in excess of five years. The solar panel power of 264 W includes an approximately 30 W margin at the end of five years (summer solstice).

Future plan

In spite of several anomalies which were observed after launch, the GMS-2 is now performing well and should provide excellent meteorological services until 1985, its expected mission life. Accordingly, the next weather watch satellite, GMS-3, is now under consideration. The GMS-3 programme will consist of two spacecraft, designated 3a and 3b. The GMS-3a will be the GMS-2 proto-flight spacecraft refurbished to provide more capability and modified to improve its reliability. The GMS-3b, will be a back-up for 3a, and will be almost identical in design to the GMS-3a. The GMS-3a was scheduled to be launched in 1984.

ACTIVE MICROWAVE SENSORS

As the baseline of designing active microwave sensors, orbit parameters and system performance requirements are tentatively settled as shown in Tables 8 and 9, respectively.

TABLE 8 Orbit parameters

	Altimeter and scatterometer	*SAR*
Height	*800 km*	*570 km*
Eccentricity	*0.004 max.*	
Orbit		*Sun-synchronous*

TABLE 9 System performance requirements

Altimeter		*Scatterometer*	
Geodetic accuracy	*50 cm*	*Wind velocity range*	*4-25 m s^{-1}*
		accuracy	*max.(2 m s^{-1}, 10%)*
Topographic accuracy	*20 cm rss*	*Wind direction*	
Wave height range	*1-20 m*	*range*	*0-360 degrees*
accuracy	*max.(0.5 m, 10%)*	*accuracy*	*±20 degrees*
Reflection coefficient	*±1 dB*	*Swath width*	*200-700 km*
Acquisition time	*Less than 6 s*	*Grid spacing*	*50 km*
SAR			
Resolution			*25 m*
Swath width			*75 km*

Radar parameters are summarized in Table 10. Total weights, sizes, and DC power requirements are not fixed yet.

Microwave altimeter

In this section, the major functional elements of the altimeter are described. A block diagram of the altimeter is shown in Fig.8. This system can be divided mainly into three sections: RF section, signal processor section and tracking processor section.

The functions of RF section are to transmit and receive radar pulses, and to process received signals with a full-deramp technique. This basic design is similar to the SEASAT-1 altimeter.

An analogue-to-digital conversion of I and Q video signals from

TABLE 10 Preliminary radar parameters

	Altimeter	*Scatterometer*	*SAR*
Frequency	*13-14 GHz*	*13-14 GHz*	*1.2-1.3 GHz*
Transmitted band width	*320 MHz*	*4 KHz*	*13 MHz*
Uncompressed pulse width	*3.2 μs*	*5 ms*	*35 s*
Compression ratio	*1024*	*-*	*450*
Transmitted RF peak power	*2 kW*	*100 W*	*1.5 kW*
Pulse repetition frequency	*1000 Hz*	*40 Hz*	*1600 Hz*
Noise figure	*5.5 dB*	*5.3 dB*	*4.5 dB*
Antenna beam width	*1.6°*	*0.5°x24° (orthogonal) 0.5°x20° (3rd antenna)*	*6.2°(range 1.0°(azimuth)*
Antenna beam centre gain	*40 dB*	*32 dB*	*34 dB*
Antenna pointing angle	*nadir*	*43°(orthogonal) 37°(3rd antenna)*	*33°(off nadir)*
Signal to noise power ratio	*≥10 dB*	*≥-15 dB*	*≥7 dB*
Surface resolution	*25 km*	*25 km*	*25 m (range) 25 m (azimuth, 4 looks)*

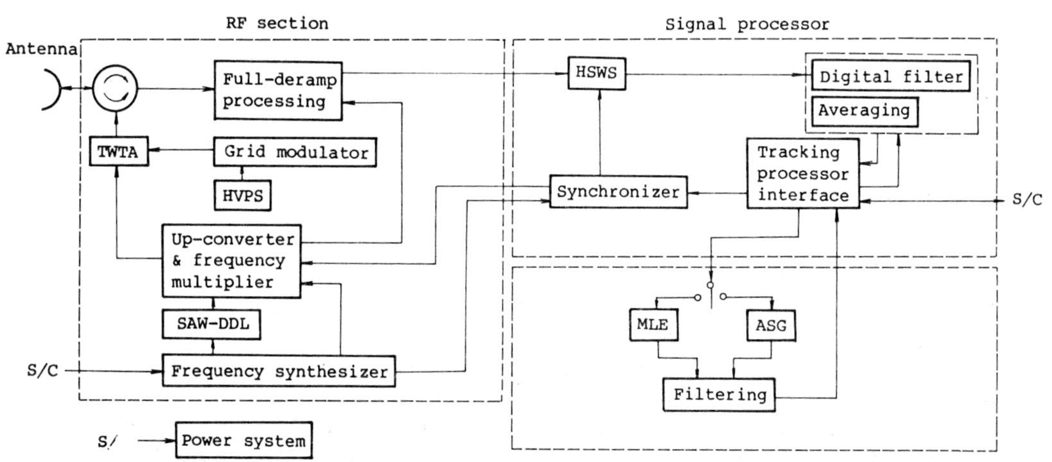

FIG.8 A block diagram of the altimeter.

RF section is accomplished in high speed waveform sampler (HSWS), which converts and stores 64 samples of these signals at a 20 MHz rate during 3.2 s. Digital filter transforms 64 samples into ones in frequency domain and averages them to provide smoothed waveform samples (50-100).

In the tracking processor section, oceanic parameters (altitude, wave height and signal-to-noise ratio) are estimated and predicted by using smoothed waveform samples. Quality of waveform samples depends on prediction accuracy, because predicted parameters control receiver trigger and AGC (automatic gain control). To improve prediction accuracy, maximum likelihood estimation (MLE) (including α-β filter) is used as an algorithm of estimation. MLE can simultaneously estimate three parameters and reduce variances of them in conparison with the adaptive split gate (ASG) α-β tracker used in the SEASAT-1 altimeter.

Some problems about MLE have been considered, as follows;

(a) MLE needs a large amount of calculation;

(b) MLE needs an accurate waveform model;

(c) MLE has not yet been used on a satellite.

The first and second problems are settled by using a recent advanced microprocessor, which has features of 16 bits/word and high speed calculation. Simulation for MLE operation has been executed in various conditions, and this system has the capability of selecting MLE or ASG. The third problem seems not to be important, considering simulation results and this configuration. Moreover, this configuration makes it easy to compare this system with the SEASAT-1 altimeter.

Microwave wind scatterometer

Microwave wind scatterometer is a pulse radar system with fan beam scanning and doppler filtering. The principle of design is basically similar to that of SASS on SEASAT-1. However, our system has a third antenna on each side of the satellite in order to remove the alias solutions of wind directions, and also has the dual independent polarity systems for transmitting and receiving signals.

Features of the system The features of the system are as follows:

(a) *Tri-directional antennas*. As mentioned above, this scatterometer has basically a three beam system. In order to determine the beam direction of the third antenna, wind vector inferring simulation was executed. Simulation results show that the most preferable direction of the third antenna is 75° in the case of Doppler radar system and the capability for wind vector determination will fairly upgrade as compared with SASS.

(b) *Footprint editing*. The observation area is located along both sides of the sub-satellite track. Each swath width is 500 km and divided into 20 unit cells (25 km x 25 km) by Doppler filter bank. In order to observe the sea closely by using the spacecraft movement, the six antennas are switched sequentially in about a 2-s interval. In an interval, four pulses and 16 pulses are assigned to the third and orthogonal antennas respectively, so that the data taken by each antenna have the same accuracy. Consequently, a 50 km x 50 km cell consists of eight unit cells in each beam (Fig.9(a)), and is observed from three different directions in as many times (Fig.9(b)). Eight unit cells are averaged in normal operation. According to the various demands for sea phenomena, closer cell constitution is also possible.

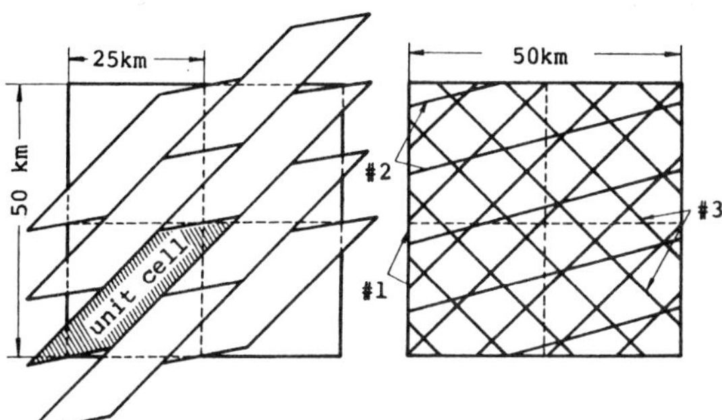

FIG.9 Footprint overview: (a) unit cells; (b) three beam pattern.

(c) *Dual polarity.* This system can measure the ocean in dual polarity (vertical and horizontal).

Synthetic aperture radar

In this section, outline of the SAR research and development model is described. Tables 9 and 10 indicate the basic SAR parameters. The SAR system consists of transmitter, receiver controller and digital section.

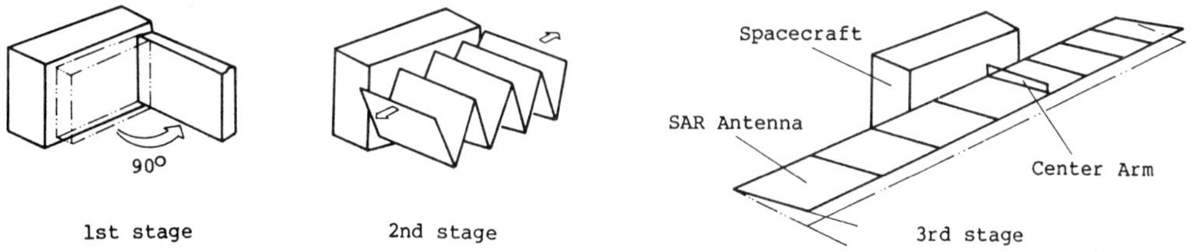

FIG.10 The deployment sequence of SAR antenna.

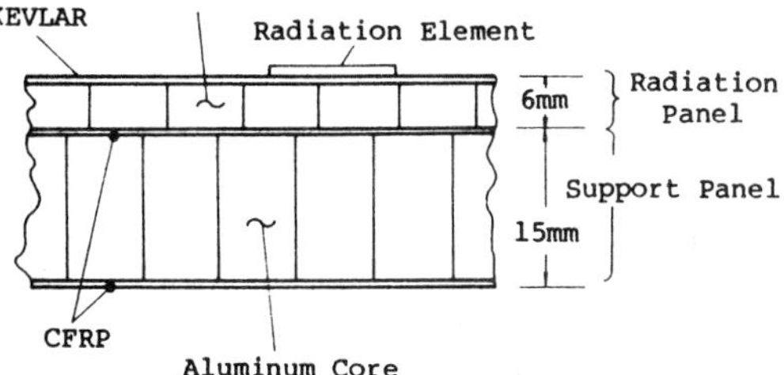

FIG.11 The configuration of SAR antenna.

The received echo is detected synchronously by the transmitted signal to get "hologram" data. The hologram data are converted into digital format to be recorded on-board or to be transmitted with an X-band data link.

The antenna is one of the components that we are taking effort in developing now. The SAR antenna consists of micro-strip array of 1024 elements and its dimension has 2.1 m x 12 m. Due to the constraints of 2.2 m diameter of H-I launch vehicle's payload section, the antenna must be deployable.

A solar panel deployment mechanism is applied to the antenna expansion. The deployment sequence consists of three stages, as shown in Fig.10. In the first stage, the antenna package is released to the right angle from the sidewall of spacecraft. In the second stage, two halves of the antenna deploy on either side of the centre arm simultaneously. In the third stage, the deployed antenna tilts to the off-nadir angle. In each stage, a spring-operated latch-up mechanism is employed for locking.

A support panel, as shown in Fig.11, consists of a honeycomb sandwich structure in order to keep the antenna panel flat in the space environment.

These are major differences from the SAR system of SEASAT-1.

Hydrological Applications of Remote Sensing and Remote Data Transmission
(Proceedings of the Hamburg Symposium, August 1983). IAHS Publ. no. 145.

Details of the INSAT meteorological applications programme of India

INDIA METEOROLOGICAL DEPARTMENT
Lodi Road, New Delhi 110003, India

ABSTRACT The Indian National Satellite (INSAT) system provides service to telecommunication, television and meteorological needs in India. The geostationary satellite is located at 74°E. A very high resolution radiometer and a DCP data relay transponder are the two basic satellite components used for meteorological applications. This paper gives an overview of each of these components, their potential application, and the data processing system required for operational use of INSAT meteorological data. The major benefits of INSAT data will be in the form of improved weather forecasting services.

Détails sur le programme d'applications météorologiques d'INSAT
RESUME Le système de satellites national indien (INSAT) répond aux besoins des télécommunications, de la télévision et de la météorologie dans l'Inde. Le satellite géostationnaire est situé à 74°E. Un radiomètre à très haute résolution et un transponder DCP sont les deux composants de base du satellite utilisés pour les applications météorologiques. Cette communication donne un aperçu sur chacun de ces deux composants, leurs applications potentielle et le système de traitement de données nécessaire pour l'utilisation opérationnelle des données météorologiques INSAT. Le plus grand avantage des données INSAT correspondra à l'amélioration des services rendus par la prévision du temps.

INTRODUCTION

The Indian National Satellite (INSAT) system is a multipurpose geostationary satellite with payloads for three distinct services, i.e., telecommunications, television and meteorology. The first satellite of the system, INSAT-1A, which was launched in April 1982 and located at 74°E over the equator, failed during September 1982 due to technical snags. The programme is being continued with the successful launch of INSAT-1B on 30 August 1983. It is located at 74°E longitude over the equator in a geostationary orbit. The satellite was operational from 15 October, 1983.

METEOROLOGICAL APPLICATIONS PROGRAMME

Satellite system

The meteorological segment of the satellite consists of two basic components. They include

(a) a two channel very high resolution radiometer (VHRR) for imaging the earth's cloud cover, and

(b) a transponder for receiving data from data collection platforms (DCPs) and relaying the received data back to the central data processing facility for further processing and dissemination to the users.

The VHRR has a nominal ground resolution of 2.75 km in the visible channel (0.55-0.75 μm) and 11 km in the infrared channel (10.5-12.5 μm). In full frame mode it has a capability of providing half-hourly pictures of the earth's cloud cover in the $20^\circ \times 20^\circ$ field of view of the earth. In the sector scan mode facility, more frequent pictures (every 6 minutes) of a limited area of the earth covering a 20° (east-west) by 5° (north-south) scan can be obtained. The data on the earth's cloud cover are transmitted in the 4 GHz band to the ground station at a data rate of approx 400 kbps.

The data collection transponder on-board INSAT is capable of receiving meteorological observations from data collection platforms (DCPs) and relaying the information to the main processing centre at Delhi. The meteorological department plans to install 100 land-based data collection platforms (DCPs) in remote and inaccessible areas of the country in a phased manner. The meteorological data are transmitted (400-MHz band) automatically by these platforms to the satellite which, in turn, relays them to the Meteorological Data Utilization Centre (MDUC) at New Delhi for processing. The satellite-based data collection system is very efficient for acquiring data from remote and inaccessible regions, where it is difficult to set up conventional meteorological stations. It is envisaged that the data will eventually be available to a wide variety of disciplines, including hydrology, snow survey and oceanography in addition to meteorology. The DCPs use 402.75 MHz on the uplink and 4-GHz on the downlink. All the DCPs are operated at the same frequency in a random access mode using a data rate of 4.8 kbps.

Data processing and applications

A Meteorological Data Utilization Centre (MDUC) has been established at New Delhi for the processing and operational use of INSAT meteorological data. The VHRR and DCP data are received at the MDUC as two independent streams of base band data. There are two independent processing segments at MDUC for processing the VHRR and DCP data. In the VHRR data processing component of MDUC system, facilities are available for production of full resolution visible and infrared images and for archival of processed data to a limited extent. The centre has facilities for interactive display and analysis. Facilities also exist for: the derivation of upper winds at two or three levels; cloud analysis; derivation of sea-surface temperature; transmission of processed low resolution satellite cloud pictures to other meteorological centres; and, derivation of cloud top temperatures and heights. The first VHRR image received from INSAT-1B and processed at MDUC on 25 September 1983 is shown in Fig.1.

The DCP data are processed in real time to obtain data of various meteorological elements such as pressure, temperature, rainfall etc.

FIG.1 First VHRR image received from INSAT-1B at the Meteorological Data Utilization Centre, New Delhi, on 25 September 1983.

The processed data are converted into a suitable format and disseminated to the users. At present the testing of the system concept is in progress.

As a part of INSAT meteorological applications programme, the India Meteorological Department is planning to implement a disaster warning system (DWS) for the efficient and reliable dissemination of warnings against approaching cyclones, directly to the areas likely to be affected. Initially the scheme is being implemented on a limited experimental basis to demonstrate the feasibility of this scheme. The plan envisages installation of 100 DWS receivers on the east coast of India. These receivers will directly receive the warning message originating from a cyclone warning centre, transmitted to INSAT-1B on C-band, which in turn, relays them to the Indian subcontinent for interception by the DWS receiving sets. In this fashion it will be possible to receive timely warnings against approaching severe cyclonic storms and take effective precautionary measures.

Benefits of INSAT applications programme

The implementation of the INSAT meteorological programme will bring much needed improvements to the meteorological observation system. The capability to get frequent cloud cover pictures over a large area will provide valuable data. The availability of INSAT data to the weather forecasters will help improve weather forecasting services of the India Meteorological Department. The major benefits will be in the form of improved weather forecasting services which are important to agriculture, fishing, aviation, hydroelectric projects, oceanography, shipping etc. Availability of more frequent observations over the oceans will improve our capability to issue timely and accurate cyclone warnings. With the improved and more accurate weather forecasts, it will be possible to improve flight planning in aviation. From the satellite data it is possible to derive sea-surface temperature (SST) which is an important meteorological parameter for understanding the air-sea interaction and for meteorological research. Precise information on SST is also important for the fishing industry. It is expected that the additional meteorological data obtained with INSAT will help in a better understanding of the behaviour of the monsoon. A precise forecast of monsoon rainfall is very important since the Indian economy depends to a large extent on the behaviour of the monsoon. The receipt of timely warnings against approaching cyclonic storms will help local authorities to take action on cyclone mitigation.

Hydrological Applications of Remote Sensing and Remote Data Transmission
(Proceedings of the Hamburg Symposium, August 1983). IAHS Publ. no. 145.

The SPOT programme: A new tool for the management of earth's resources

GÉRARD BRACHET
SPOT IMAGE, 18 Avenue Edouard Belin, F-31055 Toulouse Cédex, France

ABSTRACT The SPOT earth observation satellite programme is managed by the "Centre National d'Etudes Spatiales", the French space agency, with participation from Belgium and Sweden. It includes two satellites, SPOT 1 and SPOT 2, which will be launched in 1985 and 1987; two more satellites, SPOT 3 and 4 are planned for 1989 and 1991 in order to provide for a continuous service over 8-10 years. Launched on an heliosynchronous circular orbit at 822 km, the SPOT satellites will carry two identical high resolution electronic scanners with a swath width; 60 km; sampling interval: 10 m in the panchromatic mode (0.5-0.75 μm) and 20 m in the multispectral mode (3 bands in the visible and near infrared); optical axis steerable between +27° and -27° from vertical in the plane normal to the orbital plane. With these characteristics and the global coverage provided by two on-board recorders, the SPOT satellites will prove to be useful tools for managers and land planners in all countries. The distribution of its images, organized by the SPOT IMAGE Company, will rely on an operational service allowing users to request observations and to access to archived data.

Le programme SPOT: un nouvel outil pour la gestion des ressources terrestres
RESUME Le programme SPOT de satellite d'observation de la terre est géré par le Centre National d'Etudes Spatiales, l'Agence Spatiale Française, avec la participation de la Belgique et de la Suède. Il comprend deux satellites, SPOT 1 et SPOT 2, qui seront lancés en 1985 et 1987; deux autres satellites, SPOT 3 et 4 sont prévus pour 1989 et 1991, de façon à permettre un service continu sur 8 à 10 ans. Placés sur des orbites circulaires héliosynchrones à 822 km d'altitude, les satellites SPOT emportent deux instruments d'observation à haute resolution a balayage électronique. La largeur du champ de prise de vue est de 60 km; le pas d'échantillonnage au sol de 10 m en mode panchromatique (0.5 à 0.75 μm) et de 20 m en mode multispectral (trois bandes dans le visible et le proche infrarouge); l'axe optique des instruments peut être orienté de +27° à -27° de la verticale dans le plan perpendiculaire au plan de l'orbite. Avec ces caractéristiques et la couverture mondiale permise grâce aux deux enregistreurs de bord, les satellites SPOT seront

des outils efficaces pour les responsables de la gestion des ressources dans tous les pays. La distribution des images, organisée par la Société SPOT IMAGE, reposera sur un service opérationnel permettant aux utilisateurs de faire des demandes de prises de vue en fonction de leurs besoins et d'avoir accès aux données en archive.

THE SPOT PROGRAMME

The SPOT programme has been planned and designed as an operational and commercial system. Decided by the French government in 1978, with the participation of Sweden and Belgium, the programme is managed by the French Space Agency (CNES) which is responsible for the system development and satellite operations. SPOT 1 will be launched in early 1985 and SPOT 2, to be available for launch in early 1986, is also under construction. Plans are being made already for the launch of SPOT 3 and 4 in 1988 and onwards in order to ensure the necessary service continuity expected from an operational spaceborne remote sensing system. Indeed it is essential that new systems be operational over a sufficiently long period (at least 10 years) to allow the development of applications in those areas where remote sensing is not yet widely used.

The institutional organization of the SPOT operations has also been set up. CNES is in charge of spacecraft procurement, launch and operation and SPOT IMAGE, a commercial corporation, in charge of data distribution and all commercial relations with data users. SPOT IMAGE is developing a network of agents, distributors and subsidiaries to serve local markets; it is in the process of finalizing a pricing policy for SPOT data which is based on eventual complete cost recovery for the system (both investments amortization and operations expenses). Market studies indicate that this objective can be reached within the next ten years if the market develops as expected.

THE SPOT SYSTEM AND DATA DISTRIBUTION

Spacecraft characteristics

The SPOT spacecraft carries two identical sensors, called HRV (haute resolution visible), made of static solid state arrays of detectors (CCD) and operating in the visible and near infrared part of the spectrum. Among the innovative features of SPOT are the relatively high ground resolution of the imagery it will produce (10 m in the panchromatic mode, 20 m in the multispectral mode) and the ability of its sensors to point up to 27° east and west of the local vertical axis. This latter feature offers interesting possibilities to increase the number of opportunities to obtain views of a given area. It also permits stereoscopic observations by combining views taken at different angles from the vertical and therefore opens up the possibility of third dimension (or altitude) determination, an important requirement for cartographic applications. The principal characteristics of SPOT are summarized in Table 1.

TABLE 1 SPOT: principal characteristics

ORBIT	*Circular at 832 km* *Inclination: 98.7°* *Descending node at 10 h 30 min a.m.* *Orbital cycle: 26 days*
HAUTE RESOLUTION VISIBLE (HRV)	*Two identical instruments* *Pointing capability: ±27° east or west of the orbital plane* *Ground swath: 60 km each at vertical incidence* *Pixel size:* *10 m in panchromatic mode* *20 m in multispectral mode* *Spectral channels:* *panchromatic: 0.51-0.73 μm* *multispectral: 0.50-0.59 μm* *0.61-0.68 μm* *0.79-0.89 μm*
IMAGES TRANSMISSION	*Two onboard recorders each with 23 minute capacity* *Direct broadcast at 8 GHz (50 Mbits* s^{-1}*)*
WEIGHT	*1750 kg*
SIZE	*2 x 2 x 3.5 m plus solar panel (9 m)*

Swath width The two identical sensors (HRV) can be activated independently. Each instrument has a swath width of 60 km. When the two instruments operate in adjacent covering field, the ground coverage is 117 km.

Imaging modes SPOT operates in two modes: multispectral mode and panchromatic mode. In the multispectral mode, observations are made in three spectral bands with a pixel size of 20 m:

a green band from 0.50 to 0.59 μm
a red band from 0.61 to 0.68 μm
a near infrared band from 0.79 to 0.89 μm.

In the panchromatic mode, observations are made in a single broad band, from 0.51 to 0.73 μm with a pixel size of 10 m.

The multispectral bands have been selected to take advantage of interpretation methods developed over the last 10 years; they have been designed to allow the best discrimination among crop species and among different types of vegetation using three channels only.

The panchromatic band will offer the best geometric resolution (10 m) and will make it possible to comply with cartographic standards for maps at a scale of 1:100 000 and/or to update at a scale if 1:50 000 and in some cases 1:25 000 for thematic applications.

Field pointing flexibility, nadir and off nadir viewing One of the key features of SPOT is the steerable mirror which provides off nadir viewing capability. The instrument can be tilted sidewards (to the east or to the west) step by step from 0 to 27° allowing scene centres to be targeted anywhere within a 950 km-wide strip centred on the satellite track.

This technique provides a quick revisit capability on specific sites. For instance, at the equator, the same area can be targeted 7 times during the 26 days of an orbital cycle i.e. 98 times in one year, with an average revisit period of 3.7 days. At latitude 45°, the same area can be targeted 11 times in a cycle i.e. 157 times in one year, with an average period of 2.4 days, a maximum timelapse of 4 days and a minimum timelapse of 1 day (Fig.1).

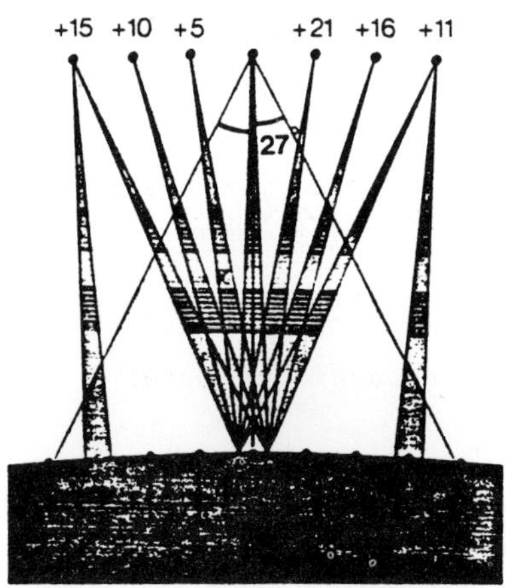

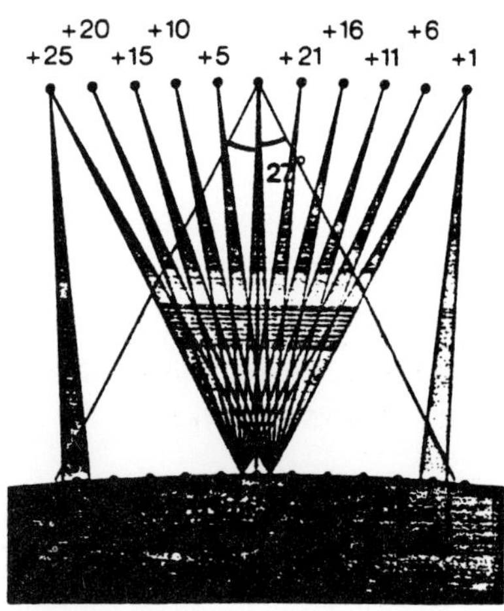

FIG.1 Typical sequence of acquisition at the equator and at latitude 45°.

The revisit flexibility allows one to:

(a) monitor phenomena which rapidly vary over time, such as crops, environmental stresses, natural disasters;

(b) improve the possibility of obtaining timely data required in many studies;

(c) improve the rate of area coverage by minimizing the effects of weather conditions.

Figure 2 illustrates the variability in obtaining complete coverage of France using cross-track viewing capability. At vertical viewing the coverage is obtained in 313 days, and in only 100 days if the depointing mode is used.

Stereoscopy The off nadir viewing capability also permits stereoscopic observations by combining views taken at different angles from the vertical. The 3D vision is obtained with the same area recorded from two different orbits, creating a parallax effect between the two scenes. Stereopairs are an important requirement in many cartographic applications: geomorphological, geological or soil maps and of course for topographic maps. SPOT will provide the

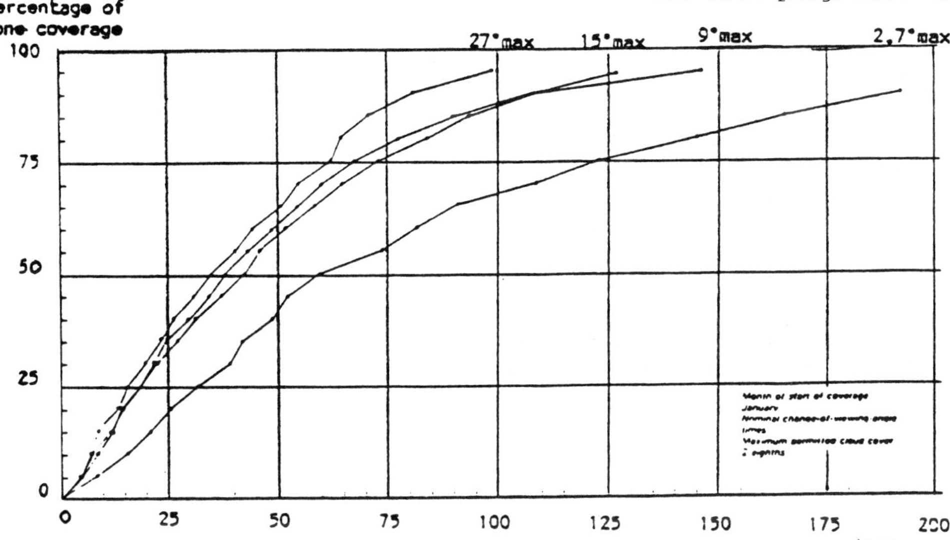

FIG.2 Time required to obtain a complete coverage of France for different maximum cross-track viewing capabilities.

opportunity to map anywhere in the world with a mapping accuracy corresponding to the 1:100 000 standard.

Image transmission Direct broadcasting operates at 8 GHz at a rate of 50 Mbits s^{-1}. The satellite carries two onboard recorders, each with 23 minutes capacity. Onboard data recording will be used over areas where there is no ground receiving facility.

Data acquisition, preprocessing and distribution

Information availability through easy and quick access to data and products is a very important factor in operational procedures. The system implemented for data acquisition as well as data distribution has been conceived to meet user needs and SPOT customers are given an active part in the system.

Basic principles are:

(a) permanent information regarding data availability;

(b) flexibility "on request" data acquisition;

(c) fast data and products distribution, based on a non discriminatory policy and the definition of marketing zones between SPOT IMAGE and various distribution centres;

(d) the protection of SPOT data by a copyright.

SPOT ground segment The SPOT system consists of (Fig.3):

(a) A satellite mission and control centre operated by CNES.

(b) Two main ground receiving stations and preprocessing centres located at Aussaguel near Toulouse, France, and at Esrange-Kiruna in Sweden. These stations receive direct data over the North polar zone, Europe and North Africa as well as worldwide data recorded on the two satellite tape recorders. Each station has a receiving capacity of 250 000 scenes per year. The preprocessing centres attached to both stations and operating in Sweden and in France, have a capacity of 70 system corrected (level 1) scenes per day or 20 precision processed (level 2) scenes per day. A level 1 scene can be preprocessed within 48 h from its acquisition at the ground station, while a precision processed scene requires 5-7 days.

(c) A network of regional receiving stations located around the world. These stations have concluded reception agreements with SPOT IMAGE. Acquisition programmes over the visibility area of each station are made by station operators and/or SPOT IMAGE.

(d) A distribution network managed by SPOT IMAGE on the basis of commercial agreements and marketing areas. Distribution involves standard data as well as value-added products.

Data bank information: the catalogue system SPOT IMAGE will build up a general catalogue of SPOT images which will contain data concerning images received and archived by all stations in the world. The catalogue system is fully computerized and designed to operate 24 h a day, 365 days a year. It will contain for each scene, information concerning: the location (geographical coordinates, orientation, etc.), acquisition mode (multispectral, panchromatic, viewing angle, stereopair), scene identification (grid number, date), quality (telemetry, cloud cover), archived products already available.

The SPOT catalogue will offer users a wide range of options concerning the processing and presentation of catalogue data. It includes statistical calculations concerning image characteristics, definition of image families and scene selection according to various criteria; alphanumeric or graphic display will be available. Besides scene characteristics and image selection, the system will analyse users data requests, record and manage data orders and manage the data acquisition programmes.

Users will access the catalogue directly in Toulouse, by conventional means (mail, telephone, telex) or through data transmission network (Transpac, Euronet, Tymnet, Telenet, Datapac).

Information exchanges between SPOT IMAGE and SPOT data users will also be possible through an electronic mailbox system. With an electronic key, users will be able to deposit in the catalogue system memory messages regarding requests for information, programming or orders. Stored messages will be read over every 6 h and the replies deposited at users disposal. For users convenience, it is expected that at least one point of contact by country (SPOT distributor) should be equipped with a fast transmission link to the SPOT IMAGE worldwide catalogue.

Data acquisition This is an innovative feature of the SPOT system. When an image is not available in archive or when a SPOT user wishes to acquire specific data with a specific time scheduling, he can request a SPOT acquisition programme. For this, the user can apply directly to SPOT IMAGE (via the catalogue system) or to a local receiving station or to a local SPOT IMAGE distribution centre.

According to the case, the user may request:

(a) unique coverage obtained during a certain period of the year;

(b) multitemporal coverage, meaning a number of coverages acquired at different periods;

(c) stereoscopic coverage, i.e. two coverages acquired in speci-

fied conditions in relation to the viewing angles used.
To do this, the user must first define the geographical area to be covered, in the form of geographical coordinates, of a polygon or a circle. For each coverage the user wants to obtain he must then indicate the general characteristics and constraints relative to image recording the especially:

(a) image recording mode: multispectral and/or panchromatic,

(b) image recording periods,

(c) the viewing angle or the range of variation comprised between -27° and +27°,

(d) the cloud cover threshold accepted from 0 to 2 per quarter of an image,

(e) eventually, the gain to be applied to detectors; two possibilities: low and high.

According to the user's needs, which are translated into programming parameters, SPOT IMAGE carries out a technical feasibility study of the request in coordination with the Mission Control Centre. In the standard procedure, a report is handed back by SPOT IMAGE within 48 h to 4 days. Accelerated procedures can be used in case of emergency. It will comprise, among others, the geometrical conditions of image recording (mosaicing of the zone to the covered), and its feasibility (probability of execution in time taking into account the climatic data of the region considered).

The user may accept (or not) these propositions. He may also modify the initial request, in which case a new study is undertaken. When the user accepts the technical conditions of execution proposed, an agreement is made between SPOT IMAGE and the user stipulating the technical and financial conditions of the execution of the programme.

SPOT IMAGE, in liaison with the user, can modify the execution of a programme in different ways:

(a) by programming directives (modification of parameters, cloud

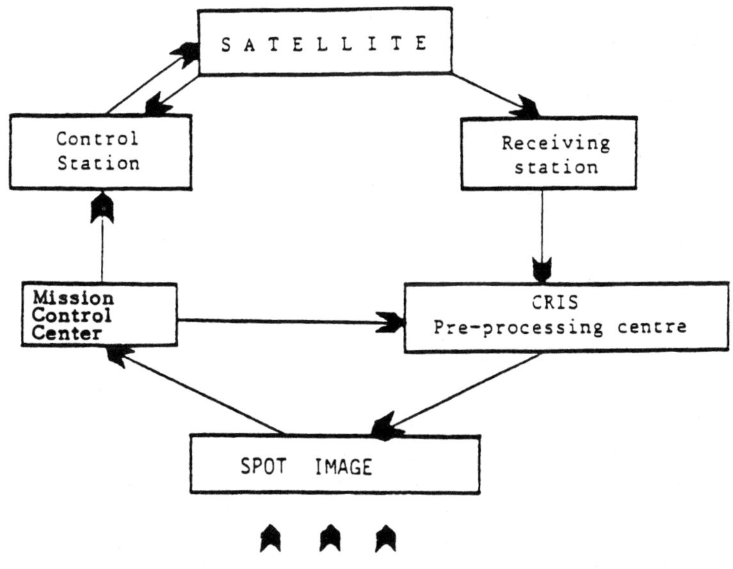

FIG.3 SPOT system diagram.

cover level, viewing angles, restriction of the range of variation);
(b) by changing from a fixed single angle to a range of variation, in order to terminate a programme ("clean-up" mode);
(c) by changing the end-of-period date (may be delayed).
The final validation of scenes is carried out after examining the quick-look images.

The user may receive, periodically or on request, a detailed report on the state of progress of his programme. This report supplies all validated scenes and the progress of coverage of the geographical zone (in simplified graphic form with statistics or in geographic/contour form).

Acquisition programmes will include long term monitoring programmes as well as emergency acquisition procedures (in case for instance of natural disasters).

Data and products distribution The Toulouse preprocessing facility (CRIS Toulouse) is designed to produce standard data such as: a level 1 (system corrected) scene within 48 h and level 2 or 5 (precision processed) within a week, with a maximum capacity of 70 scenes per day at level 1 or 20 at level 2. The Kiruna preprocessing centre (CRIS Kiruna) will have similar capacities.

SPOT IMAGE will reproduce and deliver to users standard data on CCTs and films coming from the preprocessing centres. Special and value added products will also be made available to users through a worldwide distribution network.

The term "SPOT data" applies to all SPOT scenes with standard processing while "SPOT product" refers to any product derived from the above defined data.

Whereas the distribution of SPOT data is subject to specific rules and geographical limitations, the distribution of SPOT products i.e. value-added products is not subject to any such restriction except copyrights.

CNES owns the copyright on all SPOT data. This means that any organization that wishes to distribute or sell SPOT data must first obtain a sub-license from SPOT IMAGE which has been granted by CNES an exclusive worldwide license for the distribution of SPOT data.

SPOT receiving stations will be automatically granted an exclusive sub-license for the distribution of SPOT data within their distribution zone. This sub-license is exclusive, insofar as SPOT data is concerned, within the station's distribution zone; such zones generally covering the country (or group of countries) operating the station.

SPOT IMAGE has exclusive SPOT data distribution rights in those countries that do not possess a receiving station and is currently negotiating agreements with companies, agents and the like in these different countries with a view to ensuring close contact between distributors and users and the efficient distribution of both data and products.

THE SPOT DATA SIMULATION PROGRAM

In order to prepare the user community to the use and analysis of SPOT images, an ambitious SPOT data simulation programme has been initiated since 1980. It is managed by the french "Groupement pour le Développement de la Télédétection Aérospatiale" (GDTA) of which CNES is a member; it includes two types of image simulations:

(a) Geometric simulations whereby mosaics of aerial photographs are digitized and resampled to 10 m to simulate the geometric characteristics of SPOT images under different viewing angles (this requires a digital terrain model of the area in order to take account of terrain relief in the simulation). Those simulations are used to study the usefulness of SPOT data for topographic mapping and other applications requiring stereoscopic coverage.

(b) Radiometric simulations, whereby images of certain areas are collected via an airborne scanner and data from the different channels of the scanner are processed to simulate the three spectral bands of SPOT with resampling at 20 m intervals. Such simulated images do not have the geometric quality of SPOT inages, but reflect their expected radiometric characteristics and therefore their ability to classify different types of terrain, vegetation cover, crops, etc. Many sites in France, in other European countries as well as in Africa, Bangladesh and the United States have been covered and provide a variety of useful examples for data analysis and applications. The data themselves, as well as information booklets on the image interpretation are available from SPOT IMAGE.

This SPOT data simulation programme has involved a large number of scientists and investigators in all countries where sites have been surveyed; it has proved to be of high interest both to the investigators and to the producers of the data and should pave the way to a fruitful interaction between the user community and the SPOT data producers/distributors when the spacecraft will be operating.

Hydrological Applications of Remote Sensing and Remote Data Transmission
(Proceedings of the Hamburg Symposium, August 1983). IAHS Publ. no. 145.

RADARSAT and MSAT: proposed Canadian satellite systems with hydrological applications

B. E. GOODISON
Hydrometeorology Division, Atmospheric Environment Service, 4905 Dufferin Street, Downsview, Ontario, Canada M3H 5T4
E. J. LANGHAM
RADARSAT Office, DEMR, 110 O'Connor Street, Suite 200, Ottawa, Ontario, Canada K1P 5M9
D. ATHANASSIADIS
MSAT Communication Program Manager, Department of Communications, 365 Laurier Avenue W., Ottawa, Ontario, Canada K1A 0C8

ABSTRACT Canada has been actively involved in assessing the feasibility of two quite different satellite systems proposed for launch in the late 1980s. MSAT is a geostationary communications satellite which would provide service to land vehicles, ships, aircraft and portable and fixed terminals. Mobile radio and telephone service is proposed as well as data services, one component being the DCP service offered in the 800 MHz band. Characteristics of the proposed DCP service are summarized. MSAT is a prototype commercial system; subscribers will be charged based on the time occupancy of their messages. RADARSAT is a proposed polar orbiting satellite carrying a synthetic aperture radar as its primary sensor, with a scatterometer and a high-resolution visual-infrared sensor as probable secondary sensors. Both the SAR and VIR sensors will be steerable. Baseline characteristics for payload, orbit selection and ground segments are summarized. As part of the renewable resources study team task, hydrological applications were reviewed and possible benefits assessed.

RADARSAT et MSAT: projets de systèmes satellitaires canadiens avec applications en hydrologie
RESUME Le Canada a activement contribué à l'évaluation de la possibilité pratique de réaliser deux satellites entièrement différents dont le lancement doit avoir lieu à la fin des années 1980. Le MSAT est un satellite géostationnaire de télécommunications qui servira aux véhicules terrestres, aux navires, aux aéronefs et aux terminaux mobiles et fixes. On prévoit un service pour les appareils radiotéléphoniques mobiles et fixes ainsi que des services de données dont une composante serait le service aux plates-formes de collecte des données offert dans la bande de 800 MHz. On résume les caractéristiques du service prévu aux PCD. Le MSAT est un prototype commercial. Le coût pour les abonnés sera basé sur le temps de traitement de leurs messages. Le RADARSAT est un projet de satellite

à orbite polaire doté d'un radar à ouverture synthétique comme capteur primaire, et d'un diffusomètre et d'un capteur à grande résolution dans le visible et l'infrarouge comme capteurs secondaires probables. On pourra diriger à distance les capteurs SAR et VIR. On donne le résumé des caractéristiques de base pour la charge utile, le choix de l'orbite et les segments sol. Le groupe d'étude des richesses renouvelables a examiné les applications de ces systèmes en hydrologie et évalué les avantages éventuels.

INTRODUCTION

Canada has been a leader in the field of satellite communications. It was the third country in the world to design and build a satellite; it was the first with a commercial domestic satellite system in geostationary orbit. The Government of Canada has recently been involved in assessing the feasibility of two quite different satellite systems. MSAT, or Mobile SATellite, is a proposed communications system that would provide more effective and reliable two-way radio and radio telephone services to all parts of Canada, without restriction on distance. This demonstration system is to include a DCP service using the 800 MHz band, a system which is of considerable interest to agencies expanding their DCP networks. The second programme is RADARSAT, which envisages the design, construction and launch in 1980 of a satellite carrying as its primary sensor a synthetic aperture radar (SAR). Secondary sensors which have been reviewed for their applications include a visual-infrared optical-imager, a scatterometer and a microwave radiometer.

This paper will briefly outline these two proposed satellite systems, with particular emphasis on those aspects which might have potential hydrological applications. The programmes are under continuous review; consequently, the information given should be considered subject to change at any time. There is of course no guarantee that either or both systems will reach the final launch phase.

MSAT

Background

Mobile communications may be defined as communications between two or more stations at least one of which is mobile by virtue of being installed in an aircraft, ship or land vehicle, or being transportable. At the present time, there are only terrestrial mobile communications systems in Canada - mobile radio service (MRS) and mobile telephone service (MTS). In 1979 the World Administrative Radio Conference decided to permit shared satellite and terrestrial communications services to mobile radio and telephone users in the 806-890 MHz frequency band. This has resulted in the development of cellular mobile telephone and conventional trunked land mobile radio services in the 800 MHz band.

Terrestrial systems provide cost-effective services in urban areas and also in some rural areas of Canada. However, there is an urgent need for better coverage and a higher quality of service in rural and remote areas, regions where satellites are expected to be much more cost effective than terrestrial systems. With a view to satisfying this need, the Canadian Department of Communications (DOC) entered into MSAT, which will be used for communications experiments, service development and trial services to vehicles, ships, aircraft, compact portable terminals and fixed terminals. It will complement terrestrial systems. The predominant impetus to proceed with the MSAT programme is development of a commercially viable MSAT service that will benefit service and equipment providers and users alike.

DOC is proposing to assume a lead role to implement a demonstration MSAT system and to develop a customer base of sufficient magnitude so as to ensure the commercial viability of ongoing MSAT services through subsequent commercial MSAT systems to be implemented by the private sector. Such a demonstration programme can only be undertaken with the active participation of the telecommunications carriers, the manufacturing industry and the users.

Summary of MSAT elements and services

The MSAT programme has two main elements. The MSAT Demonstration System would be comprised of a satellite in geostationary orbit, a number of earth stations for satellite control and mobile communications control, and a large complement of mobile earth stations for land vehicles, ships, aircraft and field operations. The MSAT Post-Launch Communications Programme is proposed as the vehicle for the user participation in service trials and interim commercial services on MSAT for a 7-year period after launch. The MSAT communications system is being developed to provide Canada wide coverage (including coastal waters), improved and cost-effective mobile communications in sparsely populated geographical areas, and country-wide calling capability.

The MSAT system is comprised of a space element and a number of ground elements which collectively constitute a fully integrated transmission and switching network. The space element is a geostationary satellite which will be placed in orbit in the vicinity of 106.5°W. Its position is determined by Canadian coverage requirements and available orbit slots. The ground elements' numbers, locations and types are dictated by service and cost optimization considerations.

Three broad service categories are visualized: Mobile Radio Service (MRS); Mobile Telephone Service (MTS); and Data Services (DS). Within each of these categories, different modes of operation and special features are possible. One of the modes of operation under Data Services is the DCP service offered in the 800 MHz band.

MSAT DCP services

The choice of the 800 MHz band for the provision of DCP services was based on two prime considerations. It would provide a higher level of flexibility and features than are presently available, and it would allow DCP services to be offered for a wider spectrum of applications, thus enhancing the cost effectiveness of the service offering.

The MSAT system requires a high degree of hardware and software sophistication in order to accomplish its mobile and fixed mobile communications functions. Call origination and completion, channel assignment, billing, maintenance and diagnostic procedures will be controlled through a central control driven by powerful firmware and software intelligence.

The DCP service at 800 MHz is proposed to have the following characteristics:

(a) DATA rates of up to 2.4 kbits s^{-1} resulting in shorter transmission times for messages and hence lower charges.

(b) Two-way DATA transmission capability which will permit polling of DCPs under the control of the MSAT central intelligence. The polling ability offers several advantages, among them the elimination of long silent intervals and the ease of interrogation at varied intervals. The two-way capability also allows DCPs to originate transmissions by exception in the event of unscheduled and/or emergency situations.

(c) A communications architecture that permits the direct connection between any two stations served by the system and hence the ability to transmit DCP messages directly to the headquarters or other designated locations of any given organization. This will lead to the elimination of the need for a common ground receiving station and the associated sorting and retransmission of messages by terrestrial means. Cost reduction and prompt delivery of messages are obvious advantages.

Finally, by virtue of offering the service at the 800 MHz band the limitations applying to the 400 MHz band are eliminated and hence the service can be expanded to commercial applications of data collection and industrial control. In time, such a wide base data collection and control service will be reflected in more favourable billing rates for the user.

Subscribers to the DCP service will be responsible for ensuring that their sensors are capable of interfacing with an MSAT terminal specially designed for the DCP service. Subscribers will specify the following service oriented parameters: speed of transmission (up to 2.4 kbits) and error rate required; length of message in bits or bytes; frequency and time of day that readings are required.

The system will employ a dedicated channel group for the provision of this service and each reading required will be translated into an appropriate call duration value. Given that each call will have a prescribed duration, a call list can be generated and scheduled in real time within the system. Based on this list the size of the channel group will be engineered with a specified maximum delay (grade of service) to be decided upon. The system will proceed to originate calls to the devices sequentially and in accordance with the scheduled list. The actual call established will be between the device being read and the designated terminal to which the subscriber wishes to transmit his message (dedicated terminal).

Subscribers will be charged in accordance with the time occupancy generated by their messages. This will encourage expedient conversion of presently existing slow speed devices to the maximum speed offered by the system.

The system will also offer a new industrial control service which provides a remote control capability to be used by industrial users for controlling remotely located devices from a central location. This service requires messages flowing in both directions, typically a command from the central location and a response indication returned from the controlled device to the central location.

Two major types of command-response sequences are visualized:

(a) *Immediate response:* where the response is for all practical purposes immediate and hence the circuit need not be released until the response is received.

(b) *Delayed response:* where the response is expected to arrive with a considerable time delay as dictated by the response time of the device. In this instance, it may be necessary to release the circuit after the command, and either have the device originate a random response message at a later time or initiate a second call from the central location to interrogate the device and read the response message.

Future of MSAT

Decisions on how to proceed with construction and launch of a demonstration MSAT system will have to be made. Should MSAT serve Canadians only or be expanded to cover the United States on a cost-sharing basis? If MSAT goes ahead, as either originally planned or as an immediate commercial system, decisions will be required on the cost to users and on techniques for developing markets. For hydrological applications, the DCP concept outlined above is an interesting alternative to current practice, particularly because of the proposed change to the 800 MHz band.

RADARSAT

Background

The origins of RADARSAT go back to the mid-1970s when there was a growing interest in oil and gas exploration in and around the Arctic Islands. Sea-ice, in places up to 3 m thick with ridges of ice of even greater depth, could pose problems for drill ships and tankers, and safe operations would depend on the availability of daily synoptic ice information. In 1976 a Canadian task force was established to determine the extent to which satellites could be used to meet the environmental requirements for sea ice and oceans; special emphasis was placed on the potential value of synthetic aperture radar (SAR).

In 1977 a three-year Surveillance Satellite (SURSAT) Programme was approved by the Canadian government which allowed Canadian participation in the SEASAT experiments and initiated a programme of technical developments in order to improve Canadian industrial capability in the area of SAR technology. The SURSAT programme showed that high resolution SAR imagery could provide ice information and had the potential also to monitor land resources. It was decided, therefore, to initiate the RADARSAT programme which would lead to the launch of a Canadian satellite carrying a SAR. Secondary sensors might include one or more of the following: scatterometer, optical imager, scanning microwave radiometer and altimeter.

The programme was to involve international partners, primarily to share the cost of this venture which would be very expensive for Canada. In 1980 NASA agreed to conduct joint Mission Requirement Studies to determine the extent to which such a mission could serve the needs of both countries. Earlier, Canada had joined the European Space Agency's (ESA) ERS-1 programme, concentrating on SAR technologies.

Baseline mission

The objective of the RADARSAT mission is to establish an all-weather proto-operational satellite system providing SAR image data for surveillance applications. The system should supply key users with as frequent coverage as possible, using a single satellite system, on as timely a basis as possible to demonstrate operational applications.

Mission requirement studies were conducted during the first year of the RADARSAT programme. They were concerned primarily with the availability of data (orbit selection and data processing) and the quality of data (radar design and data processing). They required the translation of user needs into mission specifications. Since user applications were varied, four study teams were established to review needs: renewable land resources, non-renewable land resources, oceanography, and sea ice. Hydrology along with agriculture and forestry made up the renewable land resources component. The results of these groups are reported in RADARSAT (1982a). The baseline mission parameters are summarized below.

Orbit The requirement for frequent sea ice information in the Northwest Passage using the SAR had a decisive influence on the selection of an orbit. The greatest coverage of this shipping route is achieved if it also represents the most northerly latitude reached by the SAR swath. This produces frequent coverage in an east-west direction in this region. A one day coverage map for Canada, plotted with a 140 km swath width is shown in Fig.1. To achieve daily coverage of any point between 71.5°N and 75.5°N, the baseline radar design has the capability of steering the radar beam across a 500 km range of access. Figure 2 illustrates this capability, showing how the radar beam might be stepped across the access swath several times during passes so that the entire shipping route is covered. This capability can also be used over land such that any part of Canada can be accessed during a three day period. As the SAR is moved within the access range, the incidence angle of the radar beam will change. For applications, the variation of radar cross section with incidence angle can assist in the identification of certain surface materials or crops and will allow for the collection of stereo radar imagery.

Although the orbit was optimized for SAR applications at high latitudes, it must also provide for good coverage by the SAR and the secondary sensors over North America, Europe and the equatorial regions and must enable the collection of a world data set by the SAR. The orbit selected has a 16 day exact repeat (at the equator) with a three day sub-cycle (at high latitudes). The orbit will be sun synchronous, at an altitude of 1001 km, an inclination of 99.5°

FIG.1 Typical one-day coverage by the SAR with nominal swath width of 140 km.

and have a descending daylight pass which crosses the equator at 09.44 h. The sun-synchronous orbit provides sun illumination at the same local time throughout the year for the optical sensor. Eclipses will occur during during every orbit for about 29 minutes.

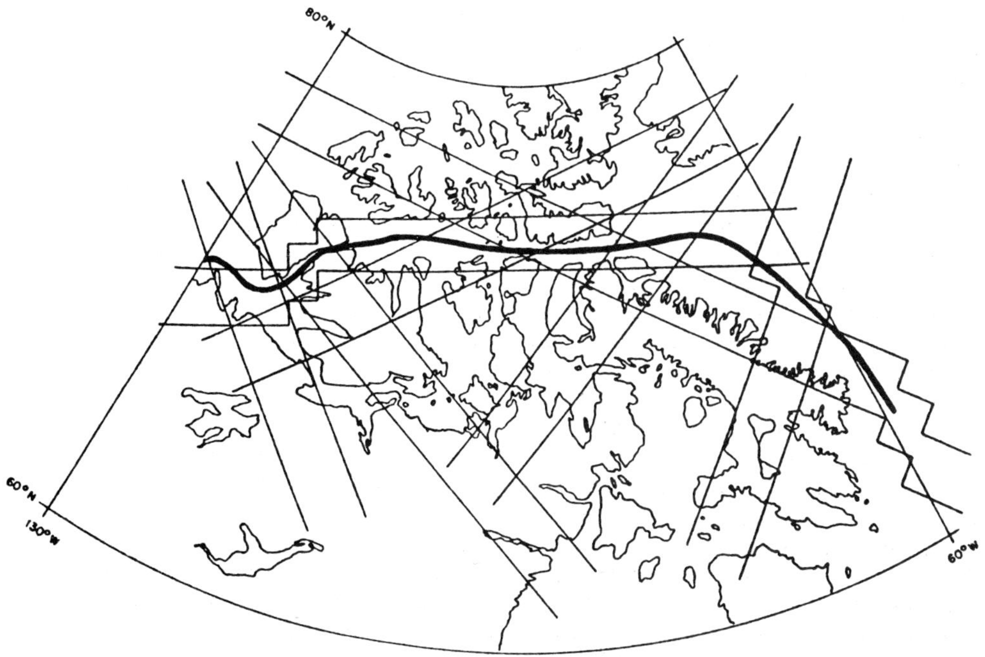

FIG.2 The use of SAR swath displacement to optimize coverage of shipping routes.

Ground segment The RADARSAT ground segment will include a Mission Control Facility, ground stations, an Ice Information Centre in Ottawa (an upgrade of Environment Canada's Ice Forecasting Centre), a comprehensive communication network and end-user facilities. The Canadian receiving station will now be at Ottawa, with a second station at Fairbanks, Alaska, providing direct readout for the western arctic.

The telemetry and ground segment components of the system concept are illustrated in Fig.3. The satellite will downlink data either directly or from on-board recorders to the primary ground receiving station. These data will then be relayed at a lower rate through a communication satellite to the Mission Control Centre in Ottawa. Processing of SAR data and data from other sensors will take place there and the products distributed to user image analysis centres and to archiving facilities.

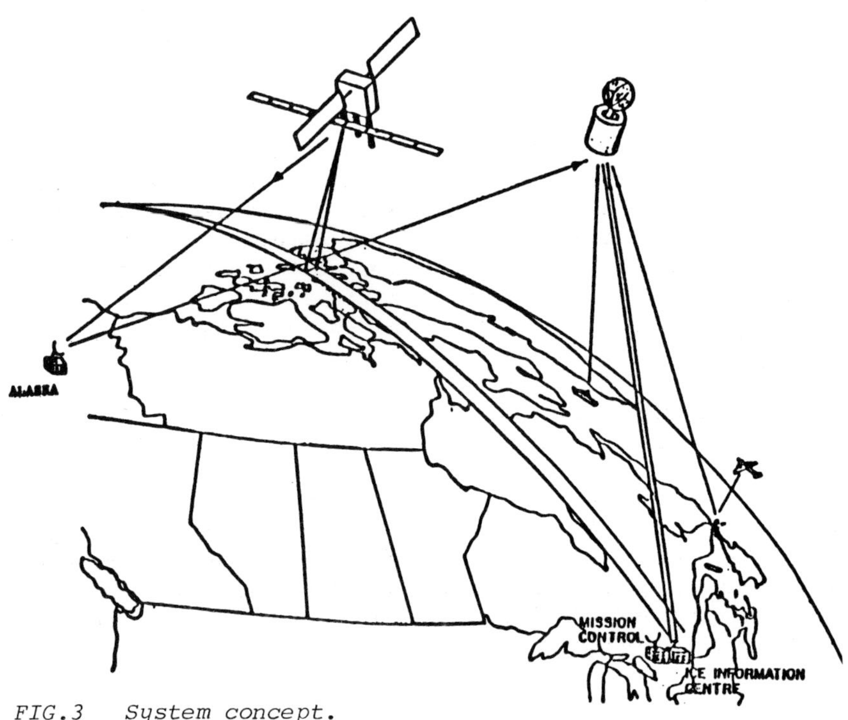

FIG.3 System concept.

Payload The SAR will be the primary sensor. Table 1 summarizes the baseline radar specifications. After careful study of existing data, the Study Teams recommended C-band over L-band, given that for technical reasons, the SAR would not be X-band.

Secondary sensors considered during Phase A included a scatterometer, visual and infrared (VIR), microwave radiometer, and altimeter. Currently, the first two sensors are the likely candidates for inclusion. The scatterometer being considered for RADARSAT is the instrument being developed for the NROSS programme. The sensor has a swath width of 715 km on either side of the satellite track and will measure wind speed and direction over the ocean surface. The

TABLE 1 Nominal RADARSAT baseline SAR

Frequency	*5.3 GHz (C-band)*
Polarization	*VV*
Altitude	*1000 km*
Inclination	*99.5°*
Accessibility swath	*≤500 km*
Incidence angles	*20°-45°*
Subswaths	*4 (equal size)*
Overlaps	*10% minimum*
Azimuth resolution	*28 m*
Looks	*4 (independent)*
Range resolution (at reference position TBD within each subswath)	*25 m*
Dynamic range	*≥30 dB*
Output power	*500 W mean*
Weight	*350 kg*

VIR sensor used as a baseline during Phase A studies was the Landsat-4 thematic mapper, but it now appears that a different instrument may be used. Swath width would be 60 km with 15 m resolution. The VIR will have a pointing capability allowing for simultaneous sensing of the same region on the ground as the SAR. Inclusion of a microwave radiometer, similar to that on SSM/I, would have been beneficial for hydrological applications, particularly snow cover mapping, but it is unlikely that it will be included.

The spacecraft platform being considered is the modified L-SAT bus, originally designed for geostationary orbit, which is being redesigned for low earth orbit. A space shuttle launch is anticipated.

As noted earlier, RADARSAT is intended to involve international partners. In 1982 a further agreement with NASA was signed in which NASA expressed an interest in providing the space shuttle launch and possibly one or two other sensors (VIR, scatterometer) for the payload. Options for contributions from others will be explored.

Applications and benefits

The focus for applications has been on the use and associated benefits of the SAR. Table 2 is a summary of various applications being investigated. It is realized that for the full benefit of radar data to be achieved, algorithms and procedures to generate products must be developed. A more complete discussion of some applications is given in Langham (1985).

The potential hydrological applications of RADARSAT were reviewed by the renewable resources study team. These are discussed more fully in RADARSAT (1982a, b) and Ramseier (1982) and are summarized in Goodison *et al.* (1985). Using SAR imagery, flood mapping and soil moisture assessment show the most promise, although the latter is often considered as an agricultural rather than as a hydrological

TABLE 2 Potential applications using radar

Sea Ice
- seasonal variation of signature
- structural characteristics for SAR
- interpretation
- C-Band scatterometery (airborne and surface)
- ship tracks

Icebergs
- detectability (as function of size, shape, sea state, incidence angle)
- discrimination (from ships)
- grounding

OCEANS

Surface Waves
- predominant wavelength and direction
- sea state

Internal Waves
- distribution and directions of propagation

Ocean Dynamics
- currents, eddies, vortices, rings

Bathymetry
- coastal
- pingoes

Hurricanes, Storms, Squalls, Windrows, Oil Slicks,
Fresh Water Slicks, Thermal Slicks, Shipping Signatures
- vessel image (function of structure orientation, incidence angle)
- wakes (vessel type, speed, direction relative to SAR, sea state)
- vessel and wake as function of sea state

RENEWABLE RESOURCES

Crop Classification and Condition
- digital analysis of multiple data sets
- digital analysis of multi-temporal data
- C-Band scatterometry (airborne and surface)

Forestry
- resource mapping
- cut areas, roads
- regrowth

Hydrology
- soil moisture
- flood mapping

GEOLOGY

SAR/VIR Visual Interpretation
Digital Interpretation of Multiple Data Sets
- SAR, VIR, geomagnetics, gamma, etc.

Stereo Presentation
- photo comparator
- holograms
- digitally generated products

application. Preliminary results on the use of SAR for snow cover monitoring, based on airborne data collected in the SURSAT programme are reported in Goodison *et al.* (1980). More recent research on this application has been conducted in Europe during the SAR-580 campaign conducted there.

A number of economic studies have been conducted covering the applications that appeared to offer the most significant benefits. Ice and ocean reconnaissance and global crop forecasting are the most dominant applications of a satellite with RADARSAT's capabilities. In hydrology, benefits in forecasting reservoir inflow, measuring soil moisture levels and monitoring snow cover were identified, although tangible benefits would be more readily realized if a microwave radiometer were included. Consequently, benefits to operational hydrology rated low. It is clear that a considerable amount of research and development is required to determine the full extent of applications of RADARSAT data in hydrology. It is realized that the VIR data could have a wide variety of uses in water resources, much like those from Landsat.

Programme status

Phase B was approved in early 1984 and will continue to late 1986. If the following phases are approved, launch is anticipated in 1990. Radar technology development activities continue. A new airborne C-band radar is scheduled for installation on the Convair-580 aircraft in late 1985. Research and applications experiments will continue as part of the airborne programme.

REFERENCES

Goodison, B.E., Whiting, J.M., Wiebe, K. & Cihlar, J. (1985) Operational requirements for water resources remote sensing in Canada: now and in the future. In: *Hydrological Applications of Remote Sensing and Remote Data Transmission* (Proc. Hamburg Symp., August 1983), 647-657. IAHS Publ. no. 145.

Goodison, B.E., Waterman, S.E. & Langham, E.J. (1980) Application of synthetic aperture radar data to snow cover monitoring. *Proc. 6th Canadian Symp. on Remote Sensing* (Halifax, Nova Scotia, 21-23 May 1980), 263-271.

Langham, E. (1985) RADARSAT enters phase B. *AIAA Progress Series* (in press).

RADARSAT (1982a) RADARSAT mission requirements document. *Report 82-7, Energy, Mines and Resources, Ottawa, Canada.*

RADARSAT (1982b) Optical sensor for RADARSAT. *Report 82-14, Energy, Mines and Resources, Ottawa, Canada.*

Ramseier, R.O. (1982) Passive microwave imaging radiometer: a candidate instrument for RADARSAT. *RADARSAT Report 82-17, Energy, Mines and Resources, Ottawa, Ontario.*

2 Data transmission

Hydrological Applications of Remote Sensing and Remote Data Transmission (Proceedings of the Hamburg Symposium, August 1983). IAHS Publ. no. 145.

Operational satellite data collection systems operated by the National Oceanic and Atmospheric Administration

DOUGLAS H. MacCALLUM
National Environmental Satellite, Data, and Information Service, National Oceanic and Atmospheric Administration, Washington, DC 20233, USA

ABSTRACT The National Oceanic and Atmospheric Administration (NOAA), a part of the Department of Commerce, operates two satellite data collection systems. The joint Franco-American Argos Data Collection and Location System (DCLS) uses the NOAA operated TIROS-N series of polar orbiting satellites. The other is the Geostationary Operational Environmental Satellite (GOES) Data Collection System (DCS) using the NOAA operated GOES spacecraft.

Systèmes opérationnels de collecte de données par satellites exploités par la "National Oceanic and Atmospheric Administration"
RESUME La "National Oceanic and Atmospheric Administration" exploite deux systèmes de collecte de données des satellites. L'un est le système coopératif Franco-American Argos, embarqué sur les satellites NOAA en orbite polaire. L'autre est le système de collecte de données des satellites GOES, en orbite géostationnaire.

ARGOS DCLS

The Argos Data Collection and Location System (DCLS) is capable of locating moving platforms as well as acquiring environmental information from either fixed or moving platforms. Argos is a cooperative programme between France and the USA. Le Centre National d'Etudes Spatiales (CNES) represents the French and both the National Oceanic and Atmospheric Administration (NOAA) and the National Aeronautics and Space Administration (NASA) represent the USA.

The Argos DCLS was developed from experience gained with the NASA Nimbus-4 interrogation, recording, and location system of 1970, the French EOLE programme 1970-1974, and the NASA Nimbus-6 random access measurement system of 1975-1979. TIROS-N, launched in October 1978, carried the first Argos DCLS instrument and was followed in June 1979 by the launch of NOAA-6 completing the initial two spacecraft segment of the programme.

These polar-orbiting spacecraft have a nominal altitude of 870 km, 98° inclination, 101-minute period, and sunsynchronous circular orbits. Sunsynchronous orbit means that the satellite crosses the equatorial plane at the same time (local solar time) each day.

For the "morning" satellite, normally these times are 0730 h (ascending or northbound) and 1930 h (descending or southbound), while the "afternoon" satellite crosses the equator at 1430 h (ascending) and 0230 h (descending). These orbital parameters allow a specific platform to come within a satellite's coverage at the same local time each day. Also, with a polar-orbiting satellite, the time and frequency of satellite visibility varies with latitude as depicted in Table 1.

TABLE 1 Latitudinal average parameters of the two spacecraft

Latitude	*Cumulative visibility time per 24 h*	*Number of passes per 24 h*			*Mean duration of pass*
		Min	*Mean*	*Max*	
0°	*80 min*	*6*	*7*	*8*	
15°	*88 min*	*8*	*8*	*9*	
30°	*100 min*	*8*	*9*	*12*	
45°	*128 min*	*10*	*11*	*12*	*10 min*
55°	*170 min*	*16*	*16*	*18*	
65°	*246 min*	*21*	*22*	*23*	
75°	*322 min*	*28*	*28*	*28*	
90°	*384 min*	*28*	*28*	*28*	

The spacecraft radio view describes a circle with a diameter of 5000 km on the earth's surface (see Fig.1). As the spacecraft orbits, the ground track of this circle makes a swath 5000 km in width across the earth. During each orbit, this swath covers both the north and south poles. Also, the swath is displaced by 25°, or 2800 km, at the equator every 24 h as a result of the rotation of the earth.

Data collection platforms are referred to as platform transmitter terminals (PTT) and may transmit analogue or digital data from up to 32 sensors. All PTT transmit on the same frequency (401.650 MHz).

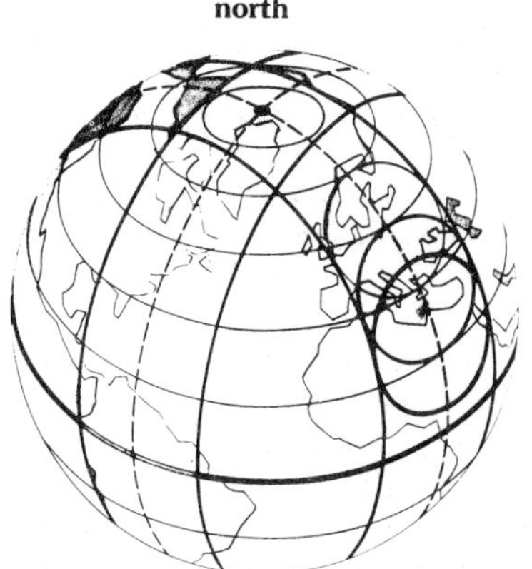

FIG.1 Spacecraft radio view.

Transmissions are made in a random manner at 40-60 s intervals for PTTs requiring location and at 100-200 s for PTTs used for data collection only. Message duration is less than one second and is limited to 256 bits. The on-board instrument is capable of receiving up to four messages simultaneously. Statistical analysis indicates that, if the same message is repeated one or more times during the approximate 10-minute period the satellite is in view of the PTT, the information will be received at least once about 99% of the time.

Location calculations are made by the Doppler shift on the carrier frequency of incoming messages to the spacecraft. The Doppler shift information is recorded onboard the spacecraft, along with the message itself, for playback at a later time. This same information also is broadcast in real time. Using this information, the altitude of the spacecraft, and the information from strategically located reference platforms used to determine precise orbits, the PTT location calculations are made. Typical accuracies for drifting buoys are 0.5-1 km for location and 0.5 m s^{-1} for speed. Accuracies for drifting balloons are 3-5 km and 1.5 m s^{-1}, respectively.

The Argos DCLS capacity is up to 4000 PTTs requiring location (at least once each 24 h) and 16 000 PTTs for data collection only (at least once each 12 h). These figures assume a worldwide distribution so that no more than 4 PTTs are transmitting simultaneously to the spacecraft.

Real time transmission of PTT messages from the spacecraft is made both at VHF (136.770 MHz or 137.770 MHz depending upon the satellite) and at S-band (1698.0 or 1707.0 MHz depending upon the satellite). However, PTT locations are not available in either of these data streams and must be computed at the direct readout station or an auxillary processing centre using the information obtained from the direct readout station. In addition, with a lack of reference PTTs, location calculations will not be as accurate as those obtained from the Argos processing centre. The normal flow of Argos DCLS data is depicted in Fig.2 and is as follows:

(a) Data are telemetered from tape recorders on the spacecraft after each orbit to a NOAA telemetry station.

(b) Data are relayed from the NOAA telemetry station via communications satellite to the NOAA processing centre in Suitland, Maryland.

(c) After decommutation and formatting at Suitland, data are relayed by a combination of landline and satellite to the Argos processing centre in Toulouse, France.

(d) Data are processed at the Argos processing centre and distributed to the users by telephone, telex, and by mail.

The average delay from the time data are collected until the processed data are available for dissemination is approximately 3-4 h. This time period includes storage onboard the spacecraft during at least one orbit.

Application to use the Argos DCLS should be made to the CNES coordination centre, Service Argos. Applications are approved by the joint Franco-American Argos Operations Committee. Data collected must be environmental to comply with international radio frequency agreements and are considered in the public domain (available to any party that requests these data) unless other arrangements are made with NOAA and CNES.

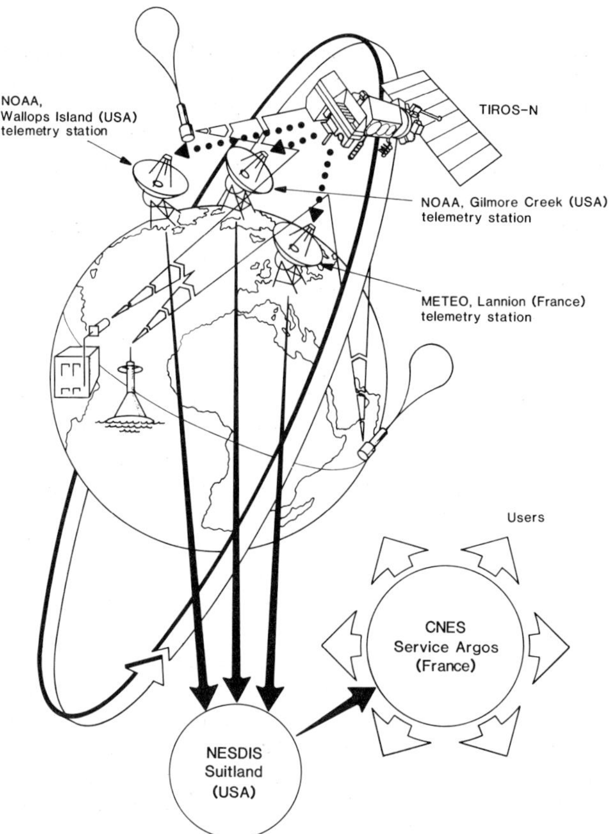

FIG.2 Argos data flow.

There are nominal charges for users of the Argos DCLS. These charges vary with type of organization (private, governmental), whether or not the organization is a member of the global processing agreement, whether or not the user obtains their data from the Argos processing centre in France or uses a direct readout ground station, and what type of data processing is required. Information pertaining to applications and charges can be obtained from: *Service Argos, Centre Spatial de Toulouse, 18 Avenue Edouard Belin, 31055 Toulouse Cedex, France.*

Some typical uses of the Argos DCLS are: drifting buoys and vessels reporting meteorological and oceanographic information; constant pressure level balloons reporting meteorological information; tracking land and marine animals; and, fixed platforms reporting meteorological, hydrological, oceanographic or seismological information.

GOES DCS

Data collection is one of the primary functions of the Geostationary Operational Environment Satellites (GOES). The system was developed by NOAA in conjunction with NASA and based upon earlier experiments with the NASA Advanced Technology Satellites (1966-1974). The GOES

DCS uses two operational geostationary satellites located over the equator at an altitude of 35 000 km. One satellite is located at 75°W longitude and the other is located at 135°W longitude. The effective range of operation is about from 75°N or 75°S latitude and, at the equator, from 0° longitude westward through 180° longitude to 150°E longitude. In the more northerly and southerly latitudes there is a narrowing of the operational area (see Fig.3). Data can be received from virtually any point in the western hemisphere excluding the polar regions.

Due to international agreements on radio frequencies, the GOES DCS is limited to the collection of environmental data only. The DCS is not used in lieu of commercial communications for collecting environmental data where such communications are available and adequate, nor is it used for point-to-point communications.

The GOES DCS is a data relay network consisting of many individual data gathering platforms frequently referred to as data collection platforms (DCPs) which can transmit their data to one of the two satellites. Each spacecraft has a capacity of 233 channels at 1.5 KHz separation of centre frequencies. This would theoretically allow more than 9000 DCPs to transmit via each spacecraft transponder in each 1-h period. However, in reality, the total number of DCP transmissions per spacecraft is closer to 6000. There are up to 200 channels available in the domestic frequency band (401.7-402.0 MHz) and 33 channels in the international frequency band (402.0-402.1 MHz). Note: The international channels are common with the international channels of the European Space Agency's Meteosat and the Japanese GMS while the domestic channels are not common with Meteosat or GMS. Channel spacing accommodates the 100 bits-per-second DCS message rates. Error rate probabilities of 10^{-5} or better can be expected.

These data are relayed through either satellite to a common Command and Data Acquisition (CDA) station at Wallops Station, Virginia, or to properly equipped ground direct readout stations at S-band (1694.5 MHz). The uplink frequency from the DCP to the satellite is UHF. Data received at the CDA are demodulated, checked for parity errors and transmission quality, and relayed by landline to Camp Springs, Maryland, where the data are disseminated to the appropriate system user. There is no processing of data into engineering units accomplished at Camp Springs before these data are disseminated. Dissemination is either in real time via dedicated circuits, or by direct dial-in on a user demand basis at low speed 110/300 and 1200 baud or at medium speed 2400 or 4800 baud (see Fig.4). Disc storage is somewhat limited and normally data storage cannot be guaranteed in excess of 24 h.

There are three basic types of DCPs in the system. Each type uses binary coded ASCII or pseudo-ASCII characters. These DCPs are type certified by NOAA prior to use in the GOES DCS. Each DCP has a unique 31-bit address which is transmitted with every message. The first type of DCP is the interrogate, which replies only when it is interrogated from the NESS ground system via the satellite. There is a variation of this type of DCP that may transmit its DCP address to the satellite via an alarm reply channel after a certain pre-set sensor threshold is reached. Upon receipt of this address on the alarm channel, the DCS ground computer will schedule a special

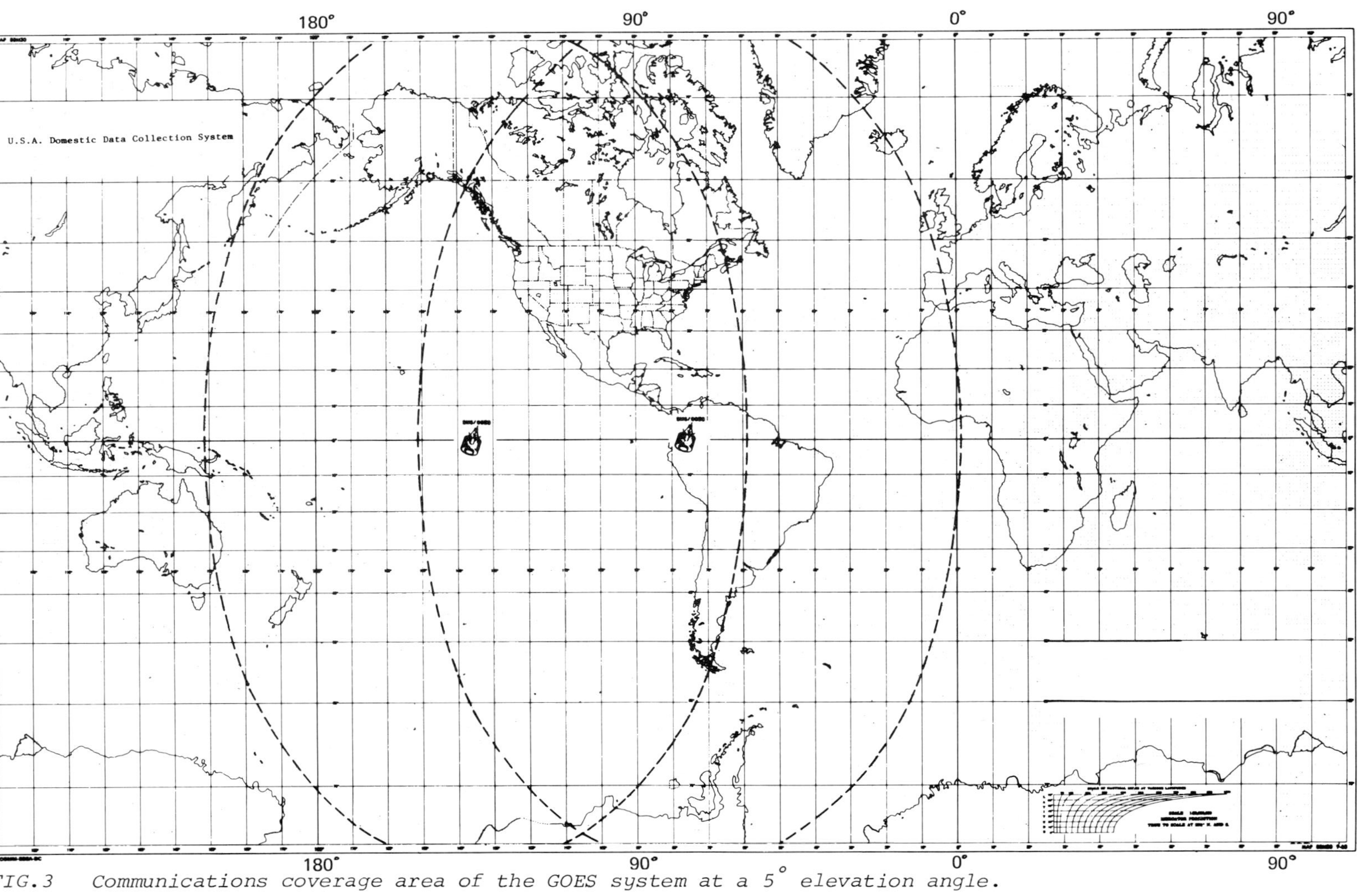

FIG.3 Communications coverage area of the GOES system at a 5° elevation angle.

interrogation of this DCP within a few minutes and the DCP will transmit its special data via the normal reply channel. The second type of DCP is self-timed and replies on its assigned time according to a pre-set internal clock. The self-timed DCPs normally are scheduled at either 3 or 4 h intervals but, in some special cases, may report more frequently. The third type of DCP reports in a random manner in response to pre-set sensor thresholds. Random reporting DCPs repeat their messages one or more times, in a random manner, to insure that at least one of their messages is received, as other random reporting DCPs on the channel may be transmitting when the first message is transmitted. Random reporting messages are brief (2-4 s including message protocol) when compared to interrogate or self-timed messages which may continue up to several minutes. Variations of the random reporting DCP may include both a self-timed and random reporting capability as well as the ability to transmit on more than one channel, depending upon the nature of the message.

The current GOES DCS ground system has 72 active domestic channels and two international channels, with a total capacity of 80 channels. There are more than 4000 DCPs in the system with 1500-2000 active at any one time. The ground system has either complete redundancy of all components, or alternate routes for data flow to insure reliability of the system. In addition, a standby GOES,

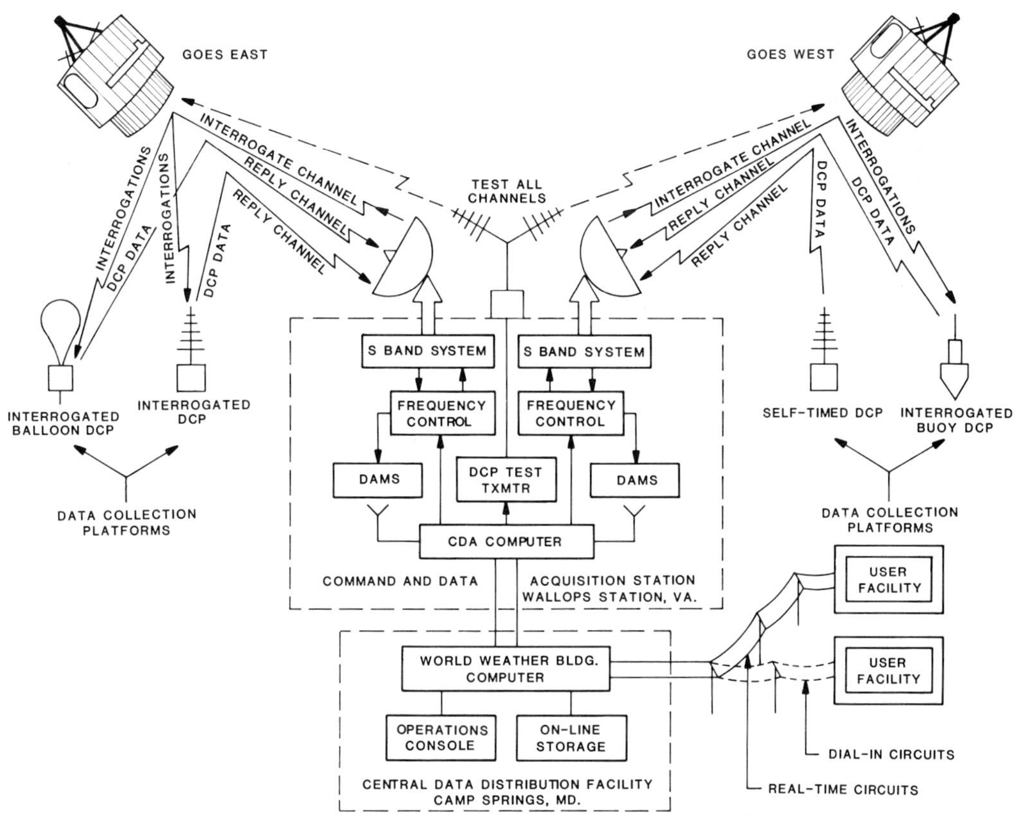

FIG.4 The GOES DCS.

located at 107°W longitude, is available to assume data collection activities in the event of operational spacecraft failure or during the two eclipse periods during the equinox when spacecraft power limitations preclude use of the satellite for data collection. To allow for efficient use of this spacecraft redundancy, all GOES DCS users have been urged to point their DCP antenna halfway between the location of the normal operational spacecraft and the standby spacecraft. In this manner, sudden changes in the active spacecraft used for DCS will not adversely affect the user's data collection activities.

Some special features of the current GOES DCS are as follows:

(a) *Time code*. Coded time data, updated at ½-minute intervals by reference to a National Bureau of Standards source, are broadcast in the interrogate signal.

(b) *Reinterrogation*. Up to 15 reinterrogations are allowed.

(c) *Remote commanding*. Interrogate DCPs can alter their electrical or mechanical operating parameters in response to a message broadcast over the interrogate channel.

(d) *Test mode/reply verify*. A DCP in the test mode, will have a reply verify transmitted upon receipt of each error free message.

(e) *Emergency interrogate schedule*. More frequent interrogations of DCP networks or segments of networks can be made by the DCS operator.

(f) *Test transmissions*. Transmissions from the test transmitter are used periodically to test each reply channel.

(g) *Diagnostic messages*. Each message is checked for errors and appropriate diagnostic information is appended to each message as necessary.

(h) *Multiple user dissemination*. Each DCP message will be sent to a primary user and up to three other users upon request.

(i) Remote access to the NOAA data base is possible in order to obtain specific information for each DCP.

(j) Appending diagnostic information from the Data Acquisition and Monitoring System (DAMS) to each message received by the NOAA ground system (see Fig.5).

The present user community consists of meteorological, hydrological, oceanographic, seismological and environmental monitoring users. By far the largest number of DCPs is involved with hydrological measurements (approximately 2600 DCPs).

The NOAA ground system is rapidly approaching saturation. The current ground system has the capacity to support approximately 5000 DCPs and the system now has more than 4000 DCPs in the data base. User plans indicate the current system will reach saturation in 1984 unless enhancements and eventual expansion are implemented.

In order to manage the system properly and to guarantee system integrity, all DCP data must be received by the NOAA ground system. Since the spacecraft are capable of supporting approximately 12 500 DCPs and 233 channels, the next expansion must be sized to support this capacity. However, due to funding and expected procurement delays, this expansion most likely will not be implemented before mid-1986. Therefore, some interim enhancement and management steps will be initiated. These may consist of limited disc expansion at both the Wallops CDA and in the World Weather Building at Camp Springs, re-allocation of disc space for operational and scheduling

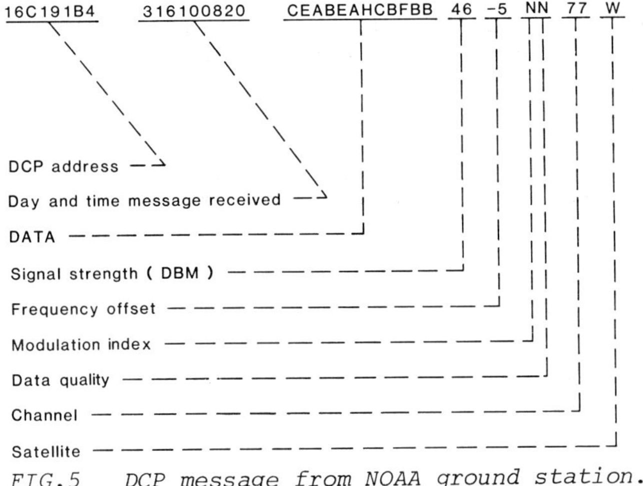

FIG.5 DCP message from NOAA ground station.

files, manual updating of DCP active/de-active status, and temporarily limiting expansion of user DCP networks.

NOAA is considering the expansion of the DCS frequency band in the follow-on geostationary spacecraft, commonly referred to as "GOES-Next". This expansion will allow more channels and larger DCP networks, the possibility of higher data rate DCPs, and, if in the proper frequency band, the incorporation on non-environmental reporting DCPs. The target date for the GOES-Next series is late in this decade.

Applications to use the GOES DCS should be forwarded to: *Chief, Data Collection and Direct Broadcast Branch (E/SP21), National Environmental Satellite, Data, and Information Service, National Oceanic and Atmospheric Administration, Washington, DC 20233*. At the present time there are no charges for using the GOES DCS other than the equipment and costs to obtain data from the NOAA distribution facility in Camp Springs, Maryland, or through a suitable ground direct readout station. As is the case with the Argos DCLS, data collected in the system must be environmental to meet international radio frequency agreements and is considered in the public domain (available to anyone who wants it) unless other arrangements are made with NOAA.

Hydrological Applications of Remote Sensing and Remote Data Transmission (Proceedings of the Hamburg Symposium, August 1983). IAHS Publ. no. 145.

Development of a distributive system for handling real time hydrological data collected by the US Geological Survey

WILLIAM G. SHOPE JR & RICHARD W. PAULSON
US Geological Survey, Water Resources Division, National Center, MS 460, Reston, Virginia 22092, USA

ABSTRACT The US Geological Survey has been collecting hydrological data using satellite data relay since the early 1970's. Until recently, data transmitted to the satellite from hundreds of automated remote locations have been received, processed, and disseminated from central computers. Although these computers offer advantages such as consolidation of resources and ease of control, the disadvantages due to increased complexity, reduced reliability, and high telephone communications costs have convinced the Survey to develop a system that will permit field offices to receive data directly from the satellite and, following on-site computer processing, distribute the data directly to water data users. Once in place, local Survey offices will, with the exception of the GOES satellite, control all phases of the satellite telemetry system from operating remote data collection sensors to providing water data users access to real time hydrological data stored in Survey computers.

Mise au point d'un système de diffusion en temps réel de l'information hydrologique acquise par l'US Geological Survey

RESUME L'US Geological Survey a collecté des données hydrologiques, retransmises par satellite, depuis le début des annees 1970. Jusqu'à maintenant l'information transmise au satellite depuis des centaines de stations automatiques éloignées a été recue, traitée et diffusée depuis des ordinateurs centralisés. Bien que ces ordinateurs aient l'avantage du regroupement des ressources et de la facilité de contrôle, les désavantages dus à une complexité accrue, à une fiabilité réduite et à un coût élevé en communications téléphoniques ont convaincu le Geological Survey de mettre au point un système qui permette aux bureaux locaux de recevoir l'information directement du satellite et après traitement par ordinateur sur place de diffuser l'information directement aux utilisateurs. Une fois installé, ce système permettra à tous les bureaux locaux du Geological Survey de contrôler, à l'exception du satellite GOES, toutes les phases du système télémetrique par satellite depuis le fonctionnement des instruments des plateformes éloignées jusqu'à la fourniture immédiate de l'information hydrologique des ordinateurs du Geological Survey aux utilisateurs.

INTRODUCTION

The US Geological Survey is the principal water resources information agency in the United States, and in cooperation with over 800 other federal, state, and local agencies, operates an extensive array of hydrological data collection stations throughout the nation. The data acquired include stage and discharge of streams, lake and reservoir levels, groundwater levels, and many indicators of the quality of surface and ground waters.

The data-collection activity has developed since the last part of the nineteenth century, and now includes more than 8000 continuous streamflow stations, 8000 partial record streamflow stations, 1000 lake and reservoir stations, 27 000 stations for monitoring groundwater levels, 8000 surface-water quality stations, and 8000 groundwater quality stations. The data collection stations are operated by Survey hydrologists and technicians from offices that are located in every state, Puerto Rico, and Guam. Several programmes within the Survey provide these offices with technical assistance in the form of computer and data-processing systems, instrumentation support, water-quality laboratory analytical services, and a research programme that develops new technologies and methodologies for data collection and analysis.

In recent years, the Survey's instrumentation programme has provided technical support and assistance to the field offices enabling installation of a modern remote telemetry capability at approximately 500 continuous streamgauging stations. This automated telemetry capability uses a series of geostationary satellites operated by the National Earth Satellite Data and Information Service (NESDIS) to relay real time hydrological data from the streamflow stations to satellite data receiving stations. The Survey's participation in the use of this technology began in the early 1970's with tests of the data collection system on the National Aeronautics and Space Administration's series of Landsat satellites (Paulson, 1974). This activity was followed in the mid to late 1970's with tests of the Geostationary Operational Environmental Satellites (GOES) that are operated by NESDIS (Shope & Paulson, 1981), and tests of a commercial satellite (Forcina & Singh, 1978) for data relay. GOES remote telemetry from Survey streamflow stations are now fully operational and are maintained by Survey field offices in cooperation with other federal, state, and local agencies that require real time hydrological data for fulfillment of their operational missions. The Survey does not usually require real time data for its interpretive studies or data reports, but the availability of such data to the Survey can be beneficial for automated data collection and for monitoring the status of instruments and data values at hydrological stations can result in a more efficient scheduling of field personnel for repair of field equipment, collection of water samples and on-site hydrological measurements.

With the planned integration of new communications and computer technologies into data-collection activities in the 1980's, the Geological Survey will be making a transition from a centralized to a distributive data collection system for acquisition, processing, and providing access to real time hydrological data by water data users. The new computer and communication technologies are beginning to have a profound effect on the way the Survey collects, transmits, stores, and disseminates hydrological data. This paper provides a description of why and how these technologies are being used to help the Survey move from a centralized system that was developed in the late 1970's and early 1980's, to a more flexible and responsive distributive data-collection system that is expected to be in place by the mid to late 1980's. The move to the distributive system will be based on information from tests at several Survey offices. The development and use of the new distributive information systems also holds promise for developing countries that seek to monitor water resources in real time or collect data from remote locations. This approach, which is based on satellite telemetry and data processing networks, could be used where a conventional communication infrastructure is absent or underdeveloped.

CENTRALIZED SYSTEM

A system of computers and communications equipment is presently in operation by NESDIS and the Geological Survey in support of real time satellite data collection. This centralized communications and data processing system was developed from the most cost-effective technologies that were available in the late 1970's. This arrangement conveys hydrological data from small battery-radios located at remote field stations to Survey field offices and cooperating agencies in real time, but suffers from problems of reliability and cost. The elements in the system and associated problems are described below.

The Geological Survey began to deploy small battery-powered radios, known as data collection platforms (DCP), at remote sites during the 1970's. These DCPs were interfaced to existing hydrological sensors and could communicate with one or more satellites. The DCP's were designed with modern electronic technology, and use microprocessors that provide much greater inherent flexibility and reliability when compared to previous instrumentation that relies on electromechanical control. The first DCPs deployed were designed to collect data from the sensor at a fixed frequency, usually every 15 or 30 minutes, accumulate many sets of data, and then at 3-h intervals telemeter the data to a GOES satellite as shown in Fig.1.

The National Oceanic and Atmospheric Administration's NESDIS operates the series of GOES satellites that have been placed in geostationary orbits above the earth's equator. These satellites, which are orbited primarily to image and monitor the earth's cloud cover and weather systems, can view the entire earth disc from an altitude of 35 000 km above the equator. As part of an international programme of environmental monitoring, the USA maintains operational satellites at 75°W and 135°W longitude. Several older satellites, located about midway between these two operational sites, are used for backup in case of a system failure in an operational satellite. Because of their location, these satellites provide an excellent vantage point from which to receive environmental data from DCP's for retransmission to ground receive sites.

Through the 1970's, the Geological Survey relied completely on the

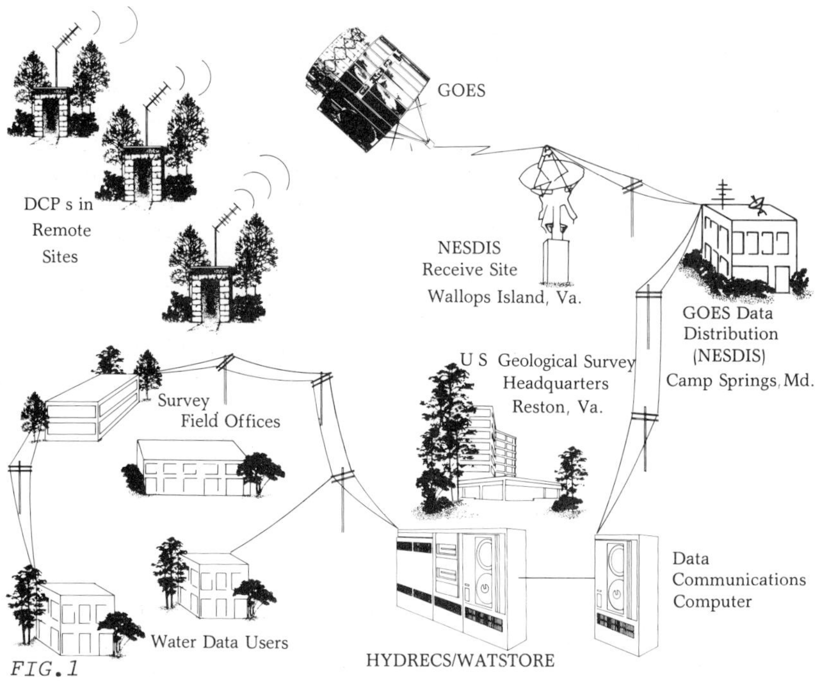

FIG.1

NESDIS Command and Data Acquisition facility located at Wallops Island, Virginia, for the reception of data telemetered from Survey hydrological stations. From the Wallops Island location, NESDIS forwards data from the satellites to a computer located in Camp Springs, Maryland, near Washington, DC and distributes the data to users via telephone lines upon request (Fig.1).

The Survey's Data Relay Project, located at the USGS National Center in Reston, Virginia, provides technical support to Survey offices in the acquisition of real time data from the NESDIS computer in Camp Springs, Maryland. The Data Relay Project has developed a real time data computer processing system, known as Hydrecs, that resides on a large general purpose interactive computer located at the National Center. Hydrological data acquired from NESDIS by a Survey data communications computer are temporarily stored in Hydrecs for interactive retrievals by Survey users and cooperators using asychronous interactive computer terminals. The Survey users can also instruct the Hydrecs system to forward hydrological data to the Survey's archival data base known as the National Water Data Storage and Retrieval System (WATSTORE) (see Showen, 1978) that resides on a large batch computer also located at the National Center. Thus, Survey and cooperator staff, in offices throughout the Nation can employ computer terminals to retrieve real time hydrological data for operational purposes, and Survey field personnel can instruct Hydrecs to automatically forward the data to the Survey's National WATSTORE system for non-real-time report generation, data analysis, and archival. Once the data have been provided to the WATSTORE system, they are available to a wide variety of water data users (also shown on Fig.1), including other federal, state, and local agencies, consultants, and the public at large.

There are a number of disadvantages and advantages to such a centralized system. The most significant disadvantage to this system is that there is a complex serial system of many computers and communications devices that must operate continuously for data to flow efficiently and reliably to the user. Moreover, elements of this serial system are under the control of different organizations located in different parts of the country and problems of contention, priority, and funding are inevitable. There are terrestrial communication systems operated by regional telephone companies that link Wallops Island, Virginia, Camp Springs, Maryland, Reston, Virginia, and users throughout the nation. They all most perform reliably for the system to function. In addition, the Hydrecs system operates on a general-purpose computer that supports a wide variety of other applications, and occasionally real time data processing is interrupted by system failure or through contention for use of the computer by other Survey users. Any single point failure in the complex serial system shown in Fig.1 can often interrupt service to *all* users of the centralized system. To real time data users that are a great distance from Reston, the cost of telecommunications from their offices to the Reston computer and the cost of computer use can be quite significant, especially if large numbers of DCPs are in operation. The applications software that is developed for the central computers is complex because it must attempt to serve a wide variety of users who have a wide range of requirements. In many cases specific user requirements cannot be met, which reduces the flexibility and control that any one user may have.

An advantage of the centralized system is that the user of the Hydrecs system need not have expertise in communications or computer operations. Beyond the simple mechanics of dialing up and signing on to the computer, the Hydrecs programs will prompt the user interactively and allow him access to the data with little knowledge of the complexity of data storage and decoding DCP data messages. Furthermore, the user need not invest any significant resources in the development of these computer programs, and is shielded from the necessity of operating earth receive site stations and computers.

IMPROVED TECHNOLOGY PROGRAMME

Beginning in the early 1980's, the Geological Survey began to plan the deployment of new solid-state, microprocessor-based technology that will have profound impacts on data collection, including a move toward a more decentralized or distributive system for remote telemetry and processing of hydrological data. Use of the new technology has enabled the Survey to design a new field data acquisition system, deploy and operate direct-readout ground stations for satellite telemetry, and develop a distributive computerized information system. These three systems, which are described below, form the cornerstones for the Survey's real time data collection network of the 1980's and beyond.

Adaptable hydrological data acquisition system

During the early 1980's, the Survey began the planning and definition of a new field data acquisition system which will replace much of the outdated data recording and telemetry systems that presently operate out of Survey hydrological field stations (Paulson *et al.*, 1982). It will be a microprocessor driven system which will be designed to meet the data collection requirements that are envisioned for the Survey through the remainder of the twentieth century. It will provide for onsite storage of data in solid-state electronic memory, or for the remote telemetry of data, either via land line or satellite. This system, which is being cooperatively developed by the Survey and National Weather Service, will provide a more flexible and reliable field system for hydrological data collection and telemetry. The new field system, which is being designed to interface with the distributive data collection networks through the use of exacting standards, will eliminate the interface problems (electromechanical control, lack of replacement parts, non-standard connections, and others) that plague the present system and will improve the quality of hydrological data.

Direct-readout ground stations

A direct-readout ground station (DRGS) is made up of an antenna, radio receive and decoding equipment, and a minicomputer that functions as the system controller. These controllers are powerful enough to control the operation of the radio receiver, decode the DCP messages, flag and disseminate alert messages, store the decoded data in a temporary file, monitor the performance of the DCP transmissions, provide access to the data by multiple users, and forward environmental data to the Distributive Information System minicomputer co-located at the Survey's field offices.

During the early 1980's, the Survey began to process and install satellite DRGS at selected Survey district offices. As opposed to the large, complicated and expensive station operated by NESDIS at Wallops Island, these DRGs are relatively inexpensive, uncomplicated, and simple to operate. Since these DRGSs do not communicate to the satellite, monitor its health, command it and its sensors, copy imagery data, or position the satellite, they can be designed solely to service the user's requirement for collection of real time telemetered environmental data. Because the DRGS can now be co-located with the user or data collection network field manager, reliability and responsiveness has been improved, more control has been returned to the field manager, and system flexibility has increased considerably. As a result of these and other factors, the use of these stations has become increasingly attractive to users of the GOES telemetry system.

Distributive information system

The Survey embarked in the early 1980's on the development of a distributive information system (DIS). When fully implemented in 1985, there will be powerful minicomputers in every major Survey office that are involved in hydrological data collection, analysis and dissemination. These minicomputers will be linked together with a dedicated nationwide communications network. Each minicomputer will form a node in this network. Software for scientific and administrative applications that now resides on central computers in the Survey's national headquarters, will be revised and distributed among the nodes of this network. The net result will be that Survey field offices will have powerful onsite capabilities for processing basic data, running hydrological simulation models, and supporting a variety of administrative and scientific applications. The system of DRGSs that are being deployed in Geological Survey field offices and the new field data acquisition systems will be interfaced with local nodes of the DIS. Real time hydrological data acquired by a nearby DRGS will be entered into the DIS and accessed by users at the local, or other nodes within the system. This configuration will provide an excellent opportunity for sharing the resources of a limited number of DRGSs, as well as providing redundant and backup support capabilities for the network of DRGSs. By October of 1983, the Survey expects to have approximately 40 DIS nodes and by June 1983, six DRGSs. By the end of the year, many of the DRGSs will be linked directly to one or more of the nodes.

DISTRIBUTED TELEMETRY

The improved technology that is being developed in the early 1980's will result in a more distributed system for the collection, processing, and distribution of remotely telemetered hydrological data (Fig.2).

Undcr a distributed mode, Geological Survey field offices will continue as with the centralized system to install and operate DCPs at Survey hydrological stations. The deployment of the new adaptable

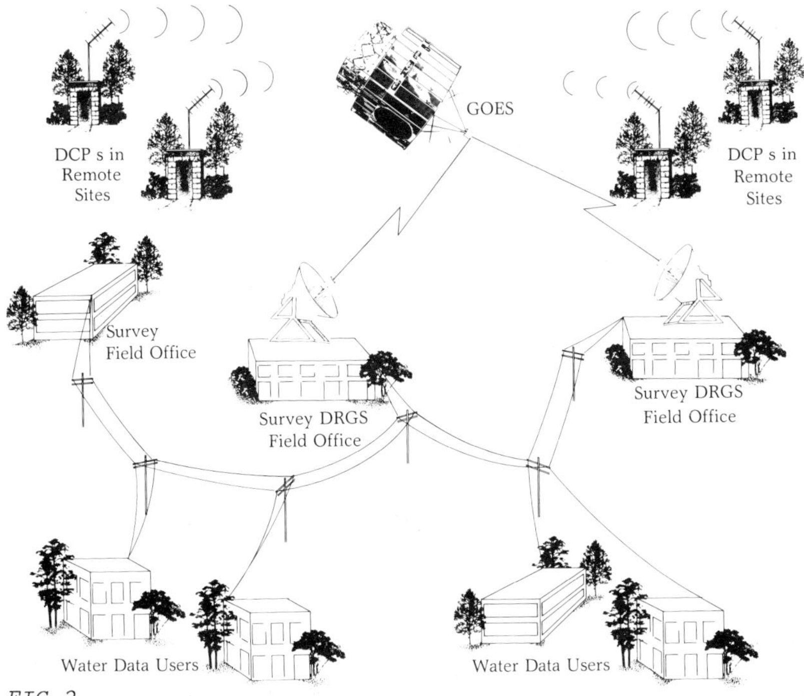

FIG.2

hydrological data acquisition systems will have the next major impact on field operations. These new systems will standardize and facilitate the transfer of data via satellite or courier (data retrieved via site visit by field technician) to the DIS network of minicomputers. Under the distributed mode, data retransmitted from the satellite will no longer be acquired from NESDIS, but from local DRGS that are owned and operated by Survey offices that are directly responsible for the operation of the hydrological data collection stations.

The processing of data acquired via satellite telemetry in the DIS minicomputer will meet four major requirements. The first requirement will be to service emergency data alarms. The system will have to service real time alarms to notify system users that emergency messages have been transmitted from DCPs that have detected extreme hydrological conditions. The second task will be to attempt to validate the data automatically in real time. There are a number of malfunctions that can occur in the sensor or other links in the system that can cause spurious data to be acquired by the telemetry system. Data validation techniques are being developed to examine absolute values, rates of change, and expected values for hydrological data from each station, so that the computer can alert the user to data that may require human review and editing. The third requirement will be for report preparation, data analysis, modelling, and long-term storage of the data. An appropriate interface between the real time data processing system in the minicomputer and the distributed WATSTORE archival system will be defined so that real time data will be forwarded to the archival system that supports the processing of all Survey hydrological data. The final major task for the computer will be to support data distribution. The DIS will respond to data requests from water data users that are attached to the minicomputer node servicing the DRGS, as well as users that gain access to the minicomputer from other nodes in the DIS network. A variety of technical and administrative routines will be developed to allow users to access and produce a wide variety of output reports that include both tables and graphs.

The Survey has developed a prototype system to perform most of these functions (not including WATSTORE functions) on a minicomputer that was in place and functioning (April 1983) before most of the DIS minicomputers were installed. This prototype system is located in Phoenix, Arizona, and is linked to the DRGS operated by the Survey's Arizona office. An evaluation of the performance of this system is being used to help define the requirements for further development of the real time system on the DIS network.

As with the centralized system, there are a set of advantages and disadvantages that exist for the distributed telemetry system. A principal advantage is that the numbers of computers and communications devices that separate the user from the DCP will be drastically reduced. It is axiomatic in such systems that the failure rate exponentially increases with the number of components in the system. Moreover, the components in the distributive system, the receive site and the local computer, are under the control of, and are generally dedicated to, the requirements of the local user and are not contested for by other major users who may have different needs. If the DRGS fails, the user can divert the DIS minicomputer to a backup site at another Survey office. The principal disadvantage will be the capital expense of the computers ($150 000-$250 000) and DRGS ($80 000) and the higher skill level required in the district staffs to operate the computers and DRGSs that are being installed. Fortunately, developments in computer software which will be coordinated from a central office, can shield the user from much of the complexity of data base operation and management.

TECHNOLOGY TRANSFER

The techniques that are being developed by the Survey may be directly applicable to developing countries where the requirements for real time data exist. Reliable DCPs and relatively inexpensive, simple to operate, and reliable DRGSs can provide a developing country with a communications system that requires none of the normal communications infrastructure that landline or terrestrial radio telemetry systems usually require. Moreover, most developing countries can gain access to geostationary satellites that are operated by the United States, the European Space Agency, and the Japanese Meteorological Agency. Moreover, the experience that the Geological Survey develops with applications software can be shared with other users who seek to use these technologies to meet their requirements.

CONCLUSIONS

As the principal federal water data collection agency of the USA, the Geological Survey operates data collection stations in cooperation with a large number of other federal, state, and local water data users. The operation of this network is influenced by the type and frequency of data that are required by users, and by the technologies that are available to help the Survey meet those requirements cost-effectively and efficiently. Based on the results of prototype tests, new communications and computer technologies are being adopted by the Survey in the early 1980's that will influence the operation of real time water data collection and processing by the Survey through the end of the century. By the middle of 1983, the Survey will have six DRGSs in operation, and by the end of 1983, many of these stations will be linked into the computerized distributive information system.

In addition to the adoption of the new technologies, the movement toward a more decentralized or distributive approach for reception and processing of data will also allow the Survey to more efficiently and effectively provide real time data for mission requirements of other agencies, and for the monitoring of the Survey's network of automated stations.

Because of the worldwide availability of GOES compatible satellites and the supporting communication equipment and computers, remote telemetry of hydrological data can also provide developing countries with a viable alternative to other data collection systems (telephone, land-based radio) that cost far more to operate and yet produce no better results.

REFERENCES

Forcina, G.P. & Singh, K. (1978) Design of an experimental data collection system using a commercial communications satellite. Preprint, XXIX Congress, International Austronautical Federalico, Dubrovnik, Yugoslavia.

Paulson, R.W. (1974) A test of an experimental polar-orbiting satellite for relaying hydrologic data. In: *Flash Floods* (Proc. Paris Symp., September 1974), 23-28. IAHS Publ. no.112.

Paulson, R.W., Billings, R.H. & Cherdak, A.S. (1982) Advanced hydrologic instrumentation activities within the Water Resources Division of the US Geological Survey. In: *Advances in Hydrometry* (Proc. Exeter Symp., July 1982), 353-359. IAHS Publ. no.134.

Shope, W.G., Jr & Paulson, R.W. (1981) Real time data collection via satellite for water management. *Transportation J., ASCE* 107.

Showen, C.R. (1978) Storage and retrieval of water resources data. In: *Collection, Storage, Retrieval and Publication of Water Resources Data*. US Geological Survey Circular 756, Washington, DC.

Hydrological Applications of Remote Sensing and Remote Data Transmission
(Proceedings of the Hamburg Symposium, August 1983). IAHS Publ. no. 145.

Collection of data using the METEOSAT DCP retransmission system

R. W. HERSCHY
Department of the Environment, Romney House,
43 Marsham Street, London SW1P 3PY, UK

ABSTRACT There are only some 30 data collection platforms (DCPs) in Europe linked to METEOSAT. One reason why users have not taken more advantage of this facility lies in the method that the data are returned from Darmstadt by land-line. Until now this return of data was via the Global Telecommunications System and the paper briefly describes this method. The new method of distribution of data by the European Space Agency (ESA) consists of retransmitting the DCP data via the satellite to small receiving stations installed by the user. These stations have a receiving dish of about 1.5 m diameter. Using spare capacity on the Weather Facsimile System (Wefax), the user's data are received directly within about 4 min of transmission. The alert facility will remain. A brief discussion of ESA's provisional future satellite programme is also presented.

Collecte de données utilisant le système de retransmission DCP lié à METEOSAT
RESUME Il n'existe en Europe que quelque 30 plates-formes de recueil de données (DCP) reliées à METEOSAT Une des raisons pour laquelle les utilisateurs n'ont pas tiré davantage parti de ce système réside dans la nature de la méthode utilisée pour transmettre les données de Darmstadt par lignes terrestres. Jusqu'à présent, cette retransmission de données s'effectuait par voie du Système de Télécommunications Planétaire selon la méthode brièvement décrite dans le présent exposé. La nouvelle méthode de diffusion de données par l'Agence Spatiale Européenne (ASE) consiste à retransmettre les données DCP par voie du satellite vers des petites stations mises en place par l'utilisateur. Ces stations sont dotées d'antennes paraboliques réceptrices d'un diamètre d'environ 1.5 m. Les données de l'utilisateur, transmises en utilisant les capacités disponibles du WEFAX (système de facsimilé météorologique), sont recues dans un délai d'environ 4 min à partir de leur transmission. Le système d'alerte subsistera. Un bref apercu du futur programme de satellites provisoire de l'ASE est également présenté.

INTRODUCTION

It has been shown that data collection platforms (DCPs) used in conjunction with geostationary satellites offer a reliable means of telemetering water management data (Herschy, 1982; Shope & Paulson, 1980). One of the problems, however, particularly in Europe, has been to find an acceptable cost effective method of receiving the data. A direct reception station which allows the user to receive DCP messages directly from the satellite is too expensive at this stage for most water management purposes. This type of station consists of a fixed-position dish antenna with a diameter of 4.5 m connected by cables to an electronic rack about the size of a filing cabinet, the entire station costing of the order of £80 000.

The high cost of these receiving stations has therefore excluded many potential users of the **METEOSAT** satellite data collection system (DCS). For this reason the European Space Agency (ESA) has devised the DCP/Retransmission system.

Data transmitted by DCPs are received at the ESA ground station at Darmstadt, West Germany, via the geostationary satellite **METEOSAT** 1 (Fig.1). A typical DCP climate station is shown in Fig.2.

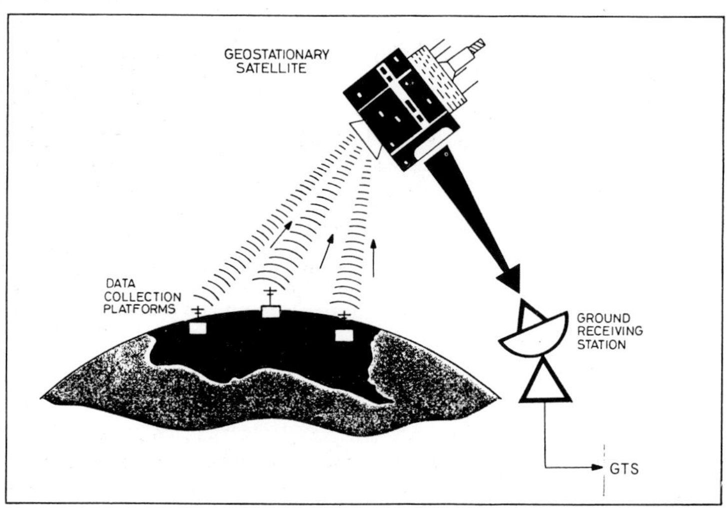

FIG.1 Data collection platforms at present transmit data at different times on specified channels to the satellite (e.g. METEOSAT, GOES, GMS etc.) for relay to the ESA ground receiving station where data are processed for distribution. If the platform user does not own a receiving station, data are received via the worldwide telex link known as the Global Telecommunication System (GTS).

The distribution of DCP messages to users at present is primarily using the GTS (Global Telecommunications System). Other means are also available such as telex and mail (for non-real-time data). All of these carriers are terrestial and require the use of existing means of communication. In many locations where DCP data could be used, these existing carriers are unreliable and expensive.

FIG.2 The automatic climate station uses an array of sensors to measure wind speed, wind direction, temperature, wet bulb depression, solar radiation, net radiation and rainfall. The data from these sensors are processed by the DCP microprocessor to compute potential evaporation using the Penman equation. The resulting data are transmitted by the DCP once per day.

THE DCP/WEFAX RETRANSMISSION SYSTEM

The European Space Agency transmits low resolution meteorological images of the earth via the Wefax link on METEOSAT 2 for reception on a secondary data user station (SDUS). This takes the form of a simple L band receiver linked to a facsimile machine. Image data are transmitted over a period of approximately 3½ min with a 27 s pause between consecutive broadcasts. The new data retransmission service utilizes this 27 s "dead" period to retransmit DCP data. By this method a modified form of SDUS is used to receive retransmitted data which can be obtained within 2-6 min of the DCP transmission with an average of 3-4 min. During the 3½ min of the image transmissions, all received DCP data from METEOSAT 1 at Darmstadt are stored in a buffer after being labelled with their time of acquisition. Upon termination of the image format, the DCP messages suitably packed, are transmitted until the buffer is empty or there is a request for a Wefax transmission. In the latter case, any remaining messages are held until the next transmission slot 4 min later. The new system is shown diagrammatically in Fig.3.

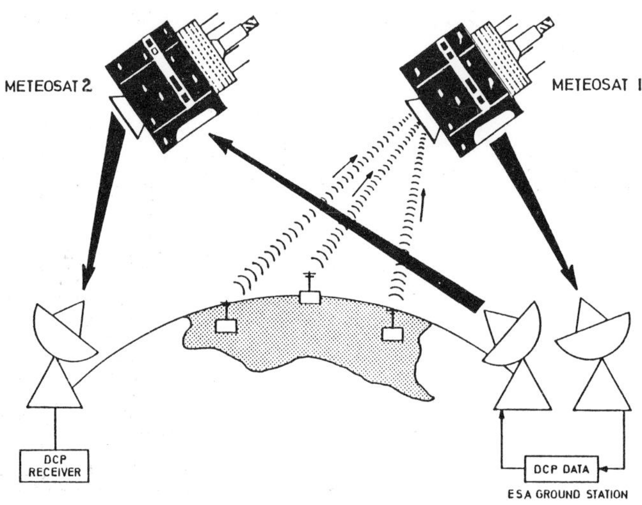

FIG.3 The DCP/Retransmission system shown diagrammatically. The DCP data are transmitted via METEOSAT 1 to ESA at the Darmstadt ground station. After processing at ESA the data are retransmitted to METEOSAT 2 for relay to the user's own ground station receiver. Two satellites are necessary since METEOSAT 2 does not have a DCP facility and METEOSAT 1 does not have a Wefax facility.

RECEIVER SYSTEM DESCRIPTION

The receiver is designed on a modular basis giving a variety of possible user options in display and storage and contains two major assemblies, the antenna unit and receiver unit the details of which are shown in Fig.4.

The antenna unit consists of a 1.5 m antenna and associated down converter. The latter amplifies the received signals, filters and down converts to VHF (1691 MHz to 133-139 MHz). Cross-site transmission to the receiver unit is carried out at this frequency. The receiver unit consists of the following sections (see Fig.4):

(a) *The second down converter* introduces a further conversion to an intermediate frequency of 10.7 MHz. This section also provides automatic frequency control and signal strength indication.

(b) *The demodulator and bit conditioner* recover the baseband signal and processes it to produce digital data and clock signals.

(c) *The format decoder* detects the presence of retransmitted data in the incoming bit stream, strips off all format coding and forwards the derived DCP data for storage and processing. The DCP data are also routed to a high speed interface.

(d) *The storage and processing section* performs the essential processing and storage required to interface the incoming DCP data with a variety of output options. Buffer storage is provided to ensure that, with the worst case data rate, the output options function without loss of data. Figures 5 and 6 show the antenna unit and receiver unit respectively. The complete system is offered at a price of about £15 000 but this is likely to be reduced depending on demand.

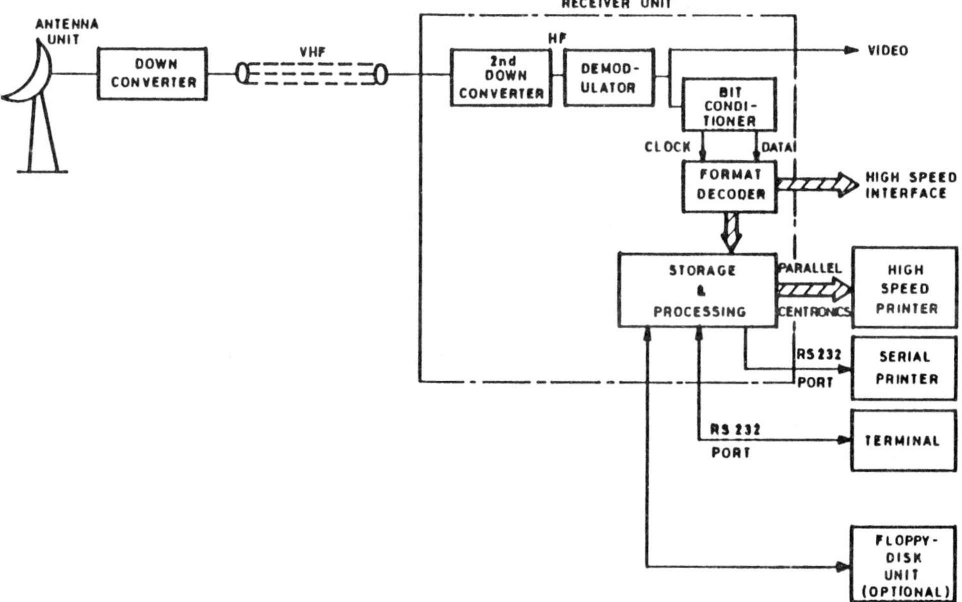

FIG.4 Block diagram of the DCP/Retransmission system.

USER FACILITIES

Certain options are available in modular sub-units such as a mini-floppy disc unit which provides a mass storage medium for DCP data storage for up to 1500 DCP messages; a high speed printer which provides hard copy of received DCP data; and a user terminal which enables full control of the receiver facilities and interfacing via an RS 232 port. If Wefax imagery is required, this can be accomplished by the addition of standard display and processing equipment; weather images and DCP data can be viewed together.

The basic receiver unit includes the facility of a direct data link which transfers all acquired DCP data via the high speed interface. All data transferred by this method are unprocessed and hence identical to the original transmitted data. This provides the facility for processing by, for example, a host computer system. Control of the DCP receiver modes is achieved via a terminal

FIG.5 The antenna unit.

connected to the RS 232 port. By this means stored DCP data can be routed to the printer and/or mini floppy disc storage. The terminal can also be used to create a look-up table in the receiver unit to enable only data from selected DCPs to be printed and/or stored. Additional header information, such as DCP names, can be entered by the user which is then printed or stored as part of the relevant data header. The use of this terminal is only required for setting up and once operating in the required mode no further interaction is required.

MECHANICAL CONFIGURATION

The antenna and down converter assembly consists of a 1.5-m-dish antenna mounted on a 120 mm outer diameter pipe with the down converter enclosure below it. The location should be such that a "line of sight" is available to METEOSAT 2. The dish antenna may, however, be up to 100 m from the receiver unit.

The receiver unit is housed in a small case which is located indoors in a position convenient to a power socket and to the printer or computer or other terminals. The front panel contains various status indicators for signal reception, channel selection switch for use with other geostationary satellites, alert indicator, DCP data indicator, stored data and Wefax data reception. The rear panel holds all the interface connectors for VHF input, high speed

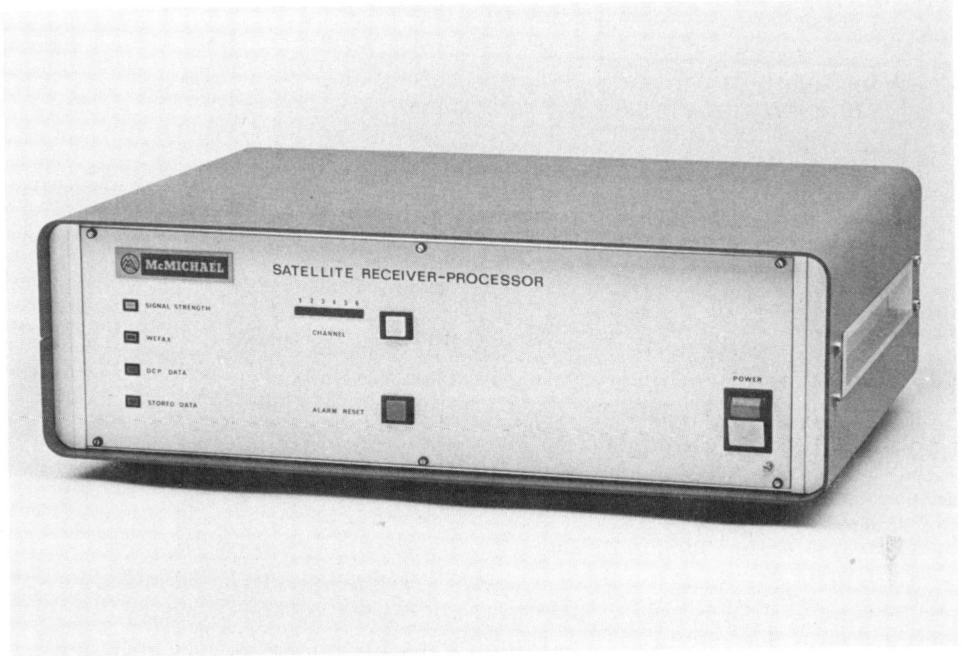

FIG.6 The receiver unit.

interface, printer output, terminal interface, floppy disc unit, video output, power input, and alert message.

USER EXPERIENCE

Three DCP receivers are now operating in the UK. These are located at Nottingham, Reading and Bath serving the Severn Trent Water Authority, the Thames Water Authority and the Wessex Water Authority, respectively. These receivers form part of the DCP pilot investigation already described and reported in Herschy (1982). The receivers were installed in late 1983.

FUTURE AVAILABILITY OF ESA GEOSTATIONARY SATELLITES

Of crucial importance to present and potential users of satellite telemetry in a future operational system is the availability of satellites. At an intergovernmental conference in March 1983, European Meteorological Services agreed to participate in an Operational METEOSAT Programme having the following content and being executed by the European Space Agency:

METEOSAT 1	expected to serve until 1985
METEOSAT 2	expected to serve until 1986
METEOSAT Prototype 2	expected launch 1985
MOP1	expected launch 1987
MOP2	expected launch 1988
MOP3	expected launch 1990

The launch of the METEOSAT Prototype 2 is officially part of the pre-operational programme. Taking an optimistic view therefore it would seem that an uninterrupted DCS will be available up to the end of 1995. On the other hand, and taking the pessimistic view, satellites cannot be guaranteed a successful launch nor can it be guaranteed that all systems are operational even after a successful launch. It will be recalled that the DCP facility on METEOSAT 2 failed to operate after launch.

It would seem, therefore, that for an operational system the availability of a satellite must be assured. In addition a spare satellite as a back-up in the event of failure would also be necessary.

If these requirements are satisfied it would appear that satellite telemetry would become a real option and indeed a cost effective alternative to present-day terrestial systems where in the UK the allocation and availability of frequencies are becoming difficult. During the UK pilot investigation no charge was made by ESA for the use of the satellite and similar arrangements are offered to contributing member countries. No such arrangement has been agreed for a future operational system and indeed it would be expected that a charge, albeit perhaps a nominal one, would be made. Other possibilities could be studied including the users renting the satellite facility. All of these matters will no doubt be the subject of discussion and negotiation in the future.

CONCLUSIONS

The development by the European Space Agency of the DCP/Retransmission system now offers the user a low cost method of satellite telemetry. The data can be received by the user within a period of 2-6 min of transmission and a variety of options are available for recording, displaying or archiving the data. The system will operate anywhere in the area covered by the ESA METEOSAT satellites. Provided the satellites are made available the system offers a cost effective alternative to terrestial telemetry.

ACKNOWLEDGEMENT Acknowledgement is made to the Department of the Environment, UK, for permission to publish this paper. Any views expressed in the paper, however, are those of the author and not necessarily those of the Department.

REFERENCES

Herschy, R.W. (1982) Towards a satellite-based hydrometric data collection system. In: *Advances in Hydrometry* (Proc. Exeter Symp., July 1982), 285-296. IAHS Publ. no. 134.

Shope, W.G. & Paulson, R.W. (1980) Real time data collection via satellite for water management. *ASCE Convention Exposition* (Florida), October 80-561.

Hydrological Applications of Remote Sensing and Remote Data Transmission
(Proceedings of the Hamburg Symposium, August 1983). IAHS Publ. no. 145.

Hydrological data collection and transmission in Sweden

GUNLÖG WENNERBERG
The Swedish Meteorological and Hydrological Institute (SMHI), Box 923, S-60119 Norrköping, Sweden

ABSTRACT Systems for automatic data collection are currently being developed in a variety of fields. At SMHI there is a data collection system comprising stations which collect data on mountain and coastal weather, water levels and temperatures in seas and rivers, and water quality, waves and currents in the sea. The data are transmitted via the telephone network or satellite. Satellite transmission means that automatic field stations can be set up where access to electricity or the telephone network is lacking. With this technique stations can easily be moved. The transmission systems result in new demands and new possibilities for sensor equipment. New remote sensing methods will also be available for monitoring waters.

Collecte et transmission de données hydrologiques en Suède
RESUME Les systèmes de collecte automatique des données se perfectionnent constamment dans les domaines les plus variés. A l'institut SMHI il existe un système pour la collecte des données sur les conditions météréologiques dans les montagnes et sur les côtes ainsi que les données sur les températures et les niveaux de l'eau dans les lacs et dans les rivières ainsi que sur la qualité de l'eau, les niveaux, vagues et courants marins. Les données sont transmises à l'aide du réseau téléphonique ou des satellites. La transmission par satellite rend possible l'installation des terminaux même dans les régions qui manquent de réseaux électriques et téléphoniques. Ainsi les terminaux dits mobiles peuvent être utilisés. La système de transmission crée de nouvelles demandes et donne de nouvelles possibilités en ce qui conserne le capteur. De plus la méthode de télédétection peut être employée pour surveiller les conditions hydrologiques.

INTRODUCTION

At SMHI some projects are at hand, which aim at improving the runoff forecasts to reservoirs and hydropower plants. Some of them concern measurements of hydrological and meteorological data, snow cover, precipitation and air temperature while others concern development of hydrological models and forecasting routines. Regarding measurements, new manually operated stations have been established. In the

Swedish mountains, however, it can be extremely difficult to find people to carry out observations, and therefore automatically operated stations are often the only way to extend the network of hydrometeorological stations in these areas. As a result, some stations, from which data are collected and transmitted automatically to SMHI, have been established.

Remote sensing methods are used to complement other measurements. Snow mapping by airborne gamma-ray spectrometry is used in mountainous areas. Weather satellites are used to study, for example, the surface temperature conditions throughout the Baltic (Wennerberg, 1980) and Landsat MSS data have been used in turbidity mapping (Wennerberg, 1981).

AUTOMATIC DATA COLLECTION AND DATA TRANSMISSION

Systems of communication have been used as far back as the Inca Empire. Theirs was made up of a system of roads and "running" messengers. A message could be carried 200 km a day. Today, however, we have other demands.

In 1968, SMHI started work on a network of automatic weather stations. The network now consists of a fully computerized system for automatic data collection. Transmission of the data is via the telephone network. The original idea behind the system was to make available to meteorologists data from places where no observers were stationed. The stations have been sited on lighthouses and in the mountains to supplement the meteorological data collected by SMHI observers. The stations installed on lighthouses have been supplemented by sensors placed in the water to measure current, temperature, salinity, tides and waves. At the request of the hydrologists, inland stations have been equipped with sensors which transmit data on water level, water quality and precipitation. Apart from the meteorologists, other current users of the data include hydrologists, power stations, mountain-rescue services, shipping and researchers.

The SMHI data collection system is based at Norrköping in Sweden. This acquisition centre automatically calls up the stations and then receives the measurements recorded by them. At present, transmission is via the public telephone network. The system is being developed, so that it will be possible to use both the telephone network and special public data transmission lines. The central station is linked by computer to the SMHI computer centre. The system permits rapid access to the data and can trigger an alarm in the event of a malfunction or a critical reading being detected. Automatic checking of the data is also possible, and the data are stored and processed at the SMHI computer centre. External users can also be linked to the data collection system via computer screen or telex.

Field measurements are collected by means of terminals, to which various types of sensors are connected. Microcomputers in the terminals enable checking, data reduction and a certain amount of data processing to be performed at the field station. Energy spectra, mean periods and significant wave heights are calculated to measure waves. For other readings, such as wind, water levels and current, mean values are calculated for 10-minute periods, and maximum and minimum values every hour. A terminal of this type can also be used in controlling the liming of acid lakes and rivers. SMHI has a team of microcomputer programmers and can offer users tailor-made software for local data collection functions (Hovberg, 1978).

It was, however, quite evident that this transmission could not fulfil the demands of hydrologists for information from mountain areas, since it is almost impossible to install telephone equipment or radio links in such areas. The Swedish telephone network is extremely good, but it doesn't include this sparsely populated area. Thus SMHI has conducted promising tests with the transmission of data via satellite. Automatic recording of precipitation and air temperatures has been in progress at a mountain station since 1978. The data are transmitted via the Argos system. The first Swedish experimental station was set up by SMHI and the Swedish Space Corporation and has functioned very well. Later another station, which also measures water level, was installed. With microcomputers in the station, mean values, e.g. temperature, water level and 24-h (0700-0700) precipitation can now be stored until they are transmitted to the satellite.

The Argos satellite transmission system is suitable for the collection of hydrological and climatic data, when real time transmission, i.e. transmission exactly at the time the reading is made, is not necessary. At present, our data are received via Toulouse, France. Data from the stations are also received in Norway. Within a year, SMHI will have acquired its own receiving station for data transmitted via satellites which will enable receiving the data when the satellite is passing directly overhead. At that time, a new data acquisition central at SMHI will be able to receive, control, store and distribute data transmitted via the telephone network and satellite telemetered data received by the antenna on the roof of the Institute (Wennerberg, 1982).

The experience of transmission via the telephone network and satellite is extremely good.

SYSTEMS FOR LOCAL DATA COLLECTION

In many cases it is not necessary, or not possible, to transmit data directly to a central receiving station. For occasional measurements, or measurements which are not required immediately, the data can be stored on magnetic tape or on plotter printouts for subsequent collection and analysis. Readings of currents and temperatures in lakes or along the coast, for example, are recorded on magnetic tape. Battery-driven instruments are suspended from a system of buoys, and the tapes and batteries are replaced at monthly or other intervals. If a large amount of data needs to be stored, the use of a minicomputer is recommended.

Simple plotters are still the most common type of equipment used to measure isolated factors, such as the water level and air temperature. In the near future, new types of memory, such as bubble memories and low-power semi-conductor memories, will enhance the prospects of this form of data collection.

NEW SENSORS FOR DATA ACQUISITION

We have noticed, however, that the use of automatic data collection systems often results in over-confidence in the validity of the collected data. The problem is not the data acquisition, as this is shown to be very reliable. The results depend mainly on the sensor at the other end of the system. Generally, the development of sensors has not followed that of the transmission systems. These new systems result in not only new demands but also in new possibilities for sensors.

At stations in mountain areas, we have to choose sensors with a low consumption of energy, as the stations are battery driven. Since a stilling well cannot be kept free from ice in northern Sweden without access to electricity or any other adequate power supply, we have chosen to put a pressure sensor at the bottom of the lake to measure the water level at the new Argos station. The sensor is a Digiquartz from Paroscientific, USA. This sensor makes it possible to measure water levels with an accuracy of 1 cm even at stations where the water level varies very much. The sensor is an oscillating quartz crystal, the frequency of which depends on the pressure. As we have to compensate for air pressure variations, these must be measured. The air pressure sensor is of the same kind.

Temperature measurements are mainly performed with Pt-100 sensors. Zener diodes are also used. This makes it possible to read increments of 0.1 °C. When better accuracy is required, we hope to be able to use quartz temperature sensors in the near future. As low power consumption is mandatory, the precipitation gauge used at our stations is a collecting bucket, which is weighed.

As to the oceanographical sensors, a new Swedish Doppler profiling current meter has just been designed, and is going to be tested this year.

As for other sensors, there is a need for solid sensors for the measurement of water quality. The sensors must be able to work under various conditions to make an extension of satellite data collection into the environmental sector possible.

FUTURE SYSTEMS

The rapid advances that have taken place in computer technology in recent years are likely to continue. This applies equally to checking and control components and to memories. Computer prices have also fallen appreciably in recent times. Consequently, it is now viable to check, reduce and process data in the field. Furthermore, storage capacity has increased substantially; semiconductors and bubble memories have made it possible to get away from printers with mechanical parts and have also facilitated further processing of the data. New data-storing media with even greater capacities will be produced. In contrast, work on the development of sensors has not advanced as fast. We can foresee, for example, the development over the next few years of new methods for measuring currents using ultrasonic and doppler techniques.

For data transmission we expect to utilize both the telephone network and the national data transmission network. The new data-collection centre at SMHI will now increase the capacity and enhance the prospects of linking a variety of stations. In future data input manually via simple terminals will be collected in the same way. This would enable data, for instance, from the manned precipitation stations, to be fed into the system without delay. It is probable that satellite telemetering stations will play a major part in the collection of data from mountain areas, sea-based stations and temporary field stations. It is planned that these data too will be transmitted via the satellite receiving station to the data-collection centre in order that they can be processed in the same way as the other data collected automatically. It is likely that conventional communication satellites will make an essential contribution to data transmission. This applies not only to the collection of data from the field stations but also to the transmission of large quantities of data from one regional centre to another.

Another technique of great interest is the meteor-burst technique, in which the reflecting properties of meteors are used for data transmission. The advantage of this system is the independence from satellites.

Radio links will also be used in the future. Fibre optics seem to be of great importance in linking systems for rather short distances.

Just now a new Swedish low energy consumption, automatic terminal, is being designed. This will be a relatively inexpensive terminal and will be of great importance in the modernization and automatization of the network for water level and discharge in Sweden. A mobile station for discharge measurements is being designed as well.

Regarding remote sensing techniques, significant results are to be expected from the development work. For monitoring water pollution, satellite-borne monitoring systems with higher resolution and more suitable spectral channels will be launched. In addition laser systems are being developed and tested for use in studying oil and other pollutants in water. These should be ready for use in the near future.

It is estimated that within about 10 years radar equipment on various platforms will be able to provide data about wave spectra, wave forms, wind conditions and water levels. Most of the development work here concerns the data processing side.

Furthermore, SMHI is planning to install a system primarily for meteorological information. This will incorporate the data from automatic stations, weather satellites and radar stations. This combination should provide better information about the amounts and intensity of precipitation and, by the end of the 1980's, information about the areal distribution of precipitation (Bodin, 1982).

REFERENCES

Bodin, S. (1982) Blueprint for the future Swedish weather service system. *Nowcasting*. Academic Press.

Hovberg, T. (1978) Meteorological and oceanographical application in Sweden of automatic data acquisition technique. *Cost 43 Seminar* (Lisbon).

Wennerberg, G. (1980) The use of weather satellite data in mapping water surface temperature. *SMHI, HB Report 41.*

Wennerberg, G. (1981) The use of Landsat-data to study turbidity in water areas. *SMHI, HB Report 48.*

Wennerberg, G. (1982) Hydrological data collection from Swedish mountain areas. *Argos Users Conference* (Paris).

Hydrological Applications of Remote Sensing and Remote Data Transmission
(Proceedings of the Hamburg Symposium, August 1983). IAHS Publ. no. 145.

Hydrological study in Greenland using the Argos system

THORKILD THOMSEN
Greenland Technical Organization, The Directorate, 20 Hauser Plads, DK-1127 Copenhagen K, Denmark

ABSTRACT Since 1976, The Greenland Technical Organization at Copenhagen has conducted hydrological studies in Greenland with a view to commencing the construction of hydropower plants. Today, these studies are to some extent made by way of automatic hydrometeorological stations of which a few are equipped for satellite transmission. These stations have been set up aiming primarily at two objectives: that of ensuring automatic station operation reliability; and, that of observing the hydrological development at the locality with a view to optimizing visits and carrying out special studies. Hydrological conditions in Greenland are conditioned by how the area is exposed in relation to the ice cap or to major local glaciers, and by the absolute location of the area in relation to the coast. The hydrological conditions may, based on the hydrographs from the drainage areas, be divided into three categories. The information required for optimization of the particular studies in Greenland, depending on the runoff, is obtained through the satellite data transmission system.

Etudes hydrologiques au Greenland au moyen du système Argos
RESUME L'Organisation Technique du Groenland effectue depuis 1976 des études hydrologiques dans ce pays en vue d'entreprendre la construction de centrales hydroélectriques. Aujourd'hui ces études sont effectuées dans une certaine mesure à des stations hydrométéorologique, dont certaines sont concues pour transmission par satellites. Les stations sont construites en vue de servir à deux buts principaux à savoir assurer un fonctionnement sûr des stations automatiques et suivre les fluctuations hydrologiques au site à étudier en vue d'optimiser les inspections et les études spéciales. Les conditions hydrologiques au Groenland sont déterminées par l'exposition du bassin par rapport à la calotte glaciaires, ou aux grande glaciers locaux et par la position de ce bassin par rapport à la côte. Au Groenland il est donc possible de distinguer trois catégories de régimes hydrologiques sur la base des hydrogrammes des bassins versants. Les renseignements nécessaires à l'optimisation de chaque étude individuelle effectuée au Groenland, qui varie selon le régime des débits, sont obtenus par la système de

transmission de données par satellite.

INTRODUCTION

The hydrological studies conducted in Greenland by the Greenland Technical Organization at Copenhagen have been initiated with a view to commencing the building of hydropower stations. These studies have concentrated on the urban communities in southwest Greenland, and on the east coast at Ammassalik and in Jameson Land. In Jameson Land, however, the scope is different from that of hydropower development.

Today, hydrological studies are being conducted in 17 different basins in Greenland (see Fig.1). Studies are carried out at varying intensities depending on the appearance and location of the basin. Automatic hydrometeorological stations in the basins used as a basis for subsequent hydrological computations are thus located around the existing urban communities and in areas with great hydrological potential.

Hydrological pilot studies related to hydropower focus on the development of long time series for the essential parameters. This is usually achieved over a considerable period for parameters such as runoff, precipitation, and temperature by using automatic stations. However, long periods of time are not available for the Greenland projects for which a result must be produced within a few years.

To provide an updated hydrological data base, the data collected from the automatic stations, of which a few are equipped for data transmission through satellites, are combined with those from intensive hydrological measuring programmes in the basins in which pre-planning is to be conducted. The objective is to ascertain the current hydrological conditions in the basins.

HYDROLOGICAL DATA SYSTEM

The framework of the hydrological data system in Greenland does, of course, vary greatly and has been extended since the beginning of 1976 (see Sørensen, 1981). The data system was introduced in 1976 by way of a few commercial stations; today, in cooperation with an electronics company, the system has been developed so as to include fully automatic stations by the Greenland Technical Organization.

The criterion for operation of the data system is that it should work under the special climatic conditions encountered in Greenland: quick variations in the weather producing high wind velocities (measured values of up to 80 m s^{-1} or 300 km h^{-1}) and severe cold. For maximum data reliability this calls for special monitoring systems.

Data collection system

The hydrological data system has been built up around a data logger with an interface for transducers and for satellite transmission (see Fig.2). The system has been designed to military specifications and has been guaranteed to work to -40°C. Slightly different transducer systems have been designed for different stations.

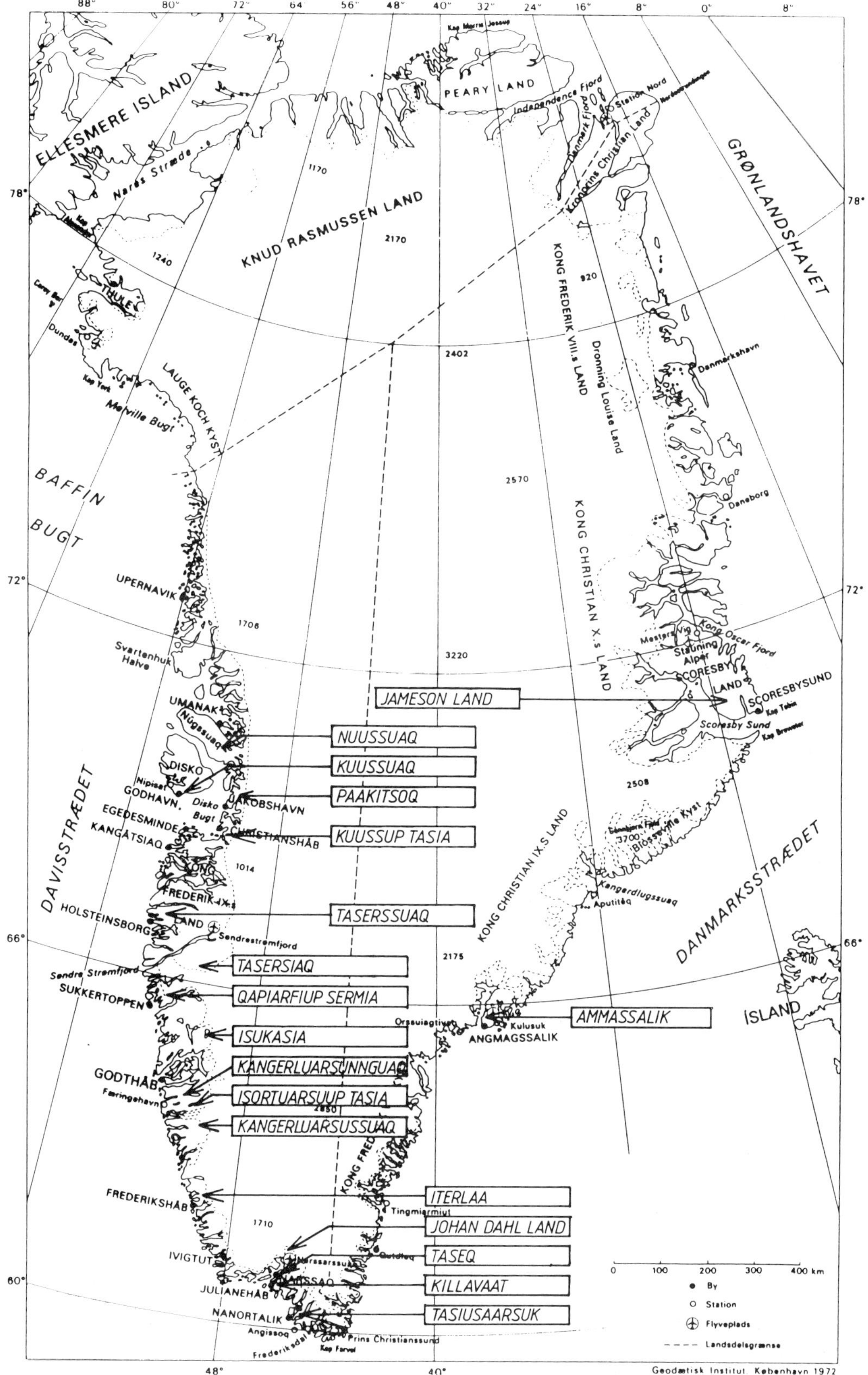

FIG.1 Greenland.

Figure 2 shows the standard data system flow diagram for a climate station and a permafrost station, respectively.

The logger energy supply is 12 V d.c. The logger can measure up to 64 single values simultaneously with a resolution of 12 bits (2^0-2^{11}) on 32 channels and 8 bits (2^0-2^7) on 32 channels. The registration interval is pre-set and may vary from continuous registration to an interval of 30 h. For each registration, the time with resolution in seconds is stated. All registrations are

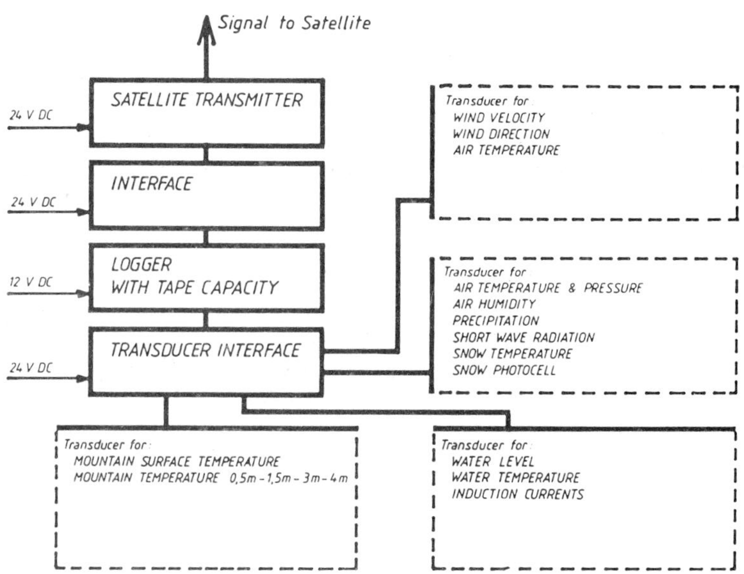

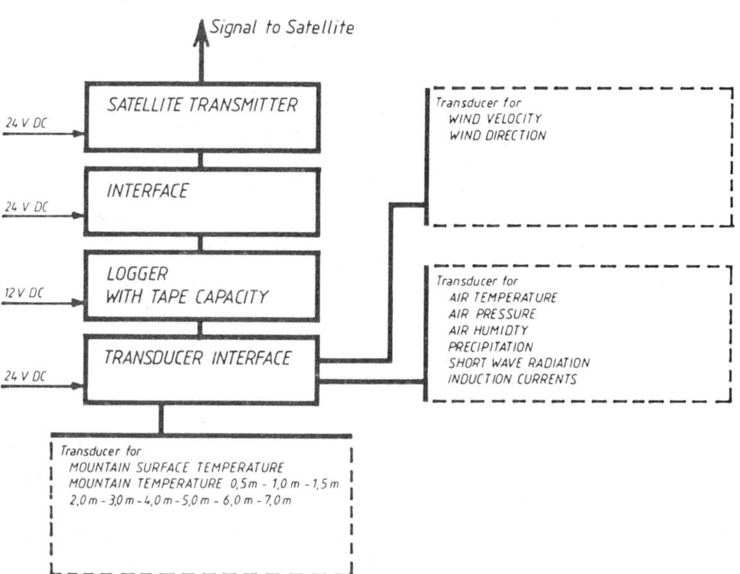

FIG.2 Climate station and permafrost station flow diagram.

stored on tape in the logger with 36-bit clock words in binary coded decimal (BCD) and channel values with 14 bits in binary code. Further, the station records certain internal electric check values such as reference potential, logger voltage, and station reference number.

On the basis of the tape and given power consumption, the station is equipped to take measurements every 3 h for one year.

Reliability of the data system

The hydrological data system developed today provides Greenland return data reliability averaging about 95%. Inspection and repair of the system may be adapted as required since satellite transmission allows for the monitoring of the operation of the stations. Transmission is effected through the Argos satellite system, as shown in Fig.3.

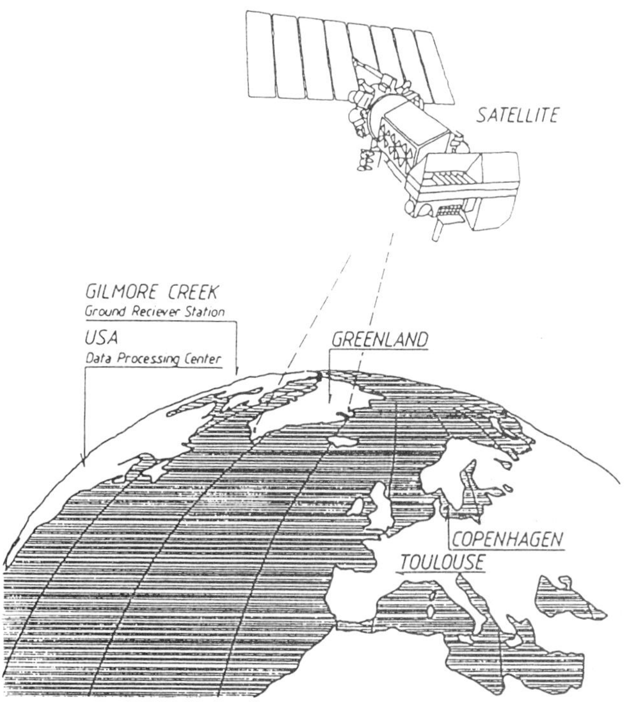

FIG.3 The Argos data transmission system.

The Greenland stations transmit the last data scan in messages at intervals of 200 s. These can be received by satellite if their transits permit. Since the orbits of the two satellites are polar, they pass over Greenland five to ten times every 24 h. The satellites will release their data after transmit over the northern hemisphere at Gilmore Creek in Alaska. After sorting of all the data in the USA, they are stored for European retrieval at Toulouse in France.

By telephone and modem, one can access the data base at Toulouse from Copenhagen and assess the operation of the stations. It is possible to eliminate inspection of those stations which are working properly, since they are expensive to inspect by helicopter. Data are accessible from the data processing centre at Toulouse about 4 h after the satellite has passed the measuring station in Greenland.

Data processing/updating

In the basins calling for major construction technical decisions, more intensive hydrological studies are being conducted at the same time in order to establish the dimensions for construction-technical schemes without having reasonably long hydrological records available. These studies include:

(a) the continuous updating of water levels;

(b) the determination of the water level/water flow relation in a lake over a chosen rise/drop in level;

(c) sedimentological or fish/biological studies at high or low water levels in the lake;

(d) snow surveying when the melt season begins;

(e) the draining of raingauges when precipitation permanently changes to rain.

The information required for the optimization of these studies and operations is obtained through the satellite data transmission system.

Hydrological conditions in Greenland depend on how a particular area is influenced by the Ice Cap or major local glaciers. Precipitation conditions in areas close to the sea also differ from those in areas affected by hydrometeorological conditions along the Ice Cap. Runoff from some drainage basins in Greenland also depends on the melting of the Ice Cap. The runoff from drainage basins with precipitation as the sole input differs considerably from that of basins in which runoff is attributable to both ablation and precipitation.

Based on the hydrographs from the drainage basins, the basins are divided into three categories:

Small basins influenced by precipitation only The hydrograph from a small drainage basins, i.e. less than 100 or 200 km^2, affected by precipitation only in the form of rain and snow on the basin, displays a major runoff peak when the snowmelt period begins. Runoff culmination is characterized by a comparatively quick drop, followed by a longer recession period. This type of hydrograph is superimposed by major or minor peaks due to precipitation events in the basin (see Fig.4). The snowmelt period begins in southwest Greenland in May/June and meltwater flow varies from a minimum of $\sim 0.1\ m^3 s^{-1}$ to a maximum of $\sim 55\ m^3 s^{-1}$. The hydrographs shown in Fig.4 are for the Tasiusarsuk basin at Nanortalik in south Greenland which has a drainage area of 17 km^2.

Larger basins influenced by precipitation only Runoff from larger areas also affected only by precipitation in the form of rain and snow is, as in the smaller areas, characterized by the melting of the snow. This water volume is so considerable that precipitation in the form of rain during the melt period throughout the summer does not show on the hydrograph. Recession runoff does

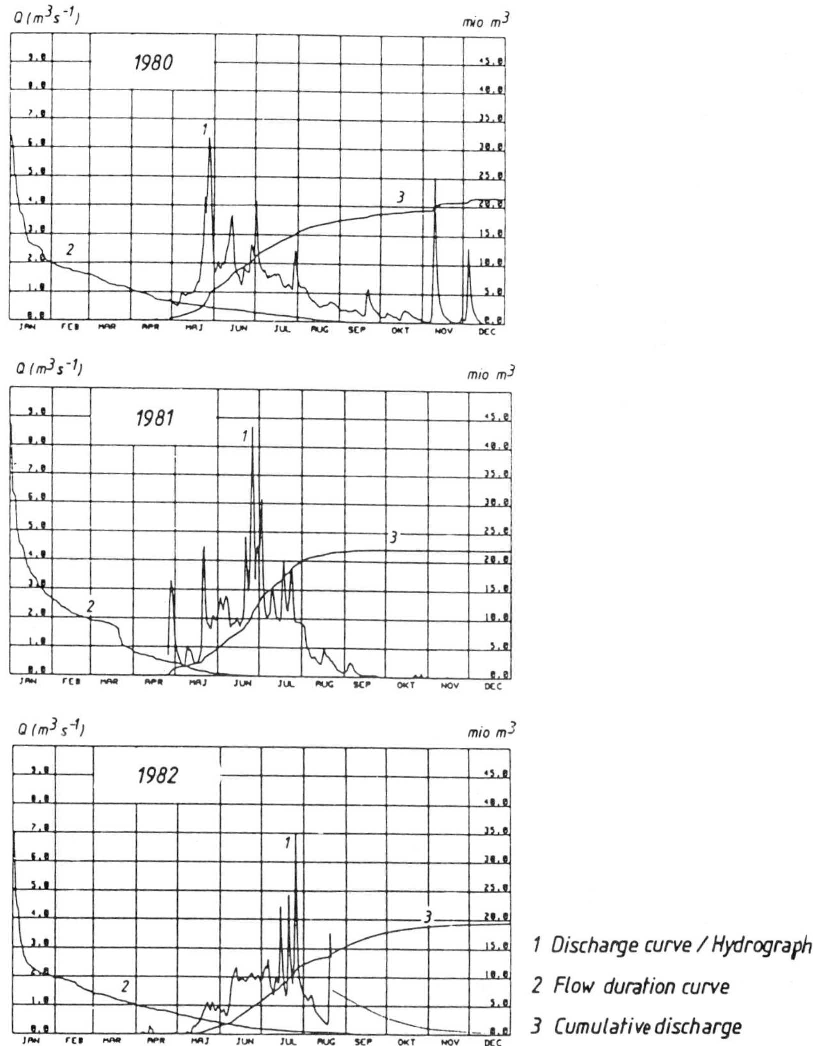

FIG.4 Hydrographs for a small drainage basin, the Tasiursarsuk basin, with an area of 17 km^2.

not decrease as fast after peak runoff as in the smaller basins, a fact partly due to a certain amount of delay through the large lake system. The hydrographs shown in Fig.5 are from Kangerluarsunnguup Tasersua which has a drainage area of 582 km^2, of which the main lake comprises 75 km^2, at Godthåb/Nuuk in west Greenland. The hydrographs represent water flow variations from $\sim$1.5 m^{3}s^{-1} to a maximum during the melting period of 40 m^{3}s^{-1}.

Basins influenced by both Ice Cap/glacier ablation and precipitation The hydrological conditions of drainage basins also affected by ablation are, as reflected by runoff, dependent on basin size. In addition to a slightly decreasing recession period, the hydrograph is characterized by a more even rise at the beginning of the melt season. During the summer period, precipitation events over the basin or cold periods are shown in part as local peaks or local dips in the hydrograph (see Fig.6). The hydrographs from the Kuussuup Tasia basin at Christianshåb/Qasigiannguit in west Greenland, shown in Fig.6, are typical of hydrographs from this type of basin.

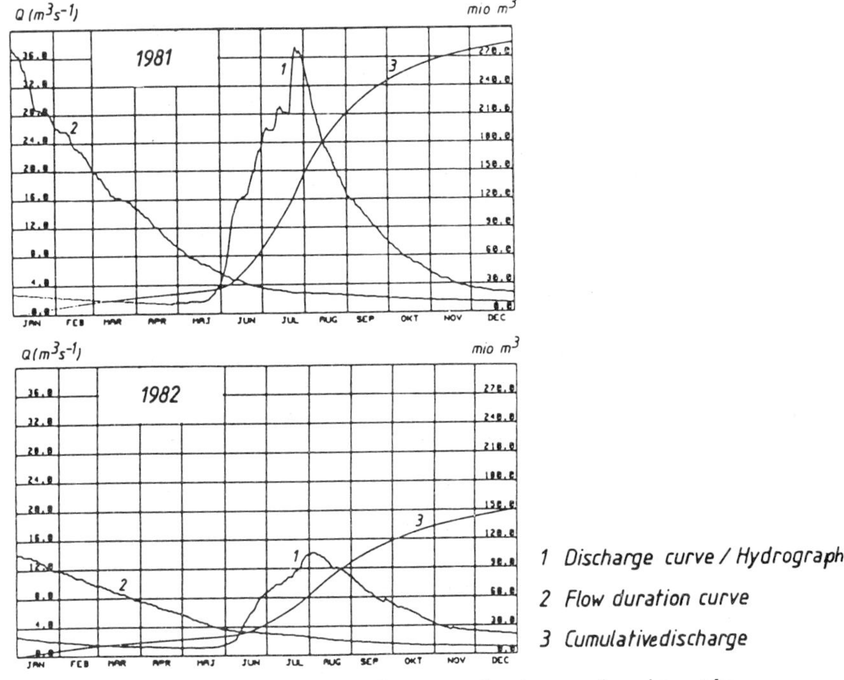

FIG.5 Hydrographs for a larger drainage basin, the Kangerluarsunnguup Tasersna, with a total area of 582 km^2 which includes a 75-km^2 lake.

The absolute water flow volume from the area is influenced by the drainage area from the Ice Cap. Streamflows of more than 2000 m^{3}s^{-1} have been registered in basins affected by ablation.

Reference is made to the traditional descriptions of the components of hydrographs given by Dunne & Leopold (1978) and Lindh & Falkenmark (1973).

CONCLUSION

This variation in hydrological response calls for more detailed planning of the particular hydrological tasks outlined above. To a considerable extent this is being achieved by the efforts being made to obtain regular and accurate data from the basins, based on the satellite retransmission from automatic stations. This method of data communication also enables a verification of local weather conditions before making a final decision on any bisits to the locality.

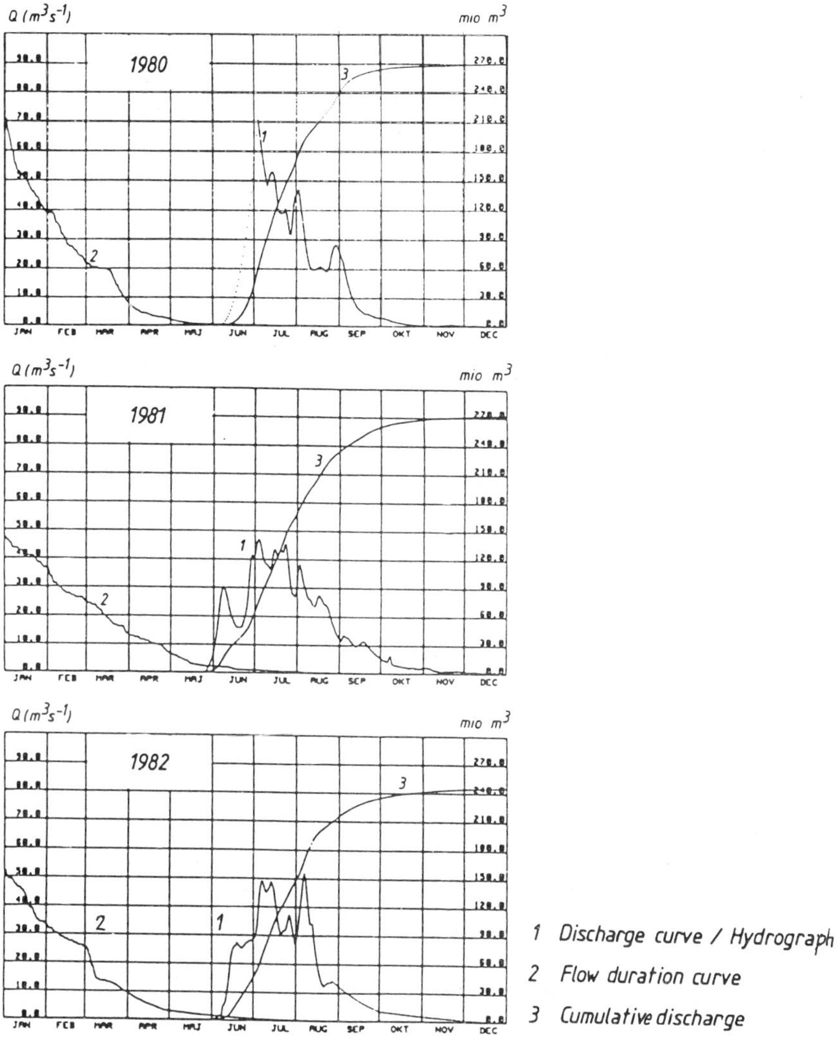

1 Discharge curve / Hydrograph
2 Flow duration curve
3 Cumulative discharge

FIG.6 Hydrographs for an ablation plus precipitation type of basin, the Kuussuup Tasia basin in west Greenland.

ACKNOWLEDGEMENT For useful discussions and critical comments while preparing this article, I would like to acknowledge the help from my colleagues Mr Arne Winther Andersen and Mr Gregers Helge Jørgensen, both civil engineers, and Mr Otto Bjørkholt, Director of OB-Consult.

REFERENCES

Dunne, T. & Leopold, L.B. (1978) Water in environmental planning, W.H. Freeman & Co., San Francisco, California.

Lindh, G. & Falkenmark, M. (1973) *Hydrologi, Andra trycknlngen.* Lund, Sweden.

Sørensen, N.V. (1981) Vandkraftundersøgelser på Grønland. Vannet i Norden. *Nordisk Hydrologisk Forening no. 1 1978,* 17-28.

Hydrological Applications of Remote Sensing and Remote Data Transmission (Proceedings of the Hamburg Symposium, August 1983). IAHS Publ. no. 145.

Emploi des satellites à orbite polaire pour la collecte des mesures effectuées aux stations hydrométéorologiques: bilan de quatre années d'utilisation

JACQUES CALLÈDE
Service Hydrologique, ORSTOM, 70-74 route d'Aulnay, 93140 Bondy, France

RESUME Depuis la mise sur orbite de METEOSAT I (novembre 1977), puis du premier satellite du système Argos (octobre 1978), le Service Hydrologique de l'ORSTOM a utilisé et évalué la technique de collecte de données par satellites. Ceci s'est concrétisé par des expérimentations ou des réalisations pratiques au Sénégal, au Canada, au Soudan, en France et au Brésil. Le télétransmission employant les satellites à défilement du système Argos s'est montré particulièrement bien adaptée à la gestion des réseaux hydrométriques. Le nombre de collectes par jour est de quatre, au moins, pour une station située sur l'Equateur, et le taux de messages correctement transmis est supérieur à 98%. Il est apparu que les pannes de fonctionnement des stations provenaient essentiellement de défauts d'alimentation en énergie électrique. A l'exploitation, une station de réception directe s'avère vite indispensable. Enfin, le système Argos présente quelques inconvénients d'exploitation liés au fait que la mission "collecte" reste secondaire par rapport à la mission "localisation". L'importance des projets (bassin du Fleuve Niger, bassin du Fleuve Amazone, Organisation de la Lutte contre l'Onchocercose en Afrique, etc.), dont certains entrent en phase de réalisation, amène à imaginer, pour la prochaine décennie, un système de satellites à vocation essentiellement hydrologique. Dans cet esprit, un système de satellites à orbite équatoriale basse, tel que prévu par le Brésil, serait des plus utiles pour la collecte des relevés hydropluviométriques de la Zone intertropicale.

Use of polar orbiting satellites for data collection of hydrometric stations: evaluation after four years
ABSTRACT The ORSTOM Hydrological Service has used and evaluated the satellite data collection system since the launching of METEOSAT I in November 1977, and that of the first Argos satellite in October 1978. This has led to experiments or developments in Senegal, Canada, Sudan, Franch and Brazil. Remote data transmission through the Argos system on NOAA orbiting satellites has been particularly suited for managing hydrometric networks. Data are collected at least four times a day at the Equator and more than 98% of messages are duly transmitted.

Any platform failures were related to faulty power supplies. A weak link in the system is the delay in receiving data from a central receive station. This delay can be eliminated if an agency has its own ground station to receive satellite transmissions directly. Finally it is difficult to use the Argos system because the "location" mission prevails over the "collecting" mission. The importance of projects such as the Niger River basin, the Amazon River basin and the Organization for the Control of Onchocerciasis in Africa, etc., some of which are under way, leads to think about a system of hydrologically oriented satellites for the next 10 years. For this purpose, a system of low equatorial orbit satellites, as foreseen by Brazil, would be very useful to collect rainfall data in the intertropical zone.

INTRODUCTION

La collecte automatique des données hydrométriques, par l'intermédiaire d'un satellite artificiel, n'a commencé - pour les hydrologues de l'ORSTOM - que vers 1970 avec le projet Eole. Il a fallu attendre 1978 pour effectuer les évaluations du système METEOSAT (le satellite METEOSAT I ayant été lancé en novembre 1977), et du système Argos (le premier satellite, Tiros-N, ayant été mis sur orbite en octobre 1978). Rappelons ici que METEOSAT est un satellite géostationnaire, tandis que le système Argos utilise des satellites à défilement, à orbites polaires.

Cette évaluation nous a montré que les satellites à défilement étaient bien adaptés pour la collecte de données hydrométriques - et même pour la prévision - lorsque deux ou trois relevés par jour sont suffisants pour décrire avec précision l'hydrogramme d'une rivière. De ce fait, le système Argos a été employé par l'ORSTOM (ou pour des opérations où l'ORSTOM intervenait à titre de conseil), sur six opérations qui ont eu lieu de 1978 à 1982, toujours pour la collecte d'informations hydrométriques: ceci nous a conduit au Sénégal, au Soudan, au Canada, en France et, enfin, au Brésil (voir Fig.1).

Le système Argos, rappelons-le, utilise deux satellites à orbite polaire (le système peut très bien fonctionner avec un seul satellite). Sa mission principale est la localisation, en coordonnées géographiques, des stations au sol. Un système assez compliqué transmet les données recueillies par les satellites sur le Centre Argos de Toulouse où elles sont traitées, puis disséminées vers les utilisateurs. Les stations au sol (appelées "balises") émettent à intervalles réguliers (40 s lorsqu'il y a localisation, 200 s lorsque seule la collecte est demandée), que le satellite soit en visibilité ou non. Si le satellite est en visibilité, il y a collecte de l'-information-sol. Le nombre de fois par jour où le satellite est en visibilité demeure fonction de la latitude du lieu: quatre à cinq fois à l'Equateur, 28 fois aux Pôles (pour deux satellites). En comparaison, le géostationnaire est toujours en visibilité de la station-sol. Une autre différence réside dans la longueur du message de collecte: 256 bits pour le système Argos, c'est-à-dire 20 fois moins que le message METEOSAT (et GOES).

Malgré ces contraintes, l'emploi du satellite à défilement s'est

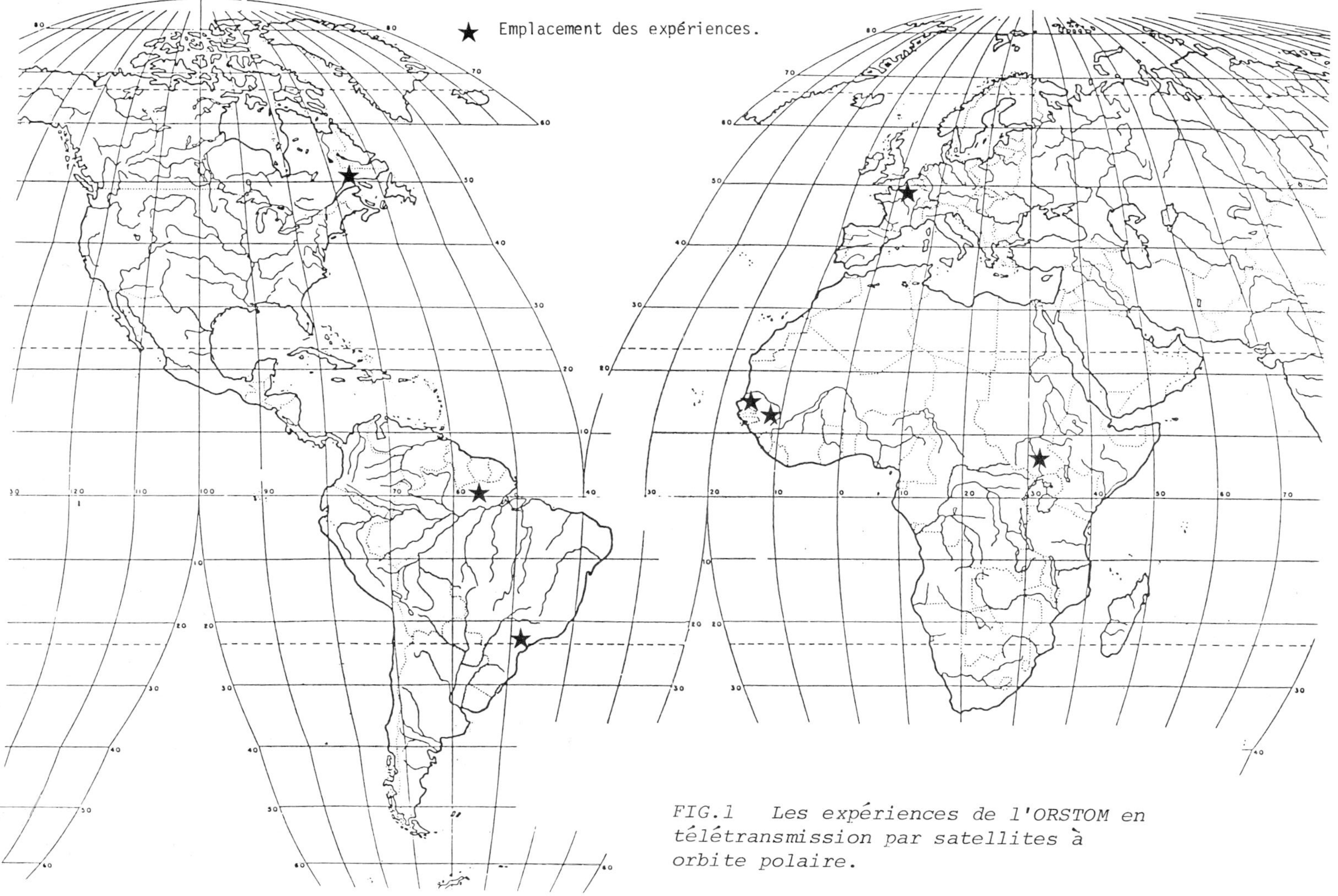

FIG.1 Les expériences de l'ORSTOM en télétransmission par satellites à orbite polaire.

révélé très prometteur, comme la pratique nous l'a montré.

UTILISATION DU SATELLITE A DEFILEMENT (SYSTEME ARGOS) PAR LE SERVICE HYDROLOGIQUE DE L'ORSTOM

De 1978 à 1982, le Service Hydrologique de l'ORSTOM a procédé à des évaluations du système de télétransmission et à des travaux de gestion gestion de réseaux hydrométriques utilisant cette technique.

- *en 1978/1979*, évaluation du système à la station hydrométrique de Kaolack (République du Sénégal) sur le Fleuve Saloum (Callède, 1979). Un codeur digital Sigtaycod était monté à l'intérieur d'un limnigraphe OTT X;
- *en 1979/1980*, participation en tant que conseil à l'évaluation du système au Canada (Province du Québec). La station hydrométrique était celle de la Malbaie, sur la Rivière Malbaie, affluent de rive gauche du Fleuve Saint-Laurent. Le limnigraphe pneumatique Leopold and Stevens était équipé d'un codeur Mémomark, du même fabricant. Notons que c'est la même électronique (balise n° 50), fabriquée par Electronique Marcel Dassault, qui a servi pour ces deux évaluations;
- *en 1980*, équipement de trois stations dans le delta intérieur du Nil Blanc (Sud) au Soudan, pour une seule campagne de mesures. Le codeur Neyrtec était directement entraîné par un système flotteur-contrepoids (Callède, 1981);
- *également en 1980*, un dispositif identique a été installé sur deux stations hydrométriques de la Rivière Falémé, affluent du Fleuve Senégal (Roche & Olivry, 1981);
- *en 1981*, le Service Hydrologique de l'ORSTOM a participé, comme conseil, à l'évaluation du système Argos pour la modernisation de l'exploitation des réseaux hydrométriques du bassin de la Seine. Nous en sommes venus à définir un nouveau type d'électronique de transmission équipé d'un système de mémorisation. Dans ce système, le limnigraphe, est interrogé toutes les 30 minutes. Le codeur était un CSEE-Sigtaycod monté à l'intérieur d'un limnigraphe OTT X (Callède *et al.*, 1982);
- *c'est en 1982* qu'une démonstration a été effectuée au Brésil. Une station hydrométrique du Paraîba do Sul a été équipée pour la télétransmission via le système Argos. Un codeur Sigtaycod a été facilement monté à l'intérieur d'un limnigraphe Hidrologia SA type LNG-9. Cette station a fonctionné d'avril à octobre 1982. En Septembre, une seconde station a été installée à Boa Vista, sur le Rio Branco. Il n'y avait pas de limnigraphe: l'indication de la hauteur d'eau était rentrée dans la balise grâce à un clavier de commande actionné deux fois par jour par l'observateur de la station hydrométrique. Enfin, une station de réception directe a été installée pour deux semaines dans les locaux du Service Hydrologique Fédéral (DCRH) à Brasilia même (Callède, 1982).

Dispositions communes à ces expériences

Toutes ces expériences utilisaient des électroniques d'émission (appelées aussi "balises") fabriquées par la Société Electronique Marcel Dassault. Il est à remarquer que la même balise (portant l'indicatif de transmission "50") a fonctionné successivement au Sénégal (1978), au Canada (1979), en France (1981) et enfin au Brésil (1982), sans la moindre défaillance.

L'antenne est généralement de type AV402 fabriquée par CIT-Alcatel. Elle se présente sous une forme particulièrement compacte.

L'alimentation en énergie électrique nécessitait une tension de 24 V pour une consommation moyenne de 72 mW (intensité en crête de 700 mA durant 0.3 s). Généralement une batterie de piles sèches, de 70 Ah de capacité, assurait une autonomie supérieure à deux ans. L'expérience brésilienne n'a pu que confirmer la nécessité de proscrire l'emploi des batteries d'accumulateur type "automobile": un tel système d'alimentation, même non connecté, se décharge complètement en trois mois.

Enfin, l'ensemble du matériel de télétransmission est suffisamment réduit pour, dans bien des cas, se loger dans les infrastructures existant déjà.

Dans la plupart des cas, la pluie était également mesurée. Un système à augets basculeurs, équipé d'un contacteur, génère une impulsion qui incrémente un compteur. C'est la valeur binaire de ce compteur qui est télétransmise.

Les résultats

Le service Argos annonçait un nombre de collectes/jour qui s'est avéré un peu pessimiste.

Nous avons, en effet, obtenu:

- pour une latitude de 07°: 8.6 collectes/jour alors qu'il en était prévu 7.5 par le Service Argos (donc 15% de mieux)
- pour une latitude de 23°: 10.4 collectes/jour alors qu'il n'en était prévu que 8.5 (soit 20% de mieux)
- pour une latitude de 49°: 13 collectes/jours alors qu'il en était prévu également 13.

Le taux de collectes exactes est remarquablement élevé. Pour une longueur de message de 32 bits, il évolue entre 98.8 et 99.9%. Pour une longueur de message de 256 bits il est de 97.6%. D'ailleurs la quasitotalité des collectes fausses proviennent d'une transmission effectuée dans de mauvaises conditions, lorsque le satellite est très bas sur l'horizon. C'est ce qui explique pourquoi le nombre de collectes/jour que nous avons observé est supérieur à ce qui avait été prévu par le Service Argos: cette prévision était basée pour des satellites ayant plus de 5° d'inclinaison au-dessus de l'horizon.

Ces résultats, associés au fait que le système Argos met en oeuvre simultanément deux satellites (l'un pouvant assumer seul la collecte en cas de panne inopinée de l'autre), permettent d'affirmer que le système Argos est parfaitement opérationnel malgré certains défauts de conception ou d'application.

Les incidents de fonctionnement

Dans l'ensemble, toutes les expériences ont fonctionné sans problème. Il suffisait de raccorder les connecteurs, de mettre sous tension électrique, et tout commençait à transmettre.

Les seules pannes (qui se retrouvent, d'ailleurs, chez nos confrères canadiens qui utilisent la télétransmission par satellite) proviennent de l'alimentation en énergie électrique. Il faut faire énormément attention à l'installation des batteries et à leur raccordement électrique. Les batteries d'accumulateur pour automobiles sont à proscrire.

Nous avons eu, également, une panne de capteur.

Le retour des données sur l'utilisateur

Il apparaît que le retour des données, du satellite vers l'utilisateur, demeure le point faible de la chaîne de télétransmission (que ce soit pour un satellite à défilement ou pour un géostationnaire).

Dans le cas du système Argos, même en employant un accès direct aux fichiers, les délais sont bien souvent supérieurs à ce qui a été promis par le Service Argos. L'utilisation de l'accès direct, lors de l'expérience Seine (Callède *et al.*, 1982) nous a montré que le matin, vers 0900 h, il n'était pas possible d'avoir les collectes plus récentes que celles du jour précédent vers 2100 h (soit 12 h de délais). De plus, ce système coûte cher: outre les frais de télex, il faut payer une redevance de 1800 francs par an et par balise (tarif 1982).

La solution employant le Système international des télécommunications metéorologiques (GTS) n'est utilisable que pour quelques stations. S'il présente l'avantage d'être gratuit, il impose par contre des délais d'acheminement qui peuvent dépasser 24 h.

En employant une station de réception directe (recevant directement la retransmission immédiate, par le satellite, des messages des balises) les délais deviennent nuls puisque les messages sont captés à chaque passage. Cette station, qui est équipée d'une antenne fixe omnidirectionnelle, est entièrement automatique. Une liaison RS232C permet un raccordement éventuel sur un ordinateur. Fabriquée par la Société CEIS-Espace, son coût raisonnable (250 000 francs) en fait la solution idéale lorsque le réseau hydrométrique équipé pour la télétransmission dépasse une dizaine de stations. Cette station a été essayée avec succès à Paris et à Brasilia: nous avons constaté que la portée pratique de la station était de l'ordre de 3500 km et la portée maximale d'environ 5500 km.

Cependant, l'emploi d'une station de réception directe va se traduire, par rapport au circuit normal du système Argos, par une baisse du nombre de collectes/jour: il faut, en effet, que le satellite soit à la fois en visibilité directe de la balise et de la station de réception (Callède, 1982; Callède *et al.*, 1982).

Nous avons utilisé, enfin, le retour en différé des fichiers créés à Toulouse par le Service Argos (fichier DISPOSE). Une fois par mois nous recevons une bande magnétique contenant la totalité de la collecte. Ce système est particulièrement précieux pour l'établissement des fichiers de hauteur d'eau. Il est simplement à regretter que le format de ce fichier n'ait pas mieux été concu pour la fonction "collecte". De plus, l'emploi d'un calendrier pseudojulien est particulièrement incommode.

PROJETS ACTUELS

Les projets actuels du Service Hydrologique de l'ORSTOM incluent les suivants:

(a) *En France*, le projet de modernisation des réseaux hydrométriques du bassin de la Seine est entré en phase exécution. Une première tranche de 20 stations hydrométriques va être installée en 1983, de même que la station de réception directe. Il en est de même pour le bassin de la Loire.

(b) *En Afrique*, un vaste projet englobant la totalité du bassin du Niger est lui aussi en cours de réalisation: 10 stations hydrométriques et une station de réception directe seront installées en 1983. Le reste (56 stations hydrométriques et sept autres stations de réception directe) seront installées en 1984 et 1985.

(c) *Un projet-pilote* de huit stations hydrométriques et une station de réception directe va être mis en exécution en mars 1984. Il concerne une partie du réseau hydrographique traité par l'Organisation Mondiale de la Santé, dans le cadre du Programme de Lutte contre l'Onchocercose. La télétransmission devrait permettre, par la connaissance immédiate du débit des rivières, de mieux gérer l'emploi des avions et des hélicoptères épandeurs d'insecticide (Le Barbé, 1982).

(d) *Au Brésil*, il est prévu un premier projet de 23 stations hydrométriques et une ou deux stations de réception directe, concernant le bassin de l'Amazone.

(e) *En Guyane Française*, deux stations hydrométriques vont être installées.

Signalons également des programmes en cours d'étude concernant la Bolivie (bassin de l'Amazone), le Cameroun (réseau hydrométrique général), l'Indonésie (collecte pluviométrique) et le Sénégal (Office de mise en valeur de la vallée du Fleuve Sénégal).

CONCLUSIONS

L'emploi d'un système de télétransmission par satellite à défilement parait particulièrement bien adapté, dans la plupart des cas, aux besoins de la gestion des réseaux hydrométriques. Dans certains cas seulement il serait nécessaire d'utiliser le géostationnaire, ce qui entraînerait des contraintes sur le terrain (contrôle des horloges) et un coût dans les équipements nettement plus élevé.

Actuellement, le seul système réellement opérationnel en Afrique et en Amérique du Sud (toujours en ce qui concerne les satellites à défilement) est le système Argos. Tel qu'il est il rend de bons services même si les hydrologues doivent s'adapter tant bien que mal à une organisation qui, manifestement, n'a jamais été prévue pour la collecte, ni pour l'hydrologie (alimentation des balises prototypes en 24 V, par exemple). Il est aussi bien regrettable que toute demande de modification mineure se traduise, aujourd'hui, par une incompréhensive fin de non-recevoir. Mais ce ne sont là que des critiques mineures pour un système remplissant son rôle et un service bien opérationnel. Je tiens à souligner ici l'efficacité du Service Argos qui nous a toujours aidés dans le développement de nos applications (notamment par le prêt de matériels).

D'après ce que nous constatons, le nombre de stations hydrométriques employant le satellite à défilement ne va qu'augmenter. Il y en aura 57 pour lesquelles l'ORSTOM intervient, dès 1983. Une évaluation prospective indiquerait, pour 1986-1990, un chiffre de 500, établi sur tous les projets dont nous avons connaissance. Il est raisonnable de penser que vers 1992, année où se clôture le système Argos, 1000 balises au moins serviront en collecte de données hydrologiques.

A ce stade nous pouvons souhaiter que les hydrologues soient enfin consultés pour que le système post-Argos réponde entièrement à leurs voeux. A moins que les mêmes hydrologues s'estiment capables de gérer eux mêmes leur propre réseau de satellites. Notons, à ce sujet, l'intérêt que représenterait un système de satellites à orbite équatoriale basse pour la couverture de la zone intertropicale (3000 km de part et d'autre de l'Equateur), ce qui permettrait une collecte toutes les 2 h avec un seul satellite. Ceci intéresserait une bonne partie de l'Amérique Latine, l'Afrique Noire et l'Indonésie.

Déjà à l'heure actuelle, le Brésil cherche à lancer un satellite de ce type qui possèdera un canal de réception compatible avec le système Argos. Nous savons que le Comité Interafricain d'Etudes Hydrauliques est intéressé par ce projet. Souhaitons qu'il aboutisse.

REFERENCES

Callède, J. (1979) Transmission par satellite des données hydrométriques. Expériences de l'ORSTOM au Sénégal et esquisse d'une technologie. *Cah. ORSTOM, série Hydrol.* XVI, No. 1, 25-53.

Callède, J. (1981) Hydrology study of the Kongor Area. ORSTOM, Paris, France.

Callède, J. (1982) *Utilisation de la Télétransmission par Satellite pour le Reseau Hydrométrique Brésilien.* ORSTOM, Paris, France.

Callède, J., Rentière, J. & Rouquerol, Y. (1982) L'emploi des balises à mémoire et de la réception directe pour les besoins des Services hydrométriques du Bassin de la Seine. Dans: *Conférence Utilisateurs Argos* (Paris, France, avril 1982). Edité par le Service Argos, Toulouse, France.

Le Barbé, L. (1982) *Analyse des Problèmes Hydrologiques Posés par les Opérations d'Épandage d'Insecticides Effectuées dans le Cadre du Programme de Lutte Contre l'Onchocercose.* ORSTOM, Lomé, Togo.

Roche, M. & Olivry, J.C. (1981) *Construction de Barrages sur les Rivières Daléma et Koila-Kobé.* ORSTOM, Dakar, Sénégal.

Hydrological Applications of Remote Sensing and Remote Data Transmission
(Proceedings of the Hamburg Symposium, August 1983). IAHS Publ. no. 145.

Hydrology and climatology of the River Amazon: GOES telemetry network

MANUEL B. DENGO
c/o Departamento de Hidrometeorología, IRHE, Apartado 5285, Panama 5, Panama
EVALDO G. M. CESAR
PHCA/SUDAM, Ave. Alte. Barroso 426, 66000 Belem, Para, Brazil

ABSTRACT The UNPD/WMO/SUDAM project "Hydrology and Climatology of Brazilian Amazon Basin" has as one of its main activities the establishment of a pilot network of telemetering stations in order to obtain hydrometeorological data using the GOES data collection system (DCS) facilities. During the second half of 1982 ten field stations were installed in the River Tocantins basin to measure water level, rainfall, humidity, temperature, atmospheric pressure and station battery voltage. A receiving site was installed at the headquarters of the Brazilian Institute of Space Research. This paper reports on the characteristics of this network, the problems during installation and initial operation, the experience gained using the GOES DCS, and comments on the future of this methodology in the Amazon basin. Recommendations are given on special support instrumentation used and on some important aspects of the GOES DCS that future users must not overlook.

Hydrologie et climatologie de l'Amazonie: le réseau télémétrique de GOES

RESUME Le projet PNUD/OMM/SUDAM "Hydrologie et Climatologie de l'Amazonie Brésilienne" compte parmi ses activités principales, l'établissement d'un réseau pilote des stations télémétriques afin d'obtenir des données hydrométéorologiques utilizant le système de collection de donneés (DCP) GOES. Pendant la seconde moitié de 1982 dix stations ont été installées dans le bassin de la riviére Tocantins pour mesurer: le niveau d'eau, les precipitations, l'humidité, la température, la pression atmosphérique et la tension de la batterie de la station. Une station de réception a été installée également dans le quartier géneral de l'Institut Brésilien de Recherche spatiale. L'objectif de cet exposé est de présenter les caractéristiques de ce réseau, les problémes rencontrés pendant l'installation et l'exploitation initiale, les expériences acquises pendant l'utilisation du GOES DCS, et de commenter l'utilisation future de cette méthodologie dans le bassin de l'Amazonie. Des recommendations out été formulées à propos de certains aspects importants du GOES DCS qui ne devraient pas être négligés par les utilisateurs futurs.

INTRODUCTION

Since 1977 the United Nations Development Programme (UNDP) and the World Meteorological Organization (WMO) have been cooperating with the government of Brazil on the project "Hydrology and Climatology of Brazilian Amazon River Basin" (Projecto de Hidrologia e Climatologia da Amazonia - PHCA) (Dengo, 1982).

Because of the extremely large size of this basin and the prevailing natural conditions, the network of existing meteorological and hydrological stations has been considered as inadequate despite the efforts of local institutions towards the improvement of the data collection system.

Under the above-mentioned project, several studies have been developed regarding different ways for improving the network of stations. Among the various alternatives, one which has been considered as mandatory is the establishment of a system of automated data transmitting stations. The main reasons for this are:

(a) the distances from the data collection points to the main population centres.

(b) the difficulties of access to the data collection sites; and

(c) the severe natural conditions of the entire region.

Among the existing methods for this type of data collection, three were closely examined, namely:

(a) telemetry via UHF/VHF radio transmission;

(b) telemetry via meteor burst; and

(c) satellite telemetry (using either a polar orbiting spacecraft or a geostationary one).

Based on technical, cost and management considerations, (Halliday, 1978), it was decided that the self-timed option of the GOES data collection system (DCS) would be used. Through WMO contacts with the US National Oceanic and Atmospheric Administration's National Environmental Satellite, Data and Information Service (NOAA/NESDIS) were established. An inter-institutional committee was formed by INPE (Brazilian Institute of Space Research), DNAEE (Brazilian Hydrological Agency), ELETRONORTE (Northern Brazil Power Authority) and SUDAM (Government Regional Development Agency for Amazonia) where the project "Hydrology and Climatology of River Amazon" has its headquarters.

The Tocantins river basin, with an area of approximately 750 000 km^2, was selected for the installation of the first 10 stations comprising the pilot network. The annual flood problems of Marabá and other riverine cities, the construction by ELETRONORTE of a giant 8000 MW hydropower station at Tucurui, the relative ease of access to different points in the basin because of the Belem-Brasilian Highway and the Trans-Amazon Road were the factors which influenced the choosing of this area for the establishment of the first network of stations.

The tasks were divided as follows:

(a) PHCA/SUDAM would buy via WMO all the necessary equipment (sensors, data collection platforms and data receiving station) and would also provide the required training for national personnel.

(b) ELETRONORTE would construct the physical bases for the field stations and would be in charge of their final installation and maintenance.

(c) INPE would be in charge of installation and operation of the receiving site and would provide the antenna to receive the signals from the satellite. As operators of the receiving station they would also be in charge of the distribution of the information to the other members of the committee.

(d) DNAEE, as the national agency for hydrology, would coordinate site selection, would watch closely all installation and operation activities, and would receive all data as input to the Sistema de Informacoes Hidrometeorologicas.

EQUIPMENT ACQUIRED

The acquisition of equipment was done through WMO headquarters. The contract, including equipment and training, was granted to Sierra Misco of Berkeley, California, who presented an integrated system consisting of:

(a) 10 sets of five sensors: river level, rainfall, relative humidity, temperature and atmospheric pressure (all made by Sierra Misco) plus one battery voltage sensor for each station in order to check the energy supply;

(b) 12 data collection platform (DCP) radio sets, 10 active plus two spares, made by La Barge;

(c) two la Barge DCP programming "Test Sets";

(d) 10 sensor to platform interfaces and 10 solar panels by Sierra Misco; and

(e) one ground receiving station made by SUTRON Corporation.

FIELD INSTALLATION

Actual field installation was possible in the second half of 1982, one year after the arrival of all of the equipment in Brazil. The one year delay was due to the difficulties encountered in developing the "Memorandum of Agreement" for using the satellite which was satisfactory to both the Brazilian Government and NESDIS.

The ground station located in Sao Jose dos Campos, was the first component of the system to be installed. This receiving system uses the antenna already existing at INPE and consists of a fully redundant station in order to offer back-up in case of a component failure. The equipment supplied by PHCA and assembled by INPE's technical staff consists of: one satellite synchronized clock, two pre-amplifiers, two downconverters, two receivers, two demodulation units, two PDP 11/03 microprocessors and one Data General Micro Nova 4X minicomputer (128 KB and magnetic tape unit) for "after reception" data processing and data distribution to users of the system.

ELETRONORTE, being responsible for the installation and maintenance of the field stations, contracted the services of Hidrologia S/A to carry out this task.

Table 1 gives the names of the selected locations of stations in the basins of the rivers Araguaia and Tocantins. Figure 1 shows the drainage basin of these rivers and the approximate location of the telemetering stations.

After successful tests of the ground-receiving station were

TABLE 1 GOES telemetry station sites

Basin	*River*	*Station name*
Tocantins	*Maranhao*	*Porto Uruacu*
Tocantins	*Parana*	*Parana*
Tocantins	*Tocantins*	*Carolina*
Tocantins	*Tocantins*	*Porto Nacional*
Tocantins	*Tocantins*	*Maraba*
Tocantins	*Itacaiunas*	*Fazenda Alegría*
Tocantins	*Tocantins*	*Tucurui*
Araguaia	*Araguaia*	*Sao Felix do Araguaia*
Araguaia	*Araguaia*	*Conceicao do Araguaia*
Araguaia	*Araguaia*	*Xambioa*

completed on 25-26 August 1982, the first of the field data collection sites was installed at Tucurui Dam on 29 August 1982.

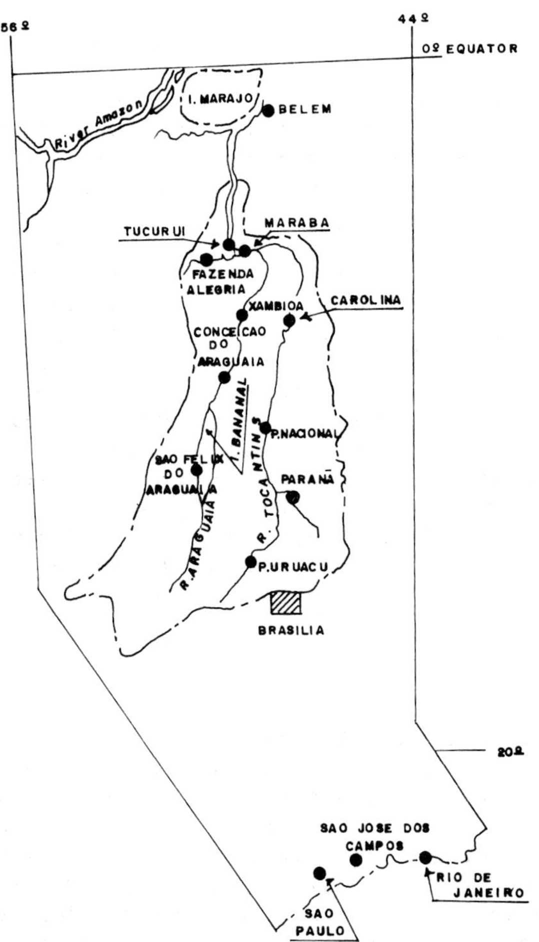

FIG.1 Location of field stations.

Carolina was the next station to be put on the air. All other installations were carried in sequence as the field crew started in Brasilia and continued installing stations along the Belem-Brasilia road all the way to Marabá. Tucurui was selected as the first site to be activated because of the logistical support existing there. As ELETRONORTE is constructing a hydroelectric power plant at the same location, there are all sorts of facilities: airport, telephones, electricity, mechanical and electrical workshops, etc. This all proved to be very important, especially the communication lines. The direct link with the ground station is of extreme importance in order to know whether the installation has been successful or not.

The deployment of the other DCPs and sensors continued without any serious problems; the main worry of the field crew was to always obtain a communication link with the ground station to verify that satellite communication had been successful. Some places offered radio-linkages, others radio to telephone interconnections, while in some cases it was impossible to have any contact with the receiving station at the time of installation. Only after returning to a point where there were telecommunication facilities available was it possible to check whether everything was correct. This source of uncertainty is an annoying factor, considering the difficulties overcome in order to reach the station site and the expense of the operation as a whole.

Following recommendations of NESDIS a new piece of equipment was bought by PHCA in order to supply information in the field indicating whether the station has correctly transmitted. This instrument is a modification of the satellite syncronized clock of the ground receiving station. The equipment is made by True Time Instruments and permits users of the GOES DCS to take advantage of the Data Acquisition and Monitoring Subsystem, known as "DAMS", while deploying or repairing platforms in the field. It is a self-contained totally portable unit which allows the field team to obtain special information emitted by the GOES DCS, known as "DAMS health messages", regarding the quality of the transmission of the DCP being installed.

This equipment was field tested early in 1983 on a routine visit to the stations, and the results were most satisfactory. The confidence of knowing what is occurring, no matter how far the field crew is from a communications link with the ground station, is worth the extra investment. This allows for timely DCP adjustments and corrections before leaving the site, thus assuring a correct installation.

MODE OF OPERATION

The platforms collect data from the sensors every half hour and transmit to the satellite every 3 h (at 1 minute intervals from one another) all the information collected in the time elapsed between two consecutive transmissions. In addition, the DCP message also contains the data set corresponding to the previous interval. This is a back-up feature that allows the recovery of valuable data whenever a transmission is lost. Once the transmission is relayed from GOES-East to Sao Jose dos Campos, it is translated into engineering units and stored in a computer equipped with a Telex interface. System users dial-up this line and obtain the information on their regular Telex terminals.

The National Department of Water and Electricity of the Brazilian Ministry of Mines and Energy has acquired an equivalent unit for its computer so that the telemetered data flow directly into the Hydrometeorological Information System files. Other users enter the received data manually into their data processing equipment. It is important to realize that this mode of operation is only possible because the system is small, and the amount of information presently produced allows manual handling. It must be acknowledged that upon expansion of the data collecting network, there will have to be an upgrading of the present data dissemination scheme.

During the period of initial operation, two types of visits to the field stations were planned: bi-monthly control visits during the first 6 months, in order to check all of the instruments installed; and emergency visits in the event of failures. The time between control visits will be extended to once every 6 months when the system is considered to be running smoothly.

The above plan has worked fine so far. It has only been necessary to visit two of the stations on an emergency basis, because of battery problems in one case and because of a DCP loss of timing in the other case.

INITIAL OPERATION RESULTS

The initial operation phase of the project has been characterized by: (a) a series of minor specific problems at both the transmission and reception sides of the system; and (b) the satisfactory behaviour of the system as a whole.

The ground receiving station had some adjustment problems mainly regarding the receivers, which had difficulties in locking the assigned frequency for GOES channel 61, which is the channel designated by NESDIS for operation of the River Tocantins System. These problems were finally solved during a visit from the manufacturers to the receiving station at Sao Jose dos Campos. This control visit was part of the contract with Sierra Misco and proved to be necessary.

The difficulties on the transmission side have been mainly due to battery failures. The batteries being used are the rechargeable gel/cell type, 12 V 23 amphours, and it is believed that the one year storage period before installation might have affected most of them as they lost the ability to maintain the charge supplied by the solar panels. Regular car batteries have been temporarily substituted in order to keep the system on the air until a definite solution is found. New gel/cell batteries should put an end to the problem. For a time it was thought that the solar panel could be draining the battery during the night. After control checks were carried out, this possibility was discarded.

There have been some problems with the platforms themselves. Two of them have been returned to the manufacturer, under warranty, because they did not accept programming. Another has had timing problems, the cause of which, at the moment of writing this paper, has not been clearly defined; La Barge technicians are going to

Brazil, under their contract with PHCA, to fix the equipment.

There have also been some problems with the sensors. The humidity and temperature sensors were out of calibration, and there were also signs of need for adjustment in some of the rainfall and river level sensors. The barometric pressure units have also caused some trouble and they are being checked in order to make them operational.

One piece of equipment that proved to be very valuable during this period, has been the receiver of the DAMS's "health" messages. It allows the field technician to be certain of the good operation of the station before leaving the site. It is also a good support tool for planning maintenance trips, as well as for general monitoring of a particular network, as it can be used from the office in order to find out how the different stations are operating. This last feature is of special importance for those users who do not have a direct down link from the satellite.

The system as a whole can be considered as having had a successful period of initial operation. It is producing results which are helping to improve the system itself by feedback, and results which are being operationally used by PHCA on river forecasting activities. It is also showing that the choice of the satellite data collection technique was the right choice, and that this is the most promising method for obtaining hydrometeorological and other environmental information in this particular area of the world. There are many parties involved in the day-to-day operation of the system, and as in any pilot scheme, everyone is learning a great deal every day both about technicalities of the system itself, and about coordination of activities among all of the participating organizations. The support from manufacturers and suppliers has been very good and the relationship with NESDIS has been excellent.

CONCLUSION

The River Tocantins telemetry network has complied with the main objectives of the development plan originally established. It is a totally operational pilot network, with a trained national personnel which has acquired the desired experience to further the application of the methodology. It has been demonstrated that this is the most feasible and technically effective way of harnessing hydrometeorological data in the difficult conditions of the River Amazon basin.

This experience has made evident a series of factors that should be considered when planning a GOES based environmental data collection network. First of all, the GOES DCS user-to-be must be aware of the fact that the system not only consists of a signal relay satellite, but also entails being a member of a complex computerized system with strict access and operational procedures (NESDIS, 1982). These procedures must be mastered by the user's technical staff in order to reap the full benefits of the system. It is only through this aggregated conception of the GOES DCS that the user can actually develop his plans in such a way that they are optimal in using the DCS resources, as well as in fulfilling his specific data collection requirements.

The future user must prepare personnel to install, service and operate the system; it is very convenient to develop a certain degree of in-house "self-sufficiency" for the whole scheme. Electronics and telecommunications technicians, data processing and communications staff are desirable personnel to be considered when staffing to meet the needs of the telemetry project.

Even for those users who are planning the installation of a receiving station, it is very important to consider a back-up link with the satellite in case of a serious failure. The most logical, and probably most cost efficient, option would be to use one of the direct "dial-up" lines that connect with NESDIS computers, where information could be temporarily stored during an emergency situation. Today's microcomputers and semi-intelligent terminals, as well as the telephone facilities available, make this option a very attractive alternative. Needless to say, whatever plans are made they should be fully discussed with NESDIS well in advance of their implementation, in order to ascertain their actual feasibility and to obtain due approval.

REFERENCES

Dengo, M.B. (1982) Developments in hydrometry in Central America and Brazil. In: *Advances in Hydrometry* (Proc. Exeter Symp. July 1982), 335-344. IAHS Publ. no. 134.

Halliday, R.A. (1978) A plan for the collection and transmission of hydrometeorological data in the Brazilian Amazon basin. *Report to UNDP/WMO project BRA/72/010.*

NESDIS (1982) *User Interface Manual* GOES Data Collection System/Data Processing System.

Scientific Procedures Applied to the Planning, Design and Management of Water Resources Systems (Proceedings of the Hamburg Symposium, August 1983). IAHS Publ. no. 147.

Hydrometeorological network for real time data collection in a Southern Hemisphere arid area

J. AMOROCHO*
University of California, Davis, California 95616, USA
P. C. FERNANDEZ, H. ROBY & J. M. FERNANDEZ
National Institute for Water Science and Technology (INCYTH), Mendoza, Argentina

ABSTRACT Summer thunderstorms are frequent and constitute the main flash flood producing events in the piedmont pre-Andean areas west of the city of Mendoza, Argentina. Studies have been conducted in a network of recording raingauges covering a 600 km^2 research area formed by nine contiguous catchments. They have led to the design of a system of VHF data transmitting stations, some of which sense rain, humidity, solar radiation and streamflow. These field installations, and an available radar station, are used to investigate time-space rainfall patterns for the formulation of distributed rainfall models for more exact hydrological forecasting.

Réseaux hydrométéorologiques pour les régions arides de l'hémisphère sud
RESUME Les averses convectives d'été out lieu fréquemment et sont à l'origine des débits extrêmes dans les piémonts des Andes, à l'ouest de la ville de Mendoza, en Argentine. Des études ont été faites dans un réseau méteorologique d'une superficie de 600 km^2, consistant en neuf bassins, versants contigus. Le résultat de ces études a été la réalisation d'un réseau de postes émetteurs de haute, fréquence (VHF), pour la transmission d'informations concernant la pluie, l'humidité, le rayonnement solaire, et le débit. Ce réseau, ainsi que un radar météorologique, sont actuellement utilisés dans l'étude de la morphologie spatiale et temporelle des précipitations, pour la formulation de modèles mathématiques, qui permettront une prévision hydrologique plus exacte.

INTRODUCTION

Over a period of several years the National Institute for Water Science and Technology (INCYTH), through its Andean regional centre has carried out hydrological investigations in the piedmont and pre-cordilleran areas which flank the city of Mendoza on the west. To implement such studies a network of eight conventional weather stations and raingauges covering approximately 600 km^2 of small

We regret to announce that Professor Jaime Amorocho died on 22 November 1983.

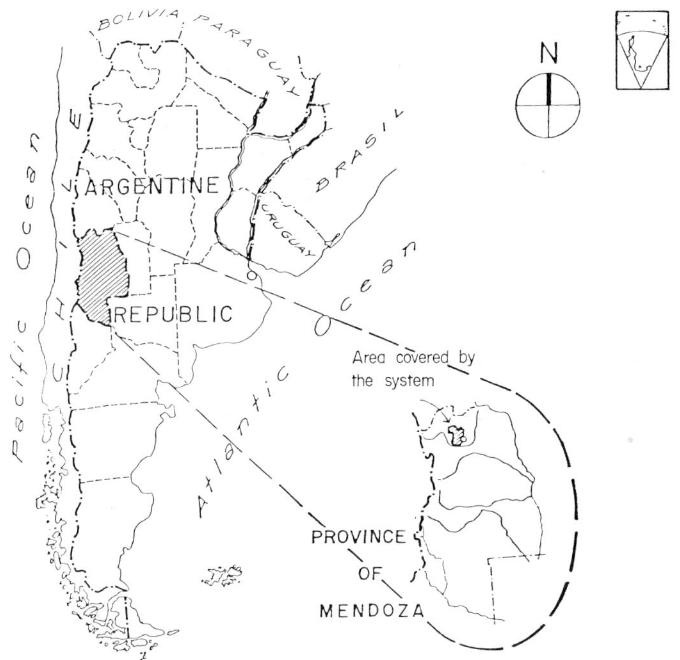

FIG.1 Location of study area. The eight conventional weather stations were installed near the eastern border of the small inset area.

contiguous basins was installed (see Fig.1).

In eight years of operation the meteorological results show that the activity of summer thunderstorms in the region is normally induced by strong low level advection of moist Atlantic air opposing upper air troughs associated with Pacific systems reaching the area across the Andes.

According to previous examination of PPI (plan position indicator) radar images, many convective cells emerge from the mountains to fall over the western Argentine plains, following the course of the Mendoza River towards the east, northeast or north along the piedmont which lies parallel to the pre-cordillera.

Organized convective cell lines advancing from the east or north-east have been sometimes observed in the area.

Previous studies advise the installation of a very dense network of raingauges to analyse accurately summer thunderstorm fields (Amorocho, 1980). A detailed economical and technical examination of various telemetering systems shows the convenience of the event reporting data system similar to that developed by the National Weather Service-River Forecast Center of California, USA (Burnash, 1979).

OBJECTIVES OF THE NETWORK

The main purpose of the system is to provide detailed data on summer thunderstorms for local and regional application.

The central and western regions of the country are formed by over

200 000 km^2 arid and semiarid lands of similar meteorological and physical characteristics. They are affected by sudden flash floods which produce considerable damage (Fernandez, 1982).

To improve the local engineering techniques in flood control and conveyance as well as the study of sediment transport and production, it is necessary to carry out detailed hydrological studies in partial areas of typical hydrological and geomorphological conditions to develop generalized models.

This task is achieved with data obtained from the network to implement and calibrate hydrological runoff models for short-term forecasting and for design. This is done by means of detailed time and space modelling of convective storms. The work by Amorocho *et al.* (1973), by the US Army Corps of Engineers (1981) and by Burnash *et al.* (1979) are the bases for the catchment models utilized by INCYTH.

Another important objective is to set up an alert system for the mitigation of the effect of flash floods on the city of Mendoza and its urban industrial and agricultural environs. This is not easy to attain because of the rapid response time of the drainage basins (some of them less than 1 h).

Due to the fact that the systems have a very short response time, the study of different alternatives has shown that the "event reporting" technology is the only means of reporting events in real time (Burnash, 1982).

The third objective refers to the calibration of distributed basin models for the design of mains and drainage channels in urban areas.

The data obtained from the real time reporting will be applied to the city of Mendoza and could be of use in many other Argentine and Latin American urban areas (Amorocho, 1980).

An important indirect objective is to install a pilot network for the country, in order to show the advantages of such technology for hydrometeorological data acquisition and real time rainfall-runoff forecasting.

DESIGN OF THE SYSTEM

Figure 2 shows the location of the network instruments, which form a set of 12 raingauges. The density used meets the requirements for a detailed time and space description of convective storms, as indicated by the radar observations available.

Previous qualitative observations of PPI and RHI (radar height indicator) radar images show fully developed single cells with 5 to 10 km lengths and 2.5 to 5 km widths. Narrow multicell systems exceeding 40 km in length were frequently observed (Amorocho, 1980).

With the cooperation of IADIZA (Argentine National Institute for Research in Arid Zones) a network of one recording and seven non-recording raingauges was installed in the summer of 1980/1981, in a small basin called Divisadero Largo. The thunderstorms registered in this network which had very high space gradients (see Figs 3 and 4; Brun *et al.*, 1981) illustrates this general condition.

Such studies, in addition to the radar observations, determined that a raingauge spacing of 1.5-3 km was desirable, and the 12

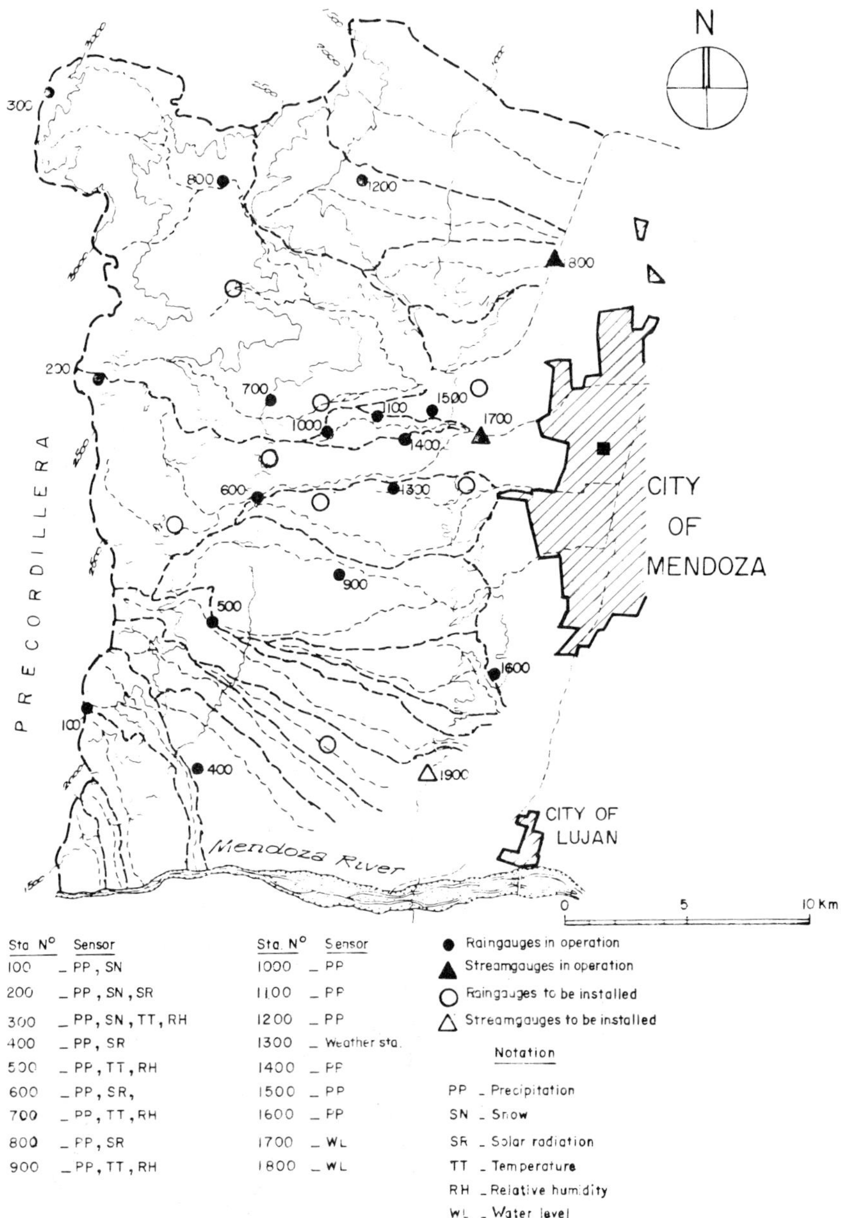

FIG.2 Location of network instruments.

recording raingauges were placed accordingly in the 36 km^2 area of study (one per 3 km^2). In one of the catchments, which has an area of 5 km^2, a streamgauge is installed at the outlet.

At the moment, seven raingauges are in operation and five more will be installed during this year. The system will also permit real time rainfall reporting and short term runoff forecasting for an area of 600 km^2.

The data are received at a central station through a binary type transmitter of VHF signals and the information is processed with a

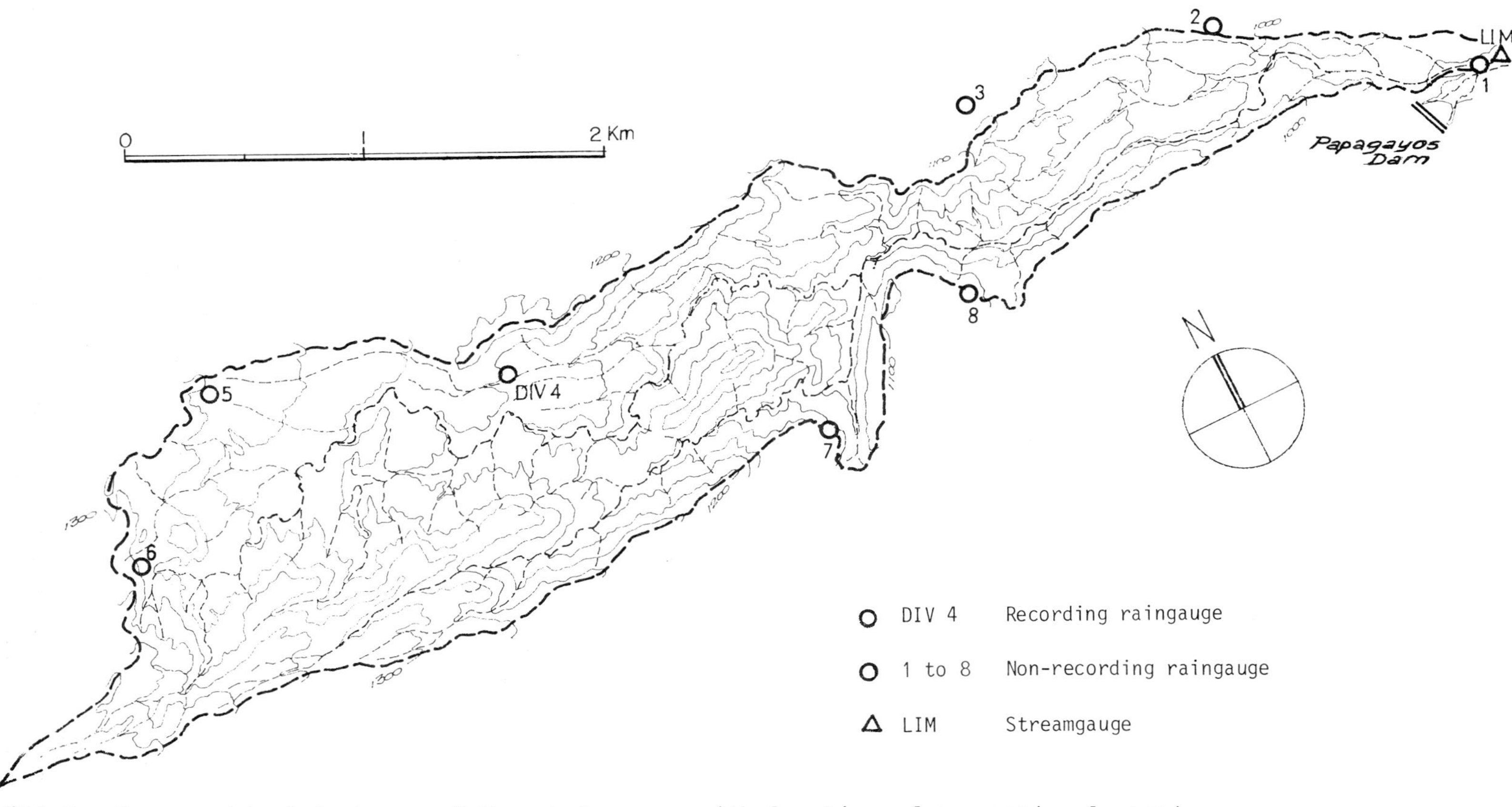

FIG.3 Topographical features of the study area, with location of conventional stations.

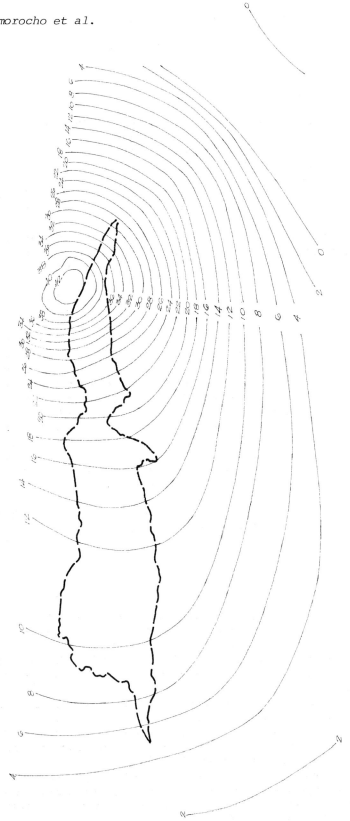

FIG.4 Approximate isohyetal map of total precipitation from a single storm cell; from data collected at conventional stations.

Tandy II minicomputer with capability for expansion.

NETWORK INSTALLATION

The criterion followed in installing the network was to obtain rows of stations at mean sea levels ranging from 3200 to 950 m in such a manner that the basin precipitation could be adequately represented, while proper reliability maintained.

All the stations can be serviced from the ground except two which only can be accessed by helicopter. The final location of the points was mapped by radio path tests carried out with 2 W portable VHF equipment.

The topographic configuration of the area, and the nearness of the stations, allow them to have individual, direct radio paths without repeaters. There are only two stations furnished with directional antennas, with an assigned frequency of 167.875 MHz.

Due to the fact that the system is operating for the study of summer thunderstorms and flash floods in detail, four stations have been furnished with sensors for humidity and temperature, four for solar radiation, and a first order weather station in the centre of the area has been instrumented for temperature, humidity, solar radiation, barometric pressure and wind velocity and direction. A type A evaporation pan will be in operation in the near future.

At the outlet of the Divisadero Largo catchment there is a concrete weir structure with a 165° V-shaped anchored steel section, which permits the measurement of low flows. To obtain the exact stage-discharge curve for such a weir a hydraulic laboratory scale model was constructed. The scales of this model were 1:10 for operating at flows ranging from 0 to 15^{3}m s^{-1} and 1:25 for flows of 15-100 $m^{3}s^{-1}$. These studies were performed at the Universidad Nacional de San Juan (1982).

Protected, and away from the streambed, was placed a bubbler gauge telemetering water level recorder. A second one will be set to the north of the region in a storm water collector channel.

REFERENCES

Amorocho, J. (1980) Report on recommendations for a hydrologic study program. INCYTH, Centro Regional Andino, Mendoza, Argentina.

Amorocho, J. *et al.* (1973) Simulation of runoff from arid and semiarid climate watersheds. Vols I, II, III, IV and V. *Dept of Water Science and Engineering, WS & Eng. Papers 3002-3006. University of California. Davis, USA.*

Burnash, R.J. (1979) Automated precipitation measurements. *National Water Service River Forecast Center, Sacramento, California, USA.*

Burnash, R.J. (1982) Real time rainfall-runoff forecasting. Today's technological revolution in flood protection. Spring meeting of the *American Geophysical Union, 1982.*

Burnash, R.J., Ferral, L. & McGuire, R. (1979) A generalized streamflow simulations system conceptual modeling for digital computers. *National Water Service, Joint Federal-State River Forecast Center, Sacramento, California, USA.*

Burnash, R.J. & Ferral, L. (1982) Examples of benefits and the technology involved in optimizing hydrosystem operation through real time forecasting. *National Weather Service, California-Nevada River Forecast Center, Sacramento, California, USA.*
Burnash, R. & Twedt, T. (1978) Event reporting instrumentation for real time flash flood warning. Conference on Flash Floods Hydrometeorological Aspects (Los Angeles, California, USA).
Brun, S., Pedrani, A. & Fernandez, J. (1981) Medicion de caudales y ajustes de modelos hidrologicos en Divisadero Largo (Streamflow measurements and adjustment of hydrologic models at Divisadero Largo). *CRICYT-LADIZA-INCYTH, Informe de Avance, Mendoza, Argentina.*
Fernandez, P.C. (1982) Estudios Hidrologicos para prevencion de aluviones. Conferencia en la reunion de la Asociacion Argentina de Geofisicos y Geodestas (Hydrologic studies for flood control. Paper presented at the Argentina Association of Geophysicists and Geodesists) (Mar del Plata, Argentina).
National Weather Service (1981). Western Region Hydrologic Service Division. Automated local evaluation in real time. Salt Lake City, Utah, USA.
US Army Corps of Engineers (1981) *HEC., HEC-I. Flood Hydrograph Package Users Manual. US Army Corps of Engineers, Davis, California, USA.*
Universidad Nacional de San Juan (1982) Estudio sobre modelo fisico vertedero aforador Divisadero Largo (Physical hydraulic model study on the streamflow measuring weir at Divisadero Largo). Instituto de Investigaciones Hidraulicas, San Juan, Argentina.

Hydrological Applications of Remote Sensing and Remote Data Transmission (Proceedings of the Hamburg Symposium, August 1983). IAHS Publ. no. 145.

Water resources sensor characteristics for GOES retransmission in Canada

J. M. WHITING
Saskatchewan Research Council, 30 Campus Drive, Saskatoon, Saskatchewan, Canada S7N 0X1

ABSTRACT Sensors are described which are used on Canadian data collection platforms (DCPs). These sensors are used on meteorological, hydrological, marine and water quality stations. Also presented are typical types, accuracy, and time response of the sensors by themselves and in field conditions with specific DCPs. The importance of the choice of the sensor is shown to have effects on the quality of the data received. Sensor calibration and field quality control are also detailed.

Les capteurs caractéristiques pour les resources hydrauliques et la télétransmission par GOES au Canada
RESUME On présente ici les capteurs qui sont employés avec les systèmes de collecte de données au Canada. Ces capteurs sont utilisés pour des stations météorologiques, hydrographiques, océanographiques et de surveillance de la qualité des eaux. On décrit les capteurs types, leur exactitude et leur temps de réponse isolés et dans les conditions de terrain, intégrés dans des systèmes de collecte des données différentes. On montre également que le choix du capteur affecte la qualité des données recues. L'étalonnage des capteurs et leur vérification pendant l'utilisation sont décrits en détail.

INTRODUCTION

Today, instrumentation consists of a complete data acquisition system instead of a single device to sense an environmental parameter at a single location. In other words, modern instrumentation includes data collection, storage, processing and dissemination involving retrieval and communication. Strictly speaking, model design should dictate the instrumentation required. Since models attempt to simulate natural mechanisms with the aid of mathematical and statistical formulation they must serve as a guide for field instrument operations.

Over the past decades, instrumentation has progressed from a piecemeal to an interdisciplinary approach. This paper will focus on the sensors presently in use by Canadian data collection platform (DCP) users. Also covered are the requirements and specifications as well as the system's basic principles and mechanisms used.

Of the three physical environments within the geosphere (atmosphere, hydrosphere and lithosphere), the atmosphere normally has the greatest mobility in its moving scale for instrumentation (Fig.1). The hydrosphere ranks second. Therefore, atmospheric

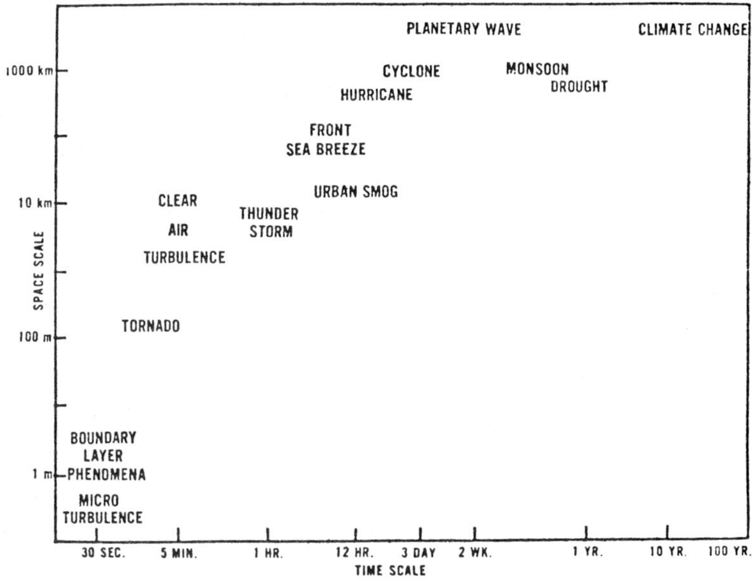

FIG.1 Time and space scales of meteorological phenomena (from Thomson et al., 1974).

instruments should detect the various forms of eddies over a wide range of scales in small increments of time and space. Figure 1 shows the time and space scales of atmospheric phenomena. The vertical scale beyond the microlayer (300 m) is not discussed (although measurements by ceilometers, scattermeters may come in the not too distant future). Figure 2 shows the time and space scales for the hydrospheric phenomena.

For example in a turbulence model, the sampling rate for wind

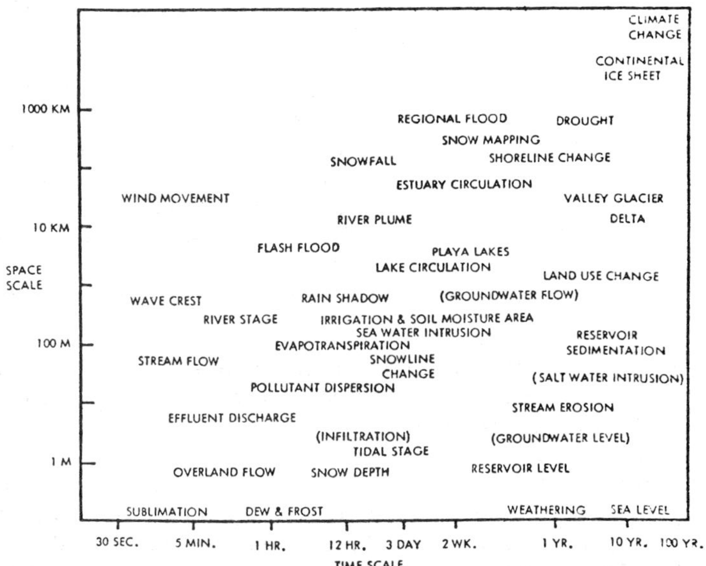

FIG.2 Time and space scales of water resources phenomena (from Thomson et al., 1974).

speed can be as high as 12 measurements per minute. Under fair weather conditions during the midday hours, one or two temperature measurements per hour would be sufficient. However during windy conditions, two to three measurements per hour would be required. In reality, however, the frequency of measurement depends upon the objective of the user (Wang & Felton, 1979). In practice, the World Meteorological Organization (WMO) has established worldwide standard hours for making surface observations (WMO, 1971, 1980).

REQUIREMENTS AND SPECIFICATIONS

When an instrument is built the performance specifications are established by calibrating and testing through comparison with a standard instrument (WMO, 1971) and by other standardized procedures. By comparing all available specifications with their own operational requirements, the user chooses the most suitable instrument. Table 1 gives the definitions used by manufacturers to make specifications.

TABLE 1 Definitions of specifications

RANGE	*Difference between extreme readouts*
LIMITATION	*Capability to give accurate readings*
ACCURACY	*Response to environmental signal or closeness to quantity or mean of series of observations or accuracy between two responses*
ERROR	*Algebraic difference*
REPRESENTATIVENESS	*Accuracy, coupling to environment, spatial and temporal coverage*
SENSITIVITY	*Change in output to known change in input*
TIME RESPONSE	*Time required for 63% of full scale change*
RELIABILITY	*Ability to retain calibration for period of time (i.e. stability or maintainability)*
RUGGEDNESS	*Period of usable data (i.e. life span)*

Independent laboratories are sometimes used which are considered reliable and have rigorous tests and standard instruments: such as the National Physical Laboratory of Great Britain or the National Bureau of Standards in the USA.

An instrument with a large range is said to have a large capacity while the small range - a low capacity. Hence, range and capacity have quite often been used loosely in the literature (Wang & Felton, 1979), particularly for those which measure volume or weight. Most sensors detect only a certain range of its complete scale accurately. The limitations are normally at the extreme ends of the scale.

Without a knowledge of the accuracy, the time and space representativeness of an environmental variate cannot be specified. The accuracy is designated as the degree to which the instrument responds to its immediate environmental signal (i.e. standard, known or true value). An alternative definition of accuracy is the closeness to a quantity or the mean of a series of observation to a reference point. In commercially available instruments the system accuracy is usually expressed either in terms of absolute (±0.1°C) or per cent of full scale (e.g. 2% FS). The latter expression is not normally suitable except in matching a sensor to the measurement system (i.e. the accuracies of the two systems should match). The error is important when considering the measurement of gradient rather than absolute values.

The output of an instrument system with high sensitivity reproduces every fluctuation. A highly sensitive thermometer may indicate a ±0.01°C change while an insensitive one would be ±2°C change.

The two terms, sensitivity and accuracy, are quite often confused. Sensitivity refers to the degree of accuracy provided by the instrument output whereas time response pertains to the speed of response. When a system involves several subsystems such as with DCPs with varying sensitivities, the compatibility becomes important. The output signal from the subsystems must be matched and amplified so that uniform sensitivities are achieved. Reliability is closely related to stability. Specifications therefore should give the operating environmental conditions (i.e. level of shock or vibration, contamination and extreme weather conditions) and the period of performance. Stability is the ability to retain calibration (e.g. several years would be high stability).

The ruggedness of an instrument is measured in the period of usable data (i.e. the life span). Most environmental instruments today are rugged. In general the cost of purchase and installation are small compared to the cost of maintenance (Wang & Felton, 1979).

Table 2 shows the wide range of parameters which can be measured. The table shows the units, range and accuracy.

SENSORS IN COMMON USE IN CANADA

In order for data quality to be of a high standard, sensors require verification of performance; installation and siting must be uniform; and a specific protocol must be standard for archiving (AES, 1982; CASI, 1983). Table 3 gives sensor parameters (for the Atmospheric Environment Service (AES) and the Water Survey of Canada (WSC)), accuracy, type, WMO precision and reporting interval (note: Canadian standards are uniform with neither WMO standards nor Table 2 specifications).

For precipitation the DCP usually measures accumulated precipitation or rate (of water equivalent). The target is an accuracy of ±0.2 mm up to 10 mm and 2% above that, but the minimum usable is ±1 mm up to 50 mm and 2% above. The normally achieved standard is ±0.2 mm (AES, 1982). In precipitation measurements, particularly in snow measurement, errors due to shieldings are

TABLE 2 Hydrospheric and atmospheric parameters

Parameters	*Units*	*Range*	*Accuracy*
Surface water temperature	°C	-40 to 40	0.01
Salinity	ppt	0 to 42	0.01%
Wave elevation	m	0 to 30	0.003
Water pressure	bar	0 to 700	0.25%
Bottom pressure variation	mbar	0 to 170	0.28
Current direction	degrees	0 to 360	1
Current speed	$m\ s^{-1}$	0.025 to 5	0.015
Infrared surface radiation	$J\ m^{-2}$	0 to 3000	2%
Transparency	$\%\ m^{-1}$	0 to 70	2%
Water level	m	-1 to 5	0.003
Tidal fluctuation	m	0 to 20	0.003
Wave height spectrum E	m^2	0.09 to 140	5%
F	$cycles\ s^{-1}$	0 to 1	-
Swell height spectrum E/Δf	$m^2\ (cycle\ s)^{-1}$	0.09 to 140	5%
F	$cycle\ s^{-1}$	0 to 0.1	0.06
Wave height	m	0 to 30	10
Swell direction	degrees	0 to 360	15%
Swell period	s	5 to 1200	0.1
Dissolved oxygen	$ml\ l^{-1}$	0.5 to 9	3%
CO_2	atm	10^{-4} to $12x10^{-4}$	1 pt/ml
Turbidity	$pt\ ml^{-1}$	1 to 1000	0.2
pH	-	1 to 13	0.01
Conductivity	$mmho\ cm^{-1}$	0.1 to 60	2
Wind direction	degrees	0 to 360	2
Wind speed	$m\ s^{-1}$	0 to 70	0.25
Wind stress	$g\ cm^{-1}$	0 to 10^7	10%
Wind run	km	0 to 260	3
Atmospheric pressure	mbar	800 to 1099	0.1
Air temperatures	°C	-65 to 50	0.1
Relative humidity	%	5 to 100	1
Dew point	°C	-40 to 40	0.2
Wet bulb temperature	°C	-40 to 40	1
Insolation	$J\ m^{-2}$	0 to 3000	1%
Ambient light	$J\ m^{-2}$	0 to 3000	1%
Precipitation intensity	$mm\ h^{-1}$	0 to 300	0.25
Precipitation amount:			
below 40 mm	mm	0 to 300	0.25
above 40 mm	mm	0 to 300	5%
Snow depth: below 40 mm/6 h	cm	0 to 20	2
above 40 mm/6 h	cm	0 to 20	10%
Wind force	$g\ cm^{-1}s^{-2}$	0 to 10^7	10%
Transmissivity	%	0 to 100	2
Pan evaporation	mm	0 to 300	0.5

Adapted from Harvey (1972).

highly variable (Goodison, 1978). The gauge should be located on level, well drained surfaces with short vegetation and in an open area which is four times the height of the closest obstruction. Canadian specifications have yet to be established for snow pillows or the parameters below the dashed line in Table 3. The weighing gauge with an optical digital encoder is the most accurate (e.g. Fischer-Porter 35-1559, now Belfort, with BEI 5V86). The potentiometric type can be connected directly to the analog input of the DCP (e.g. Belfort 5915 or 6071). The potentiometric type, however, suffers from sensitivity problems.

The specification for air temperature is shown in Table 3. However, the normally achieved value for ventilated systems is ±0.5°C and unventilated systems ±1.0°C. Ventilation can be supplied either electromechanically or by a shield which directs the sensor into the wind (e.g. Met-One 071). The probe must be shielded from solar radiation (Stevenson screen, parallel plate; Sparks, 1971 etc.). The sensor should be mounted between 1.25 and 2 m except where snow accumulation makes this impractical (up to 5 m in some cases). Maximum, minimum and mean temperatures should be based on either continuous sampling (preferred) or no less frequently than 10 minutes. The mean is the arithmetic mean for the climatological day (0601 Z to 0600 Z). The thermal lag should not be more than 30-100 s in air at 5 m s^{-1} wind speed (AES, 1982).

For relative humidity, the sensor should be accurate to 5% but preferably ±1%. Averaging is not a normal requirement. The siting and shielding is similar to that of air temperature.

Wind speed and direction should be accurate to ±10% although ±5% is preferred. The sensors are usually cup wheel or propellor type with distance constants of 2-5 m (wind direction damped to 0.3-0.7). For time sampling, the minimum sample period of 1 s should be used providing 10 minute boxcar means (AES, 1982). For 10-minute mean wind direction, vector averaging is preferred but time averaging is acceptable. The sensor should be placed on level, open terrain on a 10 m tower. The height should be adjusted to avoid effects of local obstructions.

Some DCP manufacturers make their system compatible with specific sensor manufacturers (Table 4). Table 4 gives the accuracy, threshold or limitation and the range of DCPs with specific sensors. In some cases the table also gives an expression of reliability and the time response of the total system. The typical response of the sensors by themselves is given in Table 5. The accuracy in the field can be measured manually with the sensors given in Table 6. However, the time response of the reference sensors must be compared with both the DCP sensor and the DCP.

The analog sample time in most DCPs is 1 s while motor driven potentiometers take 13 s and digital sampling takes 1-2 ms. DCPs generally require 2-66 s to reach a stable operating voltage in order to make accurate measurements of the sensors.

CONCLUSION

Sensors must be chosen that can measure the desired event. The frequency of observation must match the environment event. The sensor and the DCP response time must be compatible.

In order for DCPs to provide good data the incoming data must be

TABLE 3 Atmospheric Environment Service (AES) and Water Survey of Canada (WSC) DCP standards

Sensor	AES/WSC: Accuracy	Type	World Meteorological Precision	Organization Reporting Interval
Precipitation	±1 mm	Fisher-Porter	±2 mm below 40 mm	6 h or 1 or 3 h
		Belfort 5915	±5 mm above 40 mm	in emergencies
Snow pillow			±2 cm below 20 cm	Daily
			±5% above 20 cm	Daily
Air temperature	±1.0°C	Sonotek 4201	±0.1°C	6 h (3 h AES)
Relative humidity	5%	Pernix 800L	10%	6 h
Wind speed	1 km	45B AES Sonotek 77C	1 km	(6 h AES)
Wind direction	10°	45B Sonotek 77C		
Water level	±2 mm	BEI 5V241		3 h
Water temperature	±0.3°C			
Conductivity	±50 μHMO cm^{-1}			
pH	±0.2 ppm			
Dissolved O_2	±0.2 ppm			
Water velocity	±1 cm s^{-1}	Atlas-Flora (acoustic)		Once daily
Air pressure	±1 mbars	Pernix 215	±1 mbar	1 h
		Setra 270		
Status of operation				
Ice break-up				
Turbidity				

TABLE 4 Sensors supplied with DCPs

Sensor	Model	Accuracy	Threshold	Maximum	Comment	Temperature (°C)
BRISTOL						
Direction	Sonotek 77C	±45°	3.24 kph	240 kph		-40 to 50
Speed	Sonotek 77C	1 km	3.24 kph	240 kph		-40 to 40
Temperature	Sonotek 4201	±0.3°C				-50 to 50
Relative humidity	Pernix 800L	±5%	5%			-40 to 40
Pressure	Parosc. 215	±0.4 mbars		1034 mbars		-40 to 40
Precipitation	F-P 35	±1 mm		500 mm		-40 to 40
Rain	Belfort 5915	±4%		150 mm h^{-1}		
HANDAR						
Direction	M-1-023	±15°	2.43 kph	240 kph	5 cm ice	-50 to 70
Speed	M-1-013	2%±0.4 kph	1.94 kph	240 kph	5 cm ice	-50 to 70
Temperature	M-1-071	0.4°C	2.43 kph		with shield	-50 to 80
Relative humidity	M-1-083	±1%	1 s-90%	0.07%°C	SO_2 sens.	-40 to 80
Pressure	YS12014	±0.3%	0.15%/3K	0.0045%/°C		-34 to 82
Rain	WEA.6011	0.5% for	50 mm h^{-1}	200 mm h^{-1}		
LABARGE						
Direction	Clima.	±1.5°C	1.2 kph	225 kph	Climatronic	-40 to 50
Speed	Clima.	±1.5%	1.2 kph	225 kph		-40 to 50
Temperature	Clima.	0.15°C	0.16°C			-30 to 50
Relative humidity	Clima.	±4%	5%			-40 to 50
Pressure	Clima.	±0.4 mbars	0.3%	1038 mbars		-40 to 50
Rain	Clima.	±1%	76 mm h^{-1}			

TABLE 5 Typical sensor responses

Sensor	Type	Transmission	Time response 83% FS (s)	Accuracy	Temp. dependence
TEMPERATURE	Thermocouple	Temp. compensation Circuit (ref. junction)	1	1.5%	Bimetal response Ref. junction pt.
	Thermister	Log bridge circuit	0.5-120	0.2°C	Recorder impedence
	Platinium	Servo system	10-180	0.75°C	0°C ref. of servo
DEW POINT	Hot wire LiCl Cell	AC generator current attenuation		Approx. 5% non-linear at 0°C	-40 to 40°C
WIND SPEED	Pulse count	Photo electronic	1.5	1%	-20 to 40°C
		Electronic interface to solenoid counter	0.3	0.1 km	-40 to 40°C
	Geared potentiometer	Resistance	Direct	Higher threshold	
WIND DIRECTION	Motor potentiometer	Voltage averaging	180°/5 min	10%	-35 to 40°C
	Direct potentiometer	Resistance		10%	
RADIATION	Thermopile*	Pulse integrator	1.3 s/8 mV	0.9%	-20 to 45°C
		Amplifier		0.2%	-40 to 40°C
	Photoelectronic	Amplifier	10^{-5}	0.1 Ly min^{-1}	-45 to 40°C
PRESSURE	Piezoelectric†	Frequency response	1-2 x 10^{-5}	0.01 psi	-50 to 125°C
PRECIPITATION	Ce 137	Sodium iodide Detector	180 s	3 mm	
	Snow pillow	Mercury manometer	20	3 mm	-35 to 40°C

* Cosine response now available.

† Sensor and electronics available in correct magnitude but not standard equipment.

TABLE 6 Manual reference sensors

Sensor	Type	Transmission	Reaction time (s)	Sensor accuracy
TEMPERATURE	Mercury		180	0.01°C
	Bimetal	Lever	60	1°C
	Mercury in steel		180	
RELATIVE HUMIDITY	Human hair		30	10%
	Man-made fibre hair	Lever	25	
WIND SPEED	Reed switch	RC Circuit to	0.3 per count	1 km
	Micro-switch	solenoid counter		
WIND DIRECTION	Oil damped	Lever	Variable on	10°
	Clutch damped		viscosity	
PRESSURE	Aneroid	Lever		1 mbar
SUN DURATION	Multi-bimetal	Solenoid	10	0.1 h
	Pyroheliometer			
LIQUID PRECIPITATION	Tipping bucket	Reed switch to solenoid	0.3 per count	0.2 mm

checked weekly if not daily for data that are out of limits and range, consistent and without gaps. Table 7 gives some of the checks which should be incorporated into quality control of data. In the field, a regimented checklist should be used to check the equipment. Field calibration should not be used to adjust the electronic gain and span of sensors or DCPs. Adjustments should be made to computer programs so that raw data are not affected if mistakes are made. In an emergency, 15 h of field data can be used for in-field calibration but using three different test points. After a field trip the DCP should be monitored for 48 h to check for falling or stationary values.

TABLE 7 Indications of problems with DCPs

Sensor	
PRECIPITATION	*>180 mm* h^{-1} *or dropping*
SNOW PILLOW	*>20 mm* h^{-1} *or dropping*
AIR OR WATER TEMPERATURE	*Δ1.5°C* h^{-1}
RELATIVE HUMIDITY	*no change for more than 6 h*
WIND SPEED	*no change for more than 10 h or Δ44 KpH (especially 0 s)*
WIND DIRECTION	*no values close to 0 or 360*
WATER LEVEL	*50% drop of FS*
CONDUCTIVITY	*gradual increase or Δ100 μmhos*
pH	*Δ0.5*
DISSOLVED OXYGEN	*Δ0.5*

REFERENCES

AES (1982) *Environment Canada (DOE) Policy on Services for Communication and Archiving of Data from Automatic Stations.* AES, Downsview, Canada.

CASI (1983) *Proceedings of the First Canadian DCP Workshop* (Quebec City, Ottawa, 25-26 September 1980).

Goodison, B. (1978) Accuracy of Canadian snow gage measurements. *J. Appl. Met.* 17 (10), 1542-1548.

Harvey, G.F. (1972) *Transducer Compendium.* Inst. Soc. of America, Washington.

Sparks, W.R. (1971) *Effects of Thermometer Screen Design on the Observed Temperatures.* WMO no. 315, Geneva.

Thomson, K.P.B., Lane, R.K. & Csallany, S.C. (1974) *Remote Sensing and Water Management.* American Water Resources Ass., Urbana, USA.

Wang, J.Y. & Felton, C.M.M. (1979) *Instrument for Physical Environment Measurements*, vol. 1 (2nd edn). Miliey Information Service Inc., Oakland, USA.

WMO (1971) *Guide to Meteorological Instruments and Observing Practices.* WMO no. 8 TP 3, Geneva.

WMO (1980) *Technical Regulations, Hydrology and International Hydrological Codes.* WMO no. 555, Geneva.

Hydrological Applications of Remote Sensing and Remote Data Transmission (Proceedings of the Hamburg Symposium, August 1983). IAHS Publ. no. 145.

Technology transfer and satellite data collection

ALLEN F. FLANDERS & SUSAN F. ZEVIN
NOAA - National Weather Service, US Department of Commerce, Silver Spring, Maryland 20910, USA

ABSTRACT An international technology transfer endeavour is providing new challenges in information use and management to water resource decision makers. Under a project designated HOMS (Hydrological Operational Multi-purpose Subprogramme) the framework allows for a systematic and user-oriented approach to water resources problem solving - an alternative or complement to traditional project engineering methodology. This activity is being conducted under the auspices of the World Meteorological Organization. Each HOMS component acquires a data base or history of its own. Engineers use these documented components to plan and design new projects in similar environments. Using HOMS, water resource projects are planned as systems - total approaches to water resource problems or as individual techniques connected en eschelon or in sequence, but not requiring the operational harmony and efficiency of a system. One example is the use of satellite data collection systems to improve hydrological data acquisition. The challenge to system users is in identifying the criteria by which hydrological technology can be compared, evaluated, and interfaced to other techniques. HOMS is a prototype for other technology (information) transfer programmes, and the experience of its users and managers should become the information technology which is transferred to other disciplines.

Un transfert de technologie et des systèmes de collectes de données par satellite

RESUME Un effort international de transfert de technologie fournit aux responsables de nouvelles perspectives pour l'utilisation de l'information et la gestion des ressources hydrologiques. Dans le cadre d'un projet appelé HOMS (Hydrological Operational Multipurpose Subprogramme) la structure permet en faveur de l'usager une approche systématique et orientée vers la solution du problème des ressources hydrologiques, ce qui constitue une autre possibilité ou un complément de la méthodologie classique de l'ingénierie des projets. Cette activité se poursuit sous les auspices de l'Organisation Météorologique Mondiale. Chaque élément de HOMS acquiert une base de données ou sa propre histoire. Les ingénieurs utilisent ces éléments documentés pour planifier et élaborer, des projets nouveaux dans des environnements semblables. En se servant de HOMS, les projets concernant les ressources hydrologiques sont concus en tant que systèmes, c'est à dire une approche totale des problèmes de ressources hydrologiques, ou bien, en tant que techniques individuelles se rattachant en échelon ou en série, mais sans requérir l'harmonie opérationnelle et l'efficacité d'un système. L'utilisation des systèmes de collectes de données par satéllite pour améliorer l'obtention des données hydrologiques en est un exemple. Le défi lancé aux usagers du système concerne l'identification des critères qui permettent la comparaison, l'évaluation et l'interface de la technologie hydrologique avec d'autres techniques. HOMS est un prototype d'autres programmes de transfert de technologie (information), et l'expérience accumulée par ses usagers et gestionnaires devrait devenir la technologie d'information qui est transférée à d'autres disciplines.

INTRODUCTION

A new programme of technology transfer is being supported by the USA under the auspices of the World Meteorological Organization (WMO), a specialized agency of the United Nations. The scope of the technology transfer programme covers a broad array of items in the field of operational hydrology. Over 60 countries in WMO have joined in this effort to pool and share technology intelligence to aid developing countries in the improvement of their national meteorological and hydrological services. The programme is designated HOMS (Hydrological Operational Multipurpose Subprogramme). HOMS is a subprogramme of WMO's Operational Hydrology Programme and forms the framework for the documentation, classification, referral and implementation of operational hydrological techniques by member countries of WMO.

HOMS reflects the growing recognition in recent years of the important role of operational hydrology in economic development, and the need for more effective international action in this field. A number of major intergovernmental meetings have borne this out, in particular the UN Water Conference in 1977. In 1975 the WMO Congress decided that WMO should intensify its activities in operational hydrology, and recommended that a long-term project be undertaken for the development and application of a technology transfer system which has now come to be known as HOMS. The project offers a variety of technologies for use in hydrological and water resource projects and is undertaken as a cooperative effort by member countries, coordinated by WMO.

An example of this technology is the shared use of satellites for data collection from remote areas. One such satellite system, the Geostationary Operational Environmental Satellite (GOES) is operated for environmental users by NOAA (National Oceanic and Atmospheric Administration) of the US Department of Commerce. GOES is part of the WMO's World Weather Watch programme in which five geostationary satellites are spaced around the equator to provide global coverage.

THE HOMS PROGRAMME

HOMS consists of the organized transfer of hydrological technology used operationally in network design, observations, collection, processing and storage of data and hydrological modelling. HOMS also includes instrument catalogues, software packages, and general guidance and detailed manuals on the use of the technology under different conditions. HOMS is aimed at users who seek a high level of sophisticated technology, and at those in need of simple technology appropriate to their operating conditions. The programme uses a systems approach in classifying and cross-referencing components contributed by member countries.

HOMS is organized for direct bilateral contacts among WMO member nations and by contact through other UN agencies. To date, of the 94 members of WMO, 61 have agreed to participate in HOMS by designating officials of their National Hydrological or Meteorological Service to be the focal point for HOMS activities. These focal points and their activities are called HOMS National Reference Centres. The centres are organizational mechanisms for receiving as well as exporting operational hydrological knowledge. Where countries do not have the resources or are not organized to establish a reference centre, they may join with several other countries in the area to form a HOMS Regional Centre. Regional centres provide a link between projects of participating countries to allow (developing) countries to benefit from each other's experience and achievements. Regional centres are now established in Bangkok, Thailand, and Manila, the Philippines, representing 16 countries of Asia and the southwest Pacific. African regional centres are being established in Niamey, Niger, Nairobi, Kenya, and Kaduna, Nigeria, to foster exchange of hydrological techniques from the Nile basin in the east to the Senegal basin in the west and including some 20-24 countries. A very successful regional centre serves the Scandinavian countries of Norway, Finland, Sweden, and Denmark. Other regional centres are being considered for southern Europe (the Balkan states), the Arab countries, and two possible centres in Latin America.

Data base

The data base of HOMS is the collection of descriptions of proven hydrological technology and procedures offered by member countries. Each component or technique description is classified according to four criteria:

(a) its general use or activity category, i.e. policy, planning and organization, network design, instruments and equipment, remote sensing, methods of observation, data transmission, data storage, retrieval and dissemination, primary data processing, secondary data processing, hydrological models for forecasting and design, analysis of data for planning design and operation of water resources systems, and mathematical and statistical computations;

(b) its hydrological subsection category, i.e. groundwater, water quality, glaciology, surface water, etc.;

(c) its complexity, mostly in terms of understanding, ease of use, and implementation; and

(d) its numeric order among other components having exactly the same classification.

Classification is given in a 10 character alphanumeric field. Components are sorted by use category (section) A-X, subsection 0-99, complexity one, two, or three (three being the most complex), and by a numbering system 0-99.

The HOMS data base is presented in three forms:

(a) as a printed document in a loose leaf binder called the HOMS Reference Manual (HRM);

(b) as a data set operating under the Wylbur System at the International Computing Centre in Geneva, Switzerland; and

(c) as a storage and retrieval system operating under BASIC on a microcomputer at WMO headquarters.

There are more than 300 components contained in the first edition of the Reference Manual, contributed by some 30 countries and international organizations. Since its introduction in 1981 WMO has responded to nearly 400 requests, a majority of which were from developing countries for transfer of components. The Reference Manual is in French, Russian and Spanish and there are plans for its translation into Chinese and Arabic.

US HOMS Programme

The HOMS National Reference Centre for the US is located in the NOAA National Weather Service's Office of Hydrology (Flanders & Zevin, 1983). A Steering Committee of federal agency representatives who are delegates to the WMO's Commission for Hydrology direct overall policy and planning for the programme. The agency representatives include the Corps of Engineers, Geological Survey and Soil Conservation Service in addition to the National Weather Service. As a result of HOMS activities, the US has established closer operational hydrology ties with Canada through joint meetings of their respective HOMS National Reference Centres. The US National Reference Centre has:

(a) sent almost 50 components for inclusion in the HRM;

(b) filled over 20 requests for technical documentation of HOMS components involving more than 80 copies of components;

(c) sent more than 100 component descriptions requested from within the US and abroad.

Each technique, model, gauge, or any contribution must be an operational procedure, which is fully documented. Component descriptions proposed by US agencies are forwarded to the US HOMS National Reference Centre for review. Approved components are sent to WMO. Sample component and sequence descriptions are shown in Appendix 1 and Appendix 2.

Technology transfer The US programme transfers hydrological knowledge not only through the mail, i.e. responding to requests for documentation, but also through active participation in bilateral or multinational exchanges. In this regard, the US has completed or is participating in the transfer of HOMS components for:

(a) a real time data reporting system for Mexico;

(b) the HOMS centre in Beijing, China;

(c) real time hydrological data collection on the Yellow and Yangtze River basins in the Peoples Republic of China;

(d) tropical urban rainfall-runoff models in Malaysia;

(e) a real time hydrological forecasting system on the Arenal basin/Rio Bebedero, Costa Rica.

One challenge of HOMS is to describe and document components with detail sufficient to enable a user to readily adapt the technique to his or her operating environment. For example, a computer programme developed under one operating system may require extensive rewriting to conform to another computer's operating system. Even when operating systems and processors are identical, internal switch settings on different computers may prevent a programme from running. This situation is common on the popular 8-bit Z80 (Zilog) microprocessor based systems. Hydrologists using the HOMS programme will need to be experts in the various media used for the technology transfer as well as in the hydrological function itself (Zevin, 1982).

A good example of a HOMS component is in the use of satellites to collect hydrological data. Some of the technical details required for the successful implementation of a satellite data collection component are described in the next section.

SATELLITE DATA COLLECTION

Satellite data collection systems (DCSs) have been receiving wide attention both nationally and internationally (Flanders, 1981). These systems are particularly suited to data collection from remote areas where the more conventional means of communications are not readily available due to the lack of electricity or phone lines.

Meteorological satellites may be divided into two groups, polar orbiting and geostationary. The polar orbiting satellites circle the earth about every 90 minutes at a relatively low altitude (800-1000 km) in a poleward direction. Geostationary satellites remain at a fixed position relative to the earth, over the equator at approximately 36 000 km. The geostationary satellites always view the same area of the earth and are in constant view for data collection. Polar orbiting satellites collect data as they pass overhead within viewing (radio) range.

The WMO World Weather Watch space-based subsystem includes five geostationary satellites. Two US GOES satellites are part of this global system. When fully operational these satellites will have the capability to collect obsrvational data from hydrometeorological stations, ships, ocean buoys and other platforms.

Satellites have several advantages over UHF/VHF line-of-sight (LOS) radio systems parlicularly in mountainous areas. Though the per unit cost of satellite data collection platforms (DCPs) may be higher than LOS radio reporting system guages, the radio systems often require relay stations which add to the initial system costs and maintenance. The addition of relays may also decrease system reliability: there are more possibilities for component failures, and interference along the radio pathways; and system timing is complicated by transmitter turn-on and power-up requirements. Also, satellite DCPs can operate on low power from batteries recharged by solar cells.

THE GOES DATA COLLECTION SYSTEM

Use of the GOES DCS is limited to the acquisition of environmental data defined as observations and measurements of the physical, chemical or biological properties of the oceans, rivers, lakes, solid earth, and atmosphere (including space). Users of the DCS are responsible for the costs of the sensors and DCP radio equipment required to provide the communications link with the satellite, and any unique equipment/communications needed to receive the data at the user's facility. Design characteristics of the DCS on the GOES spacecraft require that users conform to specific technical standards that are detailed in an agreement with NOAA (1983).

The Satellite Operations Control Centre (SOCC) located outside of Washington, DC, is responsible for the command of the satellite while the telemetry to the spacecraft takes place at the Command and Data Acquisition (CDA) station at Wallops Island, Virginia. SOCC and the CDA are linked by landline. Data are distributed to users from the National Environmental Satellite, Data, and Information Services (NESDIS). Several options are available to users on methods to receive the data (Flanders, 1978): (a) dial-in service, (b) computer link, or (c) user owned down link.

Data collection platforms

There are several types of DCPs currently in use among the nearly 4000 platforms transmitting data via the two GOES satellites. These users include federal and state agencies and a number of countries in North and South America. The basic types of DCPs may be classed as INTERROGATED, SELF-TIMED, and RANDOM.

The INTERROGATED DCP is an externally actuated command receiver system. The radio set is actuated by a command initiated by the CDA station and received through the GOES spacecraft. Interrogation is on a scheduled or as needed basis. A synthesizer allows the radio set transmitter to be operated on any one of 100 selectable channels, plus one emergency channel. A lower cost, single channel DCP radio is also available that uses a crystal oscillator instead of a synthesizer.

The SELF-TIMED DCP operates on an internally actuated, self-contained preprogrammed timer system. The timer is a clock that turns on the transmitter at 1-12 h reporting intervals. A temperature compensated voltage controlled crystal oscillator with an accuracy of one part in 10^6 controls the transmitter frequency and the clock time. Any one of 50 channels is available for self-timed DCPs.

The RANDOM type DCP is coming into wide use. It can transmit continuously to insure receipt since a clock is not used or it can be activated by an event. The RANDOM type DCP uses a micro processor to recognize sensor changes and increase its reporting frequency during the event and then shut down after the event.

REFERENCES

Flanders, A.F. (1978) Environmental data management system. Spring Convention and Exhibit, Pittsburgh, Pennsylvania, Preprint 3217, Am. Soc. Civ. Engrs, New York.

Flanders, A.F. (1981) *Hydrological Data Transmission.* Operational Hydrology Report no. 14, WMO no. 559, Geneva.

Flanders, A.F. & Zevin, S.F. (1983) Lessons in HOMS building; shelter for water resources engineers. Spring Convention, Philadelphia, Pennsylvania, Preprint, Am. Soc. Civ. Engrs, New York.

NOAA (1983) Geostationary operational environmental satellite/data collection system. *Tech. Memo. NESDIS 2, Washington.*

Zevin, S.F. (1982) Statement on HOMS. At National Water Data Exchange (NAWDEX) Membership Conference and Workshop, Austin, Texas.

APPENDIX 1

HOMS COMPONENT F00.2.XX

SATELLITE DATA COLLECTION PLATFORM

1. Purpose and Objective

The Data Collection Platform Radio Set (DCPRS) allows environmental data to be relayed from a remote site to a Central Distribution Facility (CDF) via satellite. DCPRS's may be established on land or at sea on buoys and operate from solar charged batteries.

2. Description

Three basic DCPRS's are available for operation with the Geostationary Operational Environmental Satellite (GOES) system.

a) Interrogate by the Command & Data Acquisition (CDA) station in Wallops Island, Virginia, USA.

b) Self-timed message transmission initiated by the DCPRS at preselected time intervals.

c) Random transmissions determined by the event and frequency predetermined by software in the associated micro processor.

The data are received at the CDF in Suitland, Maryland for distribution to the user over land line facilities. Some users have downlinks to receive the data directly from the satellite. (See F00.2.YY)

3. Input

Analog or digital data from environmental sensors including but not limited to river, rainfall, temperature and wind measuring systems.

4. Output

Transmission of real time sensor readings to satellite (see F00.2.11).

5. Operational Requirements and Restrictions

Access to the GOES Data Collection System (DCS) is by a memorandum of agreement with the:

National Environmental Satellite and Data Information Service (NESDIS)
National Oceanic & Atmospheric Administration
U.S. Department of Commerce
Washington, D. C.

The GOES DCS is a two satellite system in geostationary orbit positioned over the equator at 75° west and 105° west longitude thereby providing coverage essentially over North and South America and the Atlantic and Pacific Oceans.

6. Form of Presentation

GOES DCS description and user information available in NOAA Technical Memorandum NESDIS 2 (1983).

7. Operational Experience

NOAA has operated the GOES DCS since the mid 1970's and currently has over 4000 DCP's in the system.

8. Originator & Technical Support

a) Originator - NOAA National Weather Service

b) Technical support - NOAA NESDIS

9. Availability

From HOMS National Reference Center for the U.S.A.

10. Conditions on Use

User agreement with NESDIS and certification of the DCPRS. Equipment available for purchase from commercial sources.

First entered: 26 April 1983 *Last updated: 26 April 1983*

APPENDIX 2

HOMS SEQUENCE XXX

SATELLITE DATA COLLECTION/RELAY SYSTEMS

1. Description

F00.2.XX: Satellite Data Collection Platform

DCP radio set allows environmental data to be relayed from a remote site via satellite to a central collection station.

F00.2.11: Data Transmission via Geostationary Satellites

GOES satellite Data Collection System (DCS)

F00.2.YY: Satellite Direct Readout Ground Stations

Enables users of the GOES DCS to receive DCP data directly from the satellite.

2. Comments

This sequence demonstrates the components necessary to collect environmental data from remote sites via the GOES satellite system and the subsequent relay or direct receipt of data by the user. This sequence may also be used in combination with other components or sequences concerning data processing, storage and retrieval. This sequence has a high level of technical complexity.

First entered: 26 April 1983 *Last updated: 26 April 1983*

Hydrological Applications of Remote Sensing and Remote Data Transmission
(Proceedings of the Hamburg Symposium, August 1983). IAHS Publ. no. 145.

The Standard Hydrologic Exchange Format (SHEF) for operational hydrological data

VERNON C. BISSELL, PHILLIP A. PASTERIS
NOAA, National Weather Service, Northwest River Forecast Center, Portland, Oregon, USA 97209

DAVID G. BENNETT
US Army Corps of Engineers, Portland, Oregon, USA 97209

ABSTRACT The Standard Hydrologic Exchange Format (SHEF) is a standardized system of encoding hydrological data transmissions for both manual and automated processing. Features of SHEF include: (a) it is readable by both man and machine, (b) a wide variety of parameters and data types are supported, (c) it has flexible time identification, (d) it uses either SI or English units, and (e) it allows flexible use of spaces and comments within the code text to enhance readability. The SHEF code is now being implemented widely in the USA and has demonstrated a broad base of appeal.

Le "Standard Hydrologic Exchange Format (SHEF)" pour les données hydrométéorologiques opérationnelles
RESUME Le "Standard Hydrologic Exchange Format (SHEF)" est un système standardisé pour mettre en code les données hydrologiques à transmettre pour le traitement manuel ainsi que le traitement automatique. Les traits caractéristiques de SHEF sont les suivants: (a) il est lisible par un homme ainsi que par une machine, (b) il supporte une large variété de paramètres et de types de données, (c) il présente une identification de temps souple, (d) il emploie les unités "SI" (Standard International) ainsi bien que les unités anglaises, et (e) il permet un emploi souple des espaces et des commentaires dans le texte encodé, ce qui augmente son efficacité. Le code SHEF est utilisé largement aux Etats Unis et il a mis en évidence un grand nombre d'utilisateurs.

INTRODUCTION

The virtual explosion in telemetering and automated exchange of operational hydrometeorological data in the last decade has resulted in almost as many ways of exchanging data as there are applications. This can be a constant nuisance to the user who must modify processing software every time a new data source becomes available. The effective sharing of hydrometeorological data in our increasingly automated world requires standards and conventions for the identification and transmission of data. The need for a standard data format which meets the needs unique to day-to-day real time hydrological operations has become painfully evident as data volumes have increased.

The standardization of data formats has two significant results. First, receiving software is minimized when processing data from many different sources. Second, some standardization of receiving data bases will result with internal identification elements (data base "keys") in one-to-one correspondence with external (transmission code) descriptors.

STANDARD HYDROLOGIC EXCHANGE FORMAT (SHEF)

The US National Weather Service (NWS) in cooperation with the US Army Corps of Engineers North Pacific Division has developed the Standard Hydrologic Exchange Format (SHEF). Detailed specification of the code has been documented by the US Department of Commerce (1982), while Bonnin & Cox (1983) have outlined features of processing software and general implementation guidelines for the Central Region of the US National Weather Service. The SHEF code meets requirements to provide both data base and external data identification for a wide range of observational data as well as for processed and forecast products. The SHEF has been adopted by the NWS for national implementation, and will be the first-recommended format for exchange of operational hydrological data between the NWS and other interests.

Functional capabilities

(a) The SHEF code is readable by both man and machine. This is a critical feature because it means the same message can be read visually by a forecaster or reservoir operator, while at the same time be fed into a computer for automatic processing. The SHEF data descriptors attempt to maximize visual recognition for the largest number of commonly used data types.

(b) The SHEF code covers observational, processed, and forecast data in the same descriptive framework, yet these data types can be distinguished from one another.

(c) A wide variety of hydrometeorological parameters are supported in order to provide the SHEF code a broad base of application and appeal. Parameters range from common river and rainfall reports to more exotic items like river ice conditions, fish counts, and lightning strikes.

(d) Routinely used stations are identified using the "station identifier", a string of up to eight alphanumeric characters which (hopefully) provide easy visual recognition. Furthermore, reports from previously unidentified locations ("stranger stations") are accepted, with location defined within one-tenth of one degree latitude and longitude. The "stranger station" concept is most useful in data-sparse areas where heavy localized rainfall is a frequent cause of flooding. It allows, for example, a report from citizen Smith that his garbage can collected 8 inches of water in 12 h. Such special reports can be used to augment standard reporting networks.

(e) Observation times can be expressed either in local time or in

Greenwich Meridian ("Z") time. Also, some processed and forecasted products can be identified by creation times as well as by time of observation or validity. This allows users to know if products are recent or too old to use.

(f) The SHEF code accepts SI units, English units, or a mixture of the two within the same message. Unique units in each of the two systems are specified for each dimensional parameter. This allows one parameter code to describe data in either system of units.

(g) Different data types are distinguished by "parameter code". All parameters in SHEF are fully represented by a seven-character code, although most transmission applications require only two or three explicit characters with the remaining five or four implicit by use of defaults. The full seven-character parameter code PEDTSEP is broken down into six descriptor keys as follows:

- (i) PE = physical element (two characters), examples are river stage, precipitation increment, power generation, discharge;
- (ii) D = duration code (one character), examples are instantaneous, hourly, daily;
- (iii) T = type code (one character), examples are observed, forecasted, and processed;
- (iv) S = source code (one character which further defines the type code, indicating how values were created or transmitted), examples are satellite telemetry, land radio, visual observer;
- (v) E = extremum code (one character), examples are maximum of day, minimum of hour;
- (vi) P = probability code (one character), examples are 5% or 95% probability of exceedance.

(h) Usually, each different parameter code used externally for data transmission will have a separate time series set aside in receiving data bases. There are times, however, when it is necessary to attach additional descriptive information to individual data values within a time series. The SHEF supports this feature which allows, for example, individual data values within a time series to be flagged as estimated or suspect.

(i) The SHEF code is very flexible in use of blanks and comment fields within coded data fields. This allows interpretive information to be added to assist casual or non-technical users in visual reading of the data. Coded data are easily intermingled with text, while a computer can efficiently discriminate coded data from comment text.

Formats

The SHEF code uses several different format structures to allow efficient transfer and readability of different data groupings. Formats used in the first version of SHEF are the ".A", ".B", and ".E" (read as "dot A", etc.) formats.

(a) The ".A" format efficiently handles data from a single station with multiple parameters and/or unevenly spaced times.

(b) The ".B" format efficiently transmits data from a group of stations having the same (or nearly the same) parameters. A single "header" defines the order in which parameters are reported. This way, parameter codes are specified only once for an unlimited number of stations. The order in which parameters are transmitted is completely flexible and is fully specified by the user in the "header" line.

(c) The ".E" format provides efficient transmission of data strings with even time spacing.

Other formats will be added to the SHEF system as use and need develop: one logical extension would be the facility to transmit gridded data, as from radar or satellite data processors. Great caution will be used when any new format type is added.

EXAMPLES

Explanation of .A example

Figure 1 shows an example of the .A format. The line is entirely self-contained and fully identifies the data values.

(a) The .A must fall in columns one and two of the data line. The "dot" in column 1 allows decoding software ease in discrimination between coded data and worded text.

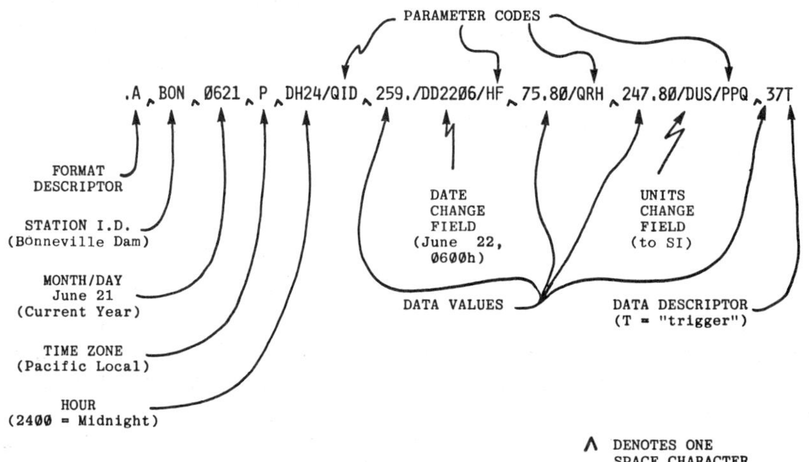

FIG.1 Example of .A format.

(b) The station identifier, BON, is a mandatory field and designates Bonneville Dam on the Columbia River in the northwestern USA.

(c) The Ø621 month-day field is mandatory, showing 21 June. The current year is assumed in this example. Special rules apply to year crossover.

(d) The P shows time zone, indicating that times shown are in Pacific local time. If the time zone designator is left off, Greenwich Meridian ("Z") time is assumed.

(e) The DH24 begins the portion of the message called the "data string". Slash characters (/) delimit individual elements within the data string. The DH24 assigns hour 24 to data values which follow (until hour is respecified).

(f) "QID 259." is called a data element, composed of two parts. The QID specifies project inflow (QI) for a 24-h period (D) of 259 kcfs. The units are defaulted to the English system since no units specifier has yet appeared in the message.

(g) The date change field DD22Ø6 changes the day and hour from midnight on 21 June to Ø6ØØ h on 22 June. Note that the month was not repeated since it did not change. This new time now applies to all subsequent data on the line.

(h) The data elements "HF 75.8Ø" and "QRH 247.8Ø" specify project forebay (HF) at Ø6ØØ h of 75.8Ø feet and mean discharge (QR) for the hour (H) ending at Ø6ØØ h to be 247.8Ø kcfs. Again, English units are implied by default.

(i) The units change field "DUS" causes subsequent data to be taken as SI units.

(j) The data element "PPQ 37T" denotes precipitation increment (PP) of 6 h duration (Q), ending at the currently effective time of Ø6ØØ h, 22 June, of 37 mm. Note that the observation is taken as SI units due to the preceding units change. The T after the 37 is an (optional) data descriptor character. In this case, the T would provide a flag to receiving software to trigger some additional processing upon receipt.

All the above description simply boils down to a message for Bonneville Dam which transmits yesterday's mean daily inflow and this morning's project forebay, hourly discharge, and 6-h precipitation. While at first glance the message may seem complicated, people become quickly accustomed to such codes and can read them very easily with a little practice.

Explanation of .B example

The example of a .B format shown in Fig.2 is a current application of SHEF for the US climatology program described by US Department of Commerce (1983). In automating the processing of data for climate analysis, the US National Weather Service has selected the SHEF code for transmittal of climatological reports. The following discussion refers to Fig.2.

(a) The .B message is composed of three parts. The first is the header line which provides time control and parameter information. Second, the message body is composed of lines containing a station identifier followed by data values in the order specified in the header line. Third, the .B message is terminated by a ".END" message line.

(b) Detailed discussion of the header line follows:

(i) The ".B" must appear in columns 1 and 2. The "dot" in column 1 provides efficient recognition of SHEF-coded data lines when intermingled with text or comment lines.

(ii) The IND designates Indianapolis, Indiana, as the originating station.

(iii) Ø331 gives the date which applies to subsequent data values (31 March of the current year). The month-day field is mandatory.

(iv) The time zone of any times specified is Central local time ("C").

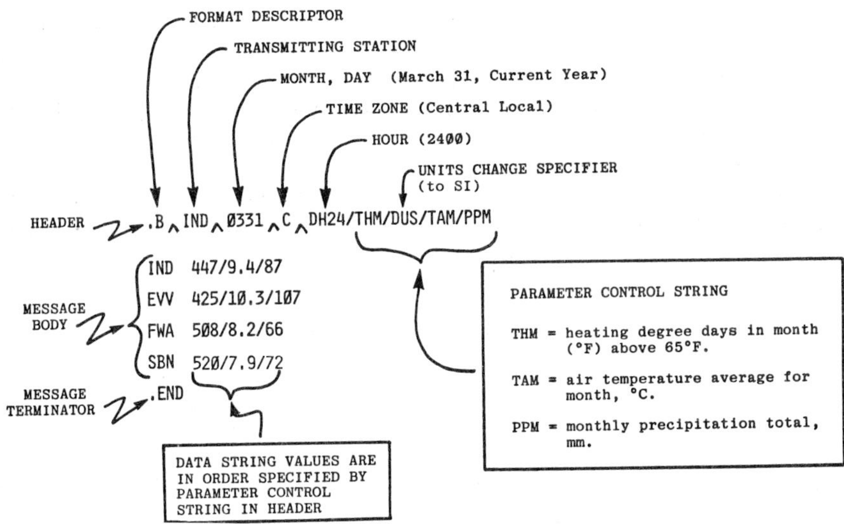

FIG.2 Example of .B format.

(v) "DH24" indicates hour 24 for subsequent data values.

(vi) "THM" begins the parameter control string, and designates accumulated heating degree days ("TH") in the month ("M") ending at the specified month-day-hour. Units will be degrees Fahrenheit since English units are the default.

(vii) "DUS" changes the unit system to SI for following parameters.

(viii) "TAM" is the parameter code indicating air temperature (TA) average for the month (M), and "PPM" is the parameter code for precipitation increment ("PP") for the month ("M").

(c) The message body lines contain the station identifier and data values. The first message body line, for example, shows that during the month of March (from header line), Indianapolis, Indiana, (IND) had 447 Fahrenheit heating degree days, an average temperature of 9.4°C, and 87 mm of precipitation. The English unit of °F was forced by the units default, while the air temperature and precipitation values are SI units since their parameter codes follow the units change specifier in the header line.

(d) The .END line terminates the .B message body. An implied ".END" is forced if any valid SHEF message line beginning with a "dot" is encountered following .B message body lines.

Explanation of .E example

The .E transmits data values with even time spacing. An example is shown in Fig.3. The report gives stage on the North Fork of the Toutle River at Kid Valley, Washington. This station is just west of Mt St Helens, which erupted explosively on 18 May 1980. Continued threat of flooding on the North Fork Toutle by breakout of lakes formed behind eruption debris or by snowmelt from hot gases and pyroclastic material during eruptions makes the station at Kid Valley very critical for effective flood warning for communities downstream. Data are telemetered through the GOES satellite routinely every hour, with data during "emergency" conditions transmitted more frequently. The data are received by the US Geological Survey (USGS) GOES downlink at Tacoma, Washington, and immediately transmitted in SHEF to NWS computers at Portland, Oregon, and Seattle, Washington.

(a) The ".E" format descriptor, "KIDW" station identifier, "Ø622" date of 22 June, and Pacific local time zone "P" follow analogously from the .A and .B examples.

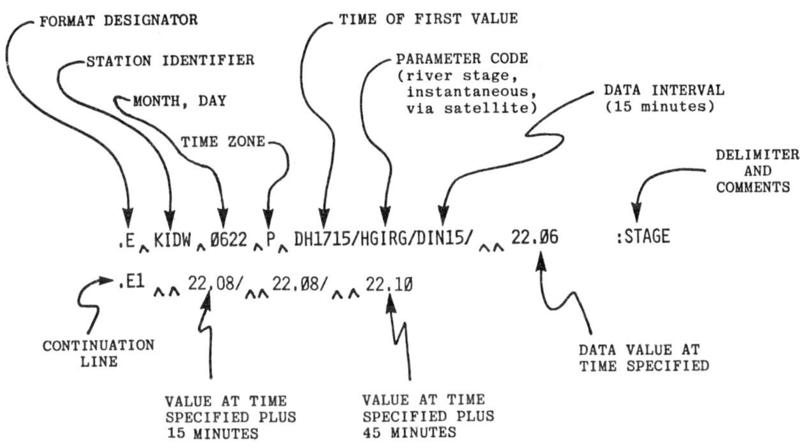

FIG.3 Example of .E format.

(b) "DH1715" indicates that the first data value will be for 1715 h (5.15 p.m.).

(c) "HGIRG" is the parameter code for data which follow. Gauge height is "HG", "I" denotes instantaneous reading, "R" denotes observed data (reading), and "G" denotes satellite data path. If it had not been desired to distinguish satellite telemetry data from other readings at this site, a parameter code of "HG" would have been sufficient since default duration is "I" and default type is "R".

(d) "DIN15" denotes data interval ("DI") is specified in minutes ("N"), and is 15 of them.

(e) The values in the data string are 15-min readings, in English units of feet since no units change specifier has been used. Thus the stage was 22.Ø6 feet at 5.15 p.m., 22.Ø8 feet at 5.30 p.m. and 5.45 p.m., and 22.1Ø at 6.00 p.m.

(f) Comments are permitted on data lines following a colon. The colon terminates line scanning for decoding. Thus the word "STAGE" following the colon in Fig.3 has no effect on automated processing of the data, but simply provides a quick aid to the visual user.

(g) The second line beginning with .E1 is simply a continuation line containing the remainder of the data string. Multiple continuation lines are allowed.

ACKNOWLEDGEMENTS The SHEF data code structure builds to a great extent on a teletype code developed by the US Army Corps of Engineers for use in the Columbia River basin. Furthermore, the thorough detail in the SHEF code specifications would not have been possible without the careful and excellent cooperation of many people both in the National Weather Service and in the US Army Corps of Engineers North Pacific Division.

REFERENCES

Bonnin, G.M. & Cox, R.S. (1983) Explanation of the Standard Hydrologic Exchange Format (SHEF) and its implementation in the Central Region. *US Dept of Commerce, National Weather Service, Kensas City, Missouri, USA, Tech. Memo, CR-67.*

US Department of Commerce (1982) *Standard Hydrologic Exchange Format (SHEF): Version I.* National Weather Service, Northwest River Forecast Center, Portland, Oregon, USA.

US Department of Commerce (1983) The "Climat" program. In: *National Weather Service Operations Manual*, chapter F-21. National Weather Service, Silver Spring, Maryland, USA.

Hydrological Applications of Remote Sensing and Remote Data Transmission
(Proceedings of the Hamburg Symposium, August 1983). IAHS Publ. no. 145.

The use of random adaptive sub-telemetry systems for satellite and meteor-burst applications

J. A. KLEPPE
Scientific Engineering Instruments, Inc., Sparks, Nevada, USA
L. G. YORI
College of Engineering, University of Nevada at Reno, Reno, Nevada, USA

ABSTRACT A system called "POPCORN-METEORNET" has been developed recently for the purpose of providing cost effective, high density data collection with a minimum of duplicative efforts. This system is privately owned and operated but can interface with such government operated systems as GOES and/or SNOTEL. The basic sub-system of the concept is a small data acquisition system connected to a microcomputer and a VHF transmitter. The unit is battery powered and sends burst of data on a random interval basis. A receiver then collects this "POPCORN" data from many sites, and then uses either a standard GOES satellite platform or a meteorburst system to carry the data into a central collecting station. The "POPCORN-METEORNET" system is currently operational in the western United States.

L'emploi de systèmes sous-télémétriques à ajustement aléatoire vis-à-vis des satellites et des météorites
RESUME La présente communication décrit le système "POPCORN-METEORNET" récemment mis au point dans le but de fournir le plus grand nombre de données à un coût restreint, avec un minimum de doubles emplois. Ce système est complètement privé mais on peut le brancher sur des systèmes gouvernementaux tels que GOES ou SNOTEL. La base du système est un petit appareil pour collecter les données branché à un ordinateur miniaturisé et à un transmetteur VHF. L'énergie du système vient de piles, et le système envoie des groupes de données à des moments irréguliers. Un poste récepteur réunit ces groupes de données "POPCORN" venus de plusieurs endroits et, à l'aide soit d'une plate-forme satellite GOES normale soit d'un système basé sur l'explosion de météorites entrant dans l'atmosphère, les renvoie à un poste récepteur contral à Sparks, Nevada, lequel se sert de satellites "naturels", à savoir des météorites, comme moyen de transmission.

INTRODUCTION

There is a continuing need for development of techniques that can be applied to increase the efficiency and cost-effectiveness of gathering measurements from many widely separated geographical locations. For example, the ever growing demands that world population growth places on the earth's finite resources requires that accurate and timely information be made available to resource management specialists. Sound management decisions can be made only if a sufficient amount of accurate data is obtained and used to create models, simulations and projections to aid in the decision-making process. The current state of computer and data processing technology permits the construction of very sophisticated models and other simulation tools. However, the limiting factor in the use of many of today's large-scale system models has been the availability of an adequate data base.

Water resource management, for instance, requires data such as snow depth, precipitation, soil moisture, air temperature, humidity, wind speed and solar flux to be measured at regular intervals at many locations. The accuracy of the resulting model then increases as data from a greater number of measurement sites are obtained. Meteorological, hydrological and geophysical parameters are but a few of the essential measurements required for wide area eco-system modelling.

The need for remote data collection is equally important in many other areas as well. Hazardous waste monitoring, transportation studies, wide area security systems, geophysical event detection, agricultural management, energy systems and resource monitoring are a few of the applications which are impacted by the availability of timely, accurate and sufficiently dense data. In response to this need, many government agencies have spent considerable effort in developing networks for gathering, processing and storing various data. However, due to the diverse nature of the missions of such groups, much duplication of effort has occurred.

The availability of a monolithic single component microcomputer has permitted the development of the "POPCORN" sub-telemetry system which is designed to provide cost-effective high density data with a minimum of duplicative effort. The existence of this low cost, versatile telemetry equipment, has in turn, given credence to the concept of a commercially operated data distribution system which is mission and user independent. This general purpose network is known as "POPCORN-METEORNET".

"POPCORN" SUB-TELEMETRY SYSTEM CONCEPTS

Scientific Engineering Instruments, Inc. (SEI), in cooperation with local governments and the University of Nevada, Reno, conducted a survey of existing technology for wide area monitoring. A subsequent report recommended a remote system based on meteor-burst communications and/or GOES satellite telemetry. It was made quite clear in the SEI report that a significant breakthrough in remote monitoring technology was indeed possible (Kleppe, 1979a).

The basis of this concept uses an innovative solution to the wide area monitoring problem called the Sub-Telemetry System (STS). An integral part of this overall system requires that continuing research efforts be directed into methods for having the data collected, processed, displayed, recorded, and finally disseminated to interested users. The long-term impact and significance that such a network can have on wide-area data gathering and control is evident. Accurate, timely information gathered can be directly supplied to researchers and planning groups for appropriate modelling and/or archiving. A key factor to the success of the STS was the development of the STS "POPCORN" system combined with a "piggyback" concept using existing and/or planned data collection networks such as the SNOTEL or GOES systems (Kleppe, 1979a, 1979b, 1982; Kleppe & Yori, 1982a, 1982b).

The STS system concept is shown in Fig.1. The data collection platform is either a GOES or standard meteor-burst site. The SEI system has a receive-only unit (STS-RX) located adjacent to the DCP. This receiver is so placed that it looks over many other data collection sites. Each of these sites uses a remote transmitter (STS-TX). These remote transmitters are of a "throw away" nature, i.e. small, low power, low cost, etc. The transmitters are programmed to transmit on a random interval, that is, no receiver or special clock is needed to self-time them. This means that one DCP site can cover an entire basin for measurements such as well depth, etc. (see Fig.1).

As an example, assume that the one DCP overlooks some 50 test wells located in a basin of interest. Each well would have a depth or quality sensor (or sensor providing any other parameter of interest). Each well would also have a STS transmitter. It is possible to calculate the data recovery from these 50 sites using the following equation (Preble, 1979; Buckelew, 1980).

$$P_s = 1 - (1 - e^{-2tM/T})^n$$

where

P_s is the probability of successfully receiving a transmission in a given time;

n is the number of transmission tries in the observation time;

t is the length of each transmission in seconds;

T is the time interval between transmissions in seconds; and

M is the number of transmitters operating on the channel of interest.

For example, assume that the transmission from each site consists of a 1-s data burst at a random interval of average value 10 min. In any given hour the probability of data recovery at the DCP (STS-RX) site would be given as

$$n = 6 \text{ transmissions/site/hour}$$

$$t = 1 \text{ second/site}$$

$$T = \frac{3600}{n} = \frac{3600}{6} = 600 \text{ s}$$

$$M = 50 \text{ sites}$$

then

$$P_s = 0.9999$$

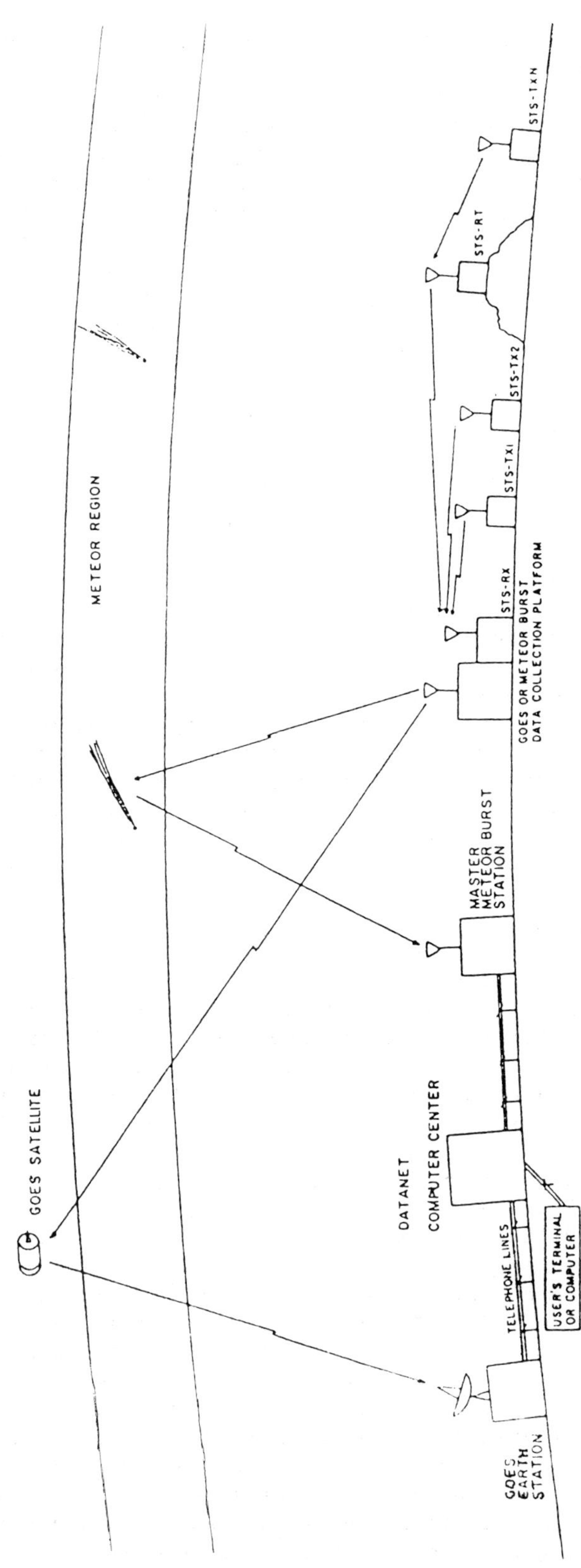

FIG.1 Block diagram of wide area computerized data collection system.

This means that there would be a data recovery (in each hour) of better than 99.9% of the 50 sites reporting. This is quite interesting since all 50 transmitters can operate in a random transit mode and use only a single transmit frequency.

Another innovative concept is the maximum use of the existing meteor-burst frequency. Since the meteor-burst system is already licensed throughout the western United States, the addition of these sub-sites is easily covered under the existing FCC license and, hence, little time is lost applying for and/or obtaining the many sub-site licenses. This concept provides a very effective means for minimizing the need for multiple frequency allocations over a selected wide area of interest.

SUB-TELEMETRY SYSTEM TECHNICAL DESCRIPTION

The SEI "POPCORN" sub-telemetry equipment consists of three major system elements; the STS-510 remote transmitter, the STS-515 repeater unit and the STS-520 receiver.

The standard STS-510 remote transmitter consists of an 8-channel analog data acquisition module and an 8-bit parallel data I/O port connected to a microcomputer, associated control electronics, and a data encoder and transmitter section. The unit is battery powered and is designed to operate for at least 60 days without recharge when set for transmission intervals of average value 10 min. The transmitter, microcomputer and data acquisition circuitry is normally powered down to conserve battery power. Transmit cycle control logic, which contains a random number generator, periodically applies power to the microcomputer which controls the measurement and transmit cycle. The processor scans the analog and digital sensor outputs and stores this data in internal RAM. Measurement data is then formatted, power is applied to the transmitter and parallel digital data is fed to a Universal Asynchronous Receiver/Transmitter (UART) circuit whose serial output is applied to the FM transmitter. The transmitter provides an output of 1.5 W using sub-carrier Frequency Shift Keyed (FSK) modulation for the data. When the transmission is complete, the cycle timing and control logic receives a "seed" which is used as the basis for generating another random number which specifies the length of time before the next transmission.

The STS-515 repeater unit contains a microcomputer controlled transceiver which is capable of receiving a transmission, checking it for errors and then determining if it should be re-transmitted based on user selectable parameters. The repeater unit is typically required only in those situations where direct radio line-of-site is not available between STS-510 transmitters and the STS-520 receiver.

The STS-520 receiver receives, provides error checking, and stores data transmitted from up to 32 "POPCORN" remote transmitters. The receiver is powered-on continuously and typically draws power from the host data collection platform (DCP). Received data are formatted and periodically transferred to the host DCP where they are "piggybacked" onto the host GOES or meteor-burst transmission. For local area data acquisition networks where a central receiving and data processing site is within radio line-of-site of sub-telemetry transmitters and/or repeaters, the STS-520 receiver may be interfaced directly to a computer via a standard RS-232 serial connection, thus eliminating the need for GOES or meteor-burst links. The receiver may also be interfaced with the telephone network through an auto-answer modem, providing that telephone network access is available at a convenient receiver site.

The sub-telemetry receiver and transmitter antennas are selected according to local requirements and can be simple "whip" or any other type of vertically polarized antenna. The STS system can also be programmed to operate on a random adaptive basis. This means the interval between transmissions can be automatically adjusted in response to changes in a particular measurement parameter.

Sub-telemetry transmitters, receivers and repeaters are small, lightweight and are packaged into standard NEMA enclosurers (H = 10", W = 8", D = 4").

THE "POPCORN/METEORNET" SYSTEM, A COMMERCIALLY OPERATED WIDE-AREA DATA COLLECTION NETWORK

The low cost of the SEI Sub-Telemetry system allows existing GOES and SNOTEL meteor-burst users to expand their data collection activities and also creates the potential for a large number of additional users to gather data without making a large investment in telemetry and data processing facilities. However, both SNOTEL and GOES networks are operated by governmental agencies with specific missions in hydrological and environmental areas. Use of these networks, especially the ground receiving stations, is limited mainly to authorized US Soil Conservation Service (SCS) and US Geological Survey (USGS) projects and a few select outside users conducting related water or environmental monitoring activities. Other potential users with monitoring applications not related to water and/or the environment would generally not be encouraged to use these networks. This does not imply a denial of access to the GOES satellite itself or privately owned meteor-burst transmitters, but the use of government owned and operated data collection and distribution facilities *is* restrictive.

It is clear that there is a need for a private network to provide data reception and distribution services, independent of the various government programmes. The SCS SNOTEL system and the USGS GOES receiving stations simply do not have the capacity or the resources to provide services to a large group of diversified users. SEI believes that the availability of its new line of sub-telemetry equipment and "POPCORN/METEORNET" will help fill these needs.

SEI's METEORNET has the immediate objective to fill this void created by the gap between limited government sponsored service and a need enhanced by an innovative advancement in low-cost measurement and telemetry technologies. The METEORNET system is located at the SEI facility in Sparks, Nevada, in the western United States and became operational in June 1983.

SUMMARY AND CONCLUSIONS

There has been a growing need for an inexpensive, reliable and versatile system that can be applied to wide-area data collection problems. Accurate and timely models usually require data densities that cannot be economically provided by expensive GOES or meteor-burst DCP's alone. The STS-"POPCORN" system does offer a cost-effective solution to the problem.

Manpower ceilings and increasing demand for more data are forcing many government agencies and private organizations to investigate automated data collection systems. The SEI "POPCORN/METEORNET" concept will provide a wide-area data collection system by maximizing joint use of both government and/or private facilities. The use of "POPCORN" and "METEORNET" type systems will allow users to turn their attention to sensor development, data analysis and modelling, etc. In this way, user resources can be expended in areas more aligned with their assigned missions and less with technical support functions.

REFERENCES

Buckelew, T.D. (1980) Down to earth satellite data collection. ASCE Conference on Broadening Horizons - Transportation and Development Around the Pacific (Honolulu, Hawaii, July 1980).

Kleppe, J.A. (1979a) Investigation into the use of remote sensing for well level measurements. Report submitted by Scientific Engineering Systems to Nevada Division of Water Resources, June 1979.

Kleppe, J.A. (1979b) The use of meteor-burst communications for well monitoring by the State of Nevada and Washoe County. Report prepared by ERDC for Nevada Division of Water Resources and Washoe County, July 1979.

Kleppe, J.A. (1982) POPCORN - a simple answer to wide area data collection. *EXPOSURES, Oceanography* 9 (6), 4-8. Oregon State University.

Kleppe, J.A. & Yori, L.G. (1982a) Remote data acquisition using random mode sub-telemetry systems. Presented at Western Snow Conference, Reno, Nevada, April 1982.

Kleppe, J.A. & Yori, L.G. (1982b) Random adaptive sub-telemetry systems for satellite and meteor-burst applications. Presented at the 19th International Symp. on Mini and Microcomputers and Their Applications (June 1982).

Preble, D.M. (1979) Demonstration of adaptive random reporting GOES data collection system. *US Army Report SCR-333-78-006, Army Engineers, Waltham, Maryland*, January.

Hydrological Applications of Remote Sensing and Remote Data Transmission
(Proceedings of the Hamburg Symposium, August 1983). IAHS Publ. no. 145.

Real time remote sensing in the Mt St Helens drainage basin

CHARLES E. ORWIG
National Oceanic and Atmospheric Administration, National Weather Service, Northwest River Forecast Center, Room 121, Custom House, 220 NW 8th, Portland, Oregon 97209, USA

ABSTRACT The eruption of Mt St Helens on 18 May 1980, brought new demands for remote sensing in the Mt St Helens area. New stream and precipitation gauges were required to monitor fully a previously data-sparse area. In addition, the installed gauges needed to be highly reliable while operating in a harsh, remote environment. The use of the expanded data network was both to monitor more closely the hydrological response and to provide the required information for a real time forecasting model. Experience with the remote sensing network over the last two years has proven its reliability, and the ability to view or be alerted by the event report as it occurs has been invaluable in real time forecasting ventures. The paper describes the operation of the network which is made up primarily of GOES platforms, meteor-burst SNOTEL stations, and a radio network of event sensing gauges. Some of the advantages and disadvantages of the network operation are discussed.

Détection à distance en temps réel dans le bassin versant du Mont Sainte Hélène

RESUME L'éruption du Mont Sainte Hélène le 18 mai 1980 a bien mis en lumière la nécessité d'un système de détection à distance dans les environs de cette montagne. Cela exigeait de nouvelles stations hydrométriques et pluviométriques afin de garder sous contrôle une région, sur laquelle, auparavant, on avait peu de données; de plus le fonctionnement des appareils de mesure installés dans cet environnement âpre et isolé devait être très fiable. L'emploi d'un réseau d'information plus étendu avait pour objet de contrôler de plus près les conséquences sur le régime hydrologique et aussi de fournir les données désirées pour un modèle de prévision en temps réel. L'expérience des deux dernières années avec le réseau de télédéction a prouvé qu'il était fiable; de plus la possibilité d'observer ou d'être alerté par le signal d'un événement au moment même où il se produit s'est avéré de grande valeur en matière de prévisions en temps réel. Le rapport décrit le fonctionnement du réseau composé en gros de plateformes GOES, de stations SNOTEL (qui utilisent les poussières météoriques pour retransmettre les données), et d'un réseau radio de stations de détection. Une discussion est ouverte sur quelques uns des avantages et inconvénients du fonctionnement du réseau.

INTRODUCTION

Often, the limiting factor in the skill in streamflow forecasting is the data system or availability of data. The more closely one wishes to monitor and forecast in a basin, the better the data system must be. Until fairly recently, the available hydrological equipment did not support detailed, real time forecasting.

The eruption of Mt St Helens radically changed the Cowlitz-Toutle river basins, which are located in the southwest portion of Washington State. The streamflow response to rainfall and snowmelt in the denuded Toutle river basin became more rapid, peaking only 8-9 h after the end of the rainfall excess. In addition, the Cowlitz County warning centre required detailed and timely warning service to keep the residents of the Cowlitz-Toutle river basins advised of important hydrological events. This paper documents the existing hydrological network prior to the eruption of Mt St Helens and presents the experience gained in applying some of the more recent data systems in the Mt St Helens drainage areas.

HYDROMETEOROLOGICAL NETWORK PRIOR TO MT ST HELENS ERUPTION

Prior to the 18 May 1980 eruption, the hydrometeorological network around Mt St Helens consisted of seven river and two precipitation gauges maintained by the US Geological Survey (USGS), which reported in an hourly radio network. The Soil Conservation Service (SCS) had four snow telemetry (SNOTEL) sites located around Mt St Helens which reported via meteor-burst communication to their master station on a twice daily schedule. The National Weather Service (NWS) operated four river gauges and five precipitation gauges. The river gauges were interrogated by telephone at least once per day, and the raingauges were a part of the ADAS system which was automatically called up by telephone at 6-h intervals. Finally, the Pacific Power and Light Company maintained a daily reporting network on the Lewis river which drains the south flanks of Mt St Helens. The existing network was adequate for forecasting and water management purposes prior to eruption, but inadequate for the detailed monitoring and forecasting required after the eruption.

DATA NETWORKS INSTALLED AFTER THE MT ST HELENS ERUPTION

One of the earliest networks installed after the eruption was the USGS system of GOES data collection platforms which replaced their radio network. When complete, this network will have more than 20 streamgauging stations, of which about one third also measure precipitation or other hydrometeorological elements. These GOES platforms broadcast emergency transmissions when a pre-set stage is exceeded as well as their regular transmissions. The frequency of the regular reports, the pre-set stage for emergency reporting, and the frequency of the emergency transmissions can all be assigned individually to each station according to demand. All of these transmissions are routed to a NWS computer in Washington, DC, from a satellite receiving station in Virginia and are routed automatically via the Automated Field Operations and Services system (AFOS) to the individual NWS offices responsible for monitoring and streamflow forecasting.

The SCS also expanded its SNOTEL meteor-burst communication network by installing additional stations to measure snow water equivalent (SWE) data around Mt St Helens. These sites also have an emergency channel reporting feature which will initiate a report when the SWE increases or decreases by a specified value or when the rainfall rate exceeds a certain value. The SNOTEL sites are primarily designed to monitor the snow pack which might be subject to pyroclastic flows. The SWE data is a vital input into the NWS and USGS models for routing of pyroclastic and mud flows down the Toutle river.

The National Weather Service has installed a land-based radio network of 16 river gauges and 15 precipitation gauges around Mt St Helens. This system is of the "event" type, which means that every time a pre-set amount of precipitation (usually 1 mm) or a change in river stage of a predetermined amount (usually 5 mm) is observed, the system transmits this information to the receiving stations. Figure 1 shows the location of all the automated reporting sites in the Mt St Helens drainage.

All river gauging sites include a radio package with antenna, and a liquid level sensor. The liquid level sensor is composed of an input shaft driven by changes in the river level, and a set of gears driving a magnetic pointer which passes over a circular board containing from two to 12 switches. As the magnetic pointer passes over a switch, an event is indicated to the radio package which transmits this information to the receiver. Several types of devices can be used to transmit the river level to the liquid level sensor input shaft; float and line, servomanometer, or gears and chain from another system. Most of the NWS river sites are driven off USGS bubblers or recorders.

The precipitation gauges are of the "tipping bucket" type. The precipitation gauge is mounted in a 30.5 cm diameter metal tube 3 m high. The tube is set in a concrete foundation about 0.7 m deep. The radio package is housed in the bottom of the tube with the antenna attached to the outside of the tube. Some of the sites have the capability to melt and measure snowfall in addition to measuring rainfall. This is an important consideration in the Mt St Helens area since winter snow is a common occurrence in upper portions of the Mt St Helens drainage. Figures 2 and 3 show a typical river and precipitation gauge.

The NWS event network has three repeaters and two receivers. The repeaters are capable of receiving all the signals from field installations and retransmitting these signals to the two receivers. The signal is sent to three locations for display of the data: the NWS Northwest River forecast center (NWRFC), the Cowlitz County warning center and the Seattle Weather Service forecast office (WSFO).

The data display at the County warning center allows the emergency services personnel to have the most current information on the rivers

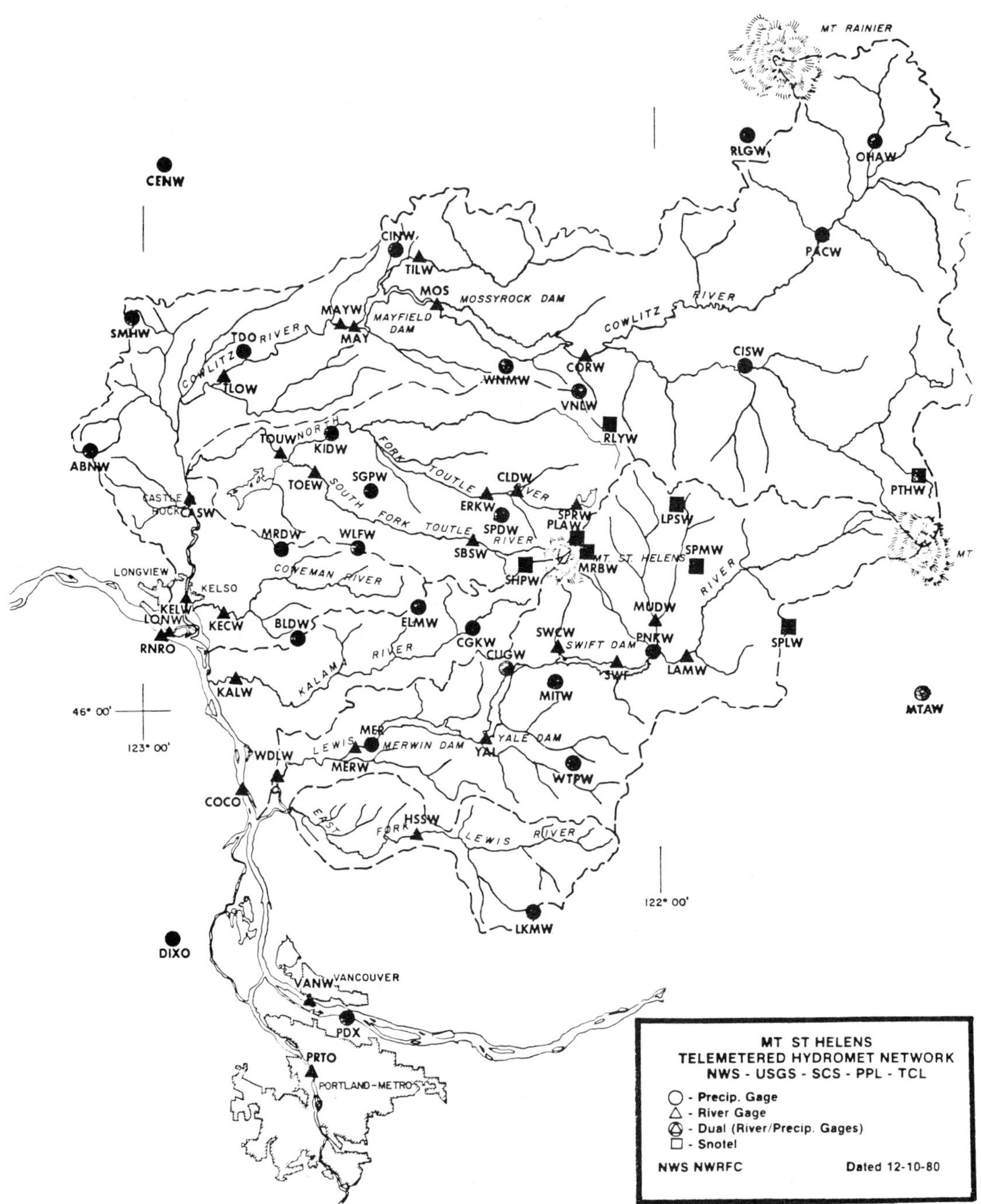

FIG.1 Map of Cowlitz River basin with hydrometeorological network.

and precipitation patterns around Mt St Helens. The data display at the NWRFC is used directly in the SSARR model for preparation of forecasts on the Toutle-Cowlitz river system. The data display at WSFO Seattle is important since that office has the primary task of issuing all warnings to the public. In addition, their office operates 24 h a day, providing close monitoring of the network at all hours (Orwig & Mathison, 1981).

During the last year, a new capability has been added to the NWS system. A criteria checking software package has been installed which monitors the incoming data as they are received. Several kinds

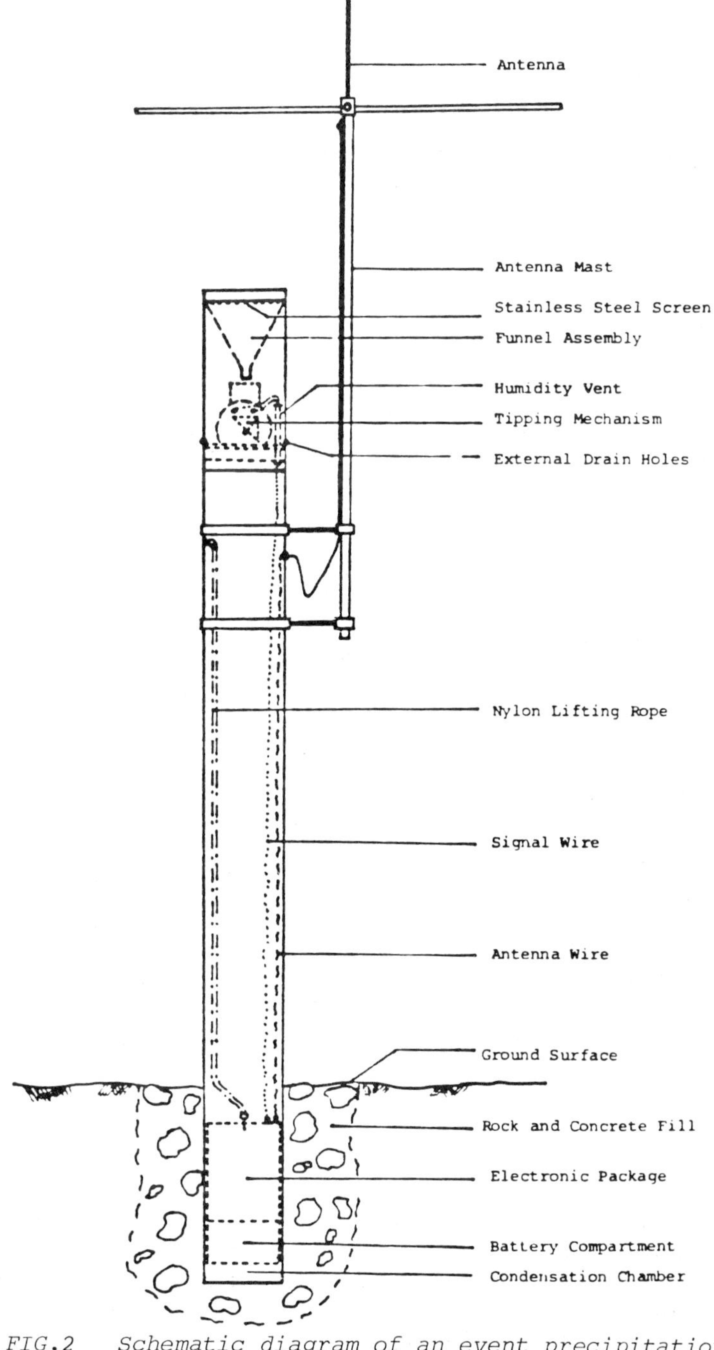

FIG.2 Schematic diagram of an event precipitation gauge.

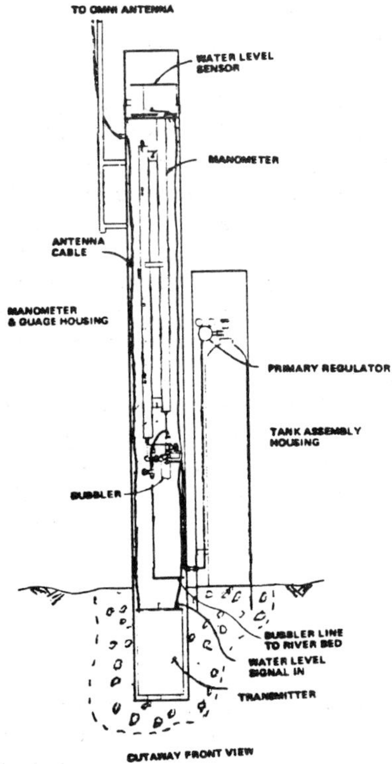

FIG.3 Schematic diagram of an event bubbler type of river gauge.

of criteria can be checked: precipitation rate, a pre-set river level, rate of change at a river site and an increase or decrease in lake elevation of a pre-set value. If any of these criteria are exceeded, an alarm/alert message is sent to the operators console at the appropriate NWS office where lights flash and a warning bell rings. Figure 4 shows a sample message as it appears on the fore-casters console. The event type reporting and the alarm/alert feature has been invaluable in the detailed real-time forecasting in the Mt St Helens area. The ability to see the event as it occurs

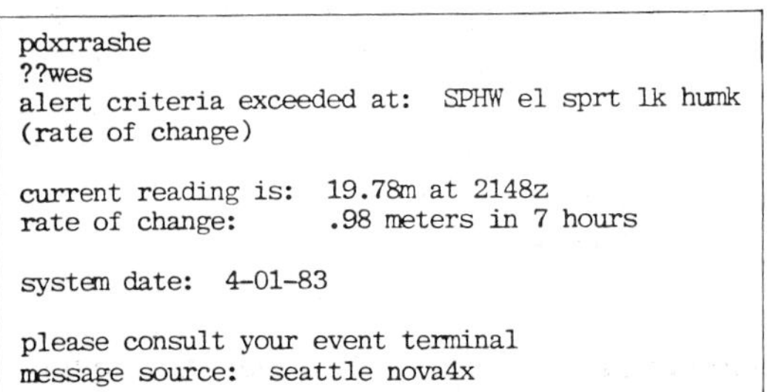
pdxrrashe
??wes
alert criteria exceeded at: SPHW el sprt lk humk
(rate of change)

current reading is: 19.78m at 2148z
rate of change: .98 meters in 7 hours

system date: 4-01-83

please consult your event terminal
message source: seattle nova4x

FIG.4 Example of alarm/alert message from event system.

and to respond immediately with the forecast model has enabled the NWS to issue some outstanding forecasts on rapidly developing flood events.

Recently the USGS and the NWS have shared in placing a trip-switch warning system in the upper reaches of the Cowlitz-Toutle river system. River channels change rapidly in the area because of the high concentration of sediment and it has proven very difficult to operate any type of standard river gauge. Also if a major breakout of a lake or a large mudflow were to occur, there is a very high chance that a conventional gauge would fail. The trip-switch system will send an event report when the switch is covered by water or when the switch is washed away. With a series of these switches placed up the hillsides, we believe that there is a good chance to measure even a catastrophic event. These trip switches serve two purposes. First, true stage readings can be obtained at discrete points where the bubbler-type river gauges measure anomalously high during events with high sediment concentrations. A secondary purpose is to provide some backup in the event of the failure of a bubbler river gauge.

OPERATIONAL ADVANTAGES OF THE VARIOUS HYDROMETEOROLOGICAL NETWORKS

The USGS GOES system for all hydrometeorological elements has proven to be quite reliable. Switching to the emergency channel when a pre-set stage is reached provides valuable data for forecasting a fast developing streamflow rise. The emergency channel reports tracked well during a pyroclastic flow event during March 1982. Since the skill in forecasting the hydrograph from a pyroclastic event is limited, the emergency channel reports every 5 minutes from some of the headwater stations were invaluable in identifying the size of the event. Also, USGS GOES reports from several of the lakes impounded by the Mt St Helens eruption are an important part in the redundant network on the lakes which are in danger of breaking out.

TABLE 1 Example of snow water equivalent available to melt by elevation zones: St Helens SWE as at 18 March 1982

	1000 m to 1250 m:			*1250 m to 1500 m:*			*1500 m to top:*		
	Ac-ft	*in.*	*mm*	*Ac-ft*	*in.*	*mm*	*Ac-ft*	*in.*	*mm*
1. North	*11587*	*40.2*	*1021*	*5522*	*54.5*	*1384*	*10272*	*77.0*	*1956*
2. East	*10979*	*39.6*	*1006*	*9612*	*54.6*	*1387*	*10176*	*79.5*	*2019*
3. South	*12699*	*39.7*	*1008*	*8568*	*55.4*	*1407*	*14015*	*79.6*	*2022*
4. West	-	-	-	*8099*	*54.2*	*1377*	*9739*	*79.4*	*2017*

Ac-ft = Acre-feet; in. = inches.

The SCS SNOTEL meteor-burst network also has performed well since its installation. The snow water equivalent (SWE) data from the network have been utilized to update a weekly report on the SWE available to melt in sectors around the mountains (see Table 1) should an eruption and a resultant pyroclastic flow occur. During the March 1982 pyroclastic flow event, the SWE data from SNOTEL provided the critical information that there was not enough snow to cause a river rise which would overtop the downstream dikes. These data also were instrumental in the issuance of a flash flood alert for the upper reaches of the river, where substantial damage did occur. These data have been very reliable. For further information on the SNOTEL one may refer to Barton & Burke (1977).

Lastly, the NWS event reporting network has provided reliable reporting of all events to date. The outstanding feature is the ability to see the event report as it happens and begin to respond immediately. This contrasts with the more standard approach of waiting until the end of an accumulation period (1, 3, 6 h) before beginning to react to a flood event. On several floods during the last winter, hydrologists have recognized the inception of heavy rain from the event reports and have stayed in the office to initiate the flood forecast. Under the old system, the hydrologist waited for the end of the next reporting period (3, 6 h) before being certain that heavy rain was falling. In some cases, he may have gone home thinking that the storm was not developing as had been forecast. The event system minimizes this problem. Also, the event type reporting makes a criteria checking programme easy to apply. This is particularly important for warning of developing flood problems during the middle of the night when the forecast centre is normally not staffed.

OPERATIONAL DISADVANTAGES OF THE VARIOUS HYDROMETEOROLOGICAL NETWORKS

As has been indicated, the networks have performed quite well overall. However, there are a few shortcomings that should be mentioned. The only shortcomings of the USGS system is that unless it is on emergency channel reporting, you must wait until the end of an accumulation period (1 or 3 h) to see the reports. Further, the expense of installing a GOES network may limit its application in some cases. The SCS SNOTEL system presently reports only twice per day in the standard network. A criteria reporting capability has been implemented around Mt St Helens, but this is not a standard, integrated part of the system at this time.

On the NWS sites there have been a few minor problems. The event system river gauges have had some problems with the bubbler lines being bent or plugged. The precipitation gauges have had minimal problems. The only problem to date was at a high elevation site where freezing rain and snow bent the antenna. Where the radio path proves to be a problem, additional repeaters may have to be added to the system. This disadvantage is balanced by the ease of installation and the relatively low cost of the event system.

CONCLUSIONS

The requirements placed upon the federal agencies to monitor and forecast on streams in the Mt St Helens area have provided a good testing ground for some new remote sensing and data transmission networks. Overall, the networks have proven to be reliable, while supplying real time data from remote sites for monitoring and forecasting purposes. Some new approaches such as the "event reporting" and the "trip switch" reporting have been especially useful and applicable to the special problems in the Mt St Helens area, and should have applications in other parts of the world.

REFERENCES

Orwig, C.E. & Mathison, J.M. (1981) Mount Saint Helens: forecasting considerations in Mount Saint Helens affected rivers. In: *Proc. Conf. on Mt St Helens: Effects on Water Resources* (8 October 1981, Jantzen Beach, Oregon, USA), 272-292. Report no. 41.

Barton, M. & Burke, M. (1977) SNOTEL: an operational data acquisition system using meteor-burst technology. In: *Proc. 45th Western Snow Conference* (18-21 April 1977, Albuquerque, New Mexico, USA), 82-97. CSU, Fort Collins, Colorado, USA.

Hydrological Applications of Remote Sensing and Remote Data Transmission
(Proceedings of the Hamburg Symposium, August 1983). IAHS Publ. no. 145.

Preliminary application of the hydrological data telemetering and flood forecasting system on the Puyang River basin

ZHANG WENYAO, REN KEREN & FENG ZHILING
The General Hydrological Station of Zhejiang, You Sheng Guan Road, Meihuabei, Hangzhou, China

ABSTRACT The Puyang River basin (3430 km^2) is located south of the city of Hangzhou. The telemetering system in which the operating mode is of the "frequency modulation and time division system with response pattern", was put into operation in 1980. The transmission includes gauging station number, water-level and rainfall values and additional information; the transfer rate is 50 baud. All facilities of the system are made in China; the comprehensive use of parity, definite-proportion, positive-negative and repetition codes is undertaken for data error-recognition and correction. More than six million data messages have been received, and data errors are not found because of the error-recognizing and correcting scheme used. Hydrological data received from gauging stations within two minutes can be put directly into the computer for data processing. After eight minutes, the discharge process, peak-stage and peak time on four stations can be printed. Analogue checking computations of 21 storm flood events from 1969 to 1980 gave a mean error of peak-discharge of 6% and a maximum of 15%. Real-time and on-line forecasting of two flood events in 1981 showed an error of peak-discharge of 9.6% and 2.3%, respectively. The results of real-time and on-line forecasting are given.

Application préliminaire de la télémesure des données hydrologiques au système de prévision des crues dans le bassin versant de la Rivière Pu Yang

RESUME Le bassin de la Rivière Pu Yang (3430 km^2) est situé au sud de la ville de Hangzhou. Le mode de fonctionnement du système de télémesure est du type: modulation de fréquence avec un système de répartition dans le temps et avec schéma de la réponse ("frequency modulation and time division system with response pattern"). Il a été mis en service en 1980. L'information transmise comprend le numéro de la station de jaugeage, le niveau de l'eau et les données concernant la pluie avec un certain nombre de données supplémentaires; le taux de transfert des données est de 50 bauds. Toutes les installations du système ont été réalisées en Chine, On a utilisé largement les codes de parité, de proportion définie, positifs et négatifs et de de répétition pour reconnaître et corriger les erreurs des données. On a reçu six millions de messages de données et jusqu'ici on n'a trouvé en définitive aucune erreur grâce au système de détection et de correction des erreurs qui a été utilisé. Les données hydrologiques reçues à partir des stations de jaugeage dans un délai de deux minutes peuvent être introduites directement dans l'ordinateur pour le traitement des données. Après huit minutes, la courbe des débits, le niveau de la pointe de crue et l'heure de son apparition à quatre stations sont imprimés. Des calculs de contrôle d'après le système mentionné plus haut, avec simulation, pour 21 crues de 1969 à 1980 ont montré que l'erreur moyenne sur le débit de pointe était de 6% et que l'erreur maximale était de 15%. Des prévisions en temps réel et des prévisions "on line" pour deux crues de 1981 ont présenté des erreurs respectives de 9.6 et de 2.3% sur le débit de pointe. On donne les résultats de ces deux types de prévision.

GENERAL VIEW OF THE BASIN

The Puyang River, a tributary of the Qietang River, is located at 120°-120.5°E and 29.5°-30.2°N. Its mainstream is 151 km and the catchment area is 3431 km^2. It has five tributaries, including the Dachen River and the Kaihua River. Seventy per cent of the basin is mountainous. The river is characterized by rapid flow in steep riverbeds upstream and impeded flood discharge by narrow and tortuous river courses running over the lowland middle and lower reaches. In addition, the flow downstream is subject to the flood and tidal backwater from the Qietang River.

Eight reservoirs are constructed upstream. The total capacity reaches 371 x 10^6m^3 (in which the flood control capacity is 188 x 10^6m^3). The protection to cultivated land on both sides of the river and to the railway, is fairly dependent on the embankment with a total length of 418 km.

With a typical sub-tropical monsoon climate over the basin, the precipitation which brings about floods is mostly caused by frontal rainfall and typhoon rainfall. Hence, there are two rainy seasons, the plum rainy season and typhoon rainy season. Annual average rainfall ranges from 1400 to 1500 mm, and annual average runoff depth from 700 mm to 900 mm.

DESCRIPTION OF COMMUNICATION FACILITIES

Twenty gauging stations, equipped with simplex VHF transceivers, with the frequency band of 150 MC, have been installed for needs of flood control over the basin. The communication system is semi-duplex and the transmitting power is from 2 to 10 W. The distribution of stations is shown in Fig.1.

COMPOSITION AND FUNCTIONS OF THE TELEMETERING SYSTEM

The telemetering system consists of 11 gauging stations, of which

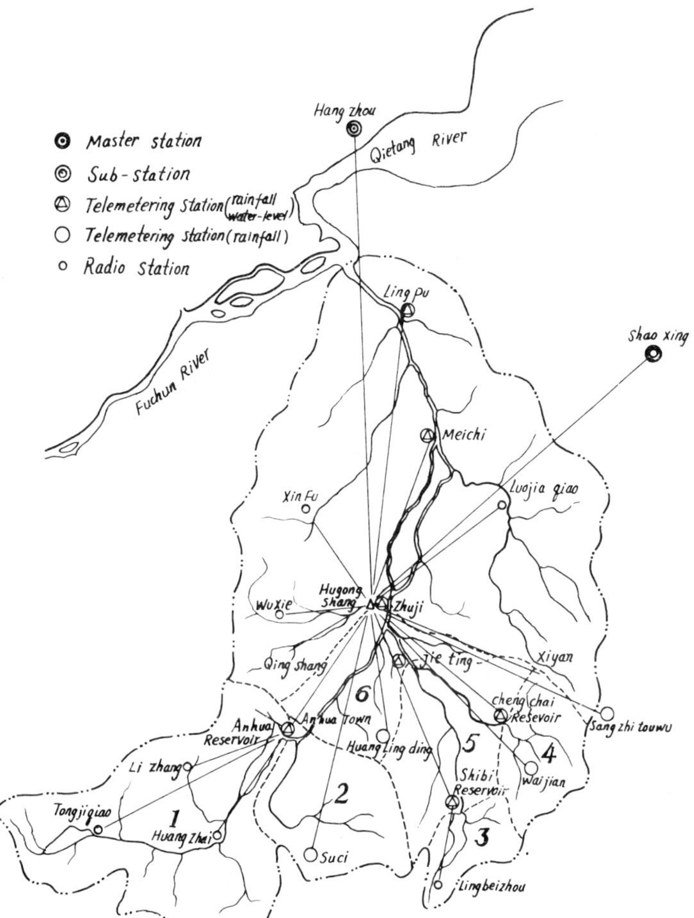

FIG.1 The network of stations.

four measure rainfall and the remainder both rainfall and water-level, of a master station (terminal station) and of a repeater station. A schematic diagram of the system is shown in Fig.2.

The operation mode adopted is of the "frequency modulation and time division system with response pattern". The telemetering radius ranges from 50 to 60 km (when topography is not a problem it can be expanded to more than 100 km). The potential number of gauging stations is 99. The ability for error-recognition and correction to data codes is powerful due to the comprehensive use of parity code, definite-proportion code, positive-negative code and repetition code in the terminal device. To save power, the power to telemetering facilities is switched on or off automatically.

Gauging stations

The gauging stations are equipped with a transceiver (XJZD-10 type), calling set, quartz clock, data set (779A type) and power supply unit (including a.c. regulation charger, nichrome storage battery group with d.c. 25 V and solar cell with power 3-5 W, etc.)

and water-level and rainfall encoder. Among them, the data set with the manual encoding keyboard is the key device.

The power to all equipment is not normally turned on until a predetermined time when the receivers are automatically switched on for 5-6 minutes. At the moment after receiving the calling signal from the master station, the power to the transmitter and other equipment is immediately turned on and the encoded data of rainfall and water-level are sent to the master station. Soon afterwards, the power to all equipment is switched off except for the receiver which returns to its standby state. The block diagram of the telemetering facilities is given in Fig.3.

Repeater station

The repeater station installed on Hugong Mountain, 330 m above sea level, near the seat of Zhuji County consists of a duplex-transceiver, directional antenna and omnidirectional antenna, quartz clock and power supply unit. Of these, the duplex-transceiver plays an

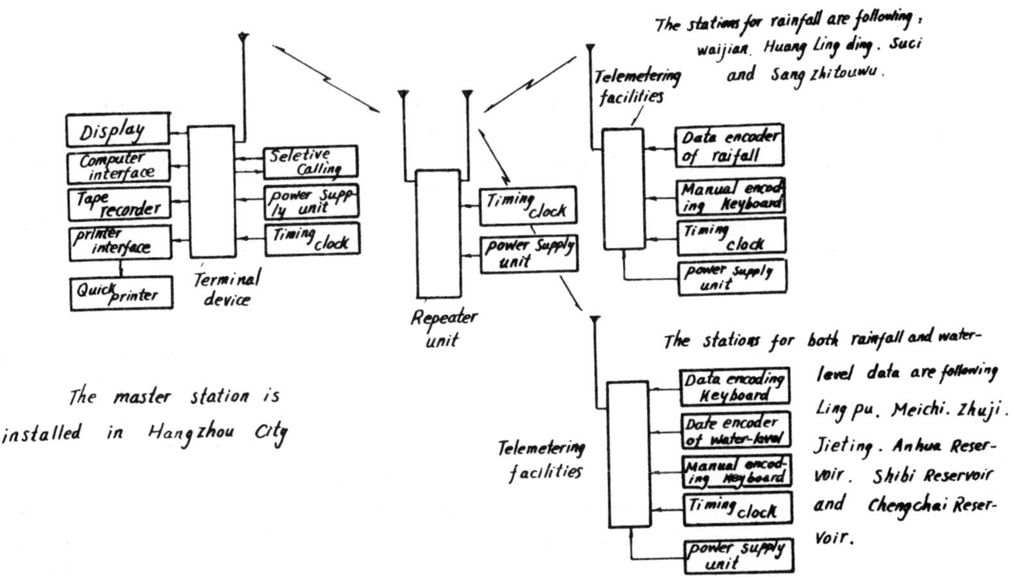

FIG.2 The telemetering system.

important role for signal repeating between the master station and each of the gauging stations. The power at the repeater station is obtained from an a.c. regulator. When the a.c. power supply breaks off under certain conditions, it can be automatically changed to d.c. power supply.

Master station

The master station, as controlling centre of the telemetering system, comprises a two-frequency simplex-transceiver (XJZD-10 type), terminal device (779B type), selective calling set, quartz clock and power supply unit. The terminal device is the key equipment; data from gauging stations can be visibly displayed on the upper part of

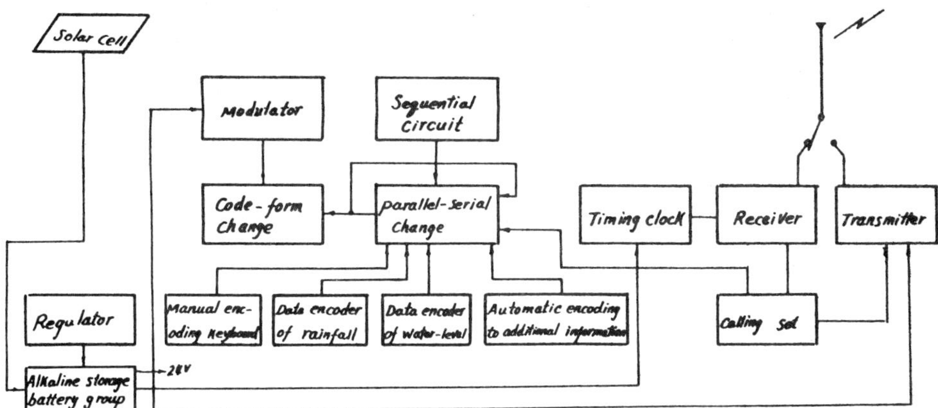

FIG.3 Block diagram of the telemetering facilities at the gauging stations.

the device alternatively and its output is connected to a printer and computer. Response signals from designated gauging stations to the master station's instructive signal are received three times, then error-recognition and correction to the codes are made. If the received data codes are normal, they are printed and output to the computer. The block diagram of equipment is in Fig.4.

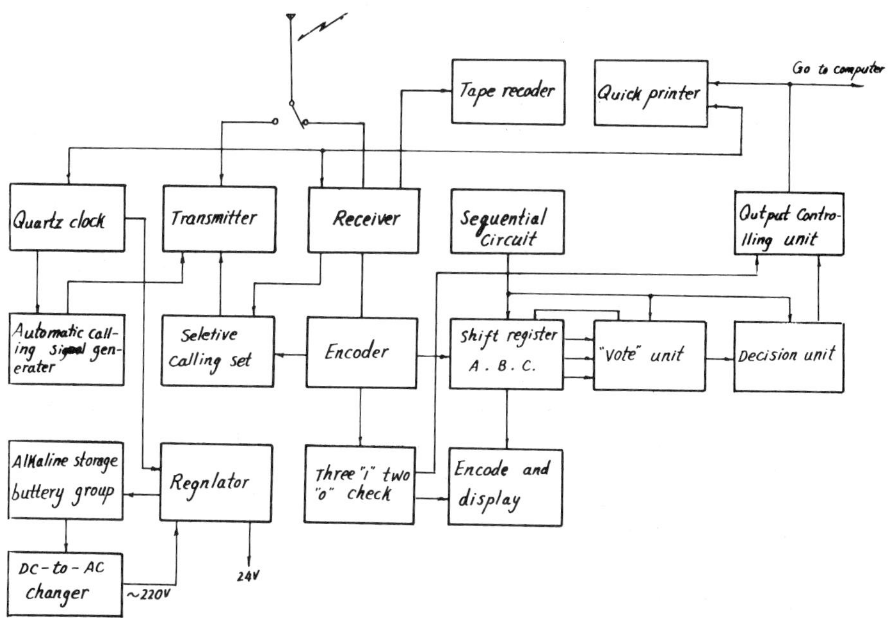

FIG.4 Block diagram of the equipment at the master station.

TRANSMISSION AND RECEPTION OF THE TELEMETERED DATA

Transmitting

(a) *Transmission error:* three "1" two "0" definite-proportion code with character of parity check is used in order to recognize code error in the course of data transmission.

(b) *Data contents and word length:* the data codes consist of the following:

gauging station number	2 digits
measured value of water level	4 digits
measured value of rainfall	3 digits
additional information	1 digit

The ten decimal digits above are equal to 50 codes of binary-coded digit, in other words, the word length is 50 bits. The additional information is used to indicate whether the power supply is normal or not, the water level reaches the warning and danger level or not at the gauging station.

(c) *Data transfer rate:* considering the reliability of data transmission, the rate of 50 baud is used.

(d) *Instructive signal recognizing:* instructive signal transmitted to gauging stations is composed of two voice-frequency, which is recognized by a demodulator.

(e) *Data transmitting:* at a predeterminated time, the power to the receiver at the gauging station is automatically switched on by a clock and is then in a standby state. When the calling signal from the master station is received, the power to the data set and transmitter is put through by signal from the demodulator. In the meantime, the sampling gate is driven to open by a sampling pulse from the data set and, water-level and rainfall codes as well as additional information are input through the gate. All these code signals are controlled by sequential circuit and shift pulse to perform the parallel-serial and code-form change. The shifted code signals control the output signals from two oscilators corresponding to "1" and "0" code respectively to modulate the fundamental wave frequency of the transmitter. Figure 5 shows the typical pulse code formation.

After data codes are sent (fourfold data code sending is made every time), the power to the transmitter is cut down and the receiver returns to its original standby state until the predeterminated time is up when the power to receiver is turned off by the clock.

Data receiving and error-recognition and correction

The performance of error-recognition and correction of data is mainly dependent on the terminal device which is composed of the decoder, sequential circuit, shifter and error-recognizing and correcting circuit.

Comprehensive use of parity code, definite-proportion code and positive-negative code for error-recognition and correction can ensure high reliability of the data input to the computer. Thus, all data errors can be checked out except that all the same double-

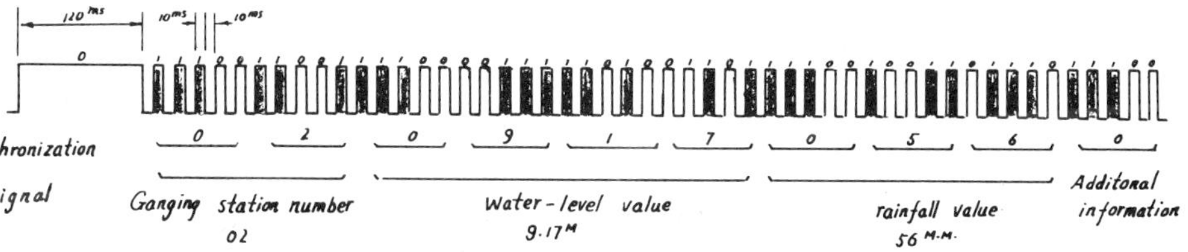

FIG.5 Typical pulse code.

error of data occurs in the same group of code while the three groups of data received from the gauging station are completely alike in the course of data transmission.

Process of data reception

The key on the calling set is pressed in a predeterminated order for about 0.5 s, the transceiver will be turned into transmitting state automatically and will send a specific double voice-frequency signal to gauging station after the frequency modulation. The transceiver returns to its receiving state as soon as the key is released. At this time, fourfold response signals from the gauging station (in which automatic clearing to any one with intense interference is made in the terminal device. If the first three are checked without errors by three "1" two "0" code, the fourth will not be allowed to enter.) are received and are input to the decoder in the terminal device to return to its original form by such processing as buffering amplification, narrow-band filtration, detection, amplitude and width recognition. The group and bit synchronizing pulse as well as "1" and "0" code are taken out from the decoder, respectively, and stored in three registers marked by A, B and C (the data stored in Shifter A are immediately encoded and displayed) under the control of the sequential circuit; they will then start shifting by shifting pulse and are input to "vote" circuit, along three routes, stored in Register A (at this moment, there is a flash on the data display unit). Moreover, the data stored in Register B and Register C return to their original position via a circle and, pushed again by shifting pulse to move the data stored in three registers out to a half adder for half-addition respectively. At the same time, the number of "1" codes which appeared are recorded. If two "1" codes occur, the data code may be mistaken due to the bad condition of the radio link, so there will be no output and complete clearing is made. If the data are correct from another reception, they are printed and entered into the computer.

FLOOD FORECASTING PROGRAMME AND FORECASTING MODEL

The Zhuji gauging station, which is an important control station with a history of 34 years, is located on the central part of the Puyang River basin. Its catchment area is 1760 km^2. The present forecasting programme is based on the rainfall-runoff relationship and the forecasting model is built on such considerations as contributing factors on the physics of runoff-formation and runoff-accumulation.

For the sake of decreasing the influence of an uneven distribution of precipitation, the basin is divided into six units, all of them using the same method of rainfall-runoff relationship, in accordance with the existing state of gauging station and reservoir distribution. The forecasting programme consists of two parts: runoff-formation computation and runoff-accumulation computation. For the first part, the method of deducting the layered evaporation contents in the soil, which is divided into three layers and computed by unit, is based on the concept that runoff formation is governed by the satisfaction of natural storage. As for the second part, the computation is made in accordance with the surface runoff and underground runoff, sloping field and river network, respectively.

A description of the computing method is illustrated below:

First, the net rainfall on each unit of the basin is obtained after deducting loss of evaporation content in soil, according to the precipitation and evaporation effectiveness as well as storage capacity on each unit. Secondly, the relevant unit graph is selected, based on the density of the surface net rainfall, which is characterized by steady seepage coefficient, to obtain the outflow hydrograph, then computing them up to each outlet section continuously by the Muskingum method. Finally, linear superposition in sequence of all unit outflow is made; thus, the forecast of the discharge process on total outlet section of Zhuji station is obtained. In addition, the discharge hydrograph on Jieting station and Anhua Reservoir station upstream can also be printed.

The forecasting model for Puyang River basin based on the programme mentioned above is illustrated in Fig.6.

SOFTWARE PROGRAMME OF COMMUNICATION INTERFACE

For real-time and on-line flood forecasting, hydrological data from the gauging stations, after error-recognition and correction of data in the terminal device, should directly enter into the computer for data processing. Since the former BASIC Interpreter used in the computer (DJS-130 type) could only perform the data input from the keyboard on the teletypewriter and photoelectric tape reader (PTR), augmentation to the BASIC Interpreter had to be made. We successfully designed the communication interface software in April 1981. The augmented Interpreter has a function that data can be put into the computer from communication equipment and satisfy the need of real-time forecasting.

During the operation of forecasting, if not receiving the data from individual gauging stations, the data input or analogue input of inserted data can be made by an operator.

COMPARISON OF FORECAST AND MEASURED FLOOD EVENTS

We selected the data from 21 storm flood events which occurred between 1969 and 1980, for checking the computation of the analogue forecast against the pattern of the real-time forecast, except the data input was by keyboard instead of communication equipment. Results show that the mean error of forecasted peak-discharge at

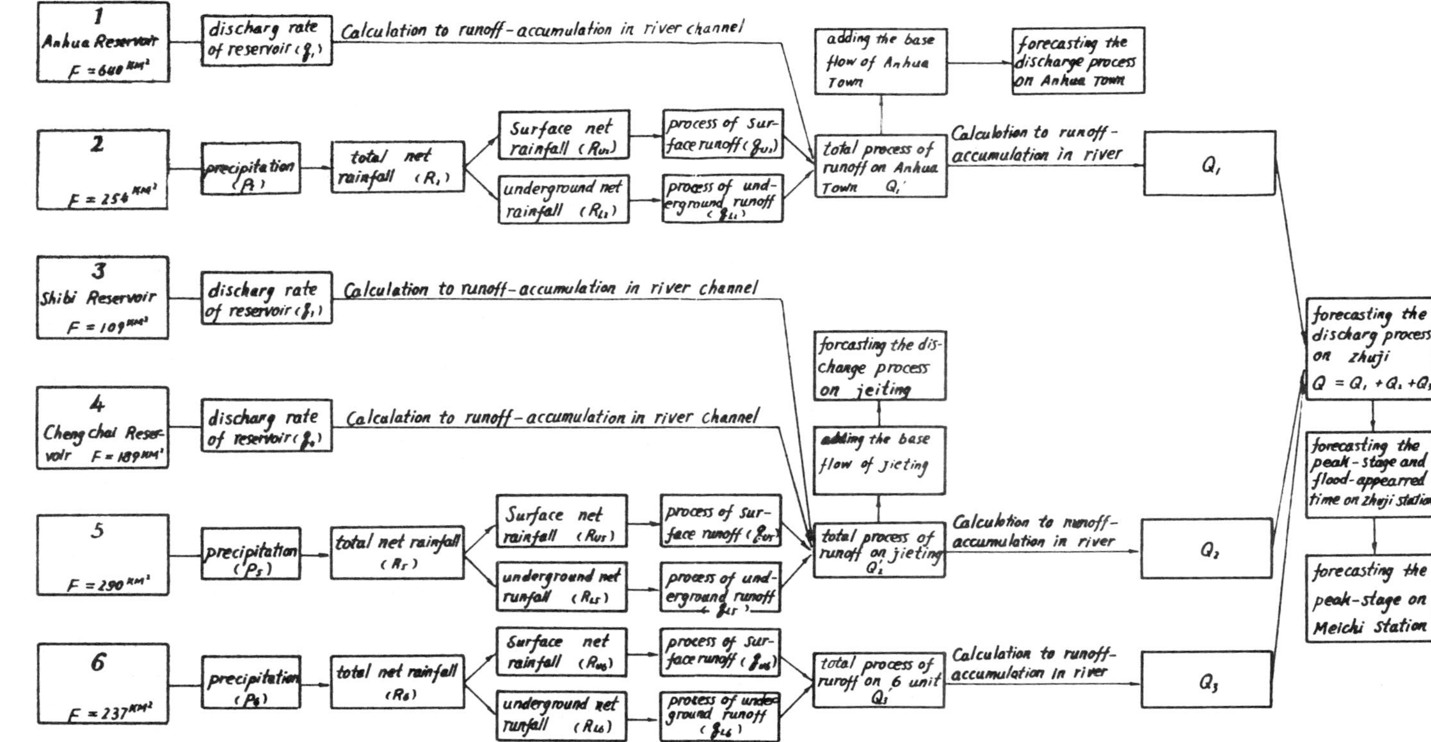

FIG.6 Mathematical model for flood forecasting.

Zhuji station was 6%, the number of storms with an error less than 10% amounted to 16, (76% of the total number), and the maximum error was 15%. As for water-level, after comparison between the forecasted and the measured, the mean error was 0.12 m, the number of storms with an error less than 0.10 m was 11 (52% of the total), less than 0.15 m was 15 (71.4%), less than 0.20 m was 17 (81%), and less than 0.25 m was 19 (90.5%). The maximum error was 0.34 m. In addition, mean time error was 2 h and the maximum was 4 h.

No significant flood events, but two small ones, occurred during 1981/1982. We took these two small storm flood events for real-time and on-line forecast interval by interval. For these two events, the error of peak-discharge at Zhuji station was +9.6% and -2.3%, error of peak-stage was +0.21% and +0.05%, respectively, and the time error was 1 h to 2 h.

CONCLUSIONS

The Hydrological Data Telemetering and Flood Forecasting System is an important component of the automation study for water-irrigation and flood-control management over the Puyang River basin. It was officially admitted into the World Typhoon Operation Experiment in 1980. All facilities used are made in China, of which the data set, timing clock and automatic changeable power supply unit were developed by ourselves. The performance is becoming more reliable after application on site for more than three years. The mean failure rates of data received in 1981 and in 1982 were 9% and 4.7%, respectively.

The comprehensive use of various kinds of codes enables the ability of error-recognition and correction to increase. Up to now, there have been six million messages received, all via the error-recognition and correction, and errors have not been found. In addition, a successful experience is that the periodic telemetering enables us to save power. The reliability of rainfall and water-level encoders is not great, so a much-needed encoder, with high reliability, must be provided.

ACKNOWLEDGEMENTS Those who took part in the study of the system include: Yu Maosong, Zhou Wuyi, Geng Luoshang, Ling Fazhong, Cheng Jikang, Jiang Baoling, Huang Ingjian, Shi Yunlian, Sun Daoun.

Hydrological Applications of Remote Sensing and Remote Data Transmission (Proceedings of the Hamburg Symposium, August 1983). IAHS Publ. no. 145.

Planning for a remote sensing and data transmission network in a hilly region for flood forecasting and warning

JAGENDRA SINGH & S. D. CHOPRA
Central Water Commission, P and D Circle (FF), Room No.814, North Wing, Sewa Bhawan, R.K.Puram, New Delhi 110066, India

ABSTRACT This paper deals with the experience the authors have gained in planning a network of remote sensing and data transmission stations in the Yamuna River basin. The drainage basin in the Himalayas has an area of 12,672 km^2 with an average elevation of above 2000 m. The elevation ranges from 290 m at the outflow site to over 6100 m at the extreme northeast end. There are three sub-basins which are interspersed with numerous north-south and east-west ridges. Map studies have been done to select five remote sensing stations for precipitation and temperature; nine for precipitation, temperature and river stage; and, eight as repeater stations for transmitting the data to the Central Flood Forecasting Station. Experience from and suggestions for map studies; precipitation distribution criteria for selection of sites; approach, physical and radio survey for suitability, are described. The information will be usefully employed in starting similar projects wherever needed.

Planification pour la télédétection et la télétransmission des données d'un réseau en régions montagneuses pour l'annonce et la prévision des crues

RESUME Cette communication présente l'expérience acquise par les auteurs dans le domaine de la planification des réseaux de télédétection et télétransmission des données dans le bassin du Fleuve Yamuna. La superficie de son bassin versant dans l'Himalaya est de 12 672 km^2 avec une altitude moyenne supérieure à 2000 m. L'altitude varie de 290 m à la station de jaugeage considérée jusqu'à plus de 6100 m à l'extrémité nord-est. Il y a trois grands sous-bassins qui sont traversés par trois chaînes de montagnes nord-est et est-ouest. Les études sur cartes ont été effectuées pour choisir cinq sites pour la mesure des précipitations et de la température, et neuf sites pour celles des précipitations, de la température et des débits, et huit stations pour transmettre les données à la Station Centrale en vue de la prévision des crues. On a expliqué en détail les résultats de cette expérience et les recommandations pour les études sur cartes des critères de distribution des précipitations pour le choix des sites, l'étude sur le terrain pour vérifier la valeur de ces sites, l'étude des transmissions radio. Ces renseignements peuvent être utilisés pour entreprendre des projets analogues là où on le désiré.

INTRODUCTION

Economic considerations are responsible for increasing encroachment on flood plains all over the world. It is becoming essential, on the parts of the Governments concerned, to provide certain safety measures to the community residing in such areas. Complete protection from flood ravages by way of structural measures, may however, not be possible, due to the prohibitive cost of flood control structures aiming at absolute safety. As a non-structural measure, advance information regarding the expected flood in any given reach does make the community conscious of the flood threat and permits it to take suitable protective measures for minimizing losses of human lives and property. Moreover, for efficient management of water resources and effective and most useful regulation/operation of reservoirs, prior knowledge of the expected inflow hydrograph into the system is increasingly important.

In most of the situations, heavy precipitation in the head waters of the drainage basin causes devastating flooding downstream in the plain areas. It becomes important to establish an efficient data collection and transmission system in the hilly upper reaches to enable the hydrologist to make use of the precipitation data for timely flood warnings to the concerned authorities and the affected people. Depending upon the requirements of each case, such a system may vary from simple, manually operated radio telephone to sophisticated automatic data-recording and transmitting systems linked with computerized flood forecasting. Such a sophisticated system has been planned on the River Yamuna.

YAMUNA BASIN

Yamuna is one the the rivers originating in the Himalayas, and has a fan shaped catchment in the hilly region (Fig.1). It flows in a southerly direction in a narrow ribbon shaped basin and passes through Delhi. During 1959, Delhi witnessed a critical flood situation, which led to the establishment of a flood forecasting unit. To provide flood warnings to the affected prople around Delhi, water levels observed at Kalanaur situated about 200 km upstream, have since been employed in the gauge to gauge correlation. During recent years, flood forecasting operations have been extended to almost all of the major drainage basins of India. It has been felt that flood forecasting could be much more useful if there was extended warning time based on precipitation in the hills.

TOPOGRAPHY

The fan-shaped Yamuna basin up to Kalanaur (Fig.2) has an area of 12 672 km^2. It is comprised of three major sub-basins - sub-basin A (Yamuna, 2287 km^2), sub-basin B (Tons, 5063 km^2) and sub-basin C (Giri, 2570 km^2). Sub-basin A has an elevation of 457 m, at the confluence of Tons and Yamuna and of 4800 m at its highest point.

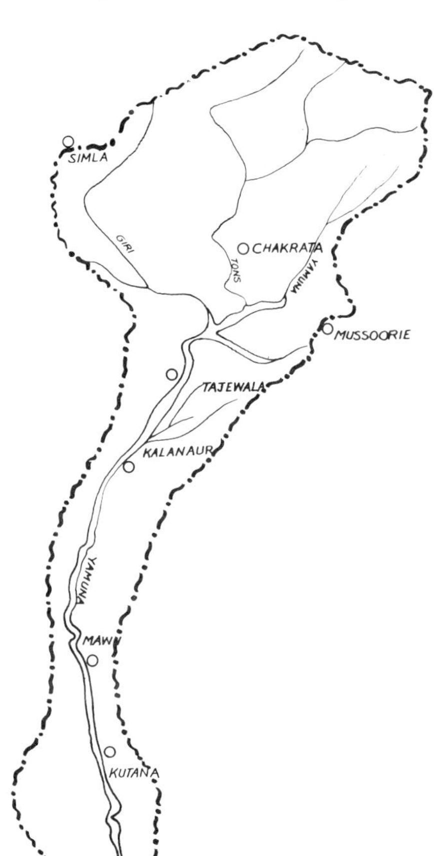

FIG.1 Yamuna basin up to Delhi.

Sub-basin B, presents a difficult terrain, with an area of about 300 km^2 toward the north-east remaining permanently snow bound. It has a minimum elevation of 457 m and maximum of 6100 m. Sub-basin C has elevations ranging from 450 to 3100 m.

CHARACTERISTICS OF RAINFALL AND FLOODS

Average annual rainfall of the basin is 145 cm. Sixty five per cent of this occurs during the south-west monsoon season from June to September. Flood-producing storms are centred usually in the lower half and occur mostly during August and September. As a result, plains downstream are faced with critical flood situations.

The gauge and discharge site at Kalanaur is the base station. It monitors the flood wave travelling downstream. In order to utilize rainfall-runoff models for predicting runoff at Kalanaur, a suitable network of data collection and transmission stations is a pre-requisite. Studies have been conducted for selection of suitable sites for such a system.

SELECTION OF SITES

River stations

On the Yamuna, the two existing sites at Lakhwar and Damta are well within the hilly reach. Keeping in view the size of the sub-basin, it was considered necessary to develop a rainfall-runoff relationship covering the whole sub-basin. For this purpose, a new gauge and discharge station at Bausan was considered necessary. At this point, the river leaves the hilly region.

On the Tons, a dam already existed at Koti for diversion of water for power generation. Keeping in view the availability of its outflow data, a gauge site was selected downstream at some distance. As the drainage area was comparatively large, another existing river station at Tuini was also selected for incorporation in the system.

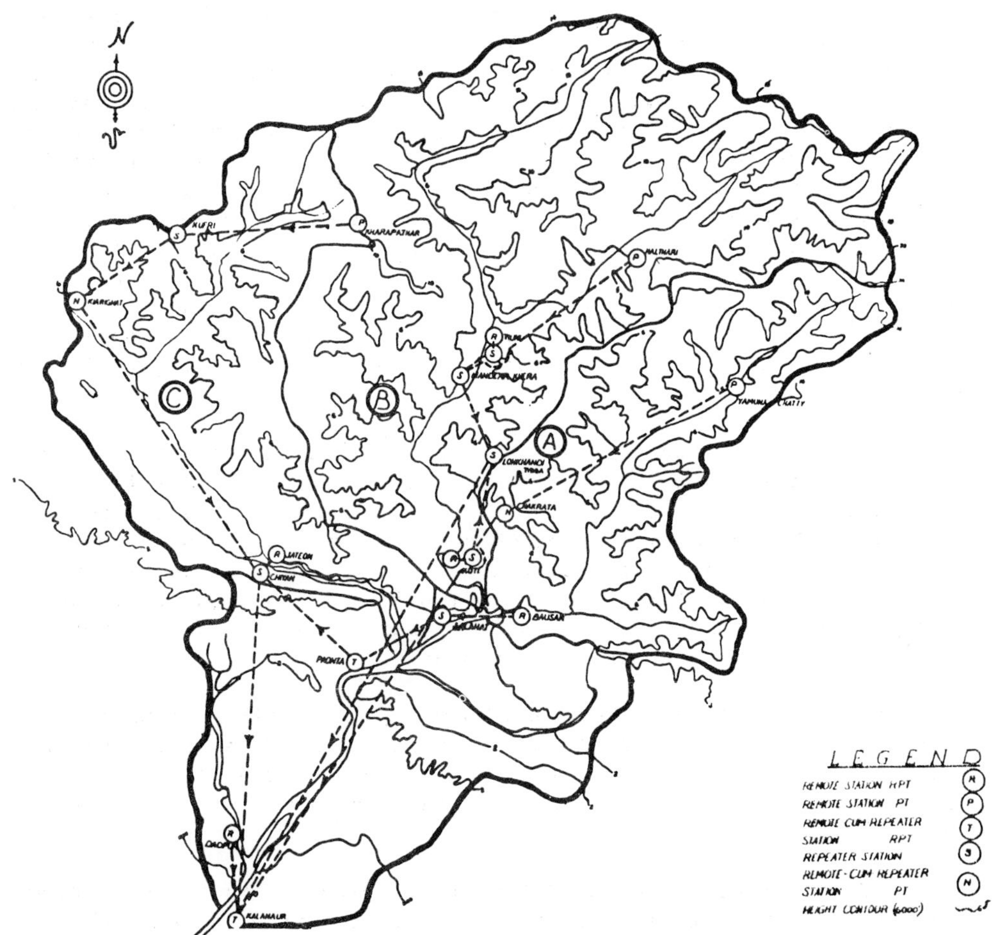

FIG.2 Yamuna basin up to Kalaraur.

On the Giri, the existing Barrage at Jateon adequately covers almost the whole of the sub-basin. With a view to utilizing the discharge data of this site, a gauging station downstream of the barrage is required.

The development of rainfall-runoff models for the three sub-basins is to be followed by the routing of the hydrographs up to Paonta and their combination with the runoff from the intermediate drainage. A water level station at Paonta needs to be established for calibration of the models.

Just upstream of Kalanaur there is a small tributary named Somb, which is prone to flash floods. One station, reporting river level, has been selected at Dadupur on this tributary to develop a flash flood warning procedure for this sub-basin. The existing base station at Kalanaur, completes the network of river stations in the basin.

Precipitation stations

There are a number of precipitation stations, but only a few stations are located at situations suitable for direct line of sight transmission. A number of repeater stations are required to transmit data to the outflow point at Kalanaur from where the data will be relayed to the central station at Delhi through repeaters at Karnal, Mawi and Kutana. Locations of water level recording and transmitting stations as selected above are essentially fixed. There is no alternative except to have repeater stations for relay of their data. Precipitation and temperature gauges have, therefore, been proposed at each of these sites. Regarding the remaining precipitation stations, representative sites are required to be located so that in each sub-basin a minimum number of repeater stations may be needed.

An attempt has been made to select, as far as possible, such locations at which, or near which, self recording raingauges already exist.

Yamuna Self recording raingauge at Chakrata has existed since 1972. The location was changed, however, to a higher elevation so that it could have direct line of sight to Kalanaur. Taking advantage of the higher elevation of Chakrata, a site was chosen near Yamuna Chatty in the upper reaches so that Chakrata could also be used as a repeater station for transmission of its data to Kalanaur. Precipitation stations at Chakrata, Bausan and Yamuna Chatty form the network for the sub-basin of Yamuna.

Tons In addition to Koti and Tuini, precipitation stations installed at the water level recording stations, data from Chakrata, which is on the catchment divide, could also be used for sub-basin B. In the upper reaches the river brings in flow from the Pabar and the upper Tons.

Detailed map studies indicated that to represent both of these upper reaches, a number of repeater stations are required. High peaks were located in this sub-basin on the toposheets and all possible alternatives were checked to find the minimum number of repeaters required. One station was located at Halthari and another at Khara-

Pathar.

Giri In addition to Khara Pathar, Kiarighat is another precipitation station. The network for Giri comprises of Khara Pathar, Kiarighat and Jateon.

The area above Kalanaur and below the three sub-basins is represented by sites at Bausan, Paonta, Koti, Jateon, Dadupur and Kalanaur, which well cover the zone, of comparatively higher rainfall intensity.

The above network had to be selected, keeping in view the limited funds which were available at the time of planning.

Selection of radio-path routes

The following procedure is generally required to be followed while selecting the radio-path routes.

(a) Take a map of suitable scale showing all roads, tracks, height contours, villages and towns.

(b) Mark the existing and proposed water level stations which are essential for incorporation into the system. These stations will also be equipped with precipitation and temperature sensors. Such stations are fixed and cannot be normally shifted to alternate sites. Hence a system has to be devised for the transmission of their data through VHF/UHF mode of transmission.

(c) Locate all hill peaks around each station and select the one which can be used as a repeater station for onward transmission of data towards the central station.

(d) Select possible areas where additional remote stations for precipitation/temperature sensors are to be set up.

(e) Check whether any of the hill peaks already selected for repeater stations can be used as additional precipitation or repeater stations for the remote stations.

(f) After check and counter check of all possible alternatives, the number of repeater stations should be reduced to a minimum. Care should be taken to see that an adequate approach facility i.e. roads/ tracks are available for maintenance operations.

(g) Take a map of scale 1" = 1 mile or 2 cm to 1 km and locate all the stations provisionally selected above.

(h) Connect every hop from remote station to repeater station and from repeater station to another repeater station etc., cutting across various height contours. Measure distance from one end for each elevation for plotting line-of-sight path. Figure 3 indicates data in respect of hop between Halthari (remote station) and Mandlar Khera (repeater station).

(i) The above line-of-sight path between two adjacent stations should be plotted (Fig.4) in K = 4/3 earth profile curve sheet. It may be seen that the plot on K = 4/3 earth curvature sheet covers a small length on the horizontal axis. Such a short distance compared to elevation difference between the two points could be assumed to have insignificant earth-curvature. Such cases may be easily plotted on ordinary graph paper (Fig.5) where the radio path clearances can be easily comprehended. Otherwise, all plottings should be done on K = 4/3 sheets. The electromagnetic wave propagation of the VHF

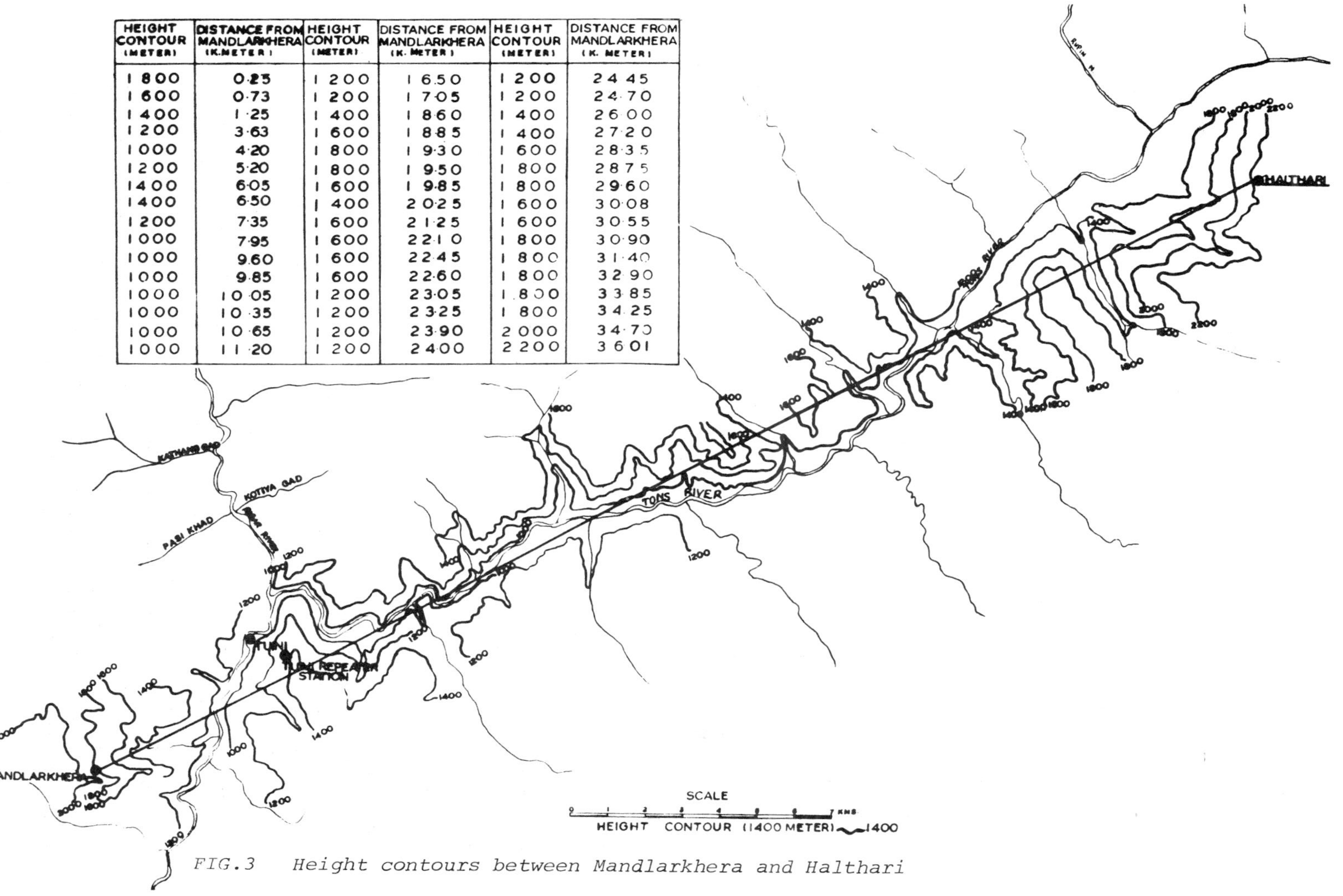

HEIGHT CONTOUR (METER)	DISTANCE FROM MANDLARKHERA (K.METER)	HEIGHT CONTOUR (METER)	DISTANCE FROM MANDLARKHERA (K. METER)	HEIGHT CONTOUR (METER)	DISTANCE FROM MANDLARKHERA (K. METER)
1800	0·25	1200	16·50	1200	24·45
1600	0·73	1200	17·05	1200	24·70
1400	1·25	1400	18·60	1400	26·00
1200	3·63	1600	18·85	1400	27·20
1000	4·20	1800	19·30	1600	28·35
1200	5·20	1800	19·50	1800	28·75
1400	6·05	1600	19·85	1800	29·60
1400	6·50	1400	20·25	1600	30·08
1200	7·35	1600	21·25	1600	30·55
1000	7·95	1600	22·10	1800	30·90
1000	9·60	1600	22·45	1800	31·40
1000	9·85	1600	22·60	1800	32·90
1000	10·05	1200	23·05	1800	33·85
1000	10·35	1200	23·25	1800	34·25
1000	10·65	1200	23·90	2000	34·70
1000	11·20	1200	24·00	2200	36·01

FIG.3 Height contours between Mandlarkhera and Halthari

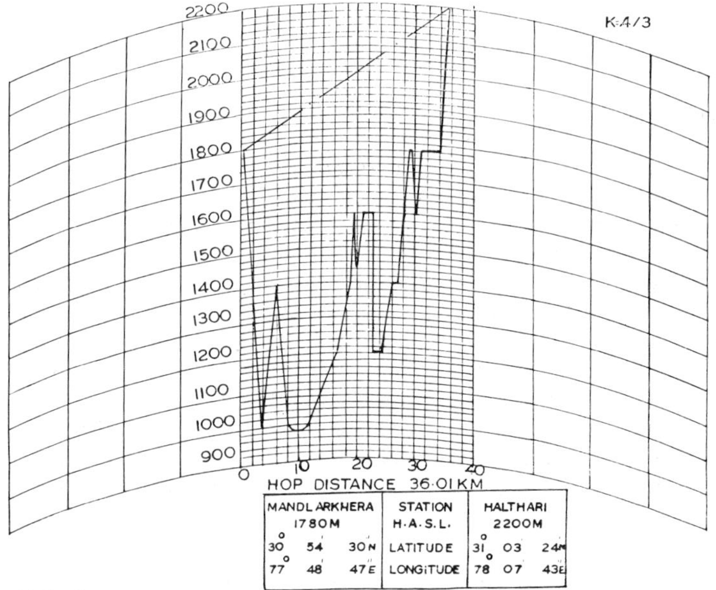

FIG.4

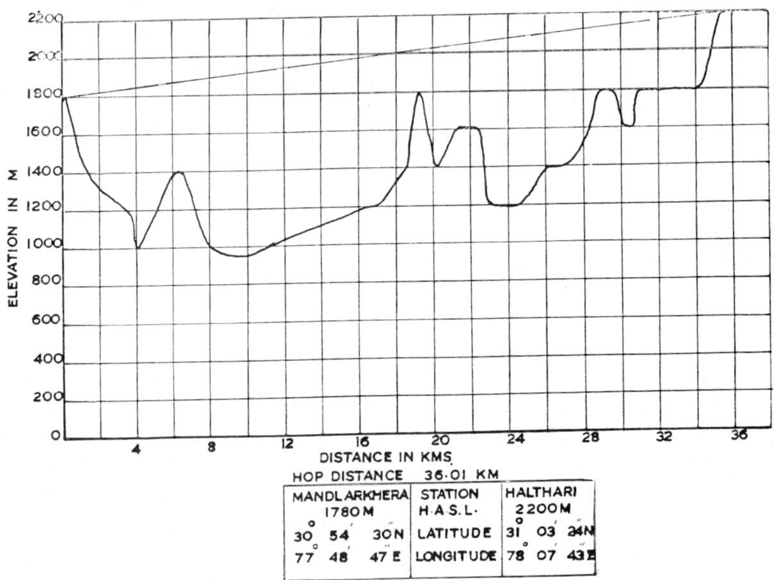

FIG.5

signal beam is normally slightly bent downward due to atmospheric refraction. This amount of bending is defined by an equivalent earth radius factor called K. The factor K, multiplied by the actual earth radius, is the radius of fictitious earth curve, corresponding to which, the wave propagation is a perfect straight line.

After finalizing the tentative locations for the different sites, the tentative tower heights are also fixed by providing some clearance for the freznel zone in addition to clearance for all obstructions.

THE FIELD STUDY

The following observations should be made during the field survey:

(a) a detailed description of each site by coordinates, access roads, physical objects for identification of an exact location recommended for tower erection;

(b) any unusual weather conditions expected in the area;

(c) physical characteristics of the site indicating the amount of levelling required, removal of rocks, trees etc;

(d) the orientation of runway, in the case of a nearby airport;

(e) the height above sea level of the site;

(f) recommended access road from the nearest main road;

(g) nearest location of available electricity supply;

(h) orientation of high tension electric line in the vicinity;

(i) future possibility of building construction along the line-of-sight path;

(j) possibility of use of nearby existing buildings/structures for the station;

(k) details of a nearby high power radar station if any.

Keeping in view all the above points, the location may be shifted suitably by 100 or 200 m, if feasible. This change is, however, subject to verification by radio survey.

In case the site is not feasible, an alternative location can be selected from map studies.

RADIO SURVEY

For radio survey for any hop, a table such as Table 1 may be prepared for facility of reference.

The first seven particulars in Table 1 will be entered from the map and field survey reports. The remaining data pertain to the communication system. The gain of the antenna depends upon the type of antenna used. Directional Yagi antenna having 10 dB gain is commonly used in VHF range. This 10 dB is taken into account in the transmitting and receiving side. The transmitter output is connected to the antenna through cable and connectors and these contribute some loss, which depends upon the type of cable used and its length between transmitter and antenna.

The path loss is the propagation loss in atmosphere between the antennae of transmitting and receiving stations. This path loss is calculated by the formula:

$$\text{Path loss in dB} = 32.44 + 20 \log D + 20 \log F$$

where D = path length in km, and F = frequency of operation in MHz.

The transmitter power is decided as per the overall requirement in the communication. If the hop length is of the order of 50 km, 5-10 W transmitter output may be required for reliable operation. During calculations the transmitter output is mentioned in dBm.

TABLE 1 Radio survey

Name of the site	*Chakrata*		*Yamuna Chatti*
Longitude	*77°53'02"E*		*78°19'56"E*
Latitude	*30°40'10"N*		*30°53'24"N*
Elevation	*2180 m*		*2240 m*
Proposed tower height	*10 m*		*10 m*
Antenna direction with respect to true north	*60.2°*		*119.8°*
Path length		*50 km*	
Gain of the antenna (Yagi)	*10 dB*		*10 dB*
Cable loss	*3.0 dB*		*3.0 dB*
Connector loss	*0.5 dB*		*0.5 dB*
Path loss		*110.46 dB*	
Transmitter power (8 W)		*39.03 dBm*	
Received power		*-58.43 dBm*	
Threshold level of the Tx/Rx		*-110 dBm*	
Fading margin		*51.57 dB*	
Frequency band		*156-176 MHz*	

$$1 \text{ mW} = 10 \log \frac{1}{1} = 10 \times 0 = 0 \text{ dBm}$$

$$1 \text{ W} = 1000 \text{ mW} = 10 \log \frac{1000}{1} = 10 \times 3 = 30 \text{ dBm}$$

$$8 \text{ W} = 8000 \text{ mW} = 10 \log 8000 = 10 \times 3.903 = 39.03 \text{ dBm}$$

When the transmitter at the furthest station is switched on, the signal is transmitted through the antenna. A certain amount of signal reached the receiving antenna. The amount of signal received by this antenna is called the received power.

Received power = transmitted power + antenna gain of transmitting station + antenna gain of receiving station - (cable and connector loss of transmitting and receiving station + path loss)
= 30.03 + 10 + 10 (3 + 0.5 + 3 + 0.5 + 110.46)
= 59.03 - 117.46
= -58.43 dBm

The threshold of the receiver is the carrier level below which the signal-to-noise ratio of the receiver will go below 20 dB. Usually for a VHF transreceiver, the threshold level is -110 dBm.

The fading margin is thus the difference between the threshold and received power. In the case above, Chakrata-Yamuna Chatty hop, it comes to 51.57 dB.

The fading margin of at least 30 dB will ensure uninterrupted communication, even if the signal gets attenuated due to unusual disturbances.

During the radio survey, apart from checking the line of sight, the disturbances from other sources are also checked using a field strength meter. Radio survey is required to be conducted to confirm that there are no problems due to the multiple reflection of the signal beam, absorption of the signal by the dense vegetation, disturbances from RF sources, or disturbances from various radar stations.

For such a survey two teams are required with the equipment listed in Table 2.

TABLE 2

	Team one	*Team two*
VHF Tx/Rx (trans-receiver)	*1*	*1*
Yagi antenna	*1*	*1*
Field strength meter	*1*	-
Magnetic compass	*1*	*1*
Batteries	*1*	*1*
HF set	*1*	*1*

The HF set is used to establish communication, because in some cases due to unexpected obstructions, it is not possible to establish the communication link using the VHF trans-receiver. Thereafter, communication is established using VHF sets. In case communication is not established, all the connectors are checked and the Yagi antenna direction is adjusted to the angle mentioned in the table using magnetic compass. Once the VHF communication is established, team one disconnects the VHF set from the Yagi antenna and the field strength meter is connected. Through the HF set, instructions are given to switch on the transmitter of the VHF set by team two, for at least 2 minutes. Within 2 minutes the field strength received is measured by the field strength meter. By adjusting the antenna direction in both sides the maximum received field strength is noted.

The observed received power is compared with the calculated one mentioned in Table 1 and if the difference between both is within 3-5 dB, it is acceptable. If the difference is more than 5 dB the reason for the additional loss has to be found through a technical check.

The presence of any other disturbance from other nearby sources in our frequency spectrum, is also verified. This can be measured by connecting the field strength meter to the Yagi antenna, and by scanning the frequency spectrum, readings can be taken for different frequencies. Continuous observations may be necessary for about 48 h to find out the consistency in the received power, for reliability of transmission.

Figure 2 shows the final sites selected along with radio paths for the telemetry system for Yamuna catchment to Kalanaur.

ACKNOWLEDGEMENTS We are grateful to Sh. Pritam Singh, Chairman, Central Water Commission for his continued encouragement to document the information and for his permission to submit it for the IAHS symposium. We are also grateful to Sh. V.G.Ghanekar, Project Director, and Mr Saul Cooper, Chief Technical Adviser (WMO/UNDP) to the Project, for valuable suggestions and technical support.

Hydrological Applications of Remote Sensing and Remote Data Transmission
(Proceedings of the Hamburg Symposium, August 1983). IAHS Publ. no. 145.

The development and construction of an adaptable limnological measuring system based on a microprocessor

G. MICHLER & B. WUSCHANSKY
Institut für Geographie der Universität München, Luisenstrasse 37, 8000 Munchen 2, FR Germany

ABSTRACT A system for continuous measurement of hydrometeorological and climatological parameters of Lake Ammer from an off-shore floating platform is described. It consists of a system of measurement (up to 32 sensors), transmission, reception and processing based on a microelectronic system. Sensors are interrogated singly, the analogue signal is digitized to transmit a serial data stream over two wires to the receiver. Decoding of the measurement value, connection to its channel number, separation and calculation in the selected measurement range are done on a microprocessor system. The temperature measurement, power supply and lightning protection systems are also described.

Mise au point et réalisation d'un système adaptable de mesures de niveaux basé sur un microprocesseur
RESUME On décrit un système de mesures continues des paramètres hydrométéorologiques et climatologiques du lac Ammer à partir d'une plateforme flottante "off-shore". Il consiste en un système de mesure (jusqu'à 32 capteurs) de transmission, de réception et de traitement basé sur des dispositifs microélectroniques. Les senseurs sont interrogés un à un, le signal analogique est digitalisé pour transmettre une série de données hydrologique au moyen de deux câbles au récepteur. Le décodage des chiffres des mesures, le rattachement à leur numéro de canal, leur séparation et les calculs dans l'intervalle de mesures choisi sont faits dans un système de microprocesseur. On décrit également la mesure de la température, la fourniture d'énergie et les systèmes de protection contre la foudre.

INTRODUCTION

Series of measurements of various important hydrometeorological and limnological parameters have mainly been carried out as single measurements at relatively infrequent intervals. Apparatus for the continuous registration of measurements on a large scale - with the exception of the supervision of water quality - have been seldom used for solving hydrogeographical and limnological problems.

Industry has offered, however, suitable and complete systems, but at a price that is not feasible for non-applied research.

In order to obtain continuous measurements of the most important hydrometeorological and climatological parameters of Lake Ammer (Ammersee, Upper Bavaria), it was possible in 1980 for the Institute of Geography at Munich University (Department of Prof. Dr F.Wilhelm) to construct, at minimal cost, a floating platform for making measurements; it was provided with a self developed and self constructed system for measurement, transmission, reception and processing electronics, based on a micro-electronic system.

As is well-known, microelectronics enter into almost all technical areas. This paper serves as an introduction to the use of such a system for continuous measurement processing on lakes.

PROGRAMME OF MEASUREMENTS

The finished platform is intended to cover the following research programme: determination of the energy turn-over at the lake surface; the evaporation above the surface of the water; the amount of energy due to the wind; the energy turnover in the lake; the temperature and density stratification in the lake; the substance turn-over in the lake; the determination of the internal seiches; the appreciation of the population dynamics of the plankton in relation to the factors of production; and, the determination of the rate of sedimentation.

Factors suitable for continuous registration are limited to those by which the recording apparatus does not call for constant attention, e.g. air temperature, humidity, wind direction, wind speed and radiation, water temperature and - already limited due to the growth of algae - conductivity, oxygen content, pH, turbidity etc. The platform which can carry 6-8 people, also serves as a base for periodic programmes for the measurement of the productivity (e.g. amount and variety of the plant plankton and the bacterial population) in the lake.

CONSTRUCTION OF THE PLATFORM

The construction of the platform will not be described here, although various important constructional details had to be taken into account. For example, a 4 m long mast carries the atmospheric measurement sensors (radiation, wind, temperature, humidity) and the two navigation lights. In a wooden box lined with sheet steel (connected with the metal parts of the platform, thus forming a Faraday shield) is found the power supply and the electronic system, protected from magnetic waves and lightning. If the navigation light fails, a circuit arrangement brings into operation a second lamp fixed below this. At this circuit a control bit is obtained, which is transmitted with the measurement values and indicates a signal in the receiver on the shore to change the bulb.

SYSTEM DESCRIPTION

Main considerations

The difficult conditions on a lake, e.g. waves, damp conditions, make it necessary to separate the sensing and the registration of the measurements. The transmission of the analogue signals, each by way of separate lines, was not possible both due to the large distance (750 m) and the large number of wires needed (for 32 sensors at least 96 lines). Analogue inputs (signals) with constant current were not suitable due to the high costs (each input channel had to be provided with its own converter) and relatively high amount of current needed.

In addition the chance of a wide application would be limited. A different length of line would make a new calibration necessary and a new cable would have to be provided. Radio transmission would also only be possible at the cost of considerable investment. The simplest solution seemed to be to interrogate the sensors singly, to digitize the analogue signal and to transmit a serial data stream by way of only two electric lines to the receiver. In the case of a cable connection only two wires are necessary and for radio transmission only one particular frequency (and not 32!).

Transmission electronics

The analogue initial signals of the sensors on the platform (analogue voltage, e.g. radiation measurements or current in the case of semiconductor sensors) are restricted to a voltage of between 0 and 10 V by use of suitable analogue circuits and operation amplifiers. The voltage is determined by the power supply from 12 V (a car battery) and the electronic units used in the transmitter. A quartz crystal with a frequency of 3.579545 controls, among other things, the address counter. In this section of the connection, the channel address is consistently raised from 0 to 31, to begin again at 0 after reaching 31. With the use of the addresses gained in this way (in 5 bit binary code), two analogue multiplexers (comparable with a step by step switch) select the appropriate sensor in order to offer the analogue initial signal as a voltage signal to the analogue digital converter (A/D converter), which transforms the analogue signal into a 12 bit parallel signal. It is capable of resolving the voltage signal from 0 to 10 V into 4096 steps. The condition of the single bits is transformed into 880 Hz and 440 Hz frequency pulses, that (as in case of Lake Ammer) can be transmitted by way of a single 2-wire cable, but also by telephone or even with a relatively cheap radio transmitter (e.g. AM or FM-walkie-talkie).

Receiver

In the receiver (located in a log-hut on the shore), there is a quartz crystal that oscillates with exactly the same frequency as the crystal in the transmitter which guarantees an absolutely synchronous encoding (transmitter) and decoding (receiver) of the data signals. The address byte, byte 1, permits the following bytes 2 and 3, that together result in the measurement value (made up of

12 bits) to be clearly connected with an address and to be combined as far as software and hardware are concerned. The decoding of the measurement value, the connection to its channel number, the separation and calculation in the selected measurement range are taken over by a microprocessor system, that - among other things - can select a printer or other peripheral recording apparatus. The microcomputer Intercept, from the firm Intersil, that was used in the system, is based on a 12-bit-C-MOS-microprocessor and is in addition provided with a 2K-memory. The C-MOS-units used in the microcomputer are also - as a result of their low current demand - able to memorize data and programmes by a simple battery buffer without a power supply. Data recording takes place in alphanumerical form by the use of a cheap metal paper printer, that prints all or single measurement values with the respective channel number and with date and time in a particular time sequence or by a change in the measurement values. Output on a floppy disc or a tape cassette is also possible. The microcomputer also processes control signals and gives a printed indication about changes in voltage, overload etc. The measurement interval can be self determined with t = 10 minutes (minimum interval = 10 minutes). Manually induced printing gives the same printed indication, however, at the time desired. By reverse A/D conversion, the selected channel can also be printed in an analogue way on a 6-dot-printer; this is particularly desirable for a first visual interpretation of certain series of measurement values. Figure 1 is a schematic of the operation of the transmitting and receiving functions.

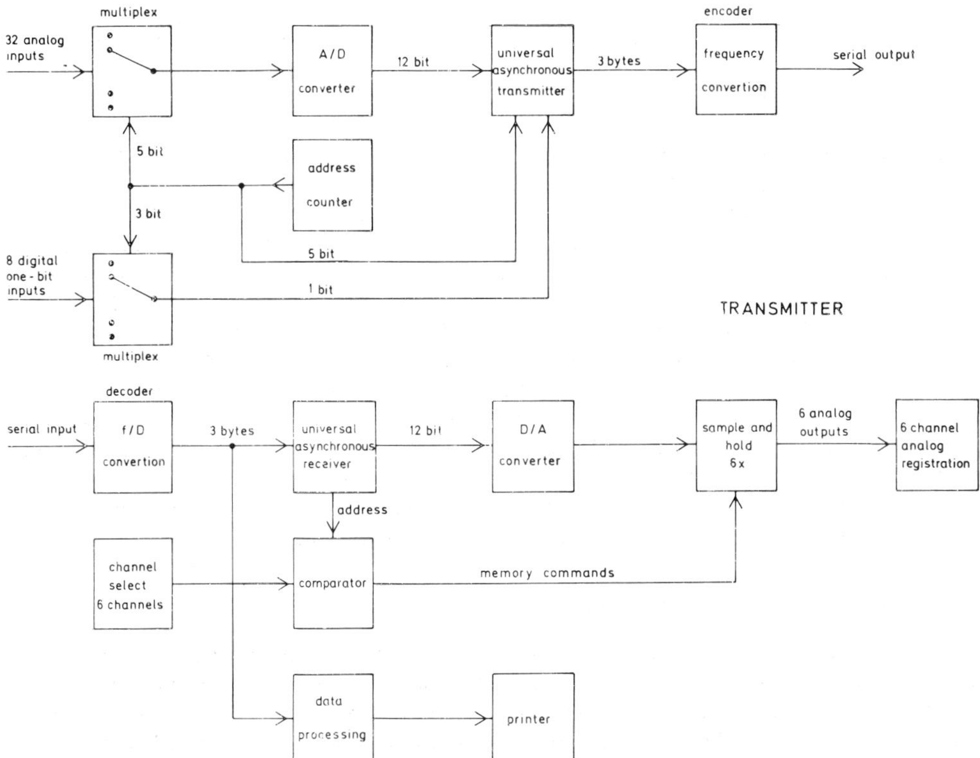

FIG.1 Block diagram of transmitter and receiver system.

Temperature measurements

A large proportion of the measuring capacity of the 32-measurement positions is necessary for the temperature measurements. Sixteen semiconductor sensors AD 590 of the firm Analog Devices ("Two Terminal IC Temperature Transducer", one has the size of a transistor, but contains a complex PTAT = "Proportional To Absolute Temperature"-circuit), that produces a change in current proportional to the change in temperature. The nonlinearity of these sensors can almost be suppressed completely by a simple circuit arrangement (two calibration resistances, a common voltage reference and a common operation amplifier). A single calibration of two temperature values that lie within the desired temperature range, is sufficient for this. Due to the fact that the PTAT sensor delivers a load independent current proportional to the change in temperature, changes in resistance, e.g. in the lines from the sensor to the platform, different lengths of the lines and even inserted resistances of several 100Ω are no importance for the measurement accuracy. The wire packet of 28 lines was protected against mechanical damage with a strengthening wire network. This network acts as a shield and results in a balancing of the electric potential and serves for the fastening of the sensors.

The sensors are sealed by a waterproof coating containing silicone Elastosil 7 and in this way are made suitable for the use in the lake.

Current supply

A 800 m long cheap standard cable (Gummischlauchleitung H 07RNF 4x) with four lines was used to provide current and was relieved of tension below the platform after which it was connected to the battery box. Two lines were used for the serial transmission of data, two were used for the power supply at a load of 56 DC V from the shore to the platform. AC current cannot be used due to the mains hum of 50 Hz induced in the parallel data transmission lines. For safety reasons and due to the difference in potential between the platform and the receiver on the shore the power supply on the shore was installed without being grounded by the use of a voltage converter. The voltage provided was delivered with the help of a load circuit arrangement to a 12 V battery on the platform, that can supply the electronic apparatus and the navigation lights for a couple of hours, if the main power supply fails. Due to the low amount of current needed (750 mA and 12 V), the transmitter (without navigation light) can be run from a car battery for a long time. In this way the use of the measurement arrangement is also possible with the help of radio transmission in remote positions.

Protection against lightning

The protection against lightning and/or against overloads (induced by lightning) is a serious problem for all electronic systems installed in the field. To remove this danger, the two data lines and the two power lines are separated using MSR overload lightning protection lightning ductors from the firm Dehn (Nürnberg).

COSTS AND POTENTIAL OF THE MEASUREMENT SYSTEM

The cost of the materials for the electronic arrangements was about £1800; funds were provided by the Deutsche Forschungsgemeinschaft. For the construction of the platform about £1400 was needed. The high variability of the electronic measurement arrangement allows the use of numerous different measurement value recorders and to be run in different stages of completion. As it is transportable, it also can be used for measurements in other scientific fields.

Hydrological Applications of Remote Sensing and Remote Data Transmission
(Proceedings of the Hamburg Symposium, August 1983). IAHS Publ. no. 145.

Remote biosensing employing fish as real time monitors of water quality events

ERIC L. MORGAN
Upper Cumberland Biological Station, Tennessee Technological University, Cookeville, Tennessee 38505, USA
KENNETH W. EAGLESON
North Carolina Department of Natural Resources, Division of Environmental Management, Biological Monitoring Group, Raleigh, North Carolina 27611, USA

ABSTRACT Recent advances in real time detection of fish physiological responses to water quality fluctuations now complement developments in remote automated physical monitoring. Not only do site-specific measurements allow verification of existing stream conditions, but they also provide sound data bases crucial to protecting and effectively managing the water resource. Employing fish breathing rate biosensing units interfaced to remote central data collection platforms equipped with physical water quality monitors, data gathered from both cold and warm water stations are transmitted at discreet time intervals via earth satellites to a land-based processing center. Viewing fish response data in light of simultaneously monitored water quality information is complementary to management needs.

Télédétection biologique en utilisant des poissons comme moniteurs en temps réel des événements affectant la qualité d'eau

RESUME Les progrès récents dans la télédétection en temps réel des réponses physiologiques des poissons aux fluctuations de la qualité d'eau complètent les dernières mises au point effectuées dans le domaine du contrôle physique automatique de cette qualité. Non seulement les mesures spécifiques à chaque site permettent la vérification des conditions existantes dans les cours d'eau, mais encore ils fournissent les données de base solides nécessaires pour protéger et gérer efficacement les ressources en eau. En utilisant le taux respiratoire des poissons, les unités de télédétection biologique sont reliées à des plates formes de collecte de données équipées avec des dispositifs de contrôle de la qualite physiqué de l'eau. Les données collectées par les stations en eau froide et chaude sont transmises à intervalles de temps discrets par satellite à un centre basé à terre. L'examen des données fournies par les réactions des poissons, à la lumière des informations sur la qualité de l'eau obtenues simultanément est complémentaire aux besoins de la gestion.

INTRODUCTION

Effective methods for rapidly evaluating the biological integrity of multipurpose water resources are becoming increasingly important as water demands intensify. In this regard, water resource managers and those responsible for monitoring water quality have long been restrained in their ability to make confident decisions. This limitation, in large part, has been the result of imposed time and manpower requirements inherent in most biological monitoring efforts. A possible solution to help alleviate these restrictions would be to employ some sort of real time automated biomonitoring device using a surrogate group of aquatic animals to detect undesirable water quality changes. Until recently, such biomonitoring applications have been limited to specific research studies and a few industrial waste water surveillance programmes (Cairns *et al.*, 1973; Cairns *et al.*, 1974; Morgan & Kuhn, 1974; Bonner & Morgan, 1976; Gruber *et al.*, 1980; Dickson *et al.*, 1980; Cairns, 1982).

Presently, monitoring programmes that include real time transmission of key physical parameters from remote stations in a basin generate continuous information on water quality not found in grab sample efforts. Recognizing the advantage of real time monitoring, certain problems may be encountered when attempting to evaluate physical data in light of the anticipated biological quality of the water resource. Of particular concern is how to interpret complex multivariate physical data in a manner that will realistically reflect biological response and ecological resiliency. A problem that is typically confronted is how to account for conditions not measured, i.e. antagonistic, additive, or synergistic effects not detected by physical monitoring alone. Since increasing evidence supports the observation that biological systems serve as good integrators of the environmental factors upon which they depend and to conditions to which they are subjected, and because their responses to various interacting factors in complex ecological systems are difficult, if not impossible, to predict from physical/chemical measures alone, real time biosensing of compensating behavioural and physiological responses has wide appeal.

In designing the work plan for remote biosensing applications, consideration had to be given to the availability of existing water quality stations equipped with remote Central Data Collection Platforms (CDCP). Two distinctly different drainages in the region were identified that had accessible platforms: (a) a warm water Cumberland River site at Carthage, Tennessee, and (b) a headwater stream in the Great Smoky Mountains National Park (GSMNP). Each drainage presented a unique set of challenges, requiring design modifications and system tailoring of the biosensing devices to meet the specific characteristics of the site. The GSMNP cold water site served as a research testing ground between 1976 and 1979 through a cooperative effort with the Park and the University. Work at the Cumberland River site was carried out as an application of remote biosensing in a warm water drainage under contract with the US Corps of Engineers, Nashville District, and in a cooperative agreement with the US Geological Survey.

A similar, but uniquely different, application of remote biosensing was included in the work plan; namely, buoy configurations. The purpose in this aspect of the study was to develop a prototype device and to bench test the complete configuration by transmitting and receiving signals in a simulated test.

METHODS AND MATERIALS

Design requirements for the remote biosensing monitor included several basic considerations. Specifically, the equipment must be designed to be relatively inexpensive and competitive with most field meters presently used in water quality monitoring. As well, the equipment would be required to operate under a wide range of weather conditions, including extremes of summer and winter temperatures, and to be powered for long periods of time by battery. Finally, the unit must be designed to interface with available remote CDCPs currently employed in various monitoring programmes to transmit physical water quality data.

Remote biosensing strategy

Specially designed biosensing chambers constructed from 10 x 30 cm plastic pipe for holding individual test fish were horizontally attached to a rack or retaining device and positioned in-stream where fish were exposed to constant flow-through conditions. The relationship of fish to chamber size was maintained at approximately 1:10, with adequate space for the test subject to accommodate to existing flows. Fish were confined within the tubular chambers by nylon screen caps clipped to alternate ends of the device. Also attached at either end were two stainless steel probes extending vertically the diameter of the chamber. These probes were then connected via co-axial cables to the preamplifier, allowing detection of the opercular voltage differentials.

Using components of the CMOS family of integrated circuits, the differential amplifier produced an eventual gain of up to 10^6 times the initial input voltage. Amplifier gain and the amplitude trigger level were adjustable to compensate for site-specific variations in water quality characteristics, i.e. conductivity and hardness. Thus, fish breath activity was amplified to give a representative analogue voltage of adequate amplitude or converted to a digital pulse prior to processing by the interface microprocessor-controller, in these particular applications by cable to streamside CDCPs.

CDCP and integrated bio/physical monitor

Breath signals generated by fish were received by the CDCP in analogue voltage or digital form, depending on the particular interface used. The data were held for any number of pre-set monitoring intervals by interface counters. Data presented to the CDCP were transmitted to the NOAA GOES satellite on six occasions each day. Broadcast data received by satellite were retransmitted to a data coordinating and processing centre (Fig.1). Depending on site-specific needs, simultaneous transmission of water quality parameters included:

temperature, dissolved oxygen (DO), hydrogen ion concentration (pH), conductance, oxidation-reduction (redox) potential, and stage height. Physical sensors were positioned in-stream alongside the fish-holding chambers.

Site-specific applications

Two remote biosensing stations were established, each designed to meet specific requirements and objectives of the drainage selected. These included: a warm-water site on the Cumberland River near

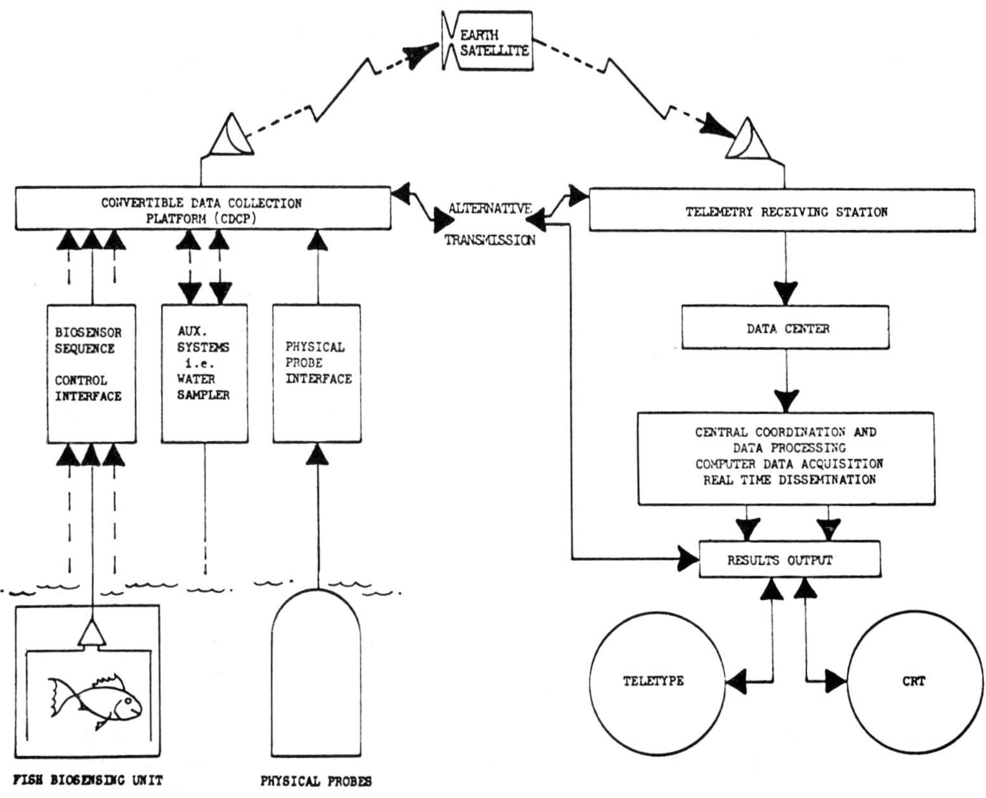

FIG.1 Remote water quality monitoring network.

Carthage, Tennessee, as a contracted project, and several research platforms on cold-water streams in the Great Smoky Mountains National Park.

In the Cades Cove basin of the GSMNP, biosensing devices were established at two separate water quality monitoring stations on Abrams Creek, each equipped with a CDCP. We chose to take this opportunity to test two types of interface units that had been designed for different modes of data input from the biosensor.

Type 1 unit was designed for interfacing to the serial port of the upstream CDCP and provided breathing rate data in analogue voltage ranging from 0 to 5 V. At the downstream site, type II interface was tested in the parallel buffered input mode by submitting digital data to the CDCP. Rainbow trout *(Salmo gairdneri)* were positioned in individual holding chambers and the remote device interfaced to the water quality platform. Sensors from an accompanying Hydrolab unit were positioned in-stream alongside the fish chambers, and during each CDCP update, simultaneous readings for selected physical parameters were taken, i.e. temperature, DO, pH, conductivity, and redox potential.

The Cumberland River CDCP site was located at Carthage, Tennessee, along the south shore under the Cordell Hull bridge. In establishing remote biosensing devices at this station, fish-holding chambers containing sunfish *(Lepomis macrochirus* or *L. cyanellus)* were attached to a rack anchored to the base of the concrete bridge support nearest the south shore. Co-axial cables attached to probes fixed to three fish chambers were connected to amplifiers levied in a waterproof container midway up the 30-m high support structure, which in turn were extended to a substation located on top of the bridge support. Here, using a battery-power source, digital signals received from the amplifiers were boosted by a line-driver device and sent across 154 m of cable to a metal building housing the monitoring equipment on shore. Signals were received by a line receiver and sent through a digital to analogue converter before interfacing to the CDCP. In this configuration, fish respiration rate data would be received at each CDCP update of 73 s. Simultaneous measurements of temperature and stage height were taken for this particular application, an update was programmed for each 15-minute interval, the data stored from each update in the CDCP, and the information in its entirety was transmitted to the satellite every 4 h.

A prototype biosensing buoy device was constructed and tested in the laboratory. Buoy components consisted of holding chambers for fish attached to a waterproof container fabricated from PVC plastic. Inside the buoyant container were housed the electrical components consisting of a d.c. power supply, amplifiers, mini-computer, and transmitter. Fish opercular responses were received by the minicomputer in digital form before conversion to a radio frequency (RF) for transmission. The RF data received from a 30 m range were interfaced to a similar minicomputer which in turn processed the information for storage to magnetic tape and for display on an accompanying terminal. Except for the terminal, the entire system was d.c. powered.

RESULTS AND DISCUSSION

Information obtained through initial tests at the GSMNP sites identified technical pitfalls and provided direction for how best to establish more permanent stations (Morgan *et al.*, 1978).

In meeting the objectives of isolating technical problems in initial applications of remote biosensing at the two CDCP equipped water quality stations in the GSMNP, the analogue (type I) interface was found to be more reliable for further consideration at the Cumberland site. The type I interface between the fish breathing activity monitor and the CDCP met all essential requirements for

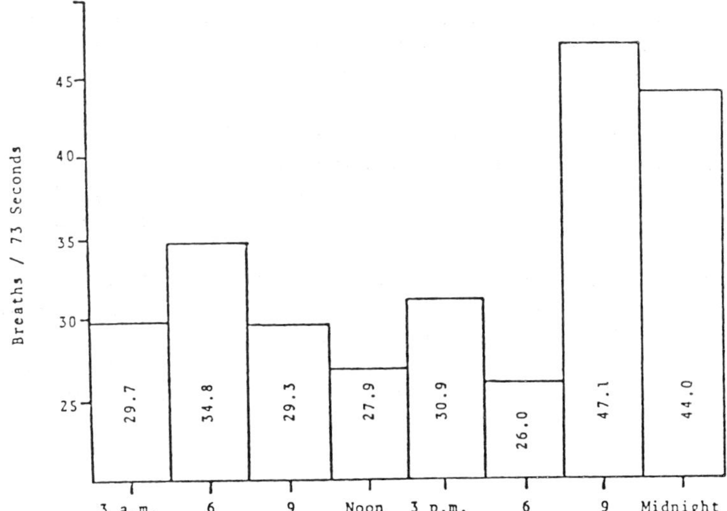

FIG.2 Respiratory rate averages of rainbow trout in the Great Smoky Mountains National Park for the period 8-17 October showing diurnal response curve.

real time biosensing at remote stations. A sample output as received from this unit is included in Fig.2. These data, expressed in volts, represent an electrical analogue of the accumulation of breathing responses counted over a 73-s interval. In this test, the data were transformed into the equivalent number of respiratory events by multiplying the analogue voltage times 12. Evaluating the simultaneously recorded physical water quality data, no unusual events were identified and the increased activity at 0600 h and again in late evening probably represents feeding behaviour responses.

Type II interface modules tested on site at the GSMNP were programmable for sampling fish breathing responses at specified time intervals and were designed to accumulate up to 999 events. Unfortunately, problems were encountered with data input to the parallel buffered port of the CDCP.

After considerable effort and several design modifications in the interface and programme changes in the CDCP microprocessor, a wiring error was found in the factory wired connector cable to the platform. With this problem corrected, digital interface modules for four biosensing devices have been fabricated for each of the two platforms available in the GSMNP. The combined biological-physical water quality monitoring stations will hopefully be employed in an acid rain study presently underway in the Park.

Application of remote biosensing devices at the Cumberland River site was attempted using the type I (analogue) interface. Though the biomonitors had been in position for more than six months, several delays developed that were beyond our control. For example, a trans-river pipeline installation immediately upstream which included blasting, prohibited placement of fish in the holding chambers even though other components of the biomonitoring system were operable. Therefore, the CDCP was removed for servicing and was not available for several more months. One final complication which further limited progress resulted from apparent lightning damage to electrical components of the entire system. These losses, combined with difficulties encountered in retrieving biosensing data via the USGS computer files, restricted the availability of fish respiratory rate data from the Cumberland River site.

In 1982 an alternate streamside monitoring site was established at the Upper Cumberland Biological Station (Tech Aqua) on Center Hill Lake. Beginning June of that year, three free-swimming bluegill were positioned in three different test chambers, i.e. horizontal cylinder, rectangular tank, oval raceway, and their breathing rates were monitored for a one-year period through to June 1983. In doing so, we were able to demonstrate that bluegill could be isolated in streamside test chambers of various designs for up to one year without difficulty and without loss of breathing-rate integrity.

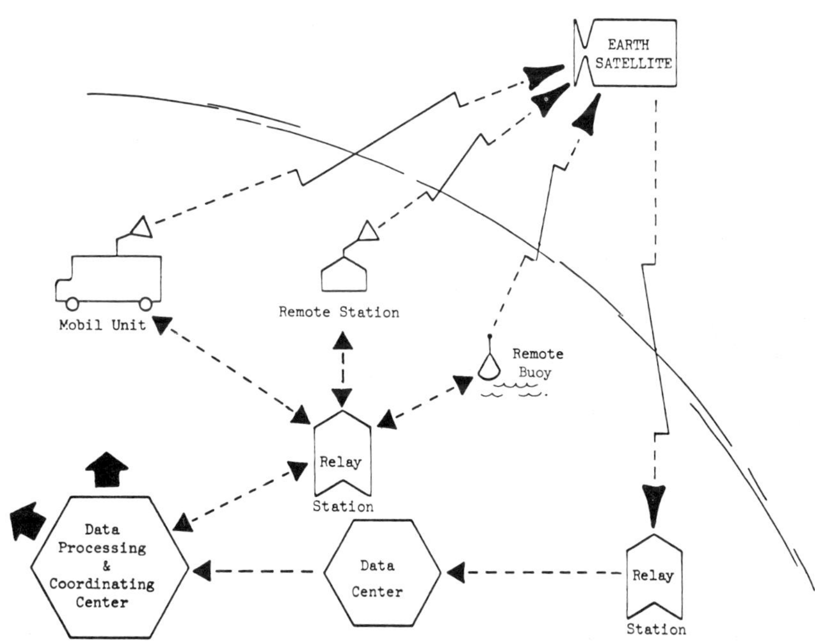

FIG.3 Regional basin monitoring network.

Through applications of remote biosensing devices at the GSMNP and the Cumberland River CDCP sites, coupled with those at the Center Hill Lake station, a set of technical questions have evolved which will require additional attention should portable site-specific units be generally accepted. For example, even though fish have been continuously maintained in various holding chambers for periods up to 12 months with no apparent change in breathing-rate integrity, we still do not know how often individual fish should be replaced following exposure to a variety of in-stream impositions. Other concerns include:

(a) Will fish continue to be responsive to subtle but chronically damaging levels of toxicants following long-term exposure to ambient water quality?

(b) To what extent will test fish serving as biosensors accommodate to sustained exposures of chronic factors?

(c) How useful and supportive will computer-managed stream ecological survey data and predictive models be when viewed in light of real time verifications of compensating behavioural and physiological responses?

(d) May computer managed baseline data sets and predictive water quality models be utilized effectively with remote site-specific data in day-by-day water resources management plans?

(e) Will these strategies provide reasonable protection for management priorities and will they be cost-effective in identifying cause-effect relationships?

Recognizing these concerns and benefiting from the advantages of recent developments in solid state micro-electronics, many of these questions are being answered and new applications of multiple species biosensors are being tested (Morgan *et al.*, 1981).

Bench tests using a buoy configuration were successful. Ongoing studies are underway to test further biosensing techniques in buoy applications (Fig.3). These remote buoys could transmit data from site-specific stations to streamside mobile units, relay stations, or satellite. Combining these advantages with permanent stations, information could be interpreted on a real time basis at a regional processing centre or relayed to specific basin centres and mobile operations.

ACKNOWLEDGEMENTS Support for this project was provided by funds made available to the Tennessee Water Resources Research Center by the following participants: Environmental Sciences Division, Oak Ridge National Laboratory; Office of Natural Resources, US Tennessee Valley Authority; and Office of Water Research and Technology, US Department of the Interior. Additional funding was provided by the US Corps of Engineers, Nashville District, and the Office of Research, Tennessee Technological University.

REFERENCES

Bonner, W.P. & Morgan, E.L. (1976) One-line surveillance of industrial effluents employing chemical physical methods and fish as sensors. *Tech. Report no. B-030TN, Tennessee Wat. Resour. Res. Center, Univ. Tennessee, Knoxville, Tennessee, USA.*

Cairns, J., Jr., Sparks, R.E. & Waller, W.T. (1973) The use of fish as sensors in industrial waste lines to prevent fish kills. *Hydrobiol.* 41 (2), 151-167.

Cairns, J., Jr, Hall, J.W., Morgan, E.L., Sparks, R.E., Waller, W.T., & Westlake, F.G. (1974) The development of an automated biological monitoring system for water quality management. In: *Trace Substances in Environmental Health* (Symp. of the 7th Annual Conference on Trace Substances in Environmental Health, USA), VII, 35-40.

Cairns, J., Jr (1982) *Biological Monitoring in Water Pollution.* Pergamon Press, Oxford, UK.

Dickson, D.L., Gruber, D., King, C. & Lubenski, K. (1980) Biological monitoring to provide an early warning of environmental contaminants. In: *Biological Monitoring for Environmental Effects* (ed. by D.L.Worf), 53-74. D.C. Heath and Company, Lexington, Maryland, USA.

Gruber, D., Cairns, J., Jr, Dickson, K.L., Hendricks, A.C. & Miller, W.R., III (1980) Recent concepts and development of an automated biological monitoring system. *J. Wat. Pollut. Control Fed.* 53 (3), 465-471.

Morgan, E.L., Eagleson, K.W., McCollough, N.D. & Herrmann, R. (1978) Biological water quality monitoring from remote stations and NASA GOES satellite. In: *Proc. of the 4th Joint Conference of Environmental Pollutants,* 886-887. Am. Chem. Soc.

Morgan, E.L., Eagleson, K.W., Herrmann, R. & McCollough, N.D. (1981) New developments in automated biosensing from remote water quality stations and satellite data retrieval for resources management. In: *Water for Survival J. Hydrol.* (L.R. Beard, guest ed.), 51 (4), 339-345.

Morgan, W.S.G. & Kuhn, P.C. (1974) A method to monitor the effects of toxicants upon breathing rates of largemouth bass *(Micropterus salmoides Lacepede).* *Wat. Res.* 8, 767-771.

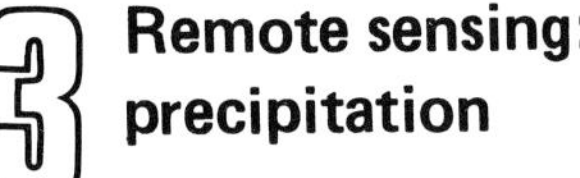

3 Remote sensing: precipitation

Hydrological Applications of Remote Sensing and Remote Data Transmission
(Proceedings of the Hamburg Symposium, August 1983). IAHS Publ. no. 145.

Rainfall evaluation by remote sensing: problems and prospects

ERIC C. BARRETT
Department of Geography, University of Bristol, University Road, Bristol BS8 1SS, UK

ABSTRACT The use of radar for precipitation research has a history of over 30 years, and of satellites more than 15 years. Much progress has been made through studies designed to understand better both the nature and distribution of rainfall, and the related characteristics of the radar and satellite data themselves. However, difficult problems remain to be solved before either type of remote sensing system could be considered fully operational for the quantification of rainfall on other than comparatively local and fragmentary bases. This paper reviews the needs for improved rainfall data, summarizes the practices which have been developed to use radar and satellites for quantitative rainfall evaluation, lists the key problems yet to be solved before such approaches can be very widely implemented, identifies and discusses the present prospects for real advancement of this science, and suggests some policies necessary to bring the operational evaluation of rainfall by remote sensing to fuller fruition.

Evaluation des chutes de pluie par télédétection: problèmes et perspectives

RESUME L'utilisation du radar pour la recherche sur les chutes de pluie date de plus de 30 ans, et, pour ce qui est des satellites, de plus de 15 ans. Beaucoup de progrès ont été effectués par suite d'études consacrées à une meilleure compréhension de la nature et de la distribution des chutes de pluie, en plus de celle des caractéristiques apparentées aux informations fournies par les radars et les satellites. Toutefois, des problèmes difficiles demeurent à résoudre avant qu'un de ces types de télédétection soit considéré pleinement opérationnel pour la quantification des chutes de pluie sur autre chose que des bases relativement locales ou très fragmentaires. Cet article examine les besoins actuels d'amélioration des données sur les chutes de pluie, résume sommairement les méthodes mises au point pour l'utilisation du radar et des satellites pour l'évaluation quantitative des chutes de pluie, énumère les problèmes clefs à résoudre avant que de tels procédés puissent être largement mis en oeuvre, identifie les perspectives actuelles pour une avance réelle de cette science, et suggère des lignes de conduite nécessaires à la pleine réalisation de l'évaluation opérationnelle des chutes de pluie par observées par télédétection.

THE NEED FOR IMPROVED RAINFALL DATA

Water is the most ubiquitous mineral on Earth. For man, rainfall is the most significant single meteorological element. Table 1 summarizes precipitation data needs as identified for a wider angle of specific applications. Unfortunately for us all, rainfall is arguably one of the most variable environmental parameters, and is both difficult and costly to measure by conventional (raingauge) devices. Thus it is scarcely surprising that the rainfall data available today are deficient for most purposes over most of the globe: the requirements listed in Table 1 are largely unmet. The key deficiencies lie in the spatial and temporal densities, the quality, and timeliness of the observations. There is even growing evidence that conventional (raingauge) supplies of data are in decline (Barrett, 1977). This is serious, for the demand for such data is growing fast, in the face of man's growing population and needs for water for life, industry, commerce, transport, recreation and science.

TABLE 1 Precipitation data requirements

Application	*Accuracy*	*Resolution: Horizontal (km)*	*Temporal*
Global climate:			
Global	*10-25%*	*200-500*	*1 week-1 month*
Continent	*10%*	*25*	*1 day*
Global weather	*10%*	*100*	*1 day*
Synoptic weather forecast	*10%*	*100*	*6-12 h*
GCM	*0.5-2 mm day^{-1}*	*100*	*1 day*
Tropical cyclone (over water)	*10-30%*	*2-20*	*0.5-6 h*
Thunderstorm/ flash flood	*10-30%*	*1-10*	*10-30 min*
Mesoscale modelling	*10-25%*	*25-100*	*15-60 min*
Crop-yield modelling	*10-30%*	*50*	*1 day*
Soil-moisture evaluation	*20%*	*20-100*	*1 day*
Water-supply forecast	*10%*	*10*	*1 week*
Hydrological structure design	*50%*	*10*	*1 week*

To meet most of our data needs over the land surfaces of the Earth would call for very dense, even networks of continuously-recording raingauges, spaced at 10 km or less. Such densities are found only in specially-instrumented test site localities. They are impractical elsewhere on grounds of cost alone. Even in an advanced western nation such as the UK, which has an unusually dense raingauge network, the average spacing of continuous recorders is only about 70 km. Surface or satellite-based remote sensing affords virtually the only hope there is of making significant improvements in the provision of precipitation data under present-day circumstances.

PRACTICES AND PROBLEMS IN REMOTE SENSING OF RAINFALL

Remote sensing has been defined as "the science of observation from a distance". It is said to be "passive" or "active" respectively depending upon whether it exploits natural emanations from the target, or artificial emanations, specially generated and transmitted by a man-made device. Signal observation and recording may be ground based, or effected at some height above the Earth by airborne or spaceborne systems. Precipitation can be monitored either from the ground or from aloft. Up to now the commonest approaches have involved ground-based active microwave (radar) systems, and spaceborne passive visible, infrared, or microwave (radiometer) systems. It is these we will review in greater detail, concentrating upon present practices, and currently-identified problems.

Radar monitoring of rainfall

Many types of radar systems have been developed for rainfall research and monitoring operations since radar was first applied to this area in the mid-1940s. A substantial literature exists, amongst which the text by Battan (1973) has become a classic.

A basic distinction separates the so-called "coherent" (or Doppler) from the "noncoherent" radars. The former exploit very stable transmitter frequencies so that the shift in microwave echoes from moving targets can be measured very precisely. Unfortunately the range of Doppler radars is restricted by signal ambiguities where high pulse repetition frequencies are used. Further, sophisticated equipment and procedures are necessary if two or three-dimensional patterns are sought after: Dopplers measure only the line-of-sight velocity components of their targets. The use of this class of radars is therefore generally restricted to meteorological research.

Non-coherent radars, the types widely used for rainfall monitoring operations, lack stable transmitter frequency, but are relatively cheap and simple to deploy for the mapping of rainfall echo patterns. Their chief uses include the following (see Browning, 1978):

(a) The qualitative determination of the dynamical structure of clouds and precipitation structures, e.g. assessment of echo shape, and patterns of precipitation associated with different weather systems, such as severe storms and mid-latitude depressions.

(b) Short-period forecasting of rainfall, e.g. involving simple extrapolation, or the expected development and/or decay of rain systems, taking account of the particular topography of the forecast area.

(c) Quantitative measurements of precipitation, e.g. by

instantaneous rain-rates, and time and/or area accumulations of rain volume.

The chief problems which have beset radar observations of rainfall include:

(a) Signal fluctuations from given intensities of rain.

(b) Vertical variations in target reflectivity, coupled with effects of the curvature of the Earth.

(c) Effects of screening and ground clutter.

(d) Accurate calibrations of radar echoes in terms of rainfall intensities in different atmospheric environments.

(e) Infra-structure requirements, e.g. power supply, trained staff etc.

(f) System costs, which are relatively high. However, estimates by the UK Water Resources Board suggest that, for a mean error of 25%, the cost-effectiveness of a calibrated radar system exceeds that of a telemetering raingauge network over areas exceeding 3000 km^2.

Satellite monitoring of rainfall

The possibility of evaluating rainfall (rain-rate and distribution) from satellite data has been considered seriously since about 1970. Interest in this possibility has grown rapidly in the last few years. The satellite approach seems particularly attractive where breadth and homogeneity of data coverage are paramount. The costs of operating satellite rainfall monitoring schemes have been at least until now, relatively low compared with surface-based alternatives. Several aspects of rainfall hydrometeorology have become amenable to satellite assessment as discussed in much greater detail by Atlas & Thiele (1982), and Barrett & Martin (1981). Associated procedures include:

(a) delimiting likely areas of rain;

(b) evaluating intensities of rain;

(c) evaluating rainfall totals accumulated through time;

(d) assessing extreme rainfall events, especially high-intensity rains;

(e) evaluating the climatology of rainfall distributions;

(f) forecasting rainfall, especially in areas open to systems approaching from poorly-observed areas;

(g) analyses of physical relationships between clouds and rain.

During the earlier years of satellite rainfall monitoring endeavours the satellite approach was viewed generally as an alternative to the ground observation (raingauge and/or radar) methods. However, more recently, the satellite and ground systems have become used much more widely as complements to each other. Today the general-purpose satellite rainfall monitoring methods best-suited to operational use are those which in one way or another integrate satellite and other data to give *improved*, rather than *alternative* assessments of rainfall. This trend seems likely to continue, except in research programmes designed to explore the intrinsic information contents of the satellite data by themselves, or to advance the basic science of rainfall monitoring by satellite.

The range of techniques developed or envisaged to evaluate rainfall using satellite data is summarized in Table 2, and in the notes which follow, which give selected recent references only for purposes of

TABLE 2 Summary of current and proposed satellite rainfall monitoring methods (after Barrett, 1982a)

Method	Chief applications	Satellite	Sensor(s)	Present status
Cloud indexing	Meteorology, climatology, hydrology, crop prediction, hazard monitoring, etc.	Polar-orbiting and/or geostationary	Visible and/or infrared	
Climatological	Crop prediction	Polar-orbiting	Visible and/or infrared	Quasi-operational (Climatological and Life history)
Life history	Severe storm assessment, meteorological research	Geostationary	Infrared	
Bispectral	Meteorological research	Polar-orbiting or geostationary	Visible and infrared	Developmental (Bispectral, Cloud physics and Passive)
Cloud physics	Cloud research and atmospheric thermodynamics	Geostationary	Infrared and microwave	
Passive	Oceanic meteorology and climatology	Polar-orbiting	Microwave	
Active	Cloud and rainfall research forecasting	? Polar-orbiting	Satellite radar (active micro-wave)	Future

exemplification.

(a) *Cloud-indexing methods.* Satellite cloud images are ascribed indices relating to cloud cover, and the probability and intensity of the likely associated rain. The central problems, surrounding the calibration of the indices and their translation into estimates of rainfall, have been addressed in many different ways. The current group leaders are the Bristol (Barrett, 1981) and the EarthSat (Heitkemper *et al.*, 1982) Methods. In their most developed forms such techniques are virtual extensions of classical meteorology.

(b) *Rainfall climatology methods.* The best-developed of these methods (Follansbee, 1976) rests on the relationship between climatologically-averaged rainfall and the long-term contribution to it by numbers of significant weather systems (e.g. mobile mid-latitude lows in China). Thus climatology, with its attendant statistical uncertainties, dictates the amount of rain deemed likely to have been carried by any one weather system.

(c) *Life history methods.* These rest on the twin premises that rains fall from colder clouds, but that the stage reached in the life-cycle of cloud significantly influences instantaneous rain rates (Griffith *et al.*, 1978; Scofield & Oliver, 1977). Such methods, with adjustments for different atmospheric environments, have been applied widely to convective situations. Some (e.g. Griffith *et al.*) are fully automated, and carry attendant advantages and disadvantages. Others (e.g. Scofield & Oliver) were designed as manual methods for severe storms and flash flood monitoring.

(d) *Bispectral methods.* These invoke the different implications of visible and infrared imagery together in objective assessments of the extent and distribution of associated precipitation. (Lovejoy & Austin, 1979). Rainfall is scaled according to comparisons with some form(s) of ground truth (gauge and/or radar data). The central assumption is that heaviest rainfall results from clouds which are both bright in the visible and cold in the infrared, but some ambiguities remain.

(e) *Passive microwave methods.* Radiometers on recent Nimbus satellites have measured naturally-emitted microwave radiation from the Earth and its atmosphere. Some data have been processed very successfully for mesoscale rainfall intensities over sea surfaces (Wilheit *et al.*, 1977), but background emissivities over land and ambiguities caused by wet ground surfaces have restricted their use over land.

(f) *Active microwave methods.* A number of technological problems remain to be solved before suggestions for satellite-borne radar are translated into the first experimental systems. The chief advantages and disadvantages of the above methods are summarized in Table 3.

Combined radar and satellite monitoring of rainfall

A few countries are developing rainfall-monitoring systems to combine the evidence of radar and satellites for the provision of improved short-period forecasts of rain. One example is the Short-Period Weather Forecasting Pilot Project of the UK Meteorological Office (Browning, 1979). Another is Project Aramis of the French Forecasting Office, as described by Gilet *et al.* (1985). The first is based on four 5.6 cm wavelength radars and image data from Meteosat.

TABLE 3 Summary of chief advantages and disadvantages of current and proposed satellite rainfall monitoring methods (see also Table 2)

Method	*Advantages*	*Disadvantages*
Cloud indexing	*Capitalizes on skill of analyst, continuously adjusted for weather, climate and terrain effects*	*Requires good training of analysts. Can be time-consuming, and cannot capitalize on full temporal coverage of geostationary data*
Climatological	*Pays detailed attention to time change factor*	*Hard to apply satisfactorily to complex situations*
Life history	*Uses full space and time resolution of geostationary data. Fully objective*	*May be applied with no visual checks, and no use of ground truth. Impossible with polar-orbiter data. Convective situations only*
Bispectral	*More powerful use of daytime data*	*Tests completed for limited situations only*
Cloud physics	*Furthers understanding of rain cloud processes*	*Applies best to convective situations*
Passive microwave	*Physically more direct than those above*	*Early promise unfulfilled. New promise needs confirmation*
Active microwave	*Most physically direct method currently envisaged*	*Untested in practice*

Instantaneous fields of precipitation, plus rainfall totals integrated for short time periods over areas defined by users are distributed from each radar site to a range of users who are currently assessing their usefulness for real time operations. Clear potential exists for further scientific and technical developments in such directions, and for a more widespread use of integrated ground, surface radar, and satellite data techniques.

PROSPECTS FOR REMOTE SENSING OF RAINFALL

Since the satellite is the more recently developed tool it is not surprising that there seems to be more scope for significant further developments in satellite rather than radar methods for use in rainfall monitoring. Consequently, it is upon satellite methods that we will mostly concentrate our attention now. The following list is ranked in order of the sequence in which such possibilities might be expected to be realized.

(a) *Runoff estimation.* Quite early studies showed that polar-orbiting satellite data could be used to provide useful basin runoff estimates for monthly periods (e.g. Davis & Weigman, 1973). Later research confirmed that, when related to streamgauge records, quite accurate daily runoff variations could be revealed by basinwide satellite rainfall evaluations, especially when geostationary satellite data were used (e.g. Amorocho, 1975). There seems to be great scope for the refinement of such techniques for basin monitoring in poorly or non-instrumented basins especially in the developing world. Both objective geostationary (life-history) rainfall monitoring techniques and manual or interactive polar-orbiting techniques perform rather similarly in respect to their areal distribution of estimated rainfall, having understandable difficulties in assessing accurately short-period point or small-area falls of rain. Since their performance improves over larger areas their greatest value may yet be seen to lie in basin runoff monitoring rather than in rainfall monitoring *per se*.

(b) *Rainfall forecasting.* The earliest suggestion that satellites could be used to provide forecasts of rainfall was made by Barrett (1973), based on polar-orbiting data. This possibility deserves further study, especially in areas or for times not covered by geostationary satellites, or not requiring the high density of forecast information which can be provided herefrom (see Browning, 1979). Intuition dictates that rainfall estimation and forecasting using polar-orbiting imagery should be easiest in latitudes dominated by frontal rains and mobile shower situations; regions dominated by such weather are near or beyond the limits of useful geostationary satellite coverage. Forecasting extreme rains from tropical storms, mesoscale systems, and severe convectional weather will also be improved as our knowledge and experience grows.

(c) *Interactive rainfall monitoring methods.* Until about 1980 satellite rainfall monitoring methods had been almost exclusively either manual (all polar orbiting, and some geostationary) or automatic (some geostationary) techniques. It is manifestly obvious to anyone who has worked in such fields that satellite image data contain some ambiguities which computers alone cannot resolve, whilst synoptic weather data contain clues to associated rainfall characteristics for which allowances cannot easily be made by objective rainfall monitoring schemes. The requirements for intended operational programmes in the USA have led, through an associated and very substantial satellite rainfall initiative, to the development of methods intended to make best possible use of both types of data using both men and machines. One expression of this is the new Interactive Flash Flood Analyzer (IFFA) system now being installed in NESDIS (the United States National Environmental Satellite Data and Information System) to improve operational support to National Weather Service field units in extreme rainfall situations (Moses, 1980). Another is the polar-orbiting rainfall monitoring project of the Applications Laboratory of NESDIS, whose object is to provide improved rainfall data from major crop-growing areas of the world as inputs to AgRISTARS (Agriculture and Resources Inventory Surveys through Aerospace Remote Sensing) by 1985. Both the EarthSat and Bristol Methods of satellite-assisted rainfall monitoring have been modified for implementation on an interactive computer system (Barrett, 1982b; Heitkemper *et al.*, 1982). Such interactive methods will promote improved rainfall estimates through:

(i) a reduction in the tedium of everyday operations;

(ii) a concentration of the analyst's attention on those aspects of the operation which a man does best; and

(iii) an improvement in the flexibility of the underlying method though an increase in the range of conventional charts and other data forms which can be made available to the analyst quickly on demand.

There is no doubt that further work in this direction will be fruitful for methodological effectiveness and efficiency.

(d) *Microwave or multispectral rainfall estimation methods*. It has long been recognized that passive microwave image data has a special potential in satellite rainfall monitoring on account of the cloud-penetration capabilities of microwave sensors. However, the use of microwave systems for rainfall monitoring over land has not fulfilled its early promise for reasons outlined earlier. Work now in progress (again under the AgRISTARS umbrella) correlating rain rates derived from weather radar with brightness temperatures measured by the scanning multichannal microwave radiometer (SMMR) aboard the Nimbus 7 spacecraft has shown that, in early tests over the central USA during the warm season, microwave radiances accounted for 76% of the variance of the radar rain (Spencer *et al.*, 1983). Whether the same might be true of other regions or other times of the year must be established next. If further research proved positive, the next generation of operational satellite rainfall monitoring methods might be microwave refinements of the interactive techniques described in (c) above, or even microwave-alone interactive methods. However, it must be noted that the sampling frequencies of current (Nimbus-7) and anticipated (DMSP-D) microwave observing systems are not sufficient for daily rainfall monitoring. Such methods and systems might, at best, be operational in the early 1990's.

(a) *Active microwave (satellite radar) methods*. The one type of possibility which draws both halves of this paper together is that rainfall might be most effectively monitored by satellite-borne active microwave sensors. This is being actively espoused by NASA (see Matthews, 1975; Atlas *et al.*, 1978), and could provide the best evidence of rainfall yet achieved from satellite altitudes. However, many problems will have to be overcome before an operational satellite rainfall radar system might be achieved. As Dennis (1963) recognized, "The basic problem facing a satellite radar designer is that of detecting a signal returned from a thin layer of precipitation against a background of circuit noise, antenna noise, and clutter signals from the earth's surface". To make matters worse the signal, once detected,will be incoherent and fluctuating. This is a particularly serious difficulty, for in radar operations rainfall values are derived from space and/or time averages of reflectivity: because rain is highly variable in space and time "precipitation data from a single satellite radar would be of negligible meteorological significance". It is because of such problems that Atlas *et al.* (1978) foresaw a system of eight satellite-borne radar systems carried by polar-orbiting satellites in four equally-spaced circular orbits, each with two satellites opposed along the orbit. This system would measure global rainfall every 3 h through either a 2 cm radar or a bispectral radar observing at perhaps 0.86 and 1.87 cm (19.35 and 37.0 GHz respectively) for better discrimination of heavy and light rain intensities. On economic grounds alone the short-term prospects for such a system are not high, but there is little doubt that satellite rainfall radar systems will be tested experimentally before long.

POLICIES FOR BROADENING THE IMPLEMENTATION OF RAINFALL REMOTE SENSING

Operational rainfall radar systems are deployed or planned in relatively few countries of the world. These are, almost without exception, countries which can also boast relatively superior raingauge networks. Although no comprehensive cost-effectiveness studies have been carried out comparing rainfall monitoring by surface radar and satellites, it has been safe to assume until very recently that radar provides more accurate data, but is more costly to operate over large areas. The future has become less certain because of the understandable wish ot the American Government to reduce its own expenditure on meteorological satellites either through cost-sharing with other countries and/or the privatization of this satellite sector. Either or both of these changes could, if they came about, prompt big increases in the unit costs of satellite images to foreign users.

It was argued at the Exeter Symposium of IAHS (Barrett, 1983) that the biggest stumbling block to a more widespread yet fully rational use of satellites to help make good existing deficiencies of rainfall data at least over land are less scientific than organizational. The need to resolve key organizational questions quickly and effectively will become all the more critical if satellite costs rise substantially. These problems include the following:

(a) The spread of remote sensing techniques for rainfall monitoring: should this be allowed to take place by natural but slow processes of local adoption, or should a plan be drawn up for global rainfall monitoring?

(b) The advantages of a "total systems" approach to the use of data from existing satellites: might some hydrological services be prepared to give up some of their autonomy in order to ensure a continuous flow of data and/or products from centralized satellite data reception and processing facilities?

(c) The configuration of satellite systems providing data for use in hydrology: if present satellites do not suit our present and anticipated data needs, is the hydrological community sufficiently well integratef to be able to press for its own dedicated satellite system ("Hydrosat")? Failure to resolve these problems will relegate satellite rainfall monitoring to the role of a third-level technique for use in and by countries whose basic data requirements are generally well-met by raingauges and surface radar and will preclude their widespread use as top-level techniques for selected applications in less well documented regions of the world.

To these questions may be added one other if worthwhile bridges are to be built between rainfall hydrometeorology and operational hydrology: does present satellite rainfall monitoring meet a *real* or only a *perceived* need of operational hydrologists? The time is ripe for a dialogue between the two groups of scientists involved. In this way established rainfall monitoring methods (developed as they were for non-hydrological applications) may be adjusted to meet further sets of needs.

REFERENCES

Amorocho, J. (1975) An application of satellite imagery to hydrologic modelling the Upper Sinu River Basin, Columbia. In: *Preprints Volume,* Symposium on the Application of Mathematical Models in Hydrology (Bratislavia, Czechoslovakia, September 1975)

Atlas, D., Bandeen, W.R., Shenk, W., Gatlin, J.A. & Maxwell, M. (1978) Visions of the future operational meteorological satellite system. In: *EASCON '78 Record* (Electronics and Aerospace Systems Convention, Arlington, Virginia, September 1978).

Atlas, D. & Thiele, D.W. (editor) (1982) *Precipitation Measurements from Space*. NASA, Goddard Space Flight Center, Greenbelt, Maryland, USA.

Barrett, E.C. (1973) Forecasting daily rainfall from satellite data. *Mon. Weath. Rev*. 101, 215-222.

Barrett, E.C. (1977) Monitoring precipitation: a global strategy for the 1980s. In: *Monitoring Environmental Change by Remote Sensing* (ed. by J.L. van Genderen & W.G.Collins), 53-58. Remote Sensing Society, UK.

Barrett, E.C. (1981) The Bristol Method of satellite-improved rainfall monitoring. In: *Precipitation Measurements from Space* (ed. by D.Atlas & D.W.Thiele), D-159-169. NASA, Goddard Space Flight Center, Greenbelt, Maryland, USA.

Barrett, E.C. (1982a) Precipitation measurements from space. *J. Climatol*. 2, 85-89.

Barrett, E.C. (1982b) AgRISTARS Stage 2: development and initial testing of the Bristol Interactive Scheme (BIAS) for satellite-improved rainfall monitoring. *Final Report, US Dept of Commerce Contract no. NA-81-SAC-00711, Univ. of Bristol, UK*.

Barrett, E.C. (1983) Organizational needs for hydrological applications of satellite remote sensing in Developing Countries. *J. Hydrol. Sci*. 28 (2), 273-281.

Barrett, E.C. & Martin, D.W. (1981) *The Use of Satellites in Rainfall Monitoring*. Academic Press, London.

Battan, L.J. (1973) *Radar Observation of the Atmosphere*. Univ. of Chicago Press, Chicago, USA.

Browning, K. (1978) Meteorological aspects of radar. *Reports on Progress in Physics* 41, 781-806.

Browning, K. (1979) The FRONTIERS plan: a strategy for using radar and satellite imagery for very short-range precipitation forecasting. *Met. Mag*. 108, 161-184.

Davis, P.A. & Weigman, E.J. (1973) Application of satellite imagery to estimates of precipitation over northwestern Montana. Technical Report no. 1, Contract no. 14-06-D-7047, Stanford Res. Inst., Menlo Park, California, USA

Dennis, A.S. (1963) *Rainfall Determinations by Meteorological Satellite Radar*. Final Report to NASA, Stanford Res. Inst., Menlo Park, California, USA.

Follansbee, W.A. (1976) *Estimation of Daily Precipitation over China and the USSR using Satellite Imagery*. NOAA Technical Memorandum, NESS 81, Washington DC, USA.

Gilet, M., Ciccione, M., Gaillard, C. & Tardieu, J. (1985) Projet Aramis: le réseau français de radars météorologiques. In: *Hydrological Applications of Remote Sensing and Remote Data Transmission* (Proc. Hamburg Symp., August 1983), 295-305. IAHS Publ. no. 145.

Griffith, C.G., Woodley, W.L., Grube, P.G., Martin, D.W., Stout, J., & Sikdar, D. (1978) Rain estimation from geosynchronous satellite imagery - visible and infrared studies. *Mon. Weath. Rev.* 106, 1153-1171.

Heitkemper, L., Cooper, J.N., Merritt, E.S., & Masonis, D. (1982) *An Interactive Meteorological Satellite Rainfall Diagnostic System designed for Global Agricultural Applications*. Final Report, US Dept of Commerce Contract no. NA-81-SAC-000174, EarthSat Corp., Bethesda, Maryland, USA.

Lovejoy, S., & Austin, G.L. (1979) The estimation of rain from satellite-borne radiometers. *Quart. J. Roy. Met. Soc.* 106.

Matthews, R.E. (ed.) (1975) *Active Microwave Workshop Report* NASA, Goddard Space Flight Center, Greenbelt, Maryland, USA.

Moses, J.F. (1980) Interactive techniques for the estimation of precipitation from geostationary imagery. In: *Preprint Volume,* Second Conference in Flash Floods (Atlanta, Georgia, March 1980).

Scofield, R.A. & Oliver, J. (1977) *A Scheme for Estimating Convective Rainfall from Satellite Imagery*. NOAA Technical Memorandum, NESS 86, Washington, DC, USA.

Spencer, R.W., Martin, D.W., Hinton, B.B., & Weinman, J.A. (1983) Satellite microwave radiances correlated with radar rain rates over land. Submitted to *Nature*.

Wilheit, T.T., Chang, A.T., Rao, M.S.V., Rodgers, E.B. & Theon, J.S. (1977) A satellite technique for quantitatively mapping rainfall rates over the oceans. *J. Appl. Met.* 16, 551-560.

Hydrological Applications of Remote Sensing and Remote Data Transmission
(Proceedings of the Hamburg Symposium, August 1983). IAHS Publ. no. 145.

Satellite-derived precipitation estimates for hydrological applications

RODERICK A. SCOFIELD
Satellite Applications Laboratory, National Environmental Satellite, Data, and Information Service, NOAA, Washington, DC 20233, USA

ABSTRACT Precipitation information is a primary requirement of hydrologists and agriculturalists around the world. There is also an important need to locate areas of heavy precipitation for making estimates for the issuance of flash flood warnings and to evaluate or predict flood potential. The raingauge network is quite limited on a global basis; consequently, on many occasions, precipitation analyses derived from conventional methods may not represent the true volume of water accumulated over an area of interest during a particular period of time. An alternative source of data are satellite-derived precipitation estimates. This paper will present satellite techniques for analysing convective, extratropical, and tropical precipitation systems. For those countries receiving geostationary satellite data, these techniques offer the meteorologists, hydrologists, and agriculturalists a simple tool for monitoring precipitation with existing resources.

Estimations des précipitations obtenues par satellites pour les applications hydrologiques

RESUME Les informations relatives aux précipitations constituent un besoin essentiel pour les hydrologues et les agriculteurs dans le monde entier. Il existe également un besoin important de localiser les zones de fortes précipitations en vue de procéder à des estimations pour la diffusion d'annonces de crues brutales et d'évaluer ou de prévoir des potentialités de crues. Le réseau des pluviométres est tout à fait limité si on le considère sur une base globale; par conséquent dans de nombreuses occasions les analyses de précipitations obtenues par les méthodes conventionnelles peuvent ne pas représenter le volume exact d'eau accumulée sur une zone donnée pendant une durée particulière. Une autre source de donnée provient des estimations de précipitations obtenues par satellites. Cette communication a pour objet de présenter les techniques de satellites pour l'analyse des systèmes de précipitations convectives, extratropicales et tropicales. Pour les pays qui reçoivent les données de satellites géostationnaires ces techniques offrent aux météorologues, aux hydrologues et aux agriculteurs un outil simple pour surveiller les précipitations avec les ressources existantes.

INTRODUCTION

Precipitation information is a primary requirement of hydrologists and agriculturalists around the world. Also, of utmost importance is the need to make estimates of areas of heavy precipitation before the issuance of flash flood warnings and to evaluate or to predict flood potential. The conventional method of acquiring precipitation data by raingauges is quite limited on a global basis; as a result, on many occasions, precipitation analyses derived from conventional methods do not represent the true volume of water accumulated over an area of interest during a particular period of time. Satellite-derived precipitation estimates supplement these data or even, in some important cases, may be the only data available. This paper presents GOES techniques for analysing three basic types of precipitation systems: convective, extratropical, and tropical cyclone.

CONVECTIVE RAINFALL TECHNIQUES

Oliver & Scofield (1976), Scofield & Oliver (1977, 1980) and Scofield (1978, 1984) have developed a technique which gives half-hourly or hourly rainfall estimates for convective systems by using GOES infrared and high resolution visible pictures. The Scofield/Oliver technique is presented in the form of a decision tree which an analyst uses to determine rainfall estimates. The technique was designed for deep convective systems that occur in tropical air masses with high tropopauses, and it is applied using infrared pictures displayed according to the digital enhancement curve (Mb curve) designed to help detect convective storm intensity.

An example of a flash flood producing thunderstorm system displayed with such a curve is shown in Fig.1. The picture shows the temperatures associated with each of the contours in the Mb curve: medium-grey (-32 to -41°C) represents the warmest tops; white (below -80°C), the coldest.

Estimates of convective rainfall are computed by comparing the changes in two consecutive pictures, using both infrared and high resolution visible. The technique is shown in Fig.2 and is divided into two main parts:

(a) The active portion of the convective system is identified; clues are presented for helping to make this decision.

(b) The half-hourly convective rainfall estimate is computed for the active portion from the following meteorological factors: (i) cloud-top temperature and cloud growth factor or divergence aloft factor, (ii) overshooting top factor, (iii) thunderstorm cluster or convective cloud line merger factor, (iv) saturated environment factor for stationary and slow moving thunderstorms, and (v) precipitable water factor for modifying estimates for thunderstorms in dry environments or with high bases. Detailed explanations of these meteorological factors are found in the previously mentioned references.

The thunderstorm system in Figs 1 and 3 produced over 15 inches of rain in a 6-h period near F. Operational estimates of over 10 inches were computed for the same area and during the same 6-h period. The flash flood rainfall at F (Figs 1 and 3) was produced by stationary

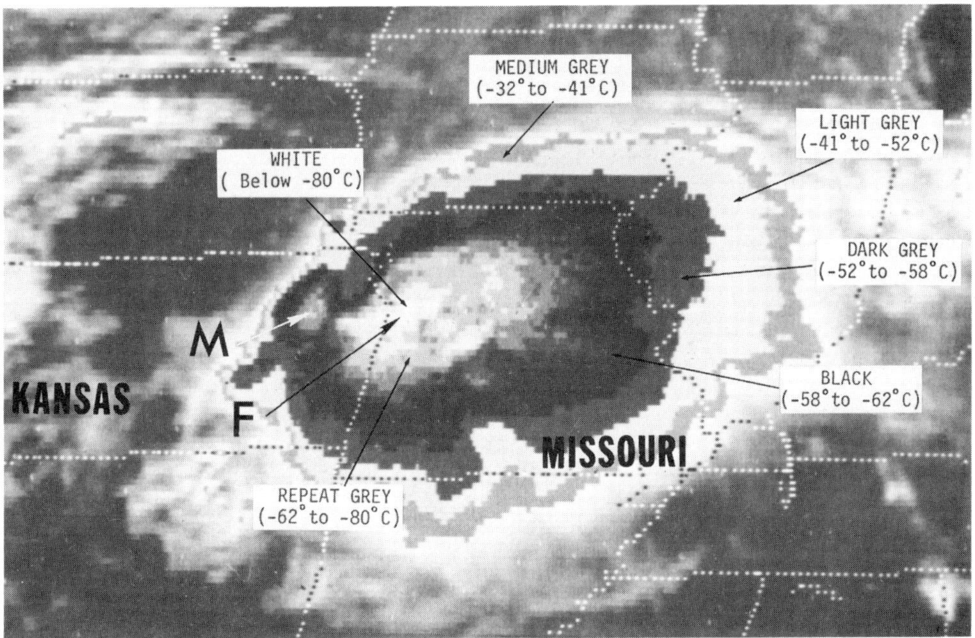

FIG.1 Enhanced infrared imagery (Mb curve), 0800 GMT, 13 August, 1982.

thunderstorms which grew rapidly and possessed overshooting tops; a merger (between 0800 and 0900 GMT) also occurred between the cluster at F and the one at M.

As mentioned above, the Scofield/Oliver technique using the infrared enhancement curve (Mb) was designed for estimating rainfall from deep convective systems with a high tropical tropopause. As shown by Scofield *et al.*, (1980), the strength of the convection is at times best estimated by a comparison of the temperature of the convective tops with the computations from the soundings determining at what height the anvil will spread out. This occurs at the stable layer near the top of the area of free convection, not at the tropopause. When this occurs, the Mb curve is not the best to use because at temperatures warmer than -62°C the Mb curve does not show the details clearly.

The convective precipitation estimation technique has been modified so that the temperature of the convection computed from a sounding is compared with the observed cloud top temperature. This computed temperature is the best measure of the expected anvil temperature and should be used for examining the anvil growth rates. Cloud top temperatures equal to or colder than the computed temperature would indicate heavier rainfall rates than warmer ones. As a result, a modification to the technique for warm tops has been developed. Using the technique as presented in Fig.2(a) and (b), the factors are modified by the following steps:

Step 1 Compute the expected temperature (equilibrium level) of the convective tops from the soundings.

Step 2 Use this temperature as the spreading anvil level and assign it the rainfall rate of the warmest repeat grey level (between -62 and -67°C).

CONVECTIVE RAINFALL TECHNIQUE

(A) RAINFALL IS COMPUTED ONLY FOR THE <u>ACTIVE</u> PORTION OF THE THUNDERSTORM SYSTEM.

The following are clues for helping to make this decision.

- IR temperature gradient is tightest around station end of anvil for a thunderstorm system with vertical wind shear (IR).
- Station is located near the center of the anvil with a tight, uniform IR temperature gradient around entire anvil for a thunderstorm system with no vertical wind shear (IR).
- An overshooting top is over the station (<u>VIS</u> and IR).
- Anvil is brighter and/or more textured (<u>VIS</u>).
- From comparing last two pictures: Station is under half of anvil bounded by edge which moves least (IR).
- Station is near 300-mb upwind end of anvil (IR, skip this clue if no upper air data available).
- Station is near the area of low-level inflow (VIS).
- Station is located under a radar echo.

(B) HALF-HOURLY RAINFALL ESTIMATES IN INCHES ARE COMPUTED FROM THE FOLLOWING FACTORS:

1.
CLOUD-TOP TEMPERATURE AND CLOUD GROWTH FACTOR [*IR*].
Determine amount that the coldest cloud tops increased within half-hour.

	>2/3° LAT	>1/3° ≤2/3° LAT	≤1/3° LAT or same	Areal decrease of shade or warming from white to rpt gray or within the rpt gray	Coldest tops 1 or more shades warmer
Med Gray (-32 to -41°C)	0.25	0.15	0.10	0.05	T
Lt Gray (-41 to -52°C)	0.50	0.30	0.15	0.10	↓
Dk Gray (-52 to -58°C)	0.75	0.40	0.20	0.15	↓
Black (-58 to -62°C)	1.00	0.60	0.30	0.20	↓
Rpt Gray* (-62 to -80°C)	1-2.00	0.60-1.00	0.30-0.60	0.30	↓
White (below -80°C)	2.00	1.00	0.60	0.40	0.10

Note: In the “Coldest tops 1 or more shades warmer” column, the page prints T in the Med Gray row and 0.10 in the White row, joined by a downward arrow. The ↓ marks in the rows between stand for that arrow.

Colder repeat gray shades should be given higher rainfall estimates.

OR

DIVERGENCE ALOFT FACTOR* [*IR and 200-mb Analysis*].

Med Gray	Lt Gray	Dk Gray	Black	Rpt Gray	White
0.15	0.30	0.40	0.60	0.60-1.00	1.00

**IR imagery shows edges of thunderstorm anvil along the upwind end forming a large angle of between 50-90 degrees pointing into the wind; 200-mb analysis often shows these storms just downwind from where the polar jet and subtropical jet separate.*

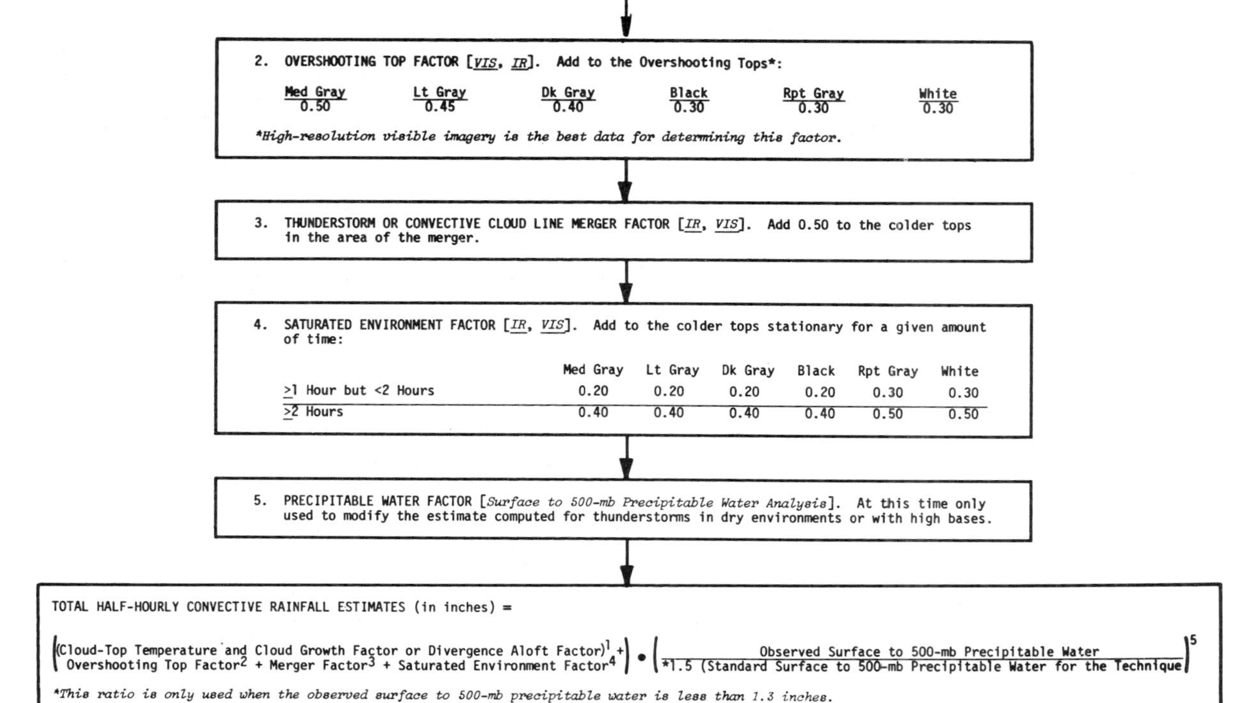

FIG.2 Convective rainfall technique.

Step 3 Compare the anvil temperature with the computed temperature. For anvil temperatures colder than the computed expected temperatures, use an appropriately higher estimated amount. For anvil temperatures warmer than the computed, adjust the estimates upward the same relative amount.

Step 4 Use the adjusted cloud top temperature to change the other factors, where applicable.

Additional information on warm tops can be found in Scofield (1984).

TROPICAL CYCLONE TECHNIQUE

Spayd & Scofield (1984) presented a technique for estimating precipitation amounts from tropical cyclones using infrared and visible data. This technique could be modified for use every 3-6h for those areas not receiving hourly imagery. Unenhanced infrared data could also be used in this technique, but using enhanced imagery yields a more detailed analysis.

The tropical cyclone technique is presented in Fig.4 and is divided into four steps:

1. The following cloud features are located in the tropical cyclone: eye or cloud system centre, wall cloud, central dense overcast area, outer banding area and area of cold convective cloud tops embedded in the outer banding.
2. Isolines are drawn around the above-mentioned cloud features.
3. Rainfall estimates are computed for the cloud features.
4. A total estimated rainfall potential is computed for the tropical cyclone before landfall.

On 12-13 September, 1979, Hurricane Frederic crossed Cuba and

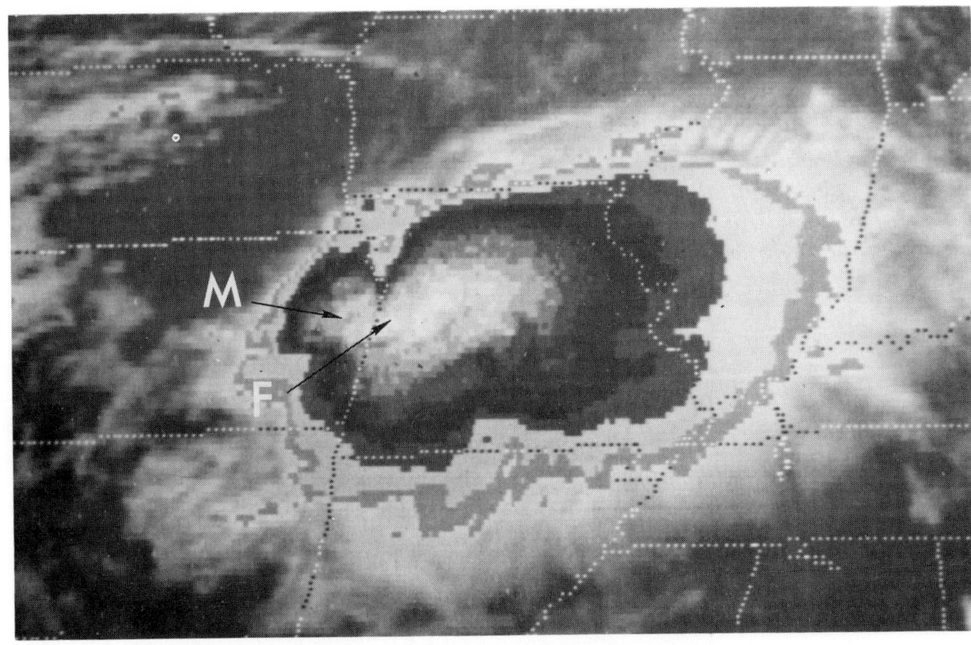

FIG.3 Enhanced infrared imagery (Mb curve), 0900 GMT, 13 August 1982.

TROPICAL CYCLONE TECHNIQUE

Locate the following cloud features in the tropical cyclone:

- Eye or cloud system center.
- Wall cloud.
- Central Dense Overcast (CDO) area.
- Outer Banding Area (OBA).
- Area of cold convective cloud tops embedded in the OBA area.

↓

From comparing two consecutive pictures, draw isolines in the second picture around the following:

- Wall cloud (approximately 20 n miles either side of the eye or the cloud system center).
- A 50 n mile radius either side of the cloud system center within the CDO; heavy rain often occurs within this radius. Use IR and VIS to help modify the size and location of the isoline. Within this isoline, coldest and brightest areas should also be analyzed; these areas often locate the heaviest rainfall within the CDO.
- Bands in the OBA that are convective.
- Within the OBA, areas of cold convective cloud tops embedded in the convective cloud bands.

↓

From comparing two consecutive pictures, compute rainfall estimates for the isolines drawn above; the underlined rainfall accumulation is normally the value used in the estimate.

↓

A. Estimates for the CDO Area and Wall Cloud	Rainfall Accumulations[1] (inches per hour)
CDO (a 50 n mile radius either side of the cyclone center; this radius can be modified by the IR and VIS).	[3]0.50-1.00-2.00[2]
Outer edge of the CDO.	0.01-0.05-0.10
Wall cloud (20 n miles either side of the cyclone center(,	[3]1.00-2.00-3.00

1. The colder the canopy temperature in the IR and the brighter and more textured the canopy is in the VIS, the higher the rainfall estimate.
2. Colder and brighter features analyzed within the CDO should be given higher rainfall estimates.
3. Cloud tops that are becoming warmer should have lower rainfall estimates.

B. Estimates for the OBA	Rainfall Accumulations[1] (inches per hour)
Outer Banding Area.	0.10-0.30-0.50
The first band from the CDO located in the onshore flow.[2]	0.50-1.00-2.00
Area of cold convective cloud tops embedded in the convective cloud bands.[3]	
Growing, becoming colder, or remaining the same.[4]	0.25-1.00-4.00[5]
Decreasing in area.[4]	0.10-0.50-1:00
Becoming warmer.[4]	0.05-0.20-0.50

1. The colder the canopy temperatures in the IR, the higher the rainfall estimate.
2. Only considered when the OBA is moving onshore.
3. These estimates are obtained from the convective rainfall technique for estimating rainfall from convective systems.
4. These categories are determined from the changes observed in the thunderstorm anvil in two consecutive pictures.
5. The more rapid the convective cloud tops grow and/or become colder, the higher the estimate.

↓

Total Estimated Rainfall Potential:

$$\frac{R_{CDO}\,D_{CDO} + R_{WC}\,D_{WC}}{V} + \frac{R_{OBA}\,D_{OBA} + R_{ECT}\,D_{ECT}}{V}$$

Where,

R_{CDO}, R_{WC}, R_{OBA}, and R_{ECT} = Rainfall rates of the CDO, wall cloud (WC) area, significant bands in the OBA, and embedded cold convective tops (ECT), respectively.

D_{CDO}, D_{WC}, D_{OBA}, and D_{ECT} = Cross sections of the cloud features in the direction of motion.

= Speed of tropical cyclone.

FIG.4 Tropical cyclone technique.

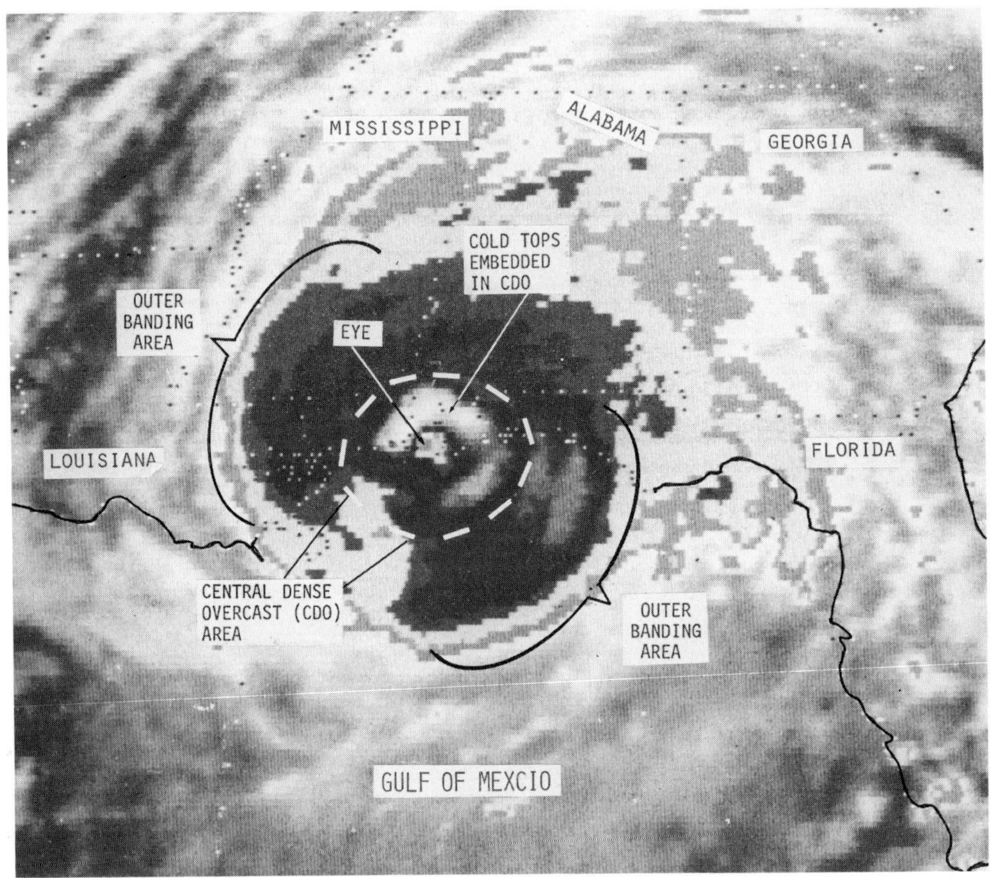

FIG.5 Enhanced infrared imagery (Mb curve) of Hurricane Frederic, 0300 GMT, 13 September 1979.

travelled northwesterly until the eye made landfall near Mobile, Alabama, at 0300 GMT (13 September). An enhanced infrared image of the hurricane during landfall is shown in Fig.5. The total estimated rainfall potential of Hurricane Frederic was calculated to be 12.9 inches at 2200 GMT, 5-h before landfall of the eye near Mobile. The observed 24-h rainfall analysis is shown in Fig.6; estimates for the tropical cyclone technique are shown in Fig.7. In this case study, the total estimated rainfall potential of the cyclone and the hourly tropical cyclone technique estimates corresponded accurately to the magnitude and placement of the heaviest rainfall.

EXTRATROPICAL CYCLONE TECHNIQUE

Scofield & Spayd (1984) are also developing a technique for estimating hourly extratropical cyclone precipitation by analysing features in the satellite and radar data and surface and upper air observations. The methodology is being developed in the form of a flow diagram or decision tree and will be easy to apply manually or be placed on a man-machine interactive system. The principal steps in the extratropical cyclone technique mentioned in the above reference are shown in Fig.8(a)-(c). In *Step 1*, areas of precipitation and the heaviest

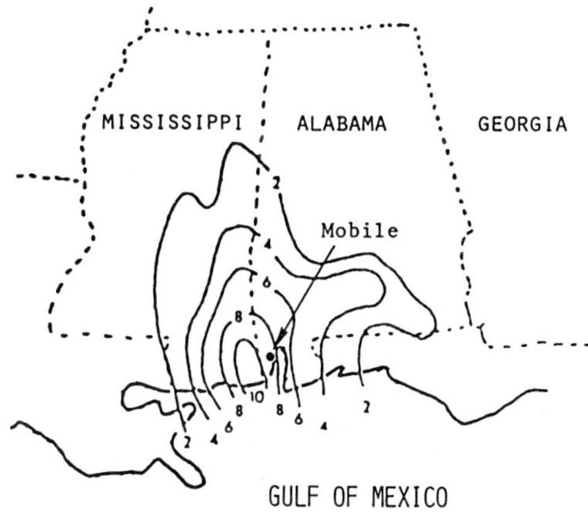

FIG.6 Observed 24h rainfall in inches 1200 GMT, 12 September to 1200 GMT, 13 September 1979.

precipitation are identified and analysed in the satellite pictures. The following categories of clues are used in making these decisions: observed precipitation in the surface and radar data, signatures in the imagery associated with precipitation in the surface and radar data, signatures in the imagery associated with precipitation and precipitation mechanisms in the atmosphere. In *Step 2*, estimates are computed based on the analyses in Step 1; in *Step 3*, the estimates are modified by the available moisture. This technique is being revised as we gain more experience and understanding in the satellite interpretation of extratropical cyclones.

VERIFICATION

Extensive verification is being planned in an operational and case study modes. Operational estimates will be saved on the NESDIS Interactive Flash Flood Analyzer and compared to precipitation

FIG.7 Tropical rainfall estimates in inches, 2100 GMT, 12 September to 1130 GMT, 13 September 1979.

EXTRATROPICAL CYCLONE TECHNIQUE

STEP 1: ANALYZE PRECIPITATION TYPES AND INTENSITIES.

Using the Schematics of Evolution and the Mechanisms, Signatures and Observations of Moderate to Heavy Precipitation, Analyze on the satellite pictures the precipitation types (showers or continuous precipitation) and intensities (ligh, moderate or heavy); dashed lines: continuous precipitation and dotted lines: showers - Label each line light, moderate or heavy.

↓

MECHANISMS, SIGNATURES AND OBSERVATIONS OF MODERATE TO HEAVY PRECIPITATION.

↓

MECHANISMS

- .To The North Of the Jet Max At The Exit Zone
And
- .To The South Of The Jet Max At The Entrance Zone
- .Location Of Maximum Warm Air Advection
- .Location Of Maximum Low Level Moisture Convergence
- .Location Of Maximum Positive Vorticity Advection
- .Upslope Flow

SIGNATURES

- .Convective Cloud Bands or Elements Remaining The Same Or Growing And Becoming Colder
- .Bright Textured Clouds In VIS; Cold Tops In The IR
- .Middle Level Clouds, Becoming Colder And Growing
- .A Comma Or Wave Head Becoming More And More Anticyclonic
- .A Comma or Wave With A Tail Growing And Becoming Colder

OBSERVATIONS

Observed Precipitation Type (showers) Or Continuous Precipitation) And Intensity (Moderate or Heavy) From Surface Reports And Radar Data:

INTENSITY	SHOWERS	CONTINUOUS PRECIPITATION
Light	1	1
Moderate	2	2
Heavy	3	3
	Radar Vip Levels	

IR SCHEMATICS OF EVOLUTION-COMMA HEAD CATEGORY.

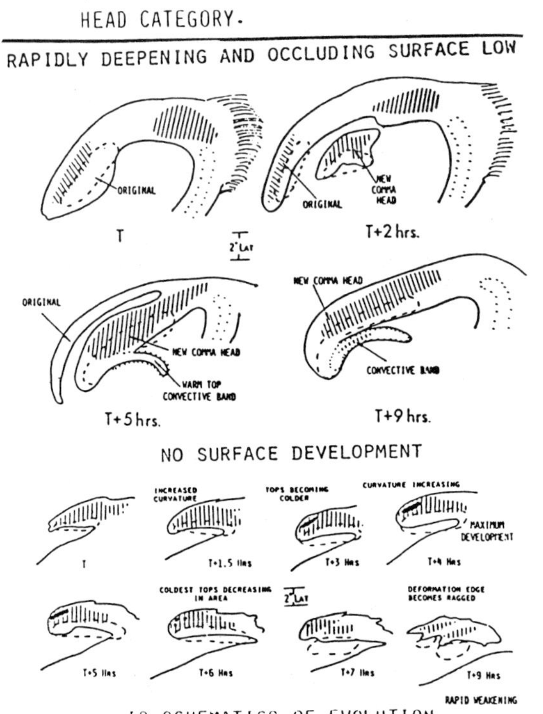

IR SCHEMATICS OF EVOLUTION-BAROCLINIC LEAF CATEGORY.

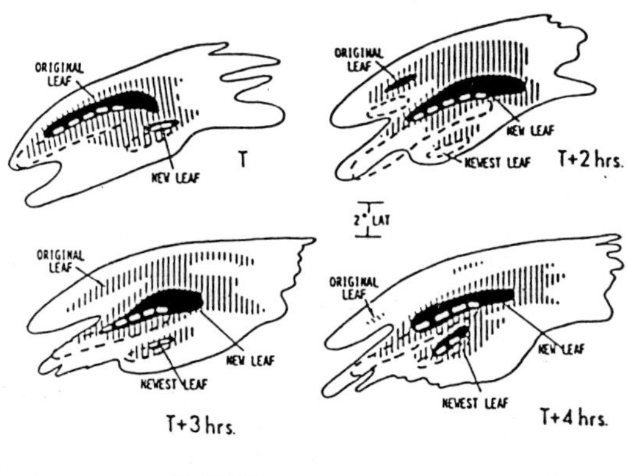

Temperature Contours

- Approximately Between - 30°C TO -40°C
- Approximately Between - 40°C TO -50°C
- Colder Than -50°C

Precipitation Types

- Area of Moderate to Heavy Continuous Precipitation
- Area of Showers

Additional Schematics on following page

FIG.8 Extratropical cyclone technique.

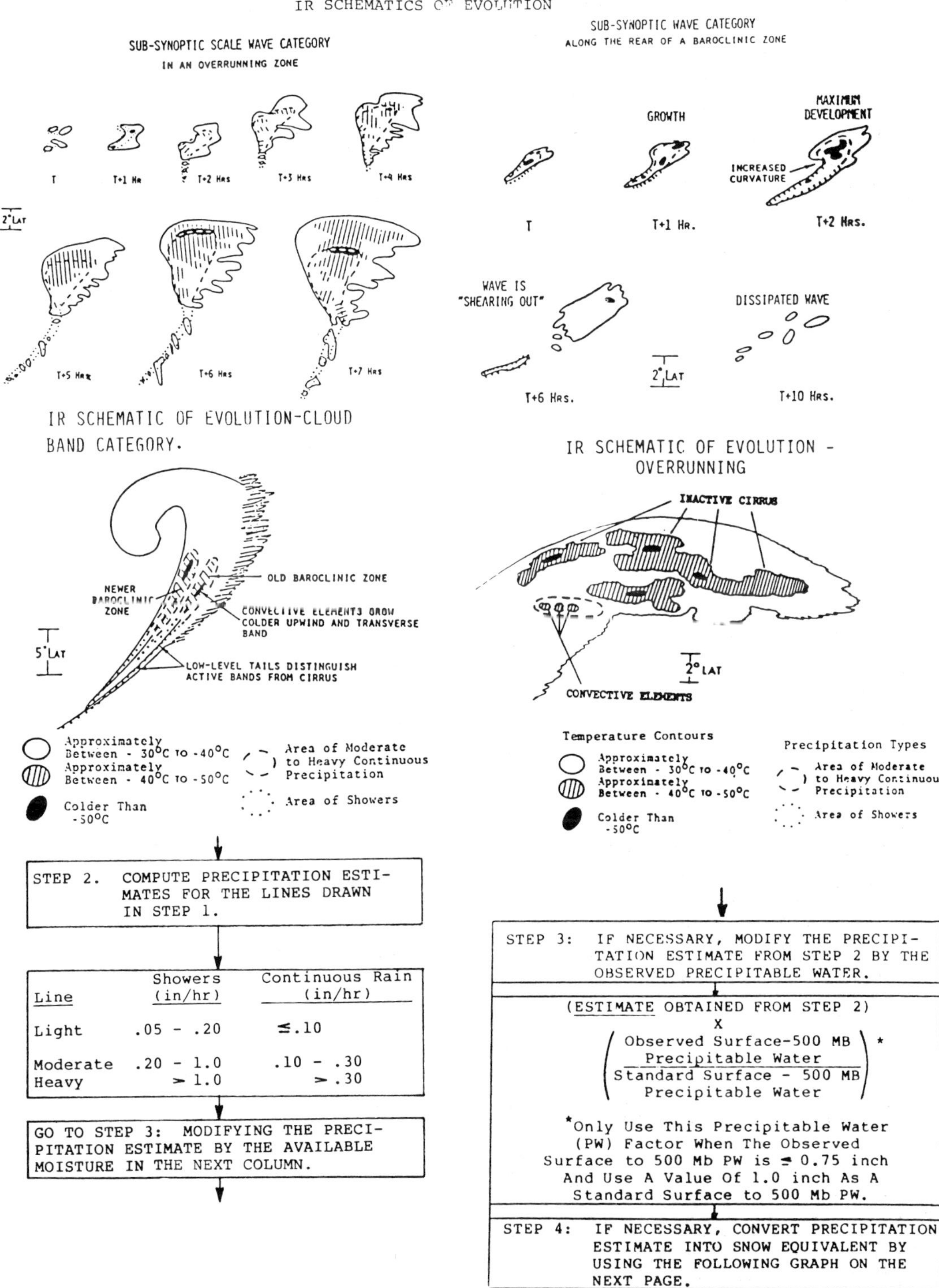

Line	Showers (in/hr)	Continuous Rain (in/hr)
Light	.05 - .20	≤.10
Moderate	.20 - 1.0	.10 - .30
Heavy	> 1.0	> .30

Fig.8 continued.

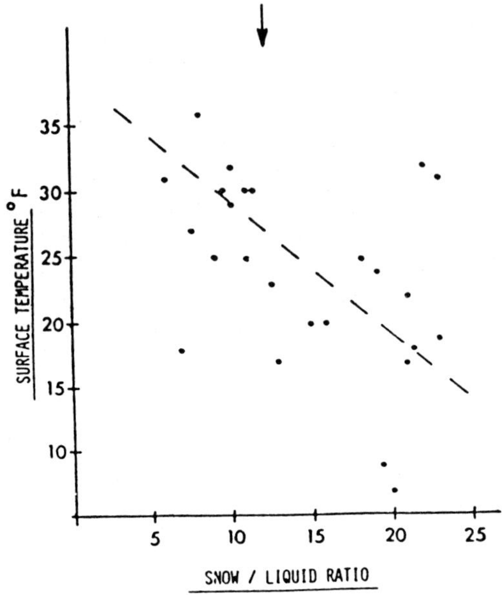

Note: These ratios may have to be adjusted for mountainous regions.

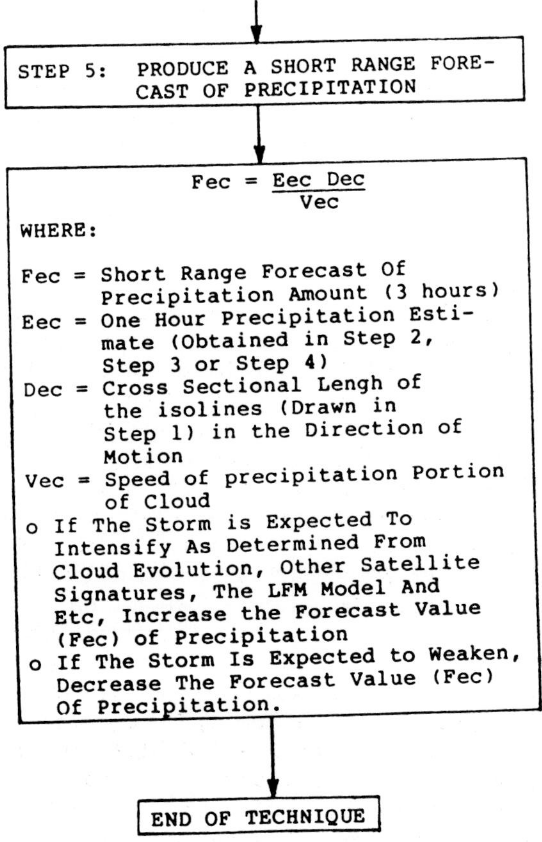

STEP 5: PRODUCE A SHORT RANGE FORECAST OF PRECIPITATION
Fec = Eec Dec / Vec
WHERE:
Fec = Short Range Forecast Of Precipitation Amount (3 hours)
Eec = One Hour Precipitation Estimate (Obtained in Step 2, Step 3 or Step 4)
Dec = Cross Sectional Lengh of the isolines (Drawn in Step 1) in the Direction of Motion
Vec = Speed of precipitation Portion of Cloud
o If The Storm is Expected To Intensify As Determined From Cloud Evolution, Other Satellite Signatures, The LFM Model And Etc, Increase the Forecast Value (Fec) of Precipitation
o If The Storm Is Expected to Weaken, Decrease The Forecast Value (Fec) Of Precipitation.
END OF TECHNIQUE

Fig.8 continued.

observations collected in real time. Case studies and statistical analyses will also be done when estimates are computed over locations where there are very dense raingauge networks.

Currently, the Synoptic Analysis Branch of NESDIS provides Weather Service Forecast Offices and River Forecast Centers with maximum rainfall estimates over a particular US county. Six-hourly isohyetal analyses have been produced for special requests. From considering only those convective systems for which the technique was designed (large, cold-topped thunderstorms occurring in moist tropical environments), our rainfall estimate for a storm event over a particular county is typically within 25% of the observed.

SUMMARY AND OUTLOOK

This paper presented techniques for estimating rainfall from thunderstorms, tropical cyclones and extratropical cyclones. For those countries receiving GOES imagery, the three techniques offer meteorologists and hydrologists a simple tool for monitoring precipitation with existing resources. Results from operational applications of these techniques and case studies are being used to verify and improve (when needed) the convective rainfall, tropical cyclone, and extratropical cyclone methodologies.

ACKNOWLEDGEMENTS The author would like to thank Vincent J.Oliver, Environmental Satellite Data Company, for his constructive criticism in the preparation of the manuscript, and also Betty Wilson for the typing and layout of the manuscript, and John Shadid and Gene Dunlap for the final draft of the figures and illustrations.

REFERENCES

Oliver, V.J. & Scofield, R.A. (1976) Estimation of rainfall from satellite imagery. Published in the preprint volumes from both the *Conference on Hydro-meteorology* (20-22 April, 1976, Ft Worth, Texas) and the *Sixth Conference on Weather Forecasting and Analysis* (10-14 May, 1976, Albany, New York), 242-245. American Meteorological Society, Boston, Maryland, USA.

Scofield, R.A. (1978) Using satellite imagery to detect and estimate rainfall from flash flood producing thunderstorms. In: *Seventh Conference on Weather Forecasting and Analysis* (16-19 October, 1978, Silver Spring, Maryland), 132-141. American Meteorological Society, Boston, Maryland, USA.

Scofield, R.A. (1981a) Analysis of rainfall from flash flood producing thunderstorms using GOES data. In: *International Symposium on NOWCASTING: Mesoscale Observations and Short-Range Prediction* (25-28 August, 1981, Hamburg, FR Germany), 51-58.

Scofield, R.A. (1981b) Satellite-derived rainfall estimates for the Bradys Bend, Pennsylvania, flash flood. In: *Fourth Conference on Hydrometeorology,* (7-9 October, 1981, Reno, Nevada), 188-193. American Meteorological Society, Boston, Maryland, USA.

Scofield, R.A. & Oliver, V.J. (1977) A scheme for estimating convective rainfall from satellite imagery. *NOAA Tech. Memo. NESS 86.*

Scofield, R.A. & Oliver, V.J. (1980) Some improvements to the Scofield/Oliver technique. In: *Second Conference on Flash Floods* (18-20 March, 1980, Atlanta, Georgia), 115-122. American Meteorological Society, Boston, Maryland, USA.

Scofield, R.A., Oliver, V.J. & Spayd, L. (1980) Estimating rainfall from thunderstorms with warm tops in the infrared imagery. In: *Eighth Conference on Weather Forecasting and Analysis* (10-13 June, 1980, Denver, Colorado), 85-91. American Meteorological Society, Boston, Maryland, USA.

Scofield, R.A., Oliver, V.J. & Spayd, L. (1982) Preliminary efforts in developing a technique that uses satellite data for analyzing precipitation from extratropical cyclones. In: *Ninth Conference on Weather Forecasting and Analysis* (28 June-1 July, 1982, Seattle, Washington), 235-244. American Meteorological Society, Boston, Maryland, USA.

Scofield, R.A. (1984) The NESDIS operational convective precipitation estimation technique. Preprints Tenth Conference on Weather Forecasting and Analysis (June 1984, Clearwater Beach, Florida). American Meteorological Society, Boston, Maryland.

Scofield, R.A. & Spayd, L.E., Jr (1984) A technique that uses satellite, radar and conventional data for analyzing precipitation from extratropical cyclones. *NOAA Tech. Memo. NESDIS 8.* US Dept Commerce, Washington, DC.

Spayd, L.E. & Scofield, R.A. (1982) A tropical cyclone precipitation estimation technique using geostationary satellite data. Unpublished manuscript.

Spayd, L.E., Jr & Scofield, R.A. (1982) A tropical cyclone precipitation estimation technique using geostationary satellite data. Unpublished manuscript.

Spayd, L.E., Jr & Scofield, R.A. (1984) A tropical cyclone precipitation estimation technique using geostationary satellite data. *NOAA Tech. Memo. NESDIS 5.* US Dept Commerce, Washington, DC.

Hydrological Applications of Remote Sensing and Remote Data Transmission
(Proceedings of the Hamburg Symposium, August 1983). IAHS Publ. no. 145.

Estimation of convective rainfall volumes with the aid of satellite data

L.-R. KRUGER, R. HARBOE & G. A. SCHULTZ
Ruhr University Bochum, 4630 Bochum, Federal Republic of Germany

ABSTRACT The scarcity of hydrometeorological ground data for design and operation of water resources systems in remote and developing areas is usually a problem. A method for estimating rainfall in these areas based on data derived from geosynchronous satellite imagery is presented in this paper. For the estimation of half-hourly rain volumes of convective cells with the aid of METEOSAT infrared data one can use the following parameters: (a) cloud-top temperature, (b) the half-hourly rate of change of this temperature, (c) size of cloud area defined by a distinct temperature threshold, and (d) the rate of change of this area with respect to time. Preliminary results obtained by means of various regression equations connecting the above-mentioned remote sensing data with simultaneously observed ground truth of a test area comprising the south of Germany are presented.

L'estimation des volumes de précipitations convectives à l'aide des données de satellites
RESUME Par suite de données hydrométéorologiques insuffisantes l'étude et l'exploitation des projets d'aménagement des eaux sont souvent problématiques dans les régions éloignées de toute voie de communication. Pour simplifier ce problème on peut se servir des techniques de la télédétection. Dans ce rapport les auteurs présentent un modèle mathématique déterministe à partir duquel il est possible d'obtenir à partir des données des satellites la hauteur des précipitations convectives tombées pendant une demi-heure. En ce qui concerne les données de la télédétection on a utilisé celles du canal infrarouge du satellite METEOSAT et on a pu en déduire les quatre paramètres suivants: (a) la température minimale des nuages, (b) le changement de cette température pendant une demi-heure, (c) la superficie des nuages plus froide qu'un seuil de température et (d) le changement de cette aire pendant une demi-heure. Les premiers résultats sous forme d'équations de régression entre les données de satellite et la hauteur de précipitations mesurées sont décrits pour l'Allemagne du sud.

INTRODUCTION

Numerous water projects, especially in arid and semiarid climates work poorly or even fail because of the inadequacies of the hydrological input data. On the one hand the network of raingauge is too sparse; on the other hand, the existing time series of measured streamflow and rainfall data are often too short to provide reliable design data. Therefore, remotely sensed information may be used to fill these gaps. In the present research work only convective rain, which is the most important type of precipitation in tropical and sub-tropical developing countries, is considered.

The basic material for the study project is the thermal infrared information - analogue and digital - from the geostationary satellite METEOSAT (reference on data information overview ESOC "area B 14", including Europe and adjacent areas). Considering the rapid change of convective systems, METEOSAT with its high rate of image production (30 minutes), seems to be suitable for rain estimation. Furthermore, the thermal infrared data even allow the cloud cells to be traced even at night.

GROUND TRUTH AND SATELLITE INFORMATION

The following four criteria were paramount in deciding which area would be most appropriate as a test area for calibration purposes:

(a) The spatial resolution of the satellite images is dependent on geographical longitude and latitude and the location of the test area within the METEOSAT image. As the spatial resolution of METEOSAT imagery - taken over the equator at 0° longitude - decreases rapidly towards the poles and away from the nadir in an east-west direction, the test area must be selected geographically not too far from the equator so that convective cells of the magnitude of about 500 km^2 can be definitely identified.

(b) The test area should have a dense network of recording raingauges.

(c) Access to recorded data from raingauge stations should be rapid and easy.

(d) Convective rains should fall frequently in the test area.

According to the above criteria, a test site comprising the south of Germany has been found most appropriate. One satellite picture element of this region represents an area of about 45 km^2. With respect to the second criterion, some 150 recording raingauges used in this study are operating south of approximately 49°N latitude; an average of one measuring station for every 500 km^2.

These recordings are used as a basis for constructing half-hour isohyetal maps. The precipitation volumes are determined from these by planimetering the area within the isohyets.

The METEOSAT infrared images, as well as the relevant digital data (tapes) - as far as these are available, were obtained from ESA in Darmstadt. Material covering all major convective events that occurred during the summers of 1978 and 1979 over southern Germany was obtained. The METEOSAT digital - magnetic tape data were processed as numerical plots (temperature values of the individual pixels) and also as symbol plots (different symbols for the pixels comprising 5°C steps and showing the areas from -25°C to areas colder than -60°C).

The next step was to relate the precipitation areas in the isohyetal maps to the respective convective cells in the infrared plots, i.e. to transfer the geographical grid of the ground maps to the plots.

Until now, the navigation problem was solved by calculating a grid for the satellite transparencies. It was presumed that METEOSAT was situated in an ideal position; landmarks were used to construct overview grids. Furthermore, the displacement error of high clouds was taken into consideration.

CONSIDERATIONS REGARDING PHYSICAL BACKGROUND

Parameters which can be derived from geosynchronous satellite infrared data and which are relevant for the determination of rain volume, are:

(a) temperature of cloud top, T_{MIN};

(b) half-hourly change in the above temperature, $\Delta T_{MIN}/\Delta t$;

(c) cloud-area size, A_i, defined by different isotherm thresholds;

(d) half-hourly changes of these cloud areas, $\Delta A_i/\Delta t$ (Scofield & Oliver, 1977; Griffith *et al.*, 1979).

For evaluation of the above parameters, some cloud physics concepts were included. It is presumed that the lower the cloud-top temperature is, the higher the possibility of the cloud going over into an icing stage and setting in motion the so called "Wegener-Bergeron-Findeisen-process" (Bergeron, 1935; Mason, 1971). A cold-topped convective cell is usually accompanied by a greater thickness of cloud. This condition affects the precipitation efficiency (droplet growth, chain reaction after Langmuir (Mason, 1971)) of the respective cloud. A rapid decrease in cloud top temperature is an indication for strong updraught within the cloud. Hereby, the hydrometeors remain longer within the cloud and increase in size, often causing the development of hailstones. In addition, an increased updraught results in an increase of moist air entrained into the cloud base; after condensation this is available as a precipitation source. The same effect is valid for a rapid expansion of the cloud area. Obviously the size of a cloud area, however defined, influences the rain volume of the entire cell.

It has been determined (Scofield & Oliver, 1980) that the environment of a cell (dry or moist) influences the amount of precipitation. This "neighbourhood effect" is visible on satellite infrared imagery by the presence of low and/or middle clouds within which the convective cell is embedded.

After these basic considerations the following general relationship has been set up:

$$R_V = f(A_i, \Delta A_i/\Delta t, T_{MIN}, \Delta T_{MIN}/\Delta t, s) \quad (1)$$

where

R_V = half-hourly rain volume;

A_i = cloud areas which are defined by different temperature - thresholds, i;

T_{MIN} = lowest temperature of cloud top;

Δt = time interval of 30 minutes (METEOSAT repetition rate);

s = environment of the cell (surroundings) (dry or moist).

DEVELOPMENT OF VARIOUS REGRESSION EQUATIONS

In order to develop a mathematical model for computation of half-hourly rain volumes with the aid of satellite data, the necessary parameters were derived from information as described above. The calibration of the model aims to minimize the value of

$$\sum_{j=1}^{n} [R_{v\ meas}(j) - R_{v\ comp}(j)]^2$$

where $R_{v\ meas}(j)$ is the measured rainfall in the half-hour interval, j; and $R_{v\ comp}(j)$ is the computed rainfall in the half-hour interval, j (j = 1,...,n). As it is not always possible from the start to determine how the individual parameters should be combined mathematically, various possibilities were tested. In these cases, models which were physically inconsistent, were not taken into account.

The derived equations are represented here only by two possibilities, one additive and one multiplicative form. In the additive form only A_i and $\Delta A_i/\Delta t$ were necessary since the inclusion of other parameters did not improve the correlation enough to justify a more complex model. The regression formula is similar to the one developed by Stout *et al.* (1979):

$$R_v = a_o + a_1 A_i + a_2 \Delta A_i/\Delta t \qquad (2)$$

For the present, the following case is in operation: $A_i = A_{-40}$ (Krüger & Schultz, 1982; Krüger, 1983), i.e. only one temperature

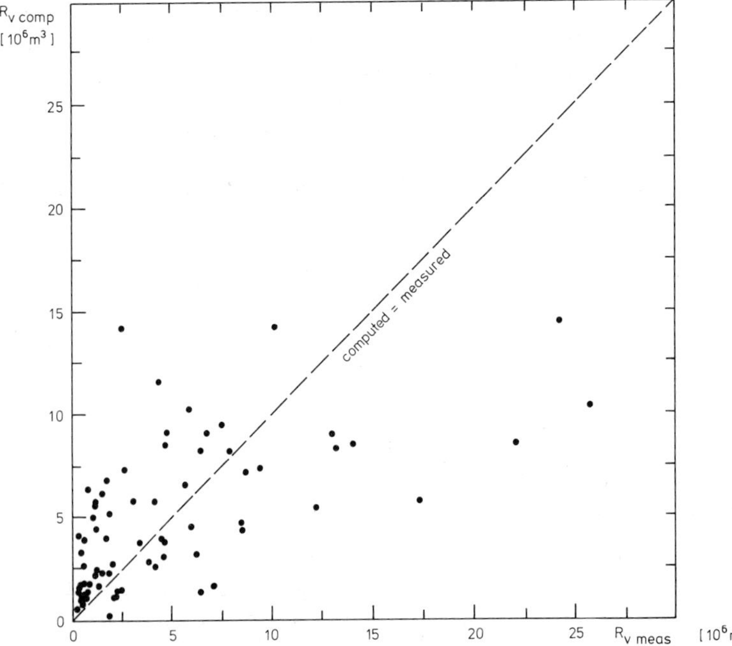

FIG.1 Comparison between measured and computed half-hourly rainfall volumes (additive model).

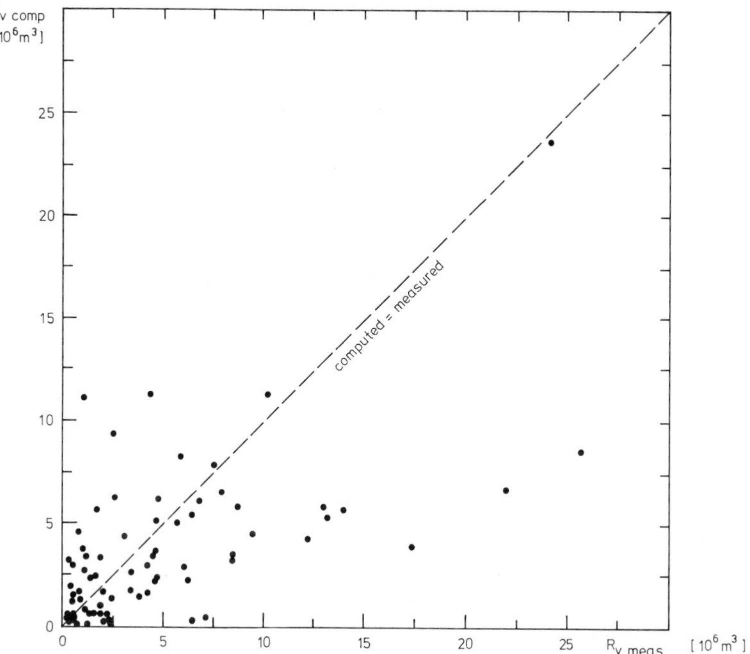

FIG.2 Comparison between measured and computed half-hourly rainfall volumes (multiplicative model).

threshold is considered. T_{MIN} is equal to the average temperature within 10% of the coldest pixels of the above defined cloud area A_i. Seven events with a total of 84 half-hour intervals were considered, but without due distinction between various environmental moisture conditions, s. From the analysis the following values for the coefficients were obtained:

$$a_o = 1.107\,0 \qquad a_1 = 0.019\,29 \qquad a_2 = 0.032\,04$$

R_v is obtained in $10^6 m^3$ when A_i is measured in pixel units of

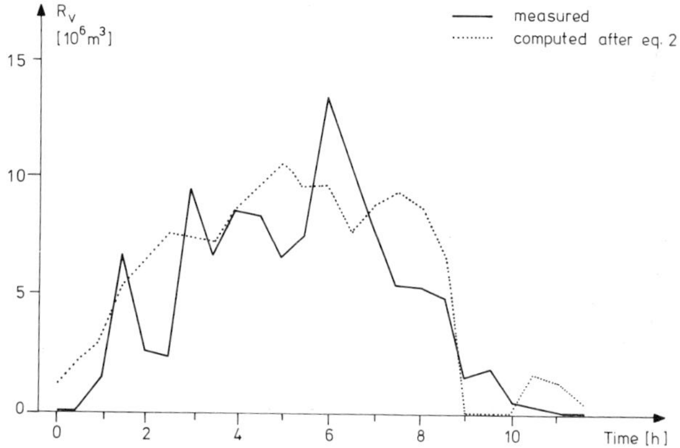

FIG.3 Rainfall volumes for one event (measured and computed).

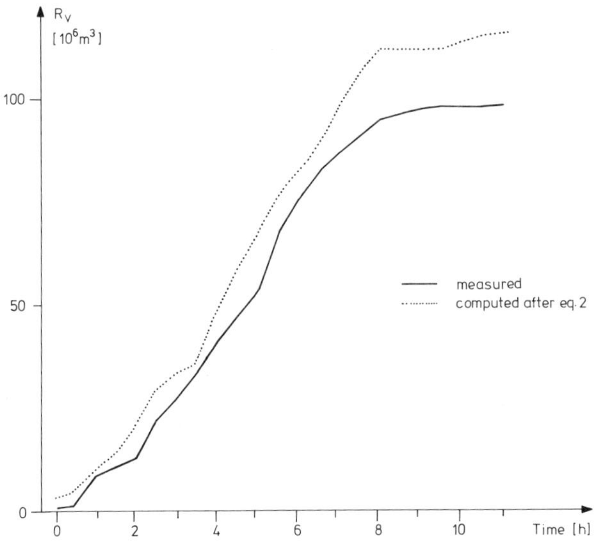

FIG.4 Accumulated rainfall volumes for one event.

approximately 45 km^2. Δt is measured in units of 30 minutes ($\Delta t = 1$). The correlation coefficient was $r = 0.626$. Figure 1 shows the relationship between computed and measured data.

In the multiplicative form four parameters were considered, such that:

$$R_v = b_o A_i^{\,b_1} \cdot e^{b_2 \Delta T_{MIN}/\Delta t} \cdot |T_{MIN}|^{b_3} \cdot e^{b_4 \Delta A_i/\Delta t} \qquad (3)$$

This case considers that rainfall volume in time Δt is the product of area (represented by A_i) and intensity (represented by all other paremeters in the equation). The calibration yields the following values of the coefficients:

b_o = 0.000 51 b_1 = 0.601 86 b_2 = -0.015 77

b_3 = 1.373 6 b_4 = 0.007 19

The temperature T_{MIN} was measured in degrees Celsius (°C).

The correlation coefficient was $r = 0.676$. Figure 2 presents the comparison between measured values and the values computed with equation (3). Other multiplicative forms of the relationship did not yield better results.

The results obtained did not satisfy completely the requirements for the necessary accuracy in estimation. Although the results are not entirely satisfactory, this may be due to an incorrect mathematical approach or to the quantity and quality of available or derived data, respectively. Nevertheless, the additive form is preferred due to its simplicity and the few coefficients that have to be estimated and will be used in the following analyses.

When data of one event are compared on a half-hourly basis, then the correlation between ground and satellite data is poor (Fig.3). On a cumulative basis, results are better, e.g. as presented by

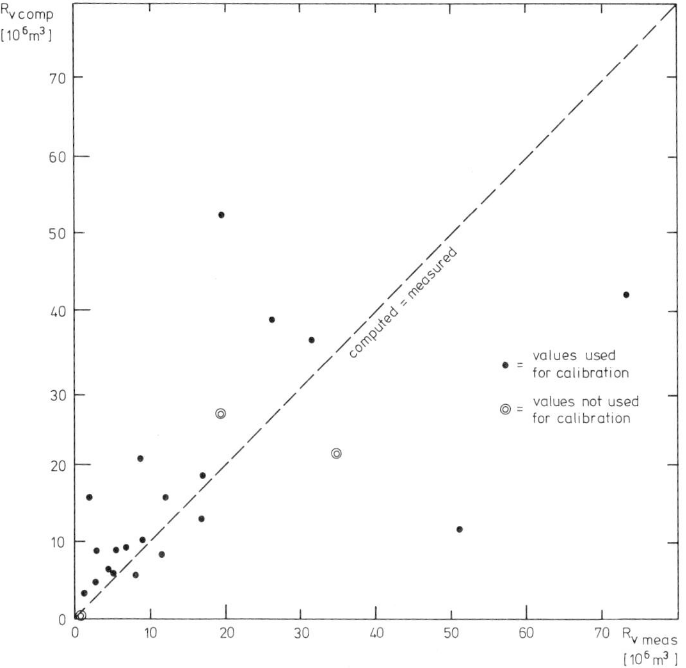

FIG.5 Comparison between measured and computed two-hourly rainfall volumes (additive model).

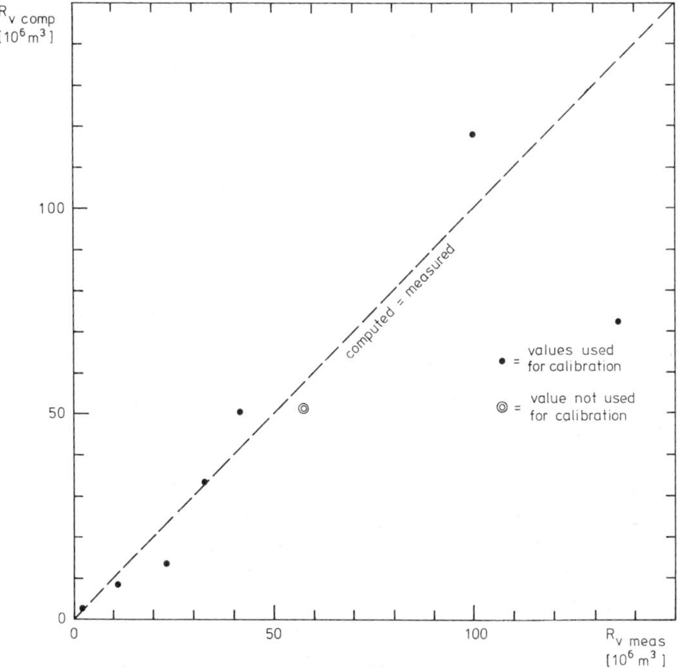

FIG.6 Comparison between total measured and total computed rainfall volume for each event.

Ingraham & Russell (1981). Computed data overestimate the total rainfall by 15% over a whole event (Fig.4).

In order to reduce the scattering of half-hourly rainfall values (e.g. Figs 1 and 2), a comparison of the data on a two-hourly basis was made. The results are shown in Fig.5 where three points were not used for calibration. As can be seen, the errors are still large. For all seven events investigated so far, total rainfall volumes, measured and computed are included in Fig.6. One event not used for calibration was underestimated by about 10%.

When analysing these results, it should be kept in mind that only raingauges were used for ground truth. If radar measurements were available, it would be highly probable that improvements in the results using the same model structures would be obtained.

After developing a deterministic mathematical model which should reveal the relationship between satellite data and precipitation, further studies would concentrate on developing a special kind of rainfall-runoff model to derive streamflow records from said precipitation. The evaluation of further events and the development of an automatic procedure for quantification of the environmental conditions by means of satellite infrared data alone may improve the results in the future.

ACKNOWLEDGEMENTS The authors wish to thank Mr Hu Siyi from the Nanjing Hydrological Institute, People's Republic of China, for his computational work.

REFERENCES

Bergeron, T. (1935) On the physics of cloud and precipitation. *Proc. 5th Assembly* IUGG, Lisbon.

Griffith, C.G., Woodley, W.L., Grube, P.G., Martin, D.W., Stout, J.B. & Sikdar, D.N. (1978) Rain estimation from geosynchronous satellite imagery - visible and infrared studies. *Mon. Weath. Rev.* 106, 1153-1171.

Ingraham, D.V. & Russell, S.O.D. (1981) Nowcasting areal rainfall over British Columbia from GOES satellite images. *Proc. International Symposium on Real-Time Operation of Hydrosystems,* vol. 1. Univ. of Waterloo, Ontario.

Krüger, L.-R. (1983) Ermittlung konvektiver Niederschläge mittels METEOSAT-Infrarotdaten. *Met. Rdsch.* 36 (2).

Krüger, L.-R. & Schultz, G.A. (1982) Ermittlung abflusswirksamer Niederschläge aus Satellitendaten. *Wasserwirtschaft* 72 (1).

Mason, B.J. (1971) *The Physics of Clouds.* Clarendon Press, Oxford, UK.

Scofield, R.A. & Oliver, V.J. (1977) *A Scheme for Estimating Convective Rainfall from Satellite Imagery.* NOAA Tech. Memo. NESS 86, Washington, DC, USA.

Scofield, R.A. & Oliver, V.J. (1980) Some improvements to the Scofield/Oliver technique. *Preprint Volume: Second Conference on Flash Floods,* (Atlanta, Georgia). American Meteorological Society, Boston, Massachusetts, USA.

Stout, J.E., Martin, D.W. & Sikdar, D.N. (1979) Estimating GATE rainfall with geosynchronous satellite images. *Mon. Weath. Rev.* 107, 585-598.

Hydrological Applications of Remote Sensing and Remote Data Transmission
(Proceedings of the Hamburg Symposium, August 1983). IAHS Publ. no. 145.

Real time inference of convective rainfall from satellite data

CECILIA GIRZ GRIFFITH, JOHN A. AUGUSTINE &
WILLIAM L. WOODLEY
Weather Research Program, NOAA/ERL, Boulder, Colorado 80303, USA

ABSTRACT Modifications have recently been made to an existing, diagnostic satellite rain estimation technique in order to calculate rainfall in real time. The technique is computer automated and uses digital, thermal infrared data from geostationary satellites to estimate summer-time convective rainfall. A simulated real time estimate for a 2½-day period over the Cauca River basin in Colombia is presented. Comparisons of these estimates with satellite estimates made from the original technique and with raingauges are shown. The real time estimates and the estimates from the original technique differ by less than 1% at the end of the 2½-day period. Time series of the area-averaged depths computed from the satellite and raingauge estimates were constructed. After the first 18 h, both satellite estimates were in phase with the raingauge estimates, but both estimated much more rain than was measured by the 14 raingauges. Plans to operate this real time satellite rain estimation technique on the Prototype Regional Observing and Forecasting Service (PROFS) during the summer of 1983 are described.

Evaluation en temps réel des averses convectives à partir des données collectées par satellite
RESUME Une technique existante d'estimation des précipitations atmosphériques par satellite a été récemment modifiée pour opérer en temps réel. Cette technique informatique exploite les données sur le rayonnement infrarouge collecté par des satellites géostationnaires, pour estimer les précipitations atmosphériques estivales convectives. Une estimation en temps réel simulée pour une période de 2½ jours est présentée pour le bassin de la Cauca en Colombie. Les résultats sont comparés avec ceux obtenus à l'aide de la technique précédente et des pluviomètres. Les estimations en temps réel et celles fournies par la technique précédente diffèrent de moins de 1% à la fin de la période de 2½ jours. Les courbes en fonction du temps de la hauteur pluviométrique moyenne pour la région ont été élaborées à partir des estimations respectivement fournies par les satellites et les pluviomètres. Après les premières 18 h, les courbes des deux techniques par satellite étaient en phase avec la courbe des pluviomètres, mais indiquaient des valeurs beaucoup plus grandes. On décrit un utilisation de cette

technique d'estimation en temps réel, qui prendrait place au cours de l'été 1983 dans le cadre du Service prototype régional d'observation et de prévision (Prototype Regional Observing and Forecasting Service (PROFS)).

INTRODUCTION

The capability to monitor rainfall in real time has many applications in meteorology and hydrology. One example is its value in the prediction of river stage by measuring the current rainfall in specific portions of the basin. With the launch of weather satellites in the 1960's, the potential for monitoring rainfall over large areas arose. The availability of high frequency imagery from the series of geostationary satellites that were launched from 1970 to the present vastly aids the study of short-term temporal variability of precipitation events.

This paper describes a recent development in computer-automated estimates of real time rainfall. There are presently several manual schemes for the estimation of convective rainfall from hard-copy imagery in real time (Follansbee, 1976; Scofield & Oliver, 1977; Barrett, 1980), but only one automated scheme (Richards & Arkin, 1981). We outline a second automated scheme, show a test and discuss the use of the scheme during summer 1983.

TECHNIQUE

A computer-automated technique to estimate summer-time convective precipitation by use of thermal infrared geostationary satellite data has been derived in south Florida (Griffith *et al.*, 1978) and widely tested. The history of the scheme presented here dates from the early 1970's when work was begun to develop a satellite rain estimation technique to investigate extra-area effects in a cloud seeding project (Meitín *et al.*, 1981). Since that time the technique has been applied to a number of settings as climatologically different as the tropical Atlantic Ocean (Woodley *et al.*, 1980; Augustine *et al.*, 1981), the United States High Plains (Griffith *et al.*, 1981), mid-latitude flash floods (Woodley *et al.*, 1978) and tropical cyclones (Waters *et al.*, 1977; Griffith & Fedor, 1984).

As originally constructed (Griffith *et al.*, 1978), the technique diagnostically calculates summer-time rainfall from convective systems by using digital, thermal infrared (IR) or visible, geostationary satellite data. Despite the better spatial resolution of the visible channel (1 km *vs.* 8 km in the IR), all recent applications have utilized only the thermal infrared data because they provide round-the-clock imagery. Raining systems are defined by the -20°C isotherm and rainfall is inferred for each convective system on an image-by-image basis. The estimated rainfall is a direct function of the area of the convective system, has an inverse relationship to the cloud top temperature of the convective system, and varies with the life history of the convective system such that more rain is inferred in the growing stage than in the decaying stage of the system's life cycle. The life history consideration not only accounts for changing cloud dynamics throughout the life cycle, but also offsets contamination from the large, inactive cirrus shield seen in the dying stage of a convective system. The life history information is keyed to the image on which the convective system achieves its maximum size. Until the maximum size of the system is measured, no rain estimates can be made for that system.

Rainfall is estimated by:

$$R_V = I \cdot [A_E/A_M] \cdot A_M \cdot (\Sigma_k\ a_k b_k) \cdot \Delta t \quad (1)$$

In equation (1), R_V is the total volumetric output (m^3) of the convective system inferred for one image; I is rainfall rate (mm h^{-1}), A_M is the maximum area (km^2) (or relative maximum area, if more than one exists) during the life of the convective system; $[A_E/A_M]$ is the average fractional coverage of echo area and is determined from empirical relationships; Δt is the interval between subsequent images (h); a_k is the fractional coverage of the system at temperatures colder than -20°C, and b_k is an empirical weighting coefficient that is inversely related to cloud top temperature and that ranges from 1.00 to 4.55. In the summation, k is incremented for temperatures as cold as or colder than -20°C. Total rainfall production for any given cloud is computed by evaluating equation (1) on every image that the convective system is seen.

Two parameters in equation (1) are functions of the life history of the cloud. Rain rate, I, can assume one of nine values that have a range from 8.2 to 23.8 mm h^{-1}. Higher rain rates occur when the system is growing than occur in the decaying stage of the life cycle. $[A_E/A_M]$ also varies with life history and furthermore is a function of maximum cloud size, A_M. For convective systems whose maximum size is less than 2000 km^2, $[A_E/A_M]$ ranges from 0.0 to 0.182. For convective systems with maximum areas between 2000 and 10 000 km^2 or greater than 10 000 km^2, the lower value is again 0.0 and the upper limit is 0.120 and 0.067, respectively. The interested reader is referred to Griffith *et al.* (1978) for additional details on the life history technique.

Because of the life history dependence, the original technique is not well-suited for real time use. The rain estimation algorithm for real time applications, referred to as the streamlined technique, still uses equation (1), but the life history dependence is eliminated. This is accomplished by replacing A_M with the size of the convective system on the image of interest and by assigning fixed values to the rain rate and fractional echo coverage terms. These latter values are fixed by assuming that each convective system exists at its maximum size on every image. This assumption then implies a rain rate of 16.7 mm h^{-1} and fractional echo coverages of 0.016, 0.047 and 0.067 for convective systems in the <2000, 2000-10 000, and >10 000 km^2 size categories, respectively.

A CASE STUDY

The impact of these simplifying assumptions was tested by running both the life history and streamlined techniques for a 2½-day period from 1800 GMT on 13 November 1978 to 0530 GMT on 16 November 1978. The area of this study is the upper basin of the Cauca River in Colombia,

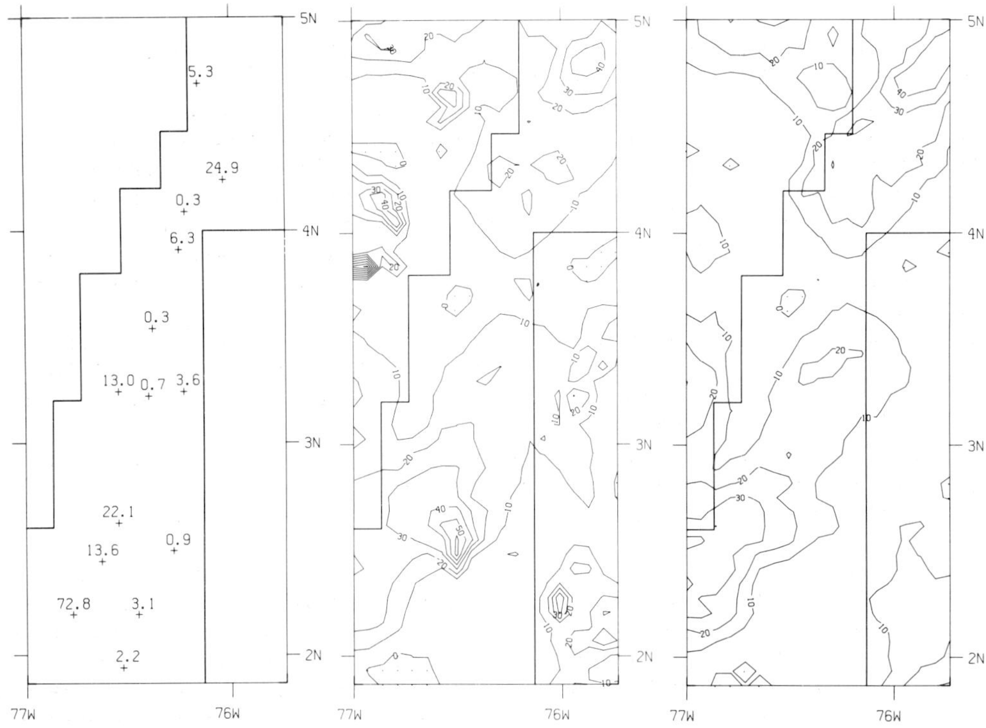

FIG.1 The area of rain estimation for the Cauca River. The Cauca drainage basin is the outlined polygon. Rain amounts (mm) are for the period from 1800 GMT on 13 November 1978 to 0530 GMT on 16 November 1978. The contour interval is 10 mm. The locations and rain amounts for the 14 raingauges are shown on the left, satellite-derived isohyets from the life history technique are in the middle, and satellite-derived isohyets from the real time technique are on the right.

South America. The Cauca is one of two major river systems that drain the Andes Mountains of western Colombia. It originates in the high mountains of southwestern Colombia between 2°N and 3°N latitude, and flows northnortheastward to nearly 9°N where it merges with Colombia's other great river system, the Magdalena. Fourteen rain-gauges within the southern half of the Cauca drainage basin were available to us. Figure 1 shows this part of the basin as resolved by the satellite (the outlined polygon).

Satellite data consisted of half-hourly images from the thermal infrared channel of GOES-East, the eastern Geostationary Operational Environmental Satellite. The thermal infrared channel senses upwelling radiation in the 10.5-12.5 μm region. The spatial resolution of these data are 8 km on a side at the satellite subpoint (75°W of the equator). At the location of the study the spatial resolution of the picture elements is not greater than the nominal resolution by more than 0.5%. Rain estimates were made from the full spatial resolution data in an 8° lat. by 12° long. box enclosing the basin.

Spatial and temporal estimates of the satellite and raingauge estimates have been made. Spatial differences in the rainfalls inferred by each satellite scheme are illustrated in Fig.1. The most obvious difference is that the streamlined technique (right) has lost the rainfall cores, particularly the 60-mm rain core in the southernmost part of the basin that was inferred in the life history technique (middle). Because the area-averaged rainfalls for the period are almost identical, some compensation must have taken place in the real time technique estimates. The compensation occurs in the extent of the remaining contours. The 20, 30 and 40-mm contours in the northeast corner of the real time plot are more extensive than their counterparts in the life history results. Likewise the 30-mm contour is more extensive in the southwest corner of the middle plot than in right-hand plot.

The sparsity of raingauges in this basin (Fig.1, left) deterred us from producing isohyets, but crude comparisons can be made. Differences between raingauge values and the satellite amounts at the corresponding locations were determined in classes of 10-mm increments. For both techniques 86% of the pairs differed by no more than one class: with the streamlined technique seven satellite-raingauge pairs were in the same class and five differed by one class, whereas with the life history technique the corresponding numbers were six apiece. In all cases where there was a one class difference, the satellite estimates were higher. Very large differences occurred at the location of the raingauge that reported 72.8 mm. There, the real time satellite estimate was in the range of 20-30 mm and the life history result was between 10 and 20 mm. The discrepancy may arise from a missing satellite image at 0230 GMT. It was during this period that the raingauge in question was recording the most rainfall.

Temporal differences were assessed from Fig.2 which shows 6-h incremental rainfalls for both satellite versions and for the raingauges. In the first 18 h, the satellite estimates are out of phase with the raingauge estimates, that is, the raingauge data show a maximum when the satellites show a minimum, but the amounts are not

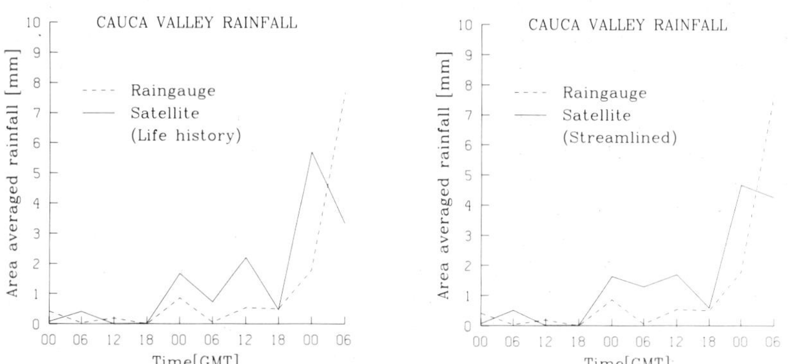

FIG.2 Time series of the satellite and raingauge area-averaged rainfalls (mm). Each point represents a 6-h accumulation. Results from the life history schemes are on the left and from the streamlined scheme on the right.

too different. Both the satellite and raingauge data show two maxima and two minima in the latter 2-day period. However, while the phase of the raingauge time series is well reproduced by the satellite schemes, the satellite techniques estimate much more rain than the raingauges register. The difference that is due to the sampling error of the raingauges, which have an average spacing of one raingauge per 1800 km^2, is presently unknown. Over the 2½-day period of calculation, the accumulated area-average rainfalls from the life history and streamlined techniques differed by less than 1% (14.62 and 14.72 mm, respectively). Compared to the estimates from the raingauges of 7.73 mm, though, both of these estimates were about 90% too high.

1983 SUMMER-TIME TEST

During the summer of 1983, the Prototype Regional Observing and Forecasting Service (PROFS) will conduct a real time test to observe and forecast weather on a regional scale. PROFS, located in Boulder, Colorado, is a system by which multiple real time meteorological data

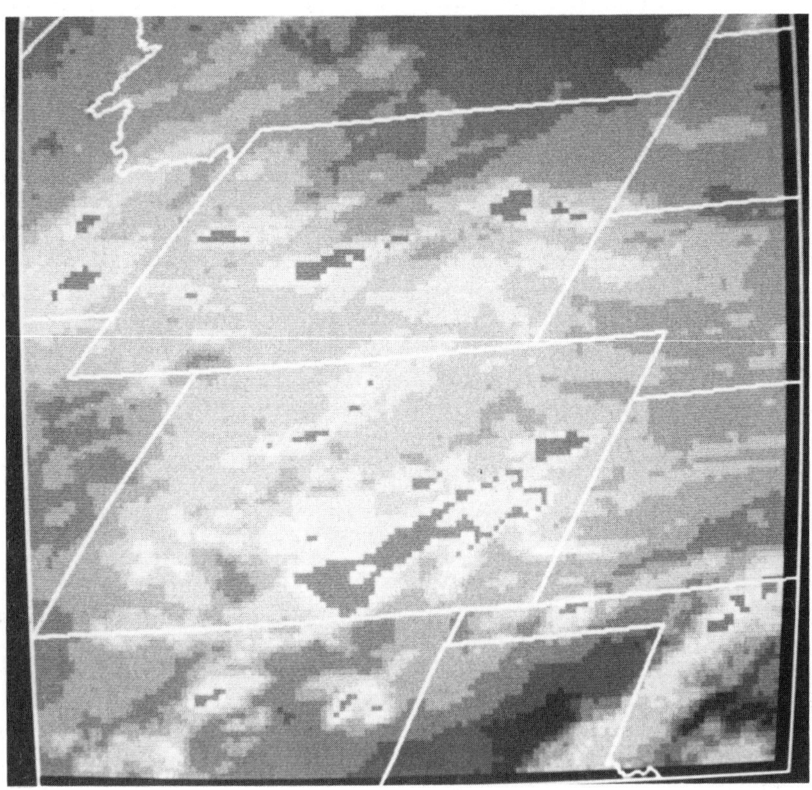

FIG.3 The thermal infrared image from GOES-EAST on 23 April 1983 at 1530 GMT. The line in the centre of the image is the border between the states of Colorado and Wyoming. The image has been enhanced so that the coldest tops are the white areas that are surrounded by the dark grey.

sets covering most of the USA are collected and analysed. The real time estimation of rainfall from GOES data will be an operating application on a PROFS VAX 11/780 computer during the summer test. Figures 3 and 4 illustrate a sample rainfall calculation from this system. Figure 3 shows a thermal infrared image centred on Colorado and Fig.4 is the corresponding inferred rainfall. Although

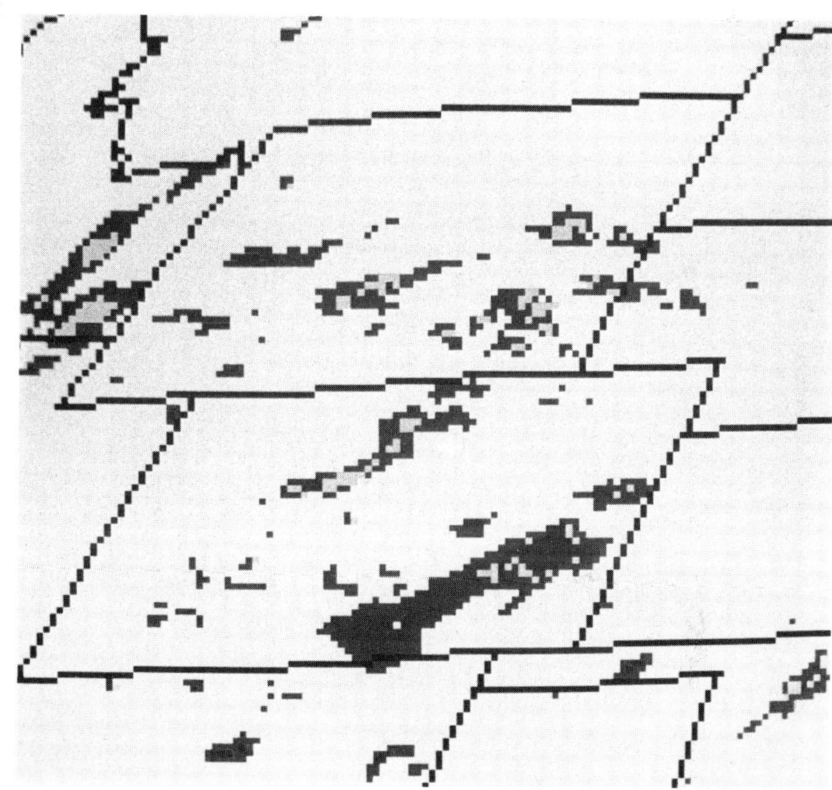

FIG.4 Rainfall inferred in real time from the IR image of Fig.3. Black represents rainfalls <1 mm h^{-1}, medium grey is 1-1.5 mm h^{-1}. A second black contour that is not distinguishable represents 1.5-3 mm h^{-1}.

there was snow, rain and drizzle reported at the surface at this time in southern Wyoming and eastern Colorado, the day was not particularly convectively active. Hence the low rainrates in Fig.4. The CPU time required to calculate the rainfall over this area is less than 5 s and the IR image can be accessed and rainfall inferred in approximately 1 min. It is hoped that the availability of real time rainfall estimates over large areas will contribute significantly to the PROFS test.

ACKNOWLEDGEMENTS Many thanks to Dr Harold Crutcher for initiating and providing us with the raingauge data for the Cauca River Valley, to Ing. Eufrasio Bernal Duffo for acquiring the raingauge data, to

Jose Meitín for his expert help with computer graphics, and finally to Paul Schultz for the photography at PROFS.

REFERENCES

Augustine, J.A., Griffith, C.G., Woodley, W.L. & Meitín, J.G. (1981) Insights into errors of SMS-inferred GATE convective rainfall. *J. Appl. Met.* 20 (5), 509-520.

Barrett, E.C. (1980) The use of satellite imagery in operational rainfall monitoring in developing countries. In: *The Contribution of Space Observations to Water Resources Management* (ed. by V.V. Salomonson & P.D.Bhavsar), 163-178. Pergamon Press, Oxford, UK.

Follansbee, W.A. (1976) Estimation of daily precipitation over China and the USSR using satellite imagery. *NOAA Tech. Memo. NESS 81, Washington, DC, USA.*

Griffith, C.G., Woodley, W.L., Grube, P.G., Martin, D.W., Stout, J. & Sikdar, D.N. (1978) Rain estimation from geosynchronous satellite imagery - visible and infrared studies. *Mon. Weath. Rev.* 106 (8), 1153-1171.

Griffith, C.G., Augustine, J.A. & Woodley, W.L. (1981) Satellite rain estimation in the US High Plains. *J. Appl. Met.* 20 (1), 53-66.

Griffith, C.G. & Fedor, L.S. (1984) Precipitation in tropical cyclones. In: *Advances in Geophysics* Academic Press, New York, New York, USA.

Meitín, J.G., Griffith, C.G., Augustine, J.A. & Woodley, W.L. (1981) A standard verification for rainfall estimation from remote platforms. In: *Precipitation Measurements from Space Workshop Report* (ed. by D. Atlas & O.W.Thiele), D-94 to D-97. NASA Goddard Space Flight Center, Greenbelt, Maryland, USA.

Richards, F. & Arkin, P. (1981) On the relationship between satellite-observed cloud cover and precipitation. *Mon. Weath. Rev.* 109 (5), 1081-1093.

Scofield, R.A. & Oliver, V.J. (1977) A scheme for estimating convective rainfall from satellite imagery. *NOAA Tech. Memo. NESS 86, Washington, DC, USA.*

Waters, M.P., III, Griffith, C.G. & Woodley, W.L. (1977) Use of digital geostationary satellite imagery for real time estimation of hurricane rain potential in landfalling storms. *Vol. of Conf. Papers: 11th Technical Conf. on Hurricanes and Tropical Meteorology* (Miami Beach, Florida, December 1977), 198-203. American Meteorological Society, Boston, Massachusetts, USA.

Woodley, W.L., Griffith, C.G., Griffin, J. & Augustine, J. (1978) Satellite rain estimation in the Big Thompson and Johnstown flash floods. *Preprints, Conf. on Flash Floods: Hydrometeorological Aspects* (Los Angeles, California, May 1978), 44-51. American Meteorological Society, Boston, Massachusetts, USA.

Woodley, W.L., Griffith, C.G., Griffin, J.S. & Stromatt, S.C. (1980) The inference of GATE convective rainfall from SMS-1 imagery. *J. Appl. Met.* 19 (4), 388-408.

Hydrological Applications of Remote Sensing and Remote Data Transmission
(Proceedings of the Hamburg Symposium, August 1983). IAHS Publ. no. 145.

Spatial transfer of precipitation data using Landsat imagery

A. K. BAGCHI
Department of Survey (School of Technology), Kwara State College of Technology, PMB 1375, Ilorin, Nigeria

ABSTRACT Estimation of areal precipitation in the Himalayas presents many problems. The terrain is highly complex and rain and snow gauges are too few. To complicate the problem the precipitation recording stations are invariably situated in the lower regions, perhaps at the lowest point. Where there is one station available in the lower region, areal precipitation can be estimated if one can transfer precipitation vertically and assume that the precipitation does not change horizontally. A method of transfer of precipitation vertically is given in Bagchi (1982). There are basins where there is not a single precipitation recording station. The nearest one available may be such that it is not realistic to assume that precipitation does not vary horizontally. The paper presents a method of horizontal transfer of precipitation from neighbouring basins. The method depends on using Landsat imagery to determine the observed linear relationship between transient snow line elevations in three neighbouring basins.

Transfert spatial des données de précipitations à l'aide de l'imagerie Landsat

RESUME L'estimation des hauteurs moyennes spatiales de précipitations dans l'Himalaya présente de nombreux problèmes. Le terrain est extrêmement complexe et les points de mesure de la pluie ou de la neige sont trop peu nombreux. Pour compliquer encore le problème les stations enregistrant les précipitations sont invariablement situées dans les parties basses, peut être au point le plus bas. Lorsqu'une station est disponible dans les régions inférieures on peut estimer la hauteur moyenne spatiale s'il est possible de transférer les précipitations dans le sens vertical en supposant qu'elles ne changent pas sur le plan horizontal. Une méthode de transfert de précipitations dans le plan vertical a été donné par Bagchi (1982). Il y a des bassins pour lesquels il n'y a même pas une seule station enregistreuse de précipitations. l'appareil disponible dans un autre bassin peut être tel qu'il n'est pas réaliste de supposer que les précipitations ne varient pas dans le plan horizontal. La communication présente une méthode de transfert horizontal des précipitations de bassins voisins. La méthode repose sur l'utilisation de l'imagerie Landsat pour déterminer la relation linéaire observée entre les altitudes de la limite transitoire des basses neiges dans trois bassins versants voisins.

INTRODUCTION

Estimation of areal precipitation in mountainous terrain is difficult because of: (a) systematic and random spatial variation in precipitation, and (b) the available precipitation recording stations are too few in number and too unrepresentative in location. Figure 1 represents a typical case in the Himalayas. Precipitation is recorded at Bhuntar, Manali and Khoksar. Manali (1900 m) is at the base of the Beas basin which soars to a height of 6000 m. Khoksar (approx. 2500 m) is situated on the other side (leeward) of the ridge. Interpolation between Manali and Khoksar data is clearly meaningless. Conceptual hydrological models, however, need zonal input of rain/snow to calculate the resultant runoff. One particular model (Bagchi, 1983b) needs the calculation of areal precipitation in the basin altitude-zone-wise. Thus, what is needed is a method of transferring precipitation vertically, from a base station upward.

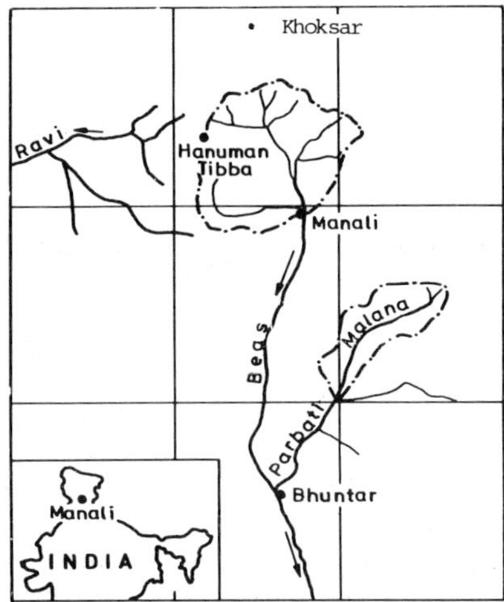

FIG.1 Location map of the Beas, Malana and Ravi rivers.

Another type of problem is the transfer of precipitation horizontally. Malana basin (Fig.1) does not have any recording station. To generate runoff in such a basin will need the transfer of precipitation from Manali to a point in Malana. Vertical transfer can be done thereafter assuming that the pattern of variation of precipitation with altitude is similar in both basins.

The question of vertical transfer was dealt with by Bagchi (1982) and will be described only generally in this paper. The present paper is mainly concerned with the horizontal transfer of precipitation.

SOME BASIC CONSIDERATIONS AND THE BASINS

If p is the recorded precipitation at Manali, let $(\gamma p + \delta)$ be the precipitation at a point X_{Malana} (situated at the same elevation as Manali) in the Malana basin. γ is a coefficient giving the systematic component of the variation of precipitation between the two points and δ is the random component. We will assume that γ is a constant and δ has zero mean, over a period which will remain undefined. Thus, for a precipitation p recorded at Manali the corresponding figure for a similarly situated point in the Malana basin is taken as γp, though this is not true on a day to day basis.

The basins are assumed to be situated in a thermally homogeneous zone meaning thereby that temperature varies only vertically. Thus, Manali and X_{Malana} have the same temperature (T_{max} and T_{min}). Also, as stated earlier, the orographic variation of precipitation is the same in the two basins.

In developing the methodology a constraint has been imposed which says that no data should be called for that are not normally available in a mountain basin in the Himalayas. The available data are: maximum and minimum daily temperature (T_{max}, T_{min}), rainfall and snowfall; all are recorded at Manali and are not available in the Malana basin.

A description of The Beas basin has been given elsewhere (Bagchi, 1982) and will not be repeated. Malana basin has similar characteristics. The basin has been divided into altitude zones (j) 200 m high as in the case of Beas.

VERTICAL TRANSFER OF PRECIPITATION

We define

$$\beta_j = \frac{\text{areal precipitation minus evapotranspiration in zone j}}{\text{point precipitation at the base (j = 1)}}$$

The values of β_j for the Beas basin as derived earlier (Bagchi, 1982) are given in Fig.2. β_j reaches its maximum value around an altitude of 3800 m with the curve flattening from 3200 to 4000 m. β_j values start falling thereafter. Higuchi (1982) mentions a case in the Nepal Himalayas where monsoon precipitation falls from 2800 m upward. He also noted a considerably higher precipitation around the peak. Higuchi's observations are based on ground measurement whereas the present methodology is based on observations of snow from satellite which do not permit the calculation of β_j beyond the permanent snow line. As a matter of fact β_j values in these zones are obtained by extrapolation. However, any error consequent upon this sudden increase in precipitation in the peak area is not likely to affect hydrological calculations significantly because the area of such a zone in a basin is so small, e.g. in the Beas basin the highest zone (5700-5900 m) covers an area of only 0.3 km^2 compared to the total basin area of 345 km^2.

HORIZONTAL TRANSFER OF PRECIPITATION

Snow is a visual manifestation of a certain meteorological situation. As in the case of vertical transfer of precipitation, the altitude of the transient snow line has been used to derive a methodology for the horizontal transfer of precipitation. Transient snow line altitudes were measured from Landsat imageries for the three basins

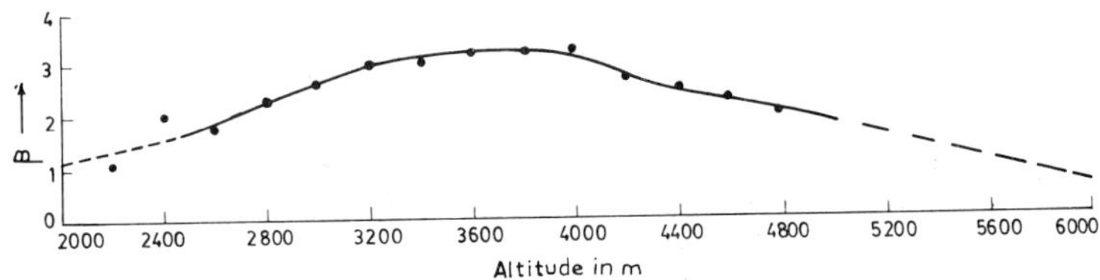

FIG.2 Variation of β with altitude.

of Beas, Malana and Ravi (Fig.1). These snow line altitudes when plotted against each other point to a linear relationship (Table 1, and Fig.3). This is striking in view of the fact that imageries of widely varying dates have been used. This temporally invariant linear trend suggests a relation between precipitation in the basins. This fact can therefore be used to transfer precipitation data horizontally.

Depth of standing snow As given elsewhere (Bagchi, 1983a) the depth of standing snow (with water equivalent w), on a day ν, in any zone (j) is given by:

$$w_{\nu j} = \frac{\beta_j}{100} \Sigma_{i=1}^{\nu} P_{i1} x_{ij} - a \Sigma_{i=1}^{\nu} (T_{max})_{ij} \quad (1)$$

in which P_{i1} = precipitation on the i-th day at the base of Manali (j = 1), x_{ij} = percentage of snowfall in the day's precipitation on the i-th day, j-th zone, a = areal value of degree-day factor (Bagchi, 1983b).

TABLE 1 Comparative study of snow altitudes in adjoining basins

Date	*Snow altitudes (m):* *Beas above Manali*	*Revi*	*Malana*
15 November 1972	*4333*	*4514*	*4388*
21 March 1973	*2437*	*2948*	-
19 April 1976	*2612*	*3250*	*3115*
3 November 1976	*4228*	*4284*	*4442*
9 December 1976	-	*4507*	*4510*
19 February 1977	*2578*	*3173*	*3149*
9 March 1977	*3052*	*3550*	*3431*
27 March 1977	*3150*	*3627*	*3498*
9 April 1978	*2709*	*3316*	*3200*
27 April 1978	*3048*	*3432*	*3363*
15 May 1978	*3402*	*3824*	*3642*
26 December 1978	*3347*	*3442*	*3431*
22 April 1979	*2990*	*3393*	*3418*
28 October 1979	*5300*	*5200*	-
3 December 1979	*3269*	-	*3505*

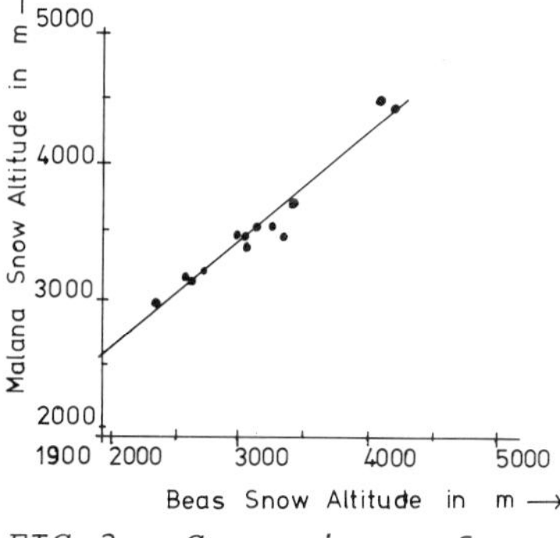

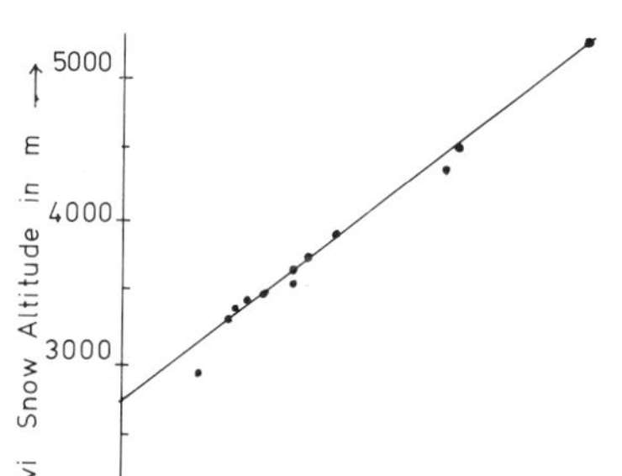

FIG.3 Comparison of snow altitudes in (a) the Beas and Malana basins and (b) the Beas and Ravi basins.

Transient snow line altitude Except in the perennial snow area the transient snow line touches a particular zone twice a year, once on its downward journey during winter and a second time in summer, while ascending. The particular zone remains under snow during the period (n days > ν) between these two days which can be determined from sequential Landsat imageries (Bagchi, 1982). Since the transient snow line appears at an elevation where the accumulated snow equals the total melt i.e. where the snow depth is zero,

$$w_{nj} = 0 = \frac{\beta_j}{100} \Sigma_{i=1}^{n} p_{i1} x_{ij} - a \Sigma_{i=1}^{n} (T_{max})_{ij} \qquad (2)$$

Horizontal transfer of precipitation In the Malana basin if the transient snow on its ascending journey appears at a zone j (counted from X_{Malana} for which j = 1), n days after the zone received the first snow of the season then

$$\frac{\beta_j}{100} \Sigma_{i=1}^{n} \gamma p_{i1} x_{ij} - a \Sigma_{i=1}^{n} (T_{max})_{ij} = 0 \qquad (3)$$

in which γp_{i1} is the precipitation at X_{Malana} (j = 1) on the i-th day. Under the assumption stated earlier, equation (3) can be solved for γ. This affords a method of horizontal transfer of precipitation.

COMMENTS AND CONCLUSION

If p be the precipitation recorded at a station in a particular basin it is now possible to estimate precipitation at a point (situated at the same elevation as the recording station) in an adjoining basin, under certain assumptions. A method of vertical transfer of precipitation was presented earlier. It is thus possible to calculate areal precipitation in a highly complex terrain. A necessary condition is that the basins should receive adequate snowfall so as to cover them almost entirely during winter and the basins should be sufficiently free from snow during summer. Though developed for Himalayan basins the methodology should find application elsewhere, provided the snow line follows the elevation contours as in the

Himalayas.

The concept presented in this paper has not been verified because of the absence of data.

ACKNOWLEDGEMENT The author is grateful to the Indian Space Research Organization for providing funds for carrying out the research under their RESPOND programme. Thanks are also due to the University of Roorkee and the Kwara State College of Technology for providing a congenial atmosphere for research. Though made under different context the suggestion for inter-basin comparison of snowline altitudes came from Professor K.G.Ranga Raju of the University of Roorkee. This is thankfully acknowledged.

REFERENCES

Bagchi, A.K. (1982) Orographic variation of precipitation in a high-rise Himalayan basin. In: *Hydrological Aspects of Alpine and High-Mountain Areas* (Proc. Exeter Symp., July 1982), 3-9. IAHS Publ. no. 138.

Bagchi, A.K. (1983a) Estimation of depth of snow from Landsat imagery. In: *Proceedings of 1983 ACSM-ASP Convention* 13-18 March, Washington, DC.

Bagchi, A.K. (1983b) Generation of streamflow in snowfed rivers using Landsat imagery. Paper presented at Symposium on Remote Sensing and Remote Data Transmission, Hamburg, August 1983.

Bagchi, A.K. (1983b) Areal value of degree-day factor. *Hydrol. Sci. J.* 28 (4), 499-511.

Higuchi, K., Ageta, Y., Yesunari, T. & Inoue, J. (1982) Characteristics of precipitation during the monsoon season in high-mountain area of the Nepal Himalaya. In: *Hydrological Aspects of Alpine and High-Mountain Areas* (Proc. Exeter Symp., July 1982), 21-30. IAHS Publ. no. 138.

Hydrological Applications of Remote Sensing and Remote Data Transmission (Proceedings of the Hamburg Symposium, August 1983). IAHS Publ. no. 145.

Projet Aramis: le réseau français de radars météorologiques

MARC GILET, MONIQUE CICCIONE, CLAUDE GAILLARD & JEAN TARDIEU
Meteorologie Nationale, EERM/CRPA, Observatoire de Magny-les-Hameaux, F-78470 Saint-Remy-les-Chevreuses, France

RESUME Pour répondre aux besoins des utilisateurs concernant la prévision des pluies à courte échéance, le Service Météorologique Français installe un réseau de radars pour la surveillance des zones pluvieuses. Il comprend 10 radars de 5 ou 10 cm de longueur d'onde. Chaque radar est équipé d'un système numérique pour la gestion de l'antenne, pour l'acquisition et le traitement des réflectivités, et pour la transmission à distance des images résultantes. Un centre de traitement, installé à Paris, recevra les images de tous les radars et établira des cartes composites des précipitations à l'échelle nationale. Ces informations serviront avec des images satellitaires à établir les prévisions des zones de précipitations à courte échéance.

Aramis project: the French weather radar network
ABSTRACT To answer user needs on rainfall short term forecasting, the French Meteorological Office is installing a network of meteorological radars. This includes ten 5 or 10 cm wavelength radars. Each radar is equipped with a digital system which controls the antenna, performs the acquisition and processing of the reflectivities and transmits the radar images. A processing centre, in Paris, will receive the radar images and produce composite pictures every 15 minutes. These data will be used together with satellite data for short term forecasting of precipitation.

OBJECTIFS DU PROJET

Le radar météorologique constitue un moyen privilégié pour détecter les phénomènes dangereux et pour évaluer de façon quasi instantanée la répartition des intensités de précipitations sur des surfaces étendues. Les études faites à l'étranger et les résultats de l'expérience HYDROMEL conduite dans la région parisienne ont abondamment démontré que dans des conditions convenables d'exploitation la qualité des mesures radar est suffisante pour satisfaire une large gamme de besoins en météorologie et en hydrologie (voir par exemple Froment, 1979).

Un des tous premiers objectifs du projet Aramis est de permettre à l'ensemble des stations départementales un accès facile aux informations radar et satellite. La manière la plus économique de réaliser cela est de concentrer les images puisque ceci permet d'utiliser pratiquement partout des lignes téléphoniques spécialisées déjà existantes (réseau "retour fac codé"). Cette concentration de données et la représentation des images radar et satellite sur une aire englobant la France permettra par ailleurs de progresser dans les trois domaines suivants:

(a) La compréhension globale de chaque situation concrète grâce à la comparaison des données fournies par les radars et les satellites avec les autres données disponibles.

(b) La prévision de la répartition des précipitations pour des échéances allant de 1 à 6 h. Dans un premier temps ces prévisions seront faites à partir des données radar seules.

(c) La climatologie des précipitations.

LES TROIS PHASES DE LA REALISATION

Les objectifs énoncés ci-dessus seront atteints progressivement, au cours des trois phases du projet, qui s'étendra sur cinq ans. On trouvera ci-dessous les principales réalisations prévues pour chacune de ces phases (voir Fig.1 pour les emplacements des radars).

Phase I - aboutissement prévu avant fin 1984

- Numérisation des radars Mélodi de Dammartin, Brest et Bordeaux.
- Numérisation du radar du Service Hydrologique Centralisateur de Perigueux (radar de Grèzes).
- Installation de radars Rodin à Toulouse, Nancy et Nantes.
- Mise en place des moyens nécessaires pour que cinq radars au moins (Dammartin, Bordeaux, Brest, Marseille, Lyon) transmettent un PPI toutes les 15 minutes vers Paris.
- Concentration sur le calculateur CDC 835 de Paris des données d'au moins cinq radars (Dammartin, Bordeaux, Brest, Marseille, Lyon) et des données du réseau britannique.
- Réalisation d'une mosaïque radar toutes les 15 minutes, en juxtaposant les données brutes des radars, et diffusion de cette mosaïque sur des lignes alimentant les stations météorologiques (terminaux METEOTEL).
- Mise en oeuvre d'un archivage des données radar et satellite a Paris.
- Diffusion depuis Paris sur les lignes alimentant les stations METEOTEL d'images METEOSAT traitées au Centre de Météorologie Spatiale de Lannion.
- Industrialisation et mise au point des terminaux de réception d'images METEOTEL.
- Installation de METEOTEL dans au moins dix stations météorologiques.
- Mise au point de la méthode de prévision de la pluie à courte échéance à partir des données radar seules qui sera opérationnelle en phase II.
- Etude des améliorations les plus urgentes à apporter aux systèmes radar.

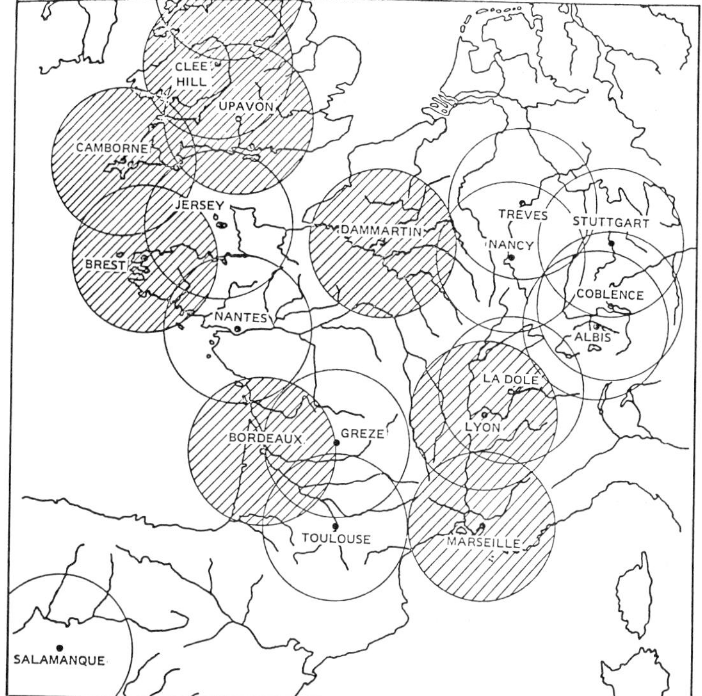

FIG.1 Image METEOTEL centrée sur 2°E long. et 47°N lat.; projection stréréographique polaire; portée théorique des radars 150 km. Zone hachurée: radars disponibles fin 1984.

Phase II - aboutissement prévu avant fin 1986

- Automatisation des radars de Nancy, Grèzes, Toulouse.
- Déplacement vers un autre site d'un radar Rodin actuellement implanté au voisinage de Toulouse pour des raisons extérieures au projet Aramis.
- Amélioration de la couverture de la région parisienne (suppression des échos de sol du radar de Dammartin ou autre solution).
- Concentration sur Paris des données de tous les radars francais portés sur la Fig.1, ainsi que de radars étrangers si cela s'avère possible.
- Mise en place sur quelques radars de moyens de mesure de lame d'eau en relation avec des utilisateurs de ce type de données.
- Mise en place à Paris d'une procédure systématique de vérification et d'analyse des données radar et satellite.
- Réalisation opérationnelle et diffusion de prévisions de pluie a très courte échéance en utilisant uniquement les données radar.
- Equipement de toutes les stations du réseau météorologique francais en terminaux METEOTEL.
- Etude de définition d'un nouveau modèle de radar météorologique adapté aux besoins d'Aramis (radar de cinquième génération).
- Etude des possibilités d'utilisation simultanée des données radar/satellite, des autres données du réseau météorologique et des résultats des modèles numériques pour l'amélioration des prévisions

à courte échéance.

- Définition d'un système opérationnel intégré pour la prévision à courte échéance.

Phase III - aboutissement prévu fin 1987

- Construction et essai du prototype du radar météorologique de cinquième génération adapté aux besoins d'Aramis.
- Mise en oeuvre du système opérationnel intégré de prévision à courte échéance.
- Intensification des échanges de données au niveau européen.

LES SOURCES DE DONNEES

Les radars actuellement existants en France qui seront utilisés pour le projet Aramis sont au nombre de dix. Trois de ces radars sont des 10 cm de type Mélodi et six sont de type Rodin. Le dixième radar est un 5 cm appartenant au Service Hydrologique Centralisateur de Périgueux. Les principales caractéristiques des Mélodi et des Rodin sont fournies par le Tableau 1.

Les radars Rodin sont d'acquisation récente. Ils sont équipés à la livraison d'un système numérique de traitement des images, le MT 750. Ce matériel permet de visualiser l'image sur un écran couleur et de la transmettre par une ligne téléphonique. Il est possible par ailleurs d'effectuer de nombreuses manipulations sur l'image comme des changement d'échelles, zooms ou excentrements. Le MT 750 a été programmé au Centre Technique et du Matériel de la Météorologie pour contrôler les mouvements de l'antenne.

Les radars Mélodi sont des matériels plus anciens, et qui n'étaient pas numérisés à l'origine. Cette numérisation a été réalisée à la Météorologie, à l'aide d'un système baptisé Saphyr. Ce matériel permet de visualiser l'image sur un écran couleur et de la transmettre par une ligne téléphonique. On peut également procéder à une variété de manipulations d'image, de façon sensiblement équivalente au MT 750. Saphyr contrôle les mouvements

TABLEAU 1 Caractéristiques des radars Mélodi et Rodin

	Mélodi	*Rodin*
Constructeur	*Omera*	*Thomson CSF*
Longueur d'onde (cm)	*10.7*	*5.3*
Fréquence de récurrence (Hz)	*250*	*330*
Durée de l'impulsion (s)	*2*	*2*
Puissance émise (kW)	*700*	*250*
Diamètre de l'aérien (m)	*4*	*3*
Largeur du faisceau (degrés)	*1.8*	*1.3*
Signal minimum détectable (dBm)	*-106*	*-112*
Système de numérisation	*Saphyr*	*MT 750*
Portée utilisée pour la centralisation (km)	*256*	*200*

de l'antenne et peut recevoir un système d'enregistrement sur bandes magnétiques.

La Fig.1 donne les emplacements des radars francais, hormis un radar Rodin dont le site n'est pas définitif. Certains radars européens dont les données pourraient avoir un intérêt pour le réseau francais figurent également sur la carte. La zone géographique couverte par cette figure correspond à la superficie de la mosaïque radar qui sera réalisée à Paris.

Pendant les premières années, les modes de balayage des radars seront simplifiés au maximum. Chaque radar devra transmettre au minimum un tour d'horizon à site bas toutes les 15 minutes. Ces données iront vers Paris et d'autres utilisateurs éventuels en passant dans la quasi totalité des cas par la station météorologique la plus proche et par le Centre Météorologique Régional (voir Fig.2). L'intervalle de 15 minutes est trop long pour de nombreuses applications, comme par exemple la mesure précise de hauteur de pluie sur de petites surfaces (voir par exemple Wilson & Brandes, 1979). Les radars appelés à faire ce type de mesure pourront balayer plus fréquemment.

Les modes d'opération initiaux seront simples pour qu'il ne soit pas nécessaire dès le début de modifier les systèmes MT 750 et Saphyr.

Les données satellitaires utilisées pour le projet Aramis seront celles de METEOSAT, en visible et en infra rouge, ou éventuellement celles de NOAA-N si METEOSAT venait à faire défaut. Ces données sont traitées au Centre de Météorologie Spatiale de Lannion en Bretagne,

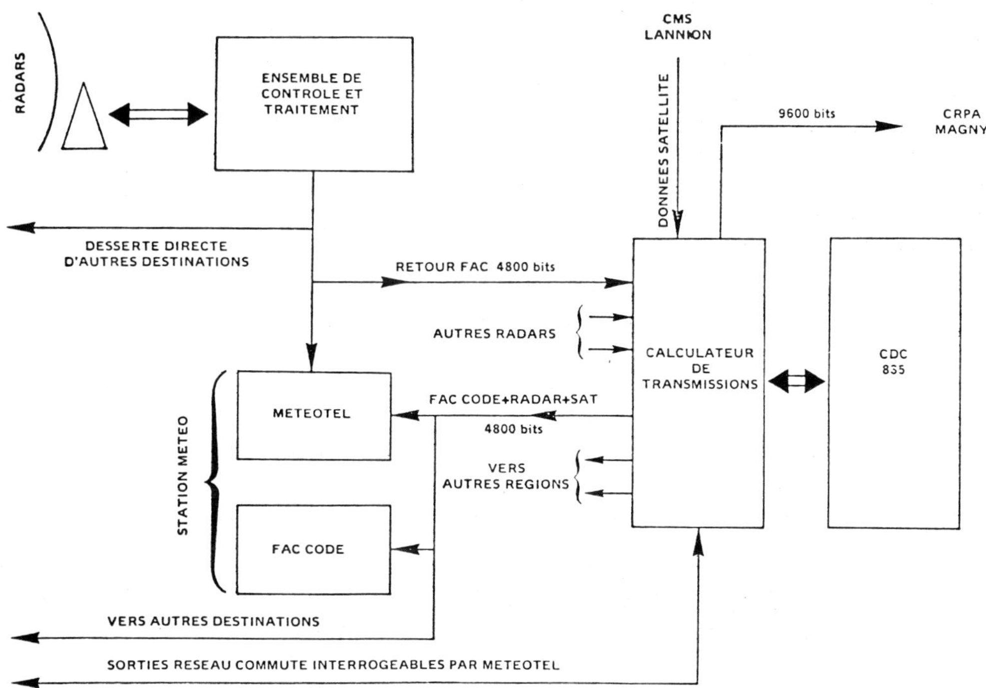

FIG.2 Principes retenus pour la concentration et la rediffusion des données satellite et radar.

et seront transmises vers Paris sous deux formats superposables au format des données radar. Le premier format, dit format METEOTEL France aura une résolution d'environ 6 x 6 km^2. Le second format, dit format METEOTEL Europe aura une résolution de 12 x 12 km^2. La projection utilisée est la projection stéréographique polaire.

CENTRALISATION DES DONNEES

Les données radar et METEOSAT seront transmises vers Paris en utilisant la plupart du temps des canaux existants, qui correspondent aux "voies retour" des lignes téléphoniques spécialisées alimentant les stations météorologiques en cartes sur des récepteurs fac similé. Au cours de la phase I et probablement de toute la phase II du projet, la centralisation opérationnelle des données sera réalisée avec des moyens informatiques dont la grande majorité existe déjà. Parallèlement, un système experimental sera mis sur pied en utilisant des moyens distincts de mini et micro-informatique, de manière à ce que les développements n'interfèrent pas avec un bon fonctionnement du réseau. Les principaux moyens utilisés pour la concentration opérationnelle, selon le principe de la Fig.3, sont les suivants:

(a) Un minicalculateur MITRA 225 baptisé COMETE 2, chargé de gérer l'ensemble des télécommunications. Il recevra les données de chacun des radars, celles de METEOSAT en provenance du Centre de Météorologie Spatiale de Lannion et les données du réseau britannique transmises depuis Bracknell. Le calculateur MITRA n'effectuera aucun traitement sur les données, et se contentera de les renvoyer par une liaison rapide en mode X25 vers le calculateur CDC 835. Après traitement sur ce calculateur, les mosaïques radar et les images satellitaires seront retournées à COMETE 2, qui les transmettra aux stations du réseau.

(b) Deux calculateurs CDC 835 et CDC 175, qui constituent actuellement l'essentiel des moyens informatiques de la Météorologie à Paris. Le CDC 835, connecté directement à COMETE effectuera la gestion routinière des données, constituera la mosaïque radar et fera les calculs nécessaires aux prévisions. Le calculateur sera en particulier relié à une console graphique EMIR. Le calculateur CYBER 175 sera utilisé pour les développements.

(c) Une console graphique EMIR, a reliée au calculateur CDC 835 par une liaison série, servira à contrôler la qualité des images. Le système EMIR est un outil de visualisation et de traitement d'image conçu pour une utilisation interactive, et destiné à équiper les Centres Météorologiques Régionaux. EMIR est décrit plus en détail au chapitre suivant.

(d) Pendant une année au moins, en attendant que le système COMETE décrit plus haut soit opérationnel, une "boîte de transfert" enverra les données arrivant sur Paris vers le Centre de Recherches en Physique de l'Atmosphère de Magny-les-Hameaux près de Paris où elles seront enregistrées. Ceci permettra une mise au point plus rapide des méthodes de traitement opérationnel des données radar et satellite.

La première étude conduite à la Météorologie sur la prévision à courte échéance des échos radar montre bien que pendant un certain

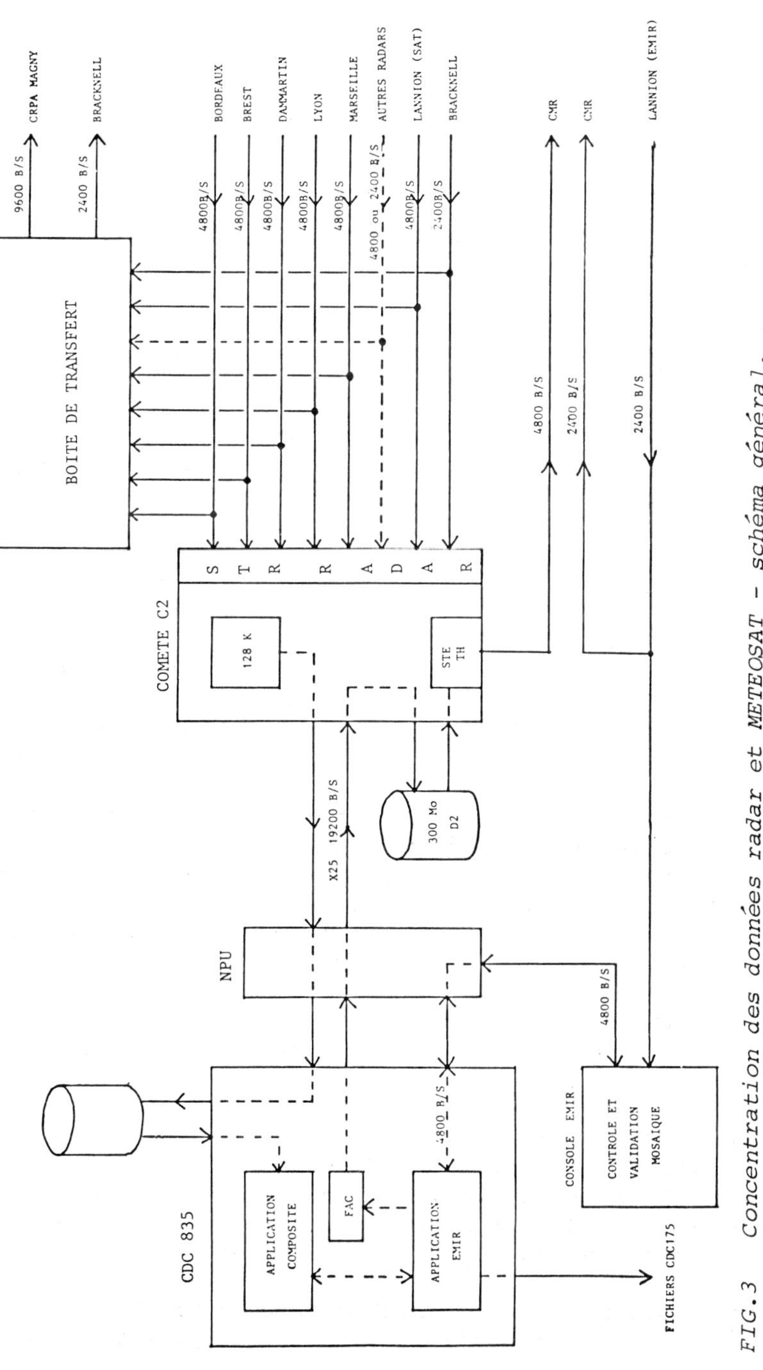

FIG.3 Concentration des données radar et METEOSAT - schéma général.

temps au moins il sera nécessaire d'employer une procédure interactive, afin de corriger certains défauts qui peuvent apparaître dans l'imagerie radar (masques, propagation anormale, etc.) et de tenir compte des aspects particuliers de chaque situation (persistance et évolution des échos, non conformité des déplacements, etc.). Ces résultats ne contredisent pas les résultats obtenus en Grande Bretagne par Browning *et al.* (1982) par exemple. Cette étude a porté sur les données d'un radar, celui de Dammartin en Goëlle, pour lequel on dispose de plusieurs années d'enregistrements. Le travail ayant été fait avec un seul radar qui présentait par ailleurs beaucoup d'échos de sol, l'échéance des prévisions a été limitée à 2 h.

On a pu tester sur différents types de situations météorologiques deux méthodes fondamentalement différentes et classiques, le suivi du centre de gravité des échos et la corrélation croisée sur l'image radar entière. Plusieurs variantes de cette dernière technique ont été essayées. Les tests ont également porté sur les dimensions de la maille utilisée pour la prévision et la vérification des résultats, ainsi que sur le pas de temps.

La méthode de prévision par suivi des échos a été rapidement éliminée, car dépendant énormément de la qualité des données (masques, informations manquantes, effets de distance) et s'appliquant mal aux échos étendus dont le centre de gravité est difficile à déterminer. La corrélation croisée est beaucoup moins sensible à ces deux inconvénients. La Fig.4 montre les résultats moyens de la comparaison des deux methodes, obtenus à partir de cinq prévisions. L'indice de qualité de la prévision utilisé est celui de Rousseau (1980). Cet indice a l'avantage d'être plus sensible que les indices employés habituellement dans la littérature.

Pour la prévision par corrélation croisée on a tout intérêt a conserver une bonne résolution sur les images de départ, surtout dans les situations convectives où les développements d'échos peuvent être très rapides. A titre d'exemple, la Fig.5 montre des résultats obtenus avec des grilles initiales de 4 x 4, 8 x 8 et 16 x 16 km^2, toutes les vérifications étant faites sur une grille de 16 x 16 km^2. On a également constaté que les calculs pouvaient être

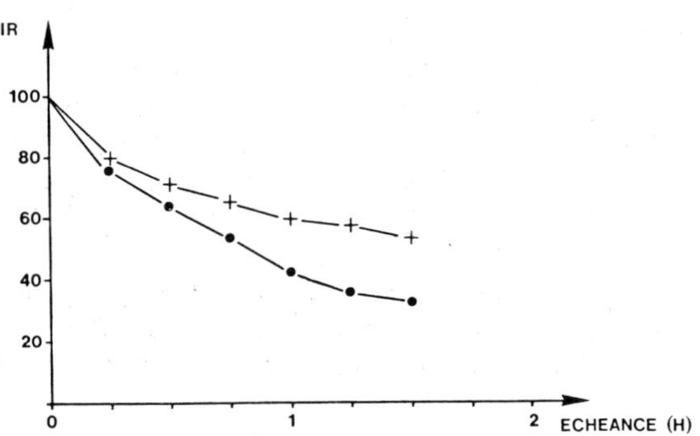

FIG.4 Comparaison de la qualité des prévisions obtenues par les méthodes de suivi d'échos (·--·) et de corrélation (+-+) pour cinq situations frontales. Les calculs sont faits sur une maille de 4 x 4 km^2 et les indices de Rousseau sont estimés sur une maille de 16 x 16 km^2.

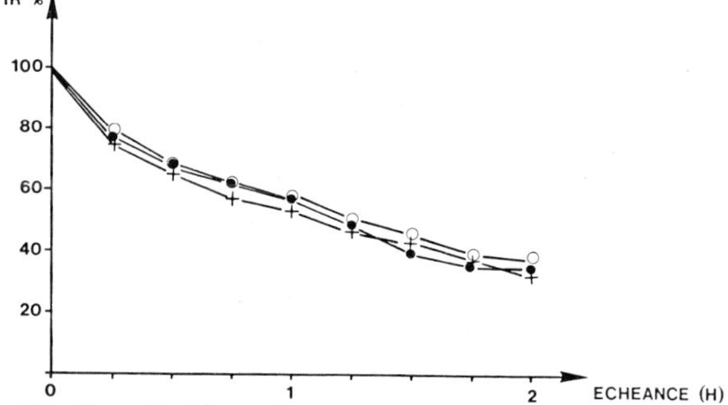

FIG.5 Indice de Rousseau en fonction du temps pour des prévisions faites avec des résolutions de départ de 4 km (o-o), 8 km (·-·) et 16 km (+-+), par la méthode de corrélation. Les résultats sont moyennés sur 12 situations frontales, pour des couvertures pluvieuses supérieures à 10%.

faits sur 1 bit, sans dégradation sensible de la qualité des prévisions. En ce qui concerne le pas dans le temps, il apparaît souhaitable pour les situations convectives de réduire l'intervalle entre images à moins de 15 minutes.

DIFFUSION

La diffusion des données se fera dans un premier temps par lignes spécialisées, soit depuis un radar pour l'image le concernant soit depuis le service central ou une station alimentée par ailleurs pour les mosaïques radar et les images satellite (voir Fig.2). Les images transmises depuis Paris vers les stations météorologiques transiteront par les canaux à 4800 b s^{-1} utilisés actuellement pour la transmission fac similé des cartes météorologiques. Ce réseau alimente pratiquement toutes les stations départementales de la Météorologie. Parallèlement, les centres météorologiques les plus importants équipés d'une console EMIR recevront également des images satellite en provenance du Centre de Météorologie Spatiale de Lannion par une ligne spécialisée à 2400 b s^{-1}.

La Météorologie a fait industrialiser deux types de stations de réception d'images; ce sont d'une part le terminal EMIR, adapté à l'usage des Centres Météorologiques Régionaux, d'autre part le terminal METEOTEL, qui équipera les stations moins importantes.

Le système EMIR, réalisé par SINTRA ALCATEL, peut être considéré comme la juxtaposition de deux éléments.

Le premier élement est un minicalculateur d'usage général avec ses périphériques; le minicalculateur est une émulation du MITRA 225 par micro-programmation d'un circuit intégré LSI 2901 à "tranche de bit".

Le deuxième élément est une console de visualisation couleur avec ses mémoires et ses processeurs vidéo ainsi que la gestion de moyens d'entrée interactifs. La console gère deux mémoires 512 x 512 x 8 bits (extensible à 12) et une mémoire alphanumérique de 24 lignes de 96 caractères. La liaison de la console au minicalculateur est une liaison accès direct mémoire à haute cadence.

Le système METEOTEL a été conçu avant tout dans un souci d'économie, dans le but d'alimenter un maximum de stations météorologiques. Dans sa version minimum, il est constitué d'un microcalculateur connecté soit sur le réseau fac similé codé à 4800 b s^{-1}, soit sur une ligne spécialisée aboutissant à un radar. La capacité mémoire est de 96 ko, soit deux images au format METEOTEL, pouvant être des images radar local, des images satellitaires ou des images radar composites. Certaines stations météorologiques seront équipées d'une ou deux possibilités supplémentaires de connection sur des lignes téléphoniques, d'une capacité mémoire de 15 images et de possibilités de sortie sur imprimante et/ou magnétophone. Toutes les versions seront équipées d'un clavier de commande permettant certaines manipulations sur les images.

Les stations METEOTEL sont concues autour d'un Bus de communication entre les cartes très répandu, le Bus IEEE 796, ce qui permettra de les faire évoluer ultérieurement en fonction des besoins qui ne manqueront pas de se préciser après leur mise en exploitation.

CONCLUSIONS

Le projet Aramis constitue une des priorités du Service Météorologique Francais. Les efforts demandés par la constitution du réseau de radars se justifieraient entièrement par les seuls besoins propres de ce service.

On entrevoit de nombreuses possibilités d'utilisation des données radar par d'autres services, comme l'aéronautique, la protection civile ou les agences de bassin. Plusieurs expériences ont déjà eu lieu dans ce sens, qui n'ont d'ailleurs pas toutes été positives. Ceci montre que le radar est un instrument qui comme tous les autres a des limites, bien qu'il puisse être adapté à beaucoup d'usages. Les expériences faites jusqu'ice n'ont pas toutes été très clairement définies à l'avance, et ceci peut expliquer qu'on soit parfois arrivé à des résultats trop embrouillés pour que leur signification ait été clairement appréhendée par les décideurs. Nous estimons que malgré des difficultés de ce type qui ne cesseront certainement pas de se présenter, les utilisations opérationnelles du radar pour la détection des phénomènes dangereux, la prévision à très courte échéance et la mesure hydrologique ont un bel avenir.

REFERENCES

Browning, K.A., Collier, C.G., Larke, P.R., Menmuir, P., Monk, G.A. & Owens, R.G. (1982) On the forecasting of frontal rain using a weather radar network. *Mon. Weath. Rev.* 110, 534-552.

Froment, G. (1979) L'expérience HYDROMEL. *Rapport technique final, Establissement d'Etudes et de Recherches Météorologiques, 77 rue de Sèvres, 92 Boulogne.*

Rousseau, D. (1980) A new skill score for the evaluation of yes/no forecasts. In: *WMO Symposium on Probabilistic and Statistical*

Methods in Weather Forecasting, (Nice, September 1980), 167-174.
Wilson, J.W. & Brandes, E.A. (1979) Radar measurements of rainfall - a summary. *Bull. Am. Met. Soc.* 60, 1048-1058.

Hydrological Applications of Remote Sensing and Remote Data Transmission
(Proceedings of the Hamburg Symposium, August 1983). IAHS Publ. no. 145.

Flood forecasting on the basis of radar rainfall measurement and rainfall forecasting

P. KLATT & G. A. SCHULTZ
Ruhr-Universität Bochum, 4630 Bochum, Federal Republic of Germany

ABSTRACT Useful and early flood forecasts require an immediate availability of the observed rainfall and runoff data as well as a quantitative precipitation forecast. For this purpose rainfall is measured by a C-band radar giving the rainfall information for the whole catchment at one point. On the basis of the rainfall observed up to the time of forecast, expected rainfall for the immediate future is forecast by a probabilistic model. Both the rainfall measured by radar and the precipitation forecast form the input into a rainfall-runoff-model which is used for the computation of real time forecasts. Results are shown for a catchment in Bavaria in southern Germany.

Prévision des crues se basant sur les précipitations mesurées par radar et les précipitations prévues
RESUME Pour augmenter la durée de l'intervalle de temps entre la prévision elle même et l'arrivée de la crue. il est nécessaire de disposer aussitôt possible d'informations sur les précipitations mesurées ainsi que d'une estimation quantitative des précipitations futures. A cet effet on propose une méthode comportant trois parties essentielles: (a) l'estimation des précipitations par radar à bande C, (b) à partir de ces informations une prévision probabiliste des précipitations futures et (c) la transformation du hyètogramme en hydrogramme à l'aide d'un modèle pluie-débit. On présente des résultats évalués dans un bassin en Bavière au sud de l'Allemagne.

INTRODUCTION

Flood forecasts are efficient only if the lead-time of the forecast is long enough to initiate flood warnings or flood protection measures (e.g. reservoir operation). In order to maximize the lead-time it is necessary to know the actual data of the flood-causing precipitation as early as possible. For this purpose radar is a useful tool. The rainfall data measured by radar form the input into a distributed mathematical rainfall-runoff model by which the flood forecast is computed. If during the rainfall the flood forecast is based solely on measured rainfall data without a forecast of future rain, the assumption is implied that there will be no rainfall after the time of forecast. This assumption is, of course, most unreasonable in the middle of a severe storm.

Therefore even a simple rainfall forecast means already an improvement. In order to solve this problem a probabilistic model was developed which forecasts the rainfall after the time when the flood forecast is issued.

RADAR-RAINFALL MEASUREMENT

A C-band-radar (~5 cm wavelength) located on an isolated mountain (1000 m a.m.s.l.) in southern Bavaria was used for radar-rainfall-measurement. The radar transmits an electronic pulse which is partially reflected by falling raindrops. The resulting "echo" is received by the radar antenna. The raw-area precipitation data are computed by means of the radar equation

$$\bar{P}_r = \frac{\pi^3}{1024 \ln 2} \frac{P_t \; h \; G^2 \; \Theta \; \Phi}{\lambda^2 \; r^2} |K|^2 \; \kappa \; Z \qquad (1)$$

where:

$\bar{P}_r$ = mean received power,
P_t = transmitted power,
h = pulse length,
G = antenna gain,
Θ, Φ = respectively the horizontal and vertical beam width to 3 dB points,
λ = wavelength,
r = echo distance,
K = complex refraction index of water,
κ = attenuation of electromagnetic radiation,
Z = radar reflectivity = $A\,R^B = \Sigma n_i D_i^{\,6}$,
R = rain intensity,
D_i = rain drop diameter.

The computed raw rainfall depth above one representative surface raingauge station is compared with the raingauge depth and a calibration factor is calculated. Finally, all of the raw data are multiplied by this calibration factor. Spatial resolution of the rainfall information is one degree azimuth and one kilometre in distance. More detailed information is given in Attmannspacher (1976).

RAINFALL FORECASTING

Since detailed, quantitative precipitation forecasting is still an unsolved problem in meteorology, a simple probabilistic approach was used in order to obtain a reasonable estimate of future rainfall while it is still raining. This estimation of future rainfall on the basis of observed rainfall is, in the sense of mathematical statistics, a conditional probability-problem. It has n dimensions, n being the number of parameters describing future rainfall. If the forecast problem is reduced to two parameters, i.e. future duration and future amount of rainfall, then a conditional probability problem of two dimensions has to be solved.

In the research project described here, 192 flood-producing

rainfall events of a special rainfall type (according to Aniol, 1971) were analysed. For this rather large sample size, a linear relation between the logarithms of duration and depth of precipitation was established. The results of the regression analysis are shown in Fig.1. The correlation coefficient is r = 0.708. Although this correlation is not too satisfactory, it can be used in order to reduce the forecasting problem to a one-dimensional conditional probability problem. This way the rainfall duration can be expressed in terms of rainfall amount and vice versa. Therefore, it is sufficient to estimate, for example, future rainfall amount and to determine the corresponding duration with the aid of the regression curve given in Fig.1.

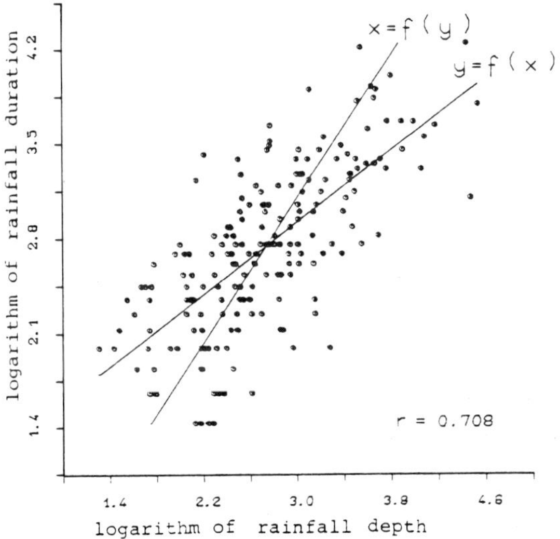

FIG.1 Linear regression between the logarithms of rainfall amount and rainfall duration.

The actual computation of future rainfall amount uses the conditional probability distributions (of rainfall amount) given the rainfall quantity already measured. The most appropriate distributions were the Pearson-III distribution and the gamma distribution which is a special case of the Pearson-III distribution. Based on these probability distributions future rainfall depth can be computed for any specified probability of non-exceedance, p (%). Table 1 gives an example of this dependence which is valid in Bavaria for a special type of rainfall. The complete rainfall forecast procedure is shown in the flow chart of Fig.2.

The analysis of all 192 observed rainfall events revealed that for a probability of non-exceedance, p = 0.6, the mean deviation between forecast and eventually observed rainfall of all of the events was equal to zero. Therefore it is suggested to use for real time forecasts at least p = 0.6. If the flood risk is very high, it may be advisable to forecast rainfall using an even higher probability of non-exceedance.

TABLE 1 Expected future rainfall depth for given observed rainfall and probability p of non-exceedance (example for southern Germany and special type of rainfall)

observed rainfall depth [mm]	expected future rainfall depth [mm]										
p [%]	50	55	60	65	70	75	80	85	90	95	99
2	12.2	13.6	15.1	16.9	19.0	21.5	24.7	28.8	34.3	45.5	71.8
4	10.3	11.7	13.2	15.0	17.1	19.6	22.8	26.9	32.9	43.6	69.9
6	9.5	10.8	12.3	14.1	16.2	18.7	21.8	26.0	32.0	42.7	69.3
8	8.2	9.6	11.1	12.9	15.0	17.5	20.7	24.8	30.9	41.7	68.3
10	8.0	9.4	11.0	12.8	14.9	17.5	20.7	25.0	31.1	41.9	68.7
12	8.4	9.8	11.5	13.3	15.6	18.2	21.5	25.8	32.0	43.0	69.8
14	8.2	9.7	11.3	13.2	15.4	18.0	21.3	25.6	31.9	42.8	69.5
16	8.6	10.1	11.8	13.7	16.0	18.7	22.0	26.4	32.7	43.7	70.7
18	9.0	10.6	12.3	14.3	16.6	19.3	22.7	27.2	33.5	44.7	71.8
20	9.5	11.0	12.8	14.8	17.2	20.0	23.4	27.9	34.4	45.6	72.9
22	9.9	11.5	13.3	15.4	17.8	20.6	24.1	28.7	35.2	46.6	74.0
24	10.3	12.0	13.8	15.9	18.3	21.2	24.8	29.4	36.0	47.5	75.1
26	10.7	12.4	14.3	16.4	18.9	21.8	25.5	30.1	36.8	48.4	76.2
28	11.2	12.9	14.8	17.0	19.5	22.5	26.1	30.9	37.6	49.3	77.3
30	11.6	13.4	15.3	17.5	20.1	23.1	26.8	31.6	38.4	50.2	78.3
32	12.0	13.8	15.8	18.1	20.7	23.7	27.5	32.3	39.2	51.1	79.4
34	12.5	14.3	16.3	18.6	21.2	24.3	28.1	33.0	40.0	51.9	80.4
36	12.9	14.8	16.8	19.1	21.8	24.9	28.8	33.7	40.7	52.8	81.5
38	13.3	15.2	17.3	19.7	22.4	25.6	29.4	34.5	41.5	53.7	82.5
40	13.8	15.7	17.8	20.2	22.9	26.2	30.1	35.2	42.3	54.5	83.5
42	14.2	16.2	18.3	20.7	23.5	26.8	30.8	35.9	43.0	55.4	84.5
44	14.6	16.6	18.8	21.3	24.1	27.4	31.4	36.6	43.8	56.2	85.5
46	15.1	17.1	19.3	21.8	24.7	28.0	32.0	37.3	44.6	57.1	86.5
48	15.5	17.6	19.8	22.3	25.2	28.6	32.7	37.9	45.3	57.9	87.4
50	16.0	18.0	20.3	22.9	25.8	29.2	33.3	38.6	46.1	58.7	88.4
52	16.4	18.5	20.8	23.4	26.3	29.8	34.0	39.3	46.8	59.6	89.4
54	16.8	19.0	21.3	23.9	26.9	30.4	34.6	40.0	47.5	60.4	90.3
56	17.3	19.4	21.8	24.5	27.5	31.0	35.2	40.7	48.3	61.2	91.3
58	17.7	19.9	22.3	25.0	28.0	31.6	35.9	41.4	49.0	62.0	92.2
60	18.2	20.4	22.8	25.5	28.6	32.2	36.5	42.0	49.7	62.8	93.2
62	18.6	20.8	23.3	26.0	29.1	32.8	37.1	42.7	50.5	63.6	94.1
64	19.0	21.3	23.8	26.6	29.7	33.4	37.8	43.4	51.2	64.4	95.0
66	19.5	21.8	24.3	27.1	30.3	33.9	38.4	44.0	51.9	65.2	96.0
68	19.9	22.2	24.8	27.6	30.8	34.5	39.0	44.7	52.6	66.0	96.9
70	20.4	22.7	25.3	28.1	31.4	35.1	39.6	45.4	53.3	66.8	97.8
72	20.8	23.2	25.8	28.7	31.9	35.7	40.3	46.0	54.1	67.6	98.7
74	21.3	23.7	26.3	29.2	32.5	36.3	40.9	46.7	54.8	68.4	99.6
76	21.7	24.1	26.8	29.7	33.0	36.9	41.5	47.4	55.5	69.1	100.5
78	22.1	24.6	27.3	30.2	33.6	37.5	42.1	48.0	56.2	69.9	101.4
80	22.6	25.1	27.8	30.8	34.1	38.0	42.7	48.7	56.9	70.7	102.3
82	23.0	25.5	28.3	31.3	34.7	38.6	43.3	49.3	57.6	71.5	103.2
84	23.5	26.0	28.8	31.8	35.2	39.2	43.9	50.0	58.3	72.2	104.1
86	23.9	26.5	29.2	32.3	35.8	39.8	44.6	50.6	59.0	73.0	105.0
88	24.4	26.9	29.7	32.8	36.3	40.3	45.2	51.3	59.7	73.7	105.8
90	24.8	27.4	30.2	33.3	36.9	40.9	45.8	51.9	60.4	74.5	106.7
92	25.2	27.9	30.7	33.9	37.4	41.5	46.4	52.5	61.0	75.3	107.6
94	25.7	28.3	31.2	34.4	37.9	42.1	47.0	53.2	61.7	76.0	108.4
96	26.1	28.8	31.7	34.9	38.5	42.6	47.6	53.8	62.4	76.8	109.3
98	26.6	29.3	32.2	35.4	39.0	43.2	48.2	54.5	63.1	77.5	110.2
100	27.0	29.7	32.7	35.9	39.6	43.8	48.3	55.1	63.8	78.3	111.0

FLOOD FORECASTING

Rainfall measured by radar plus rainfall forecasts following the procedure described above form the input into a mathematical rainfall-runoff model for forecasting flood hydrographs.

As a test catchment, a southern tributary of the River Danube, the Günz River, was chosen with the river-gauges Lauben (318 km²) and Nattenhausen (526 km²). Radar-rainfall-measurements are feasible over the whole catchment area.

Rainfall-runoff model

In order to make use of the high resolution of the radar data both

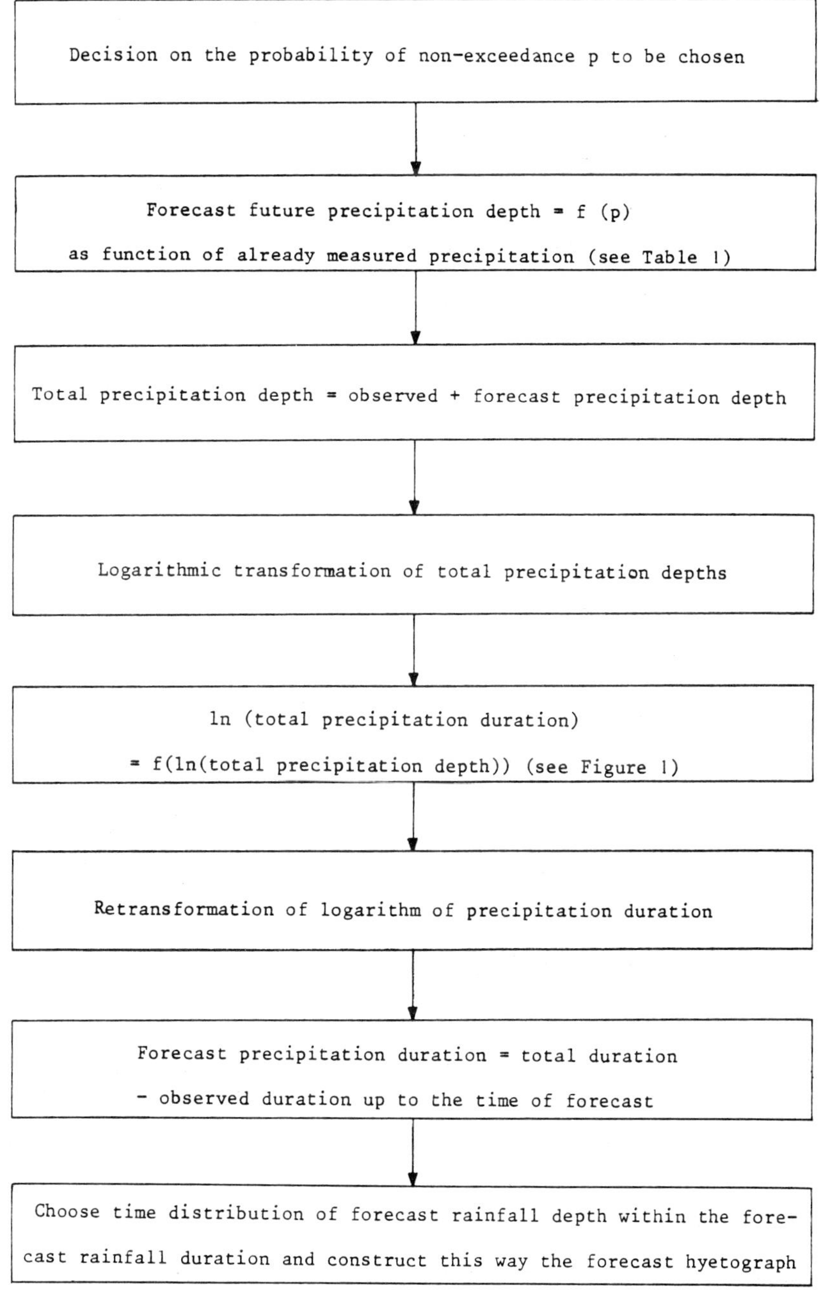

FIG.2 Rainfall forecast procedure.

in space and in time, a rainfall-runoff model of the distributed system called HYREUN model II (Schultz, 1969; Anderl *et al.*, 1976) was selected.

The excess rain hyetographs are computed with the aid of a time-varying runoff coefficient, ψ

$$r_{eff} = r_{obs} \quad \psi_{end}(1 - e^{-at}) \qquad (2)$$

with

r_{eff} = excess rain,
r_{obs} = observed rainfall,
ψ_{end} = final runoff coefficient,
a = constant, and
t = time.

The baseflow was chosen as a linear, slightly increasing function. In order to improve the forecast accuracy the observed flood

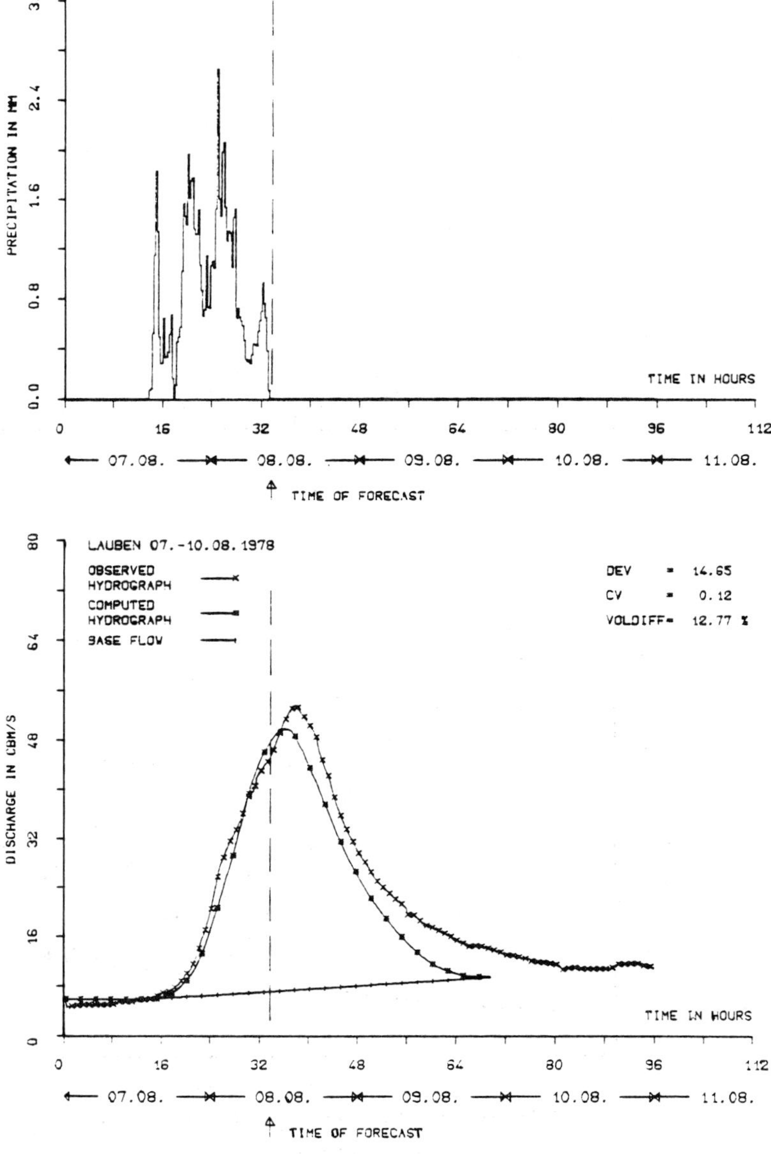

FIG.3 Flood forecast based on radar rainfall measurement.

hydrograph up to the time of forecast is used as an indirect input for real-time re-calibration of the model parameters.

Results

Figure 3 shows an example of a flood forecast after the end of the rainfall event compared to the observed hydrograph. The forecast shows a satisfactory accuracy. The peak and time to peak are in good agreement, while the flood volume is about 10% underestimated.

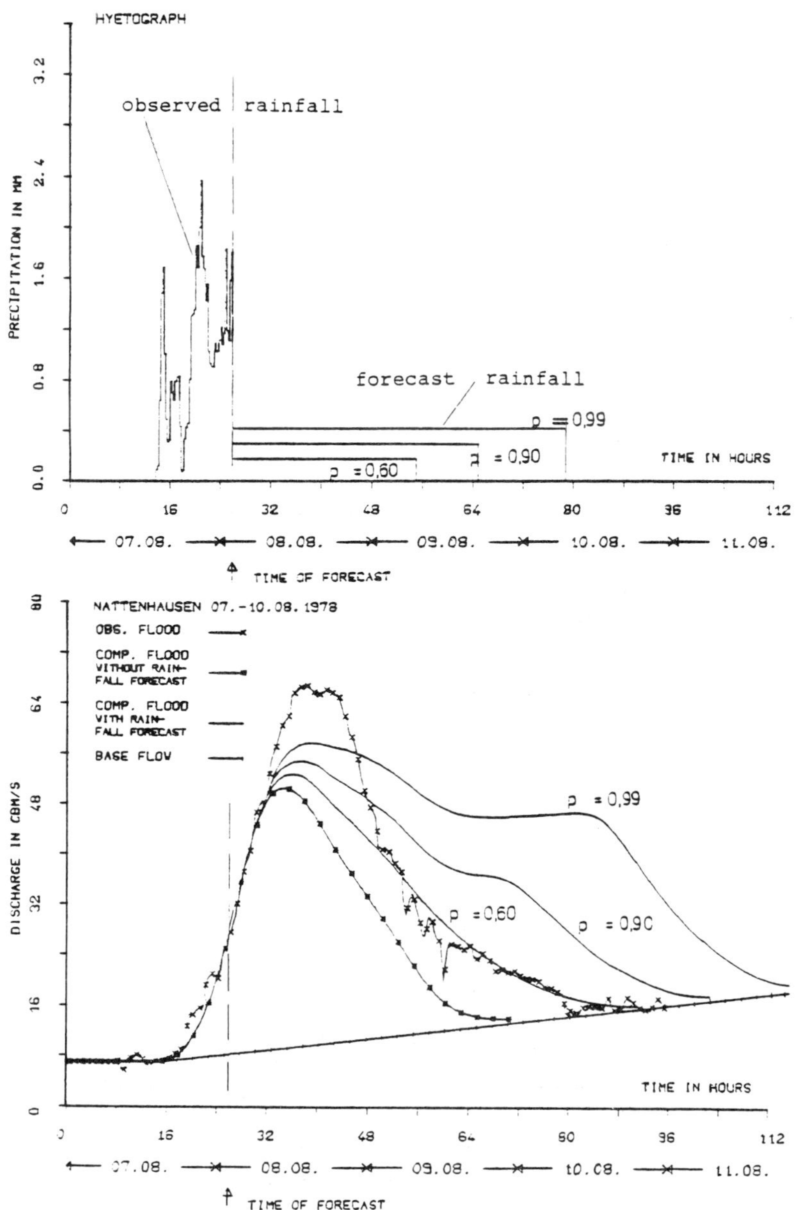

FIG.4 Flood forecast based on radar rainfall measurement and rainfall forecast.

This example shows the performance of an adequate rainfall-runoff model used for flood forecasting. The result is, however, not surprising, since the whole rainfall information is available at the time of forecast and almost the whole rising limb of the actual flood is known and thus used for adjustment of the model parameters. Considerably more difficult and less accurate is a forecast issued *before* the end of the causative rainfall. In this case less

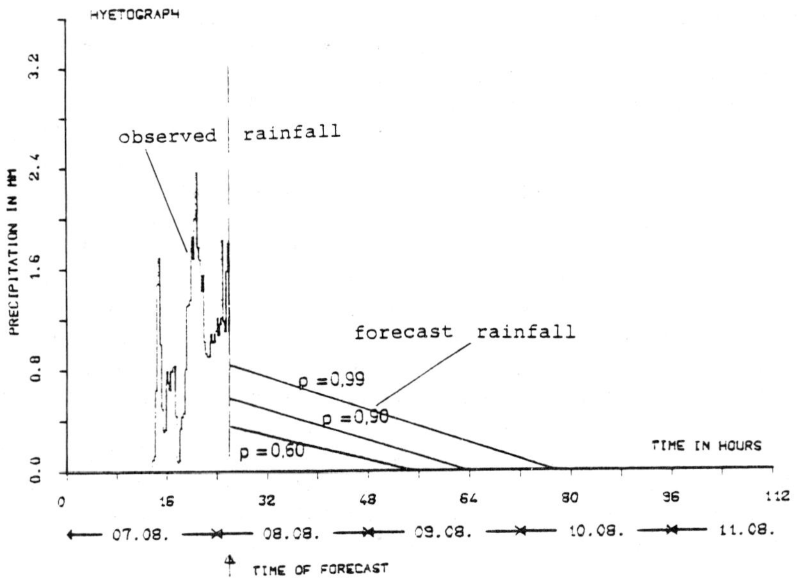

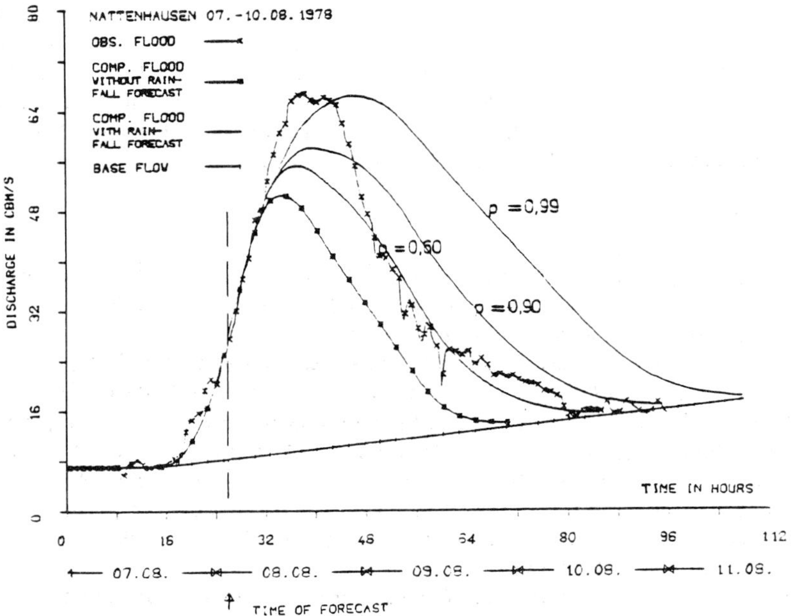

FIG.5 Flood forecast based on radar rainfall measurement and rainfall forecast.

information about the actual rainfall and the actual flood hydrograph is available. Therefore, a rainfall forecast is required and the resulting flood forecast is dependent on the chosen probability of non-exceedance of the future rainfall.

With the aid of the probabilistic model as described previously, future rainfall is estimated according to its depth and duration and the chosen probability of non-exceedance. In order to serve as input into a rainfall-runoff model, however, the time distribution of rainfall intensity within the duration must also be specified. Since no information about the future rainfall distribution is available, a realistic assumption is required. One possible assumption is to expect rainfall of constant intensity.

Figure 4 shows an example of a flood forecast while the rain is still falling, using this assumption about future rainfall. In the diagram four different examples of potential forecasts are given: (a) no future rainfall, (b) future rainfall with $p = 0.60$, (c) future rainfall with $p = 0.90$, (d) future rainfall with $p = 0.99$. It is obvious that even for $p = 0.99$ the flood peak is underestimated. The duration of the total flood is overestimated for $p > 0.6$. This negative result is due to the unrealistic assumption about future rainfall intensity distribution. Figure 5 shows the same conditions except that the rainfall intensity is assumed to be linearly decreasing. The resulting forecast flood hydrograph is much more accurate than the one shown in Fig.4.

Unfortunately, up to now there is only a small number of radar-observed floods available for testing the developed method. Therefore, at present it is not possible to present a statistical analysis of the accuracy of this technique.

ACKNOWLEDGEMENTS The authors wish to thank Dr W.Attmannspacher of the German Weather Service for providing the radar rainfall data and the Bavarian Institute of Water Resources for providing the runoff data. Thanks are also due to the German Research Foundation for financial support of the research work. The computations were carried out at the Computer Centre of the Faculty of Civil Engineering of the Ruhr-University Bochum.

REFERENCES

Anderl, B., Attmannspacher, W. ' Schultz, G.A. (1976) Accuracy of reservoir inflow forecasts based on radar rainfall measurements. *Wat. Resour. Res.* 12 (2), 217-223.

Aniol, R. (1971) Sommerniederschlag am Hohenpeissenberg und Wetterlage. *Sonderbeobachtungen des met. Observatorinms Hohenpeissenberg, No. 17.*

Attmannspacher, W. (1976) Radarmessungen zur Bestimmung von Flächenniederschlägen. *Die Naturwissenschaften* 63, 313-318.

Schultz, G.A. (1969) Digital computer solutions for flood hydrograph prediction from rainfall data. In: *The Use of Analog and Digital Computers in Hydrology* (Proc. Tucson Symp., 1968), vol. 1, 125-137. IAHS Publ. no. 80.

Schultz, G.A. & Klatt, P. (1980) Use of data from remote sensing sources for hydrological forecasting. In: *Hydrological Forecasting* (Proc. Oxford Symp., April 1980), 75-82. IAHS Publ. no. 129.

Hydrological Applications of Remote Sensing and Remote Data Transmission
(Proceedings of the Hamburg Symposium, August 1983). IAHS Publ. no. 145.

SARAH: outil de traitement des images météorologiques

JEAN TARDIEU
Météorologie Nationale EERM/CRPA, Observatoire de Magny les Hameaux, F-78470 Magny les Hameaux, France

RESUME L'interprétation simple et rapide des situations météorologiques nécessite la représentation visuelle et la manipulation aisée de l'ensemble des données acquises. La chaîne SARAH (SAtellite RAdar Hydrologie) permet la manipulation sous un format standardisé d'images envoyées par les satellites, composées à partir des enregistrements des radars ou synthétisées à partir des réseaux de capteurs ou des résultats des modèles mathématiques de simulation ou de prévision météorologique.

SARAH: tool for interpreting meteorological images
ABSTRACT The quick and easy interpretation of meteorological situations requires a clear visual representation and easy manipulation of available data. The SARAH (SAtellite RAdar Hydrology) system allows the analysis on a standard format of satellite and composite radar images as well as from meteorological analysis maps derived from the raingauge network or from numerical weather prediction or simulation models.

INTRODUCTION

La représentation de l'état du fluide qu'est l'atmosphère terrestre a toujours été un problème majeur en météorologie. L'utilisation opérationnelle des satellites porteurs de caméra, de radars et de tout instrument à grand champ d'observation a conduit les centres météorologiques à développer diverses techniques d'analyse de l'atmosphère par traitement des images.

La restitution sur un même maillage des données provenant des satellites et des radars avait été proposée, dans le cadre du projet HIPLEX, par Reynolds & Smith (1979) qui ont montré l'intérêt pour la recherche et la prévision du traitement interactif des images. Différents expérimentateurs ont utilisé des systèmes analogues pour l'analyse combinée des informations fournies par les radars et les satellites (Bellon *et al.*, 1980; Collier, 1981). Il est possible d'ajouter d'autres informations provenant de réseaux météorologiques standards ou complémentaires (Beran & MacDonald, 1981; Saker, 1982; Purdom, 1981).

A l'Etablissement d'Etudes et de Recherches Météorologiques, dans le cadre du traitement des données acquises pendant l'expérience LANDES 79, nous avons développé une chaîne permettant de restituer dans un même quadrillage géographique, des images issues de capteurs à grand champ d'observation (radar à acquisition numérique, satellite etc.). Pour les besoins de la recherche, nous complètons cette chaîne par la visualisation d'autres données provenant des capteurs en service dans les réseaux météorologiques. Enfin, sous ce format, sont représentés les champs prévus par les modèles météorologiques.

DESCRIPTION DE LA CHAINE DE TRAITEMENT

Pour réaliser cette chaîne, nous avons utilisé les possibilités en moyens de calcul et en systèmes de traitement des images qui étaient disponibles à l'EERM, notamment un calculateur CDC 175 et le système METEOSCOPE.

Cette chaîne a été conçue pour être d'un emploi simple et facilement évolutive en fonction des disponibilités ou de l'évolution des matériels.

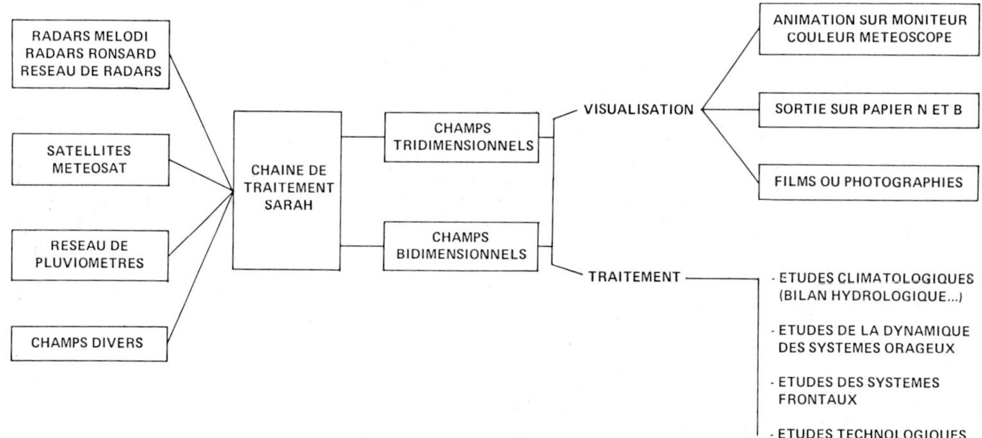

FIG.1 Synoptique de la chaîne SARAH.

La Fig.1 montre les principales étapes du traitement. La partie principale est un fichier numérique bi ou tridimentionnel en points de grille d'un format fixe.

en entrée: les données préalablement enregistrées sur bandes magnétiques numériques

1ére étape: la restitution des données sur une grille décrite suivant un projection géographique classique

2éme étape: interprétation des résultats, visualisation de ces champs

La grille utilisée est décrite suivant les projections Lambert ou Mercator. La projection Lambert est utilisée pour les cartes géographiques de France; elle minimise les déformations pour les régions situées sous nos latitudes. Actuellement, nous améliorons les programmes pour utiliser la projection stéréographique polaire, projection couramment employée par les météorologistes Européens.

VISUALISATION DES IMAGES

Diverses possibilités de visualisation ont été développées notamment en utilisant les imprimantes électrostatiques. Mais le traitement le plus souple consiste à utiliser le METEOSCOPE, système de traitement interactif des images numériques. Ce système est étudié, réalisé et commercialisé par la société Numelec-Sein sous le nom de Pericolor 1000. Dans l'état actuel, le système comprend:

- un moniteur de télévision de 51 cm
- huit plans mémoire 256x256 de 8 bits (ou 4 de 16 bits)
- quatre plans marqueurs de 1 bit

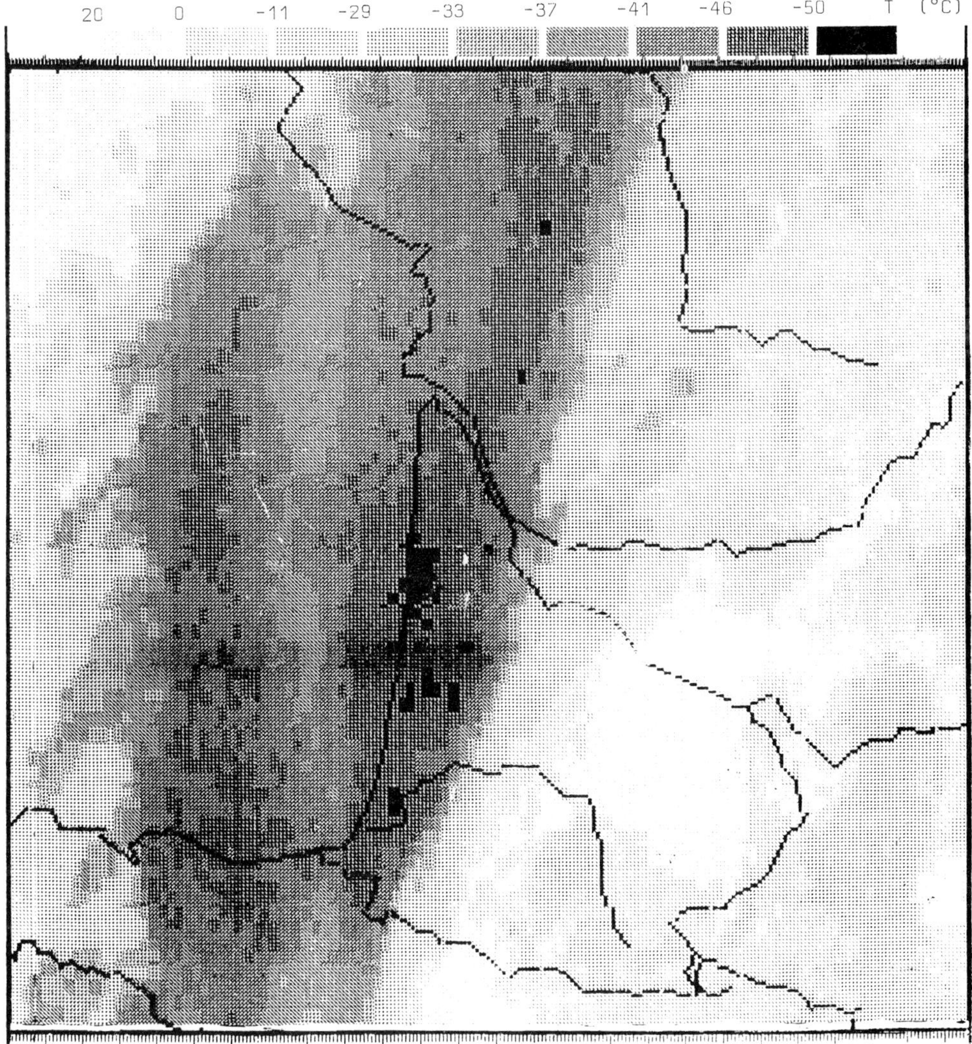

FIG.2 METEOSAT canal infra-rouge à 11 30 TU. L'image est restituée sur une projection Lambert 30/60, centrée sur Bordeaux-Merignac. Le pixel mesure 2 km de côté au centre de l'image. Les teintes de gris correspondent à la température de rayonnement au niveau du satellite.

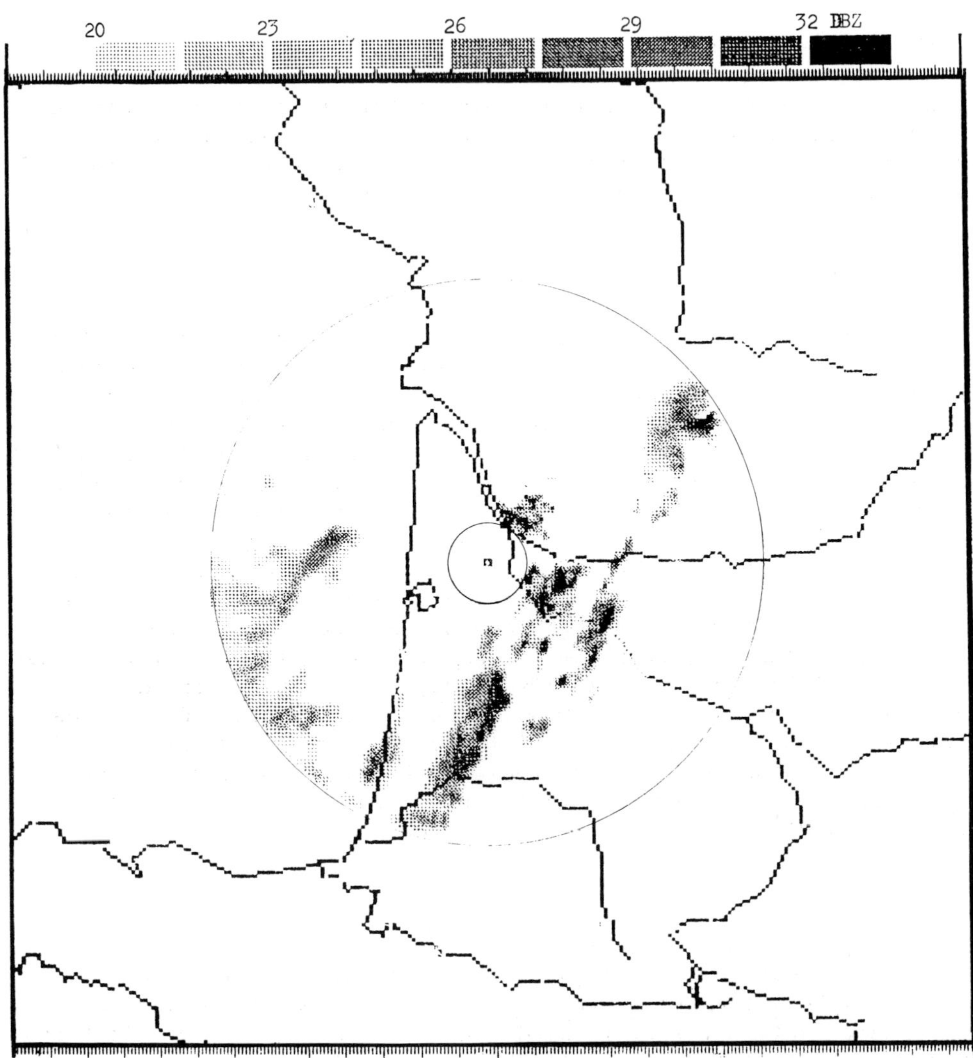

FIG.3 Echos enregistrés par le radar MELODI de Bordeaux-Merignac à 11 51 TU. L'image est restituée sur la même projection que pour la Fig.2. La chaîne numérique sur la radar, dans la configuration utilisée, acquiert les informations entre 10 et 138 km (limites matérialisées par des cercles). Les échos à l'est du radar sont des échos non-météorologiques (échos fixes).

- un plan alphanumérique de 36 lignes de 50 caractères, permettant l'affichage des commentaires et le dialogue avec le système.
- un micro-processeur Intel 8080A, disposant d'une mémoire morte de 32 Ko et d'une mémoire vive de 8 Ko. Il permet, grâce à un logiciel d'emploi simple, de gérer les plans images, marqueurs et alphanumériques, ainsi que le traitement des images (zoom, décadrage, animation, opérations arithmétiques ou booléennes entre deux ou plusieurs images ou sous-images etc.).
- une liaison avec un mini-ordinateur, actuellement un HP2100, qui

possède, entre autres, deux disques de 5 Mo, quatre dérouleurs de bandes magnétiques, une mémoire de 64 Ko. Cette liaison permet le transfert d'images dans les deux sens, l'écriture des plans marqueurs et caractères ainsi que les modifications de l'ensemble des paramètres pour la gestion des images. Le HP2100 doit être remplacé cette année par un mini-ordinateur plus récent.

APPLICATIONS

Actuellement, le système permet l'animation à cadence assez rapide (environ 1 image/seconde) d'un nombre quelconque d'images archivées sur bandes magnétiques, donc pouvant provenir d'autres centres de recherche. Il est aussi utilisé pour l'analyse par animation, du comportement des modèles numériques de prévision ou de simulation de l'atmosphère (Tardieu *et al*, 1982). Il permet en outre de comparer le résultat des simulations numériques avec les phénomènes réels.

L'intercomparaison peut se faire de manière aisée, soit visuellement par utilisation du METEOSCOPE, soit par programme numérique, grâce à l'utilisation conjuguée de fichiers de format standardisé.

Sur les Figs 2 et 3, est présentée une application, prise le 15 août 1979, pendant la campagne LANDES 79. Ce jour-la, un front froid a traversé l'Europe. Dans la région visualisée (sud-ouest de la France), le système frontal organisé en bandes, a donné des pluies isolées, d'intensité moyenne (1 à 10 mm h^{-1}). Sur les Figs 2 et 3, nous pouvons observer que les précipitations, visibles sur l'image radar, ont lieu sur la face avant des bandes de nuages visibles sur la photo satellite.

CONCLUSION

Actuellement outil d'investigation, le METEOSCOPE peut devenir un outil d'exploitation permettant la diffusion, sous forme animée, des données satellites et radars, conjointement avec le résultat des modèles de prévision. En particulier, l'utilisation conjointe sur des projections identiques, d'animations d'images de satellites, et d'images synthétisées à partir d'un réseau radar, ainsi que celles réalisées à partir des résultats de modèles numériques, devient la base d'une surveillance du temps à courte échéance sur la France.

REFERENCES

Bellon, A., Lovejoy, S. & Austin, G.L. (1980) Combining satellite and radar data for the short-range forecasting of precipitation. *Mon. Weath. Rev.* 108, 1554-1566.

Beran, D.W. & MacDonald, A.E. (1981) Design of a short-range forecasting system. Dans: *Mesoscale Observation and Short Range Prediction* (Proc. IAMAP Symp., Hamburg, August 1981).

Collier, C.G. (1981) A system for the combined use of the data from multiple radars and satellites in the United Kingdom. Dans: *Mesoscale Observation and Short Range Prediction* (Proc. IAMAP Symp., Hamburg, August 1981).

Purdom, J. (1981) Combining satellite and conventional data for very short range forecasting purposes. Dans: *Mesoscale Observation and Short Range Prediction* (Proc. IAMAP Symp., Hamburg, August 1981).

Reynolds, D. & Smith, E. (1979) Detailed analysis of composited digital radar and satellite data. *Bull. Am. Met. Soc.* 60, 1024-1037.

Saker, N. (1982) The design of FRONTIER interactive display system. *COST 72 Workshop/Seminar on weather radar* (Reading, UK).

Tardieu, J., Audouin, J.M., Pham, H.L. & Rousseau, D. (1982) Le METEOSCOPE: une aide à la mise au point et à l'exploitation des modèles numériques de météorologie. *Note interne non publiée no.39 de l'EERM,* Direction de la Météorologie, France.

Hydrological Applications of Remote Sensing and Remote Data Transmission (Proceedings of the Hamburg Symposium, August 1983). IAHS Publ. no. 145.

Rainfronts, fractals and rainfall simulations

S. LOVEJOY* & D. SCHERTZER
Météorologie Nationale, EERM/CRMD, 2 Avenue Rapp, 75007 Paris, France

ABSTRACT Rain areas as seen by radar show a complex of bands, lines and other structures. Fluctuations in both time and space can occasionally be very large. Radar and satellite data from Canada, Spain, France and the tropical Atlantic on scales from 1 to 1000 km are analysed in the context of fractals, i.e. objects with structure at all scales. It is possible to construct fractal rainfall models of the evolution of rainfields that are fairly realistic both visually and statistically. In particular, the models presented have the following properties: realistic "complexity" of shapes (as measured by the fractal dimension); realistic distribution of fluctuations; realistic distribution of rainfronts; and, realistic distribution of rain areas.

Simulation de fronts de pluie, des structures fractales et des précipitations

RESUME Les régions de pluie, vues par radar, ont des formes très compliquées avec des bandes, des lignes, et d'autres structures de toutes tailles. De temps en temps, les fluctuations dans l'espace et dans le temps sont exceptionnellement importantes. A l'aide de données radars et satellitaires on analyse les formes et les fluctuations sur une gamme d'échelle allant de 1 a 1000 km, en divers lieux. Ces analyses, couplées avec la théorie des objets fractals (c.a.d. ayant une structure à toutes échelles) ont permis la construction de modèles aléatoires de la pluie. Ces modèles dépendent de trois paramètres et produisent des simulations de l'évolution de champs de pluie ayant un comportement globalement réaliste comme en témoigne la visualisation de ces simulations. En particulier, ces simulations ont les propriétés suivantes: une bonne "complexité" des formes (qui est mésurée par la dimension fractale); des fluctuations réalistes; une bonne distribution des longueurs de fronts; une bonne distribution des aires de pluie.

INTRODUCTION

A striking feature of rainfall is its extreme spatial and temporal variability. Over a wide range of time and space scales, sudden changes occur so frequently that rainfall has been intuitively described as "erratic". An equally striking feature evident on any radar rain map (e.g. Fig.1) is that rain areas appear to be bounded by straight-line structures. This fact is sufficiently important to

*Current address: Physics Department, McGill University, 3600 University St., Montreal, Quebec, Canada.

FIG.1 A radar rain map at 3 km altitude taken by the ship Quadra in the tropical Atlantic. Symbols in numerical and then alphabetical order indicate rain rates on a log scale, eight symbols per decade in rain rate. Resolution is 4 x 4 km. An asterisk indicates sea clutter (i.e. noise - centre only), and the maximum radar range (220 km). Note the prevalence of straight lines, commonly referred to as "bands".

have given rise to a large specialist literature concerning the nature and phenomenology of these "fronts" and "bands". Erratic or "intermittent" behaviour was tackled by Mandelbrot (1973, 1977, 1982) and Mandelbrot & Wallis (1968), who, by incorporating such behaviour in the notion of fractals, suggested a simple and direct connection between a certain kind of erratic behaviour and straight-line structures. The present paper establishes that rainfall from diverse regions of the earth is indeed erratic in this sense, and confirms that rain areas are bounded by a hierarchy of straight-line structures, the largest of which are commonly identified with "fronts".

THE NOAH EFFECT

The change in rain intensity over a short distance may be denoted by ΔR and the probability of observing a change (or fluctuation) can be denoted by $Pr(\Delta R > \Delta r)$, with ΔR exceeding Δr. When

$$Pr(\Delta R > \Delta r) \sim (\Delta r)^{-\alpha} \text{ with } \alpha < 2,$$

large fluctuations occur so frequently that the function changes discontinuously (see Fig.2). Mandelbrot showed this rule to be central to the description of one sort of erratic behaviour, which he called the "Noah effect" (Mandelbrot & Wallis, 1968), after the extreme rainfall fluctuation responsible for the biblical flood. (For the "Joseph effect", see Mandelbrot (1977, 1982)).

The purpose of this paper is to establish that this poetic term also fits more mundane evidence: the author discovered that fluctuations in rainfall from diverse regions follow the above rule, $(\Delta r)^{-\alpha}$, with $\alpha \sim 5/3$. The key properties of distributions of this form are (a) that the probability concentrated in their tails is so large that the variance is infinite, and (b) that in random samples drawn from such a distribution the largest value is almost surely of the same magnitude as the sum of all the others. To applied statisticians, the behaviour seemed so peculiar that the distribution $(\Delta r)^{-\alpha}$ was dismissed *a priori* from statistical

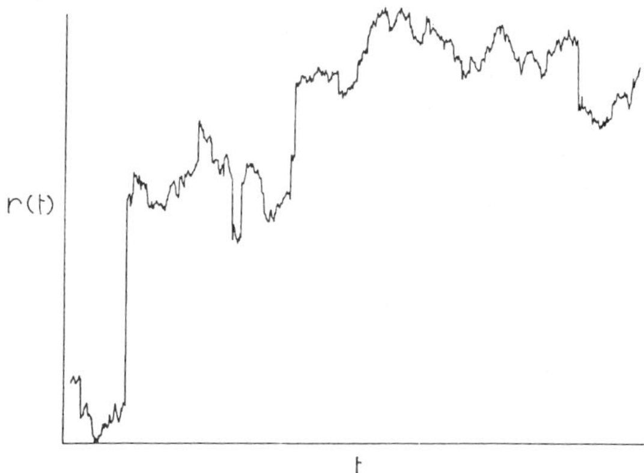

FIG.2 A Monte-Carlo simulation of a rainfall time series (r(t)) constructed by adding 1300 consecutive independent random variables from the distribution $\Delta r^{-1.65}$. *Positive and negative changes were equally likely. Note that in any interval, most of the change in r(t) is due to one large "jump", hence the term "erratic".*

modelling. Mandelbrot argues, to the contrary, that this behaviour makes the scaling distribution eminently suitable in many areas of modelling. Indeed, when a random function is constructed by summing these random variables (Fig.2), the function is discontinuous, and the largest discontinuity often dominates over the change due to all the others. This is true for all subintervals, yielding erratic behaviour at all scales. In the present specific case, the largest discontinuities can be identified with rain fronts, but there is a whole hierarchy of lesser discontinuities. Figure 3 shows computer simulations of this effect in the two spatial dimensions rather than the temporal one, showing that the discontinuities evident in Fig.2 appear here as straight line structures (see later sections and Lovejoy & Mandelbrot (1985)).

A further striking feature of the hyperbolic distribution resides in its scaling: when the rule $Pr(\Delta R > \Delta r) \sim (\Delta r)^{-\alpha}$ is extended down to $\Delta r = 0$, the result becomes invariant with respect to scale changes. Thus, this paper establishes that rainfront intensities are scaling. To the student of turbulence, the value $\alpha = 5/3$ for the scaling exponent is most suggestive, but the author did not yet seek to explain its occurrence here.

Lovejoy (1982) has recently shown that the projections of rain area shapes have no characteristic length scales and are therefore fractals. This finding expressed mathematically the intuitive view of cloud and rain shapes as composed of billows upon billows down to very small sizes. Adding the result reported in the present paper, we find that rain areas are bounded by fractals which are discontinuous at all scales, and are bounded by straight line structures. The horizontal rain field is thus composed of a large number of fronts, the largest of which dominate the others and yield the bands and fronts characteristic of radar rain maps. The erratic nature of rain is important not only in explaining the morphology of rain, but also because these large random fluctuations in rain are a potentially serious impediment to deterministic forecasting.

EMPIRICAL EVIDENCE FOR THE NOAH EFFECT

This section sketches the procedure followed to establish that rain fluctuations do indeed exhibit the Noah-effect. A direct connection with rainfronts will be made later. It is natural to observe the fluctuations in the flux of rain from an isolated rain area. This was done with radar data with 4 x 4 km spatial and 5 minute temporal resolution, from Canada (Montreal), Spain, and the tropical Atlantic. Because rain areas frequently split apart or merge together, it is necessary to establish criteria for their selection. In Fig.4 only those areas that maintained their identity for at least 100 minutes, with only minor splits, were selected. Rain areas were followed until a major split or merger occurred, after which the area was considered "dead" (see Tsonis & Austin, (1981) for details). Less than 10% of all areas satisfied these criteria. Because some minor splitting is allowed, but merging forbidden, decreases in flux are slightly favoured, outnumbering increases by about 20%.

The straight-line behaviour evident on the log-log plot (Fig.4) is a sensitive indicator of hyperbolic distributions (Mandelbrot,

1960), particularly for $\alpha < 2$. When the distributions from Spain, Montreal, and the tropical Atlantic are normalized so as to yield the same flux, the Δr distributions cannot be statistically distinguished by Komolgorov-Smirnov tests. If the positive and negative Δr's are normalized separately, they are also distributed similarly.

More support for the hypothesis of $(\Delta r)^{-1.65}$ behaviour comes from Fig.5, where a different rain area selection criteria was used. All areas that neither split nor merged on two consecutive scans were used - about 50% of the areas present. During the 3 h during which data were collected, the total flux of all storms increased by 40%, however, positive and negative Δr's were almost equal in number (238 and 213 respectively). Most of the increase is therefore due to the fact that the large positive Δr's exceed by ~50% the large negative Δr's (Fig.5). Subintervals during which the flux decreased yielded similar distributions except that the relative magnitude of the distributions of large positive and large negative Δr's was different. In all cases, the $\Delta r^{-1.65}$ asymptotic behaviour was unaffected.

Digression on the predictability of rain fluxes

Comparison of the distributions of Δr for different time intervals (Δt) yields important information on the existence of time scales in the atmospheric processes that produce rain. When such processes involve a typical time interval T, we expect the shape of the Δr distributions to be different for $\Delta t < T$ and $\Delta t > T$, hence the distances between the curves in Fig.4 to be different for $\Delta t > T$ or $\Delta t < T$. In fact, the data show similarly shaped curves, differing by a factor 2^H as Δt is doubled. Because of the close link between time and space scales, the apparent absence of time scales between 5 and 40 minutes is consistent with the fractal geometry of rain and cloud shapes between 1 km^2 and 1.2×10^6 km^2, reported by Lovejoy (1982).

It should be noted that the scaling exponent, H, is a generalized structure function exponent, a generalization necessary in the present case where the structure function does not exist due to the infinite variance of Δr. The scaling exponent H is apparently the same in the three regions examined, and was estimated in two ways. The distance between successive Δr curves, determined directly, yields $H = 0.69 \pm 0.06$. Alternatively, a straight line with slope -1.65 can be fitted, determining the intercept with the line "probability = 1". If this intercept is regarded as a function of Δt, linear regression yields $H = 0.59$. It was shown (Mandelbrot, 1977, 1982) that for Noah erratic fluctuations, the condition for independence is $H_{ind} = 1/\alpha$. This possibility is not excluded by our data, which for $\alpha = 1.65$ yields $H_{ind} = 0.61$.

If fluctuations are independent, then forecasts of future changes in flux cannot be made on the basis of the previous rainflux history. This last conclusion was tentatively reached elsewhere (Tsonis & Austin, 1981) and is clearly incompatible with rain models postulating a well-defined storm lifecycle.

(b)

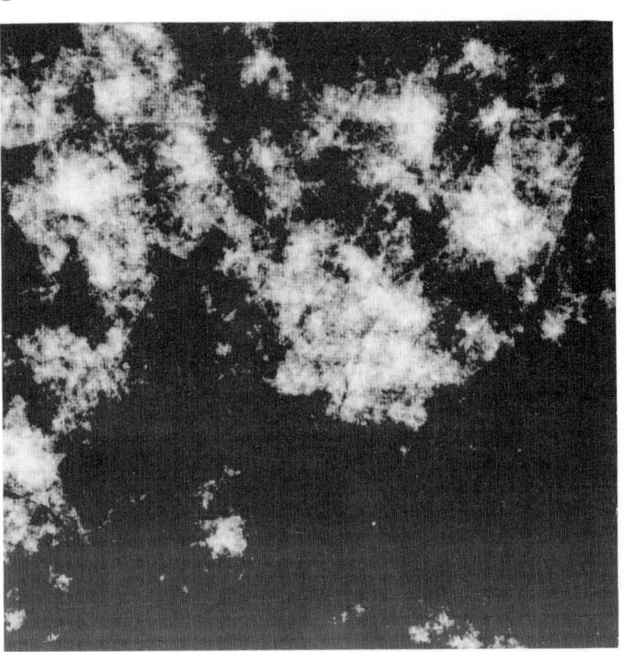

(a)

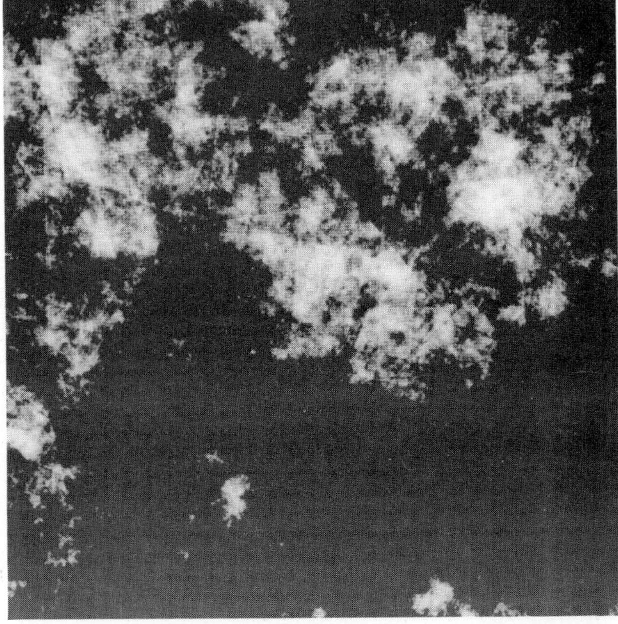

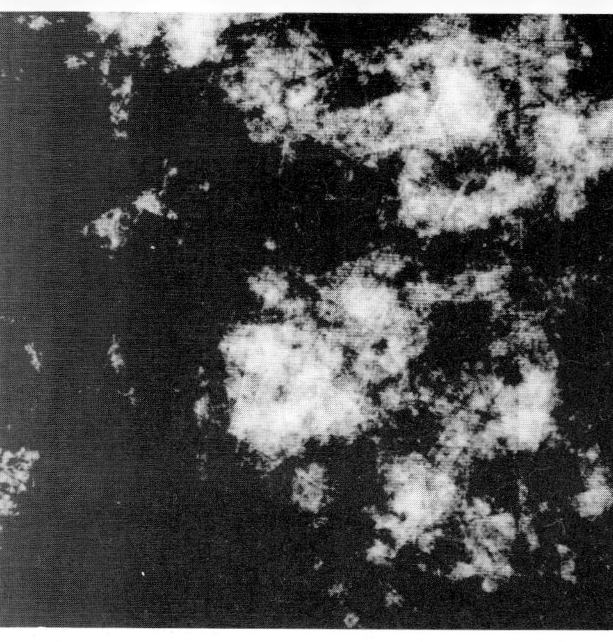

(c)

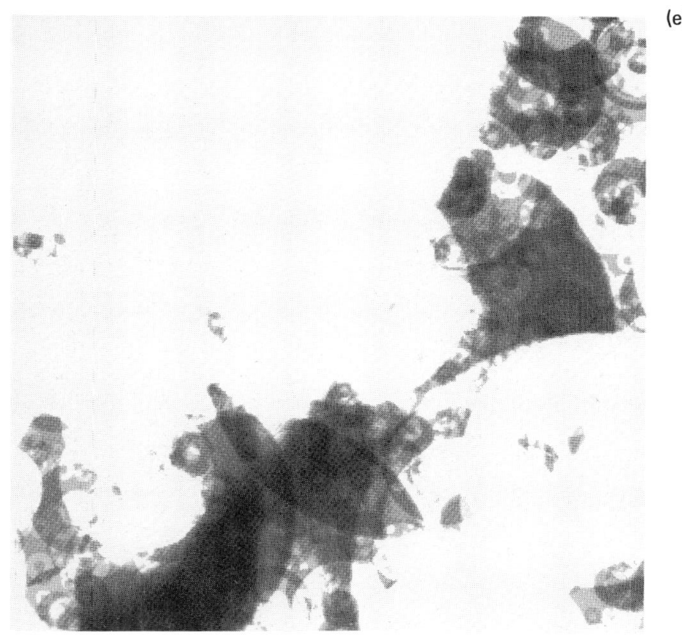

(e)

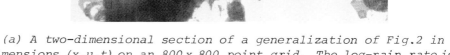

(d) *FIG.3* (a) A two-dimensional section of a generalization of Fig.2 in three dimensions (x,y,t) on an 800×800 point grid. The log-rain rate is represented by the intensity of the white. This "front" type model is constructed from the addition of 250 000 straight-line discontinuities of which the strongest are still visible. The cloud-like appearance of the result is unsurprising because of the geometric simularities between the cloud and rain fields (see Lovejoy (1982) of Fig.7).

(b) Same as (a) but at a time corresponding to 16 grid points later.

(c) Same as (b) but 16 grid points later.

(d) An example of the "annular eddy" model descibed in Lovejoy & Mandelbrot (1985), on a 400×400 point grid by the addition of 60 000 annuli (see (e)). The log-rain rate structures here are segments of enormous annuli.

(e) An intermediate stage in the construction of an "annular eddy" type model on an 800×800 point grid with a quarter of the density of the annuli of (d). Increasung the density results in a field similar to (d).

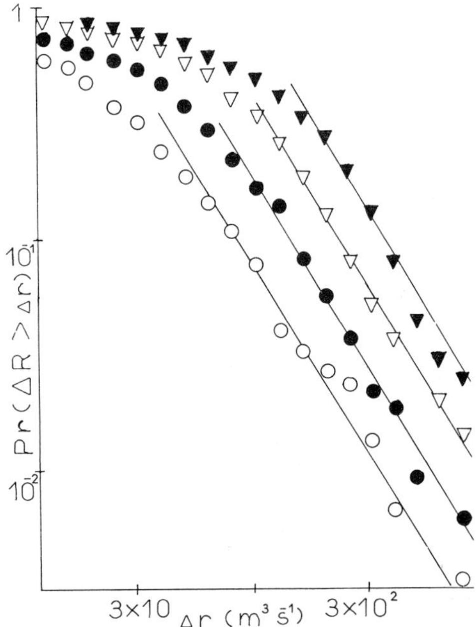

FIG.4 The probability ($Pr(\Delta R > \Delta r)$) of a random change in rain flux (ΔR) exceeding a fixed Δr; negative Δr only. White circles are 5 minutes apart, black circles are 10, white triangles are 20, and black triangles are 40. Straight lines have slopes of -1.65. Data are from two afternoons in Spain, and 21 different rain areas selected as described in the text.

AN EMPIRICAL STUDY OF RAIN AND CLOUD FRONTS

The existence of straight-line structures in the rain field has been inferred indirectly from the existence of (a) the Noah effect, and (b) the observed scaling (fractal) nature of both the fluctuation probability distribution, and the area-perimeter relation (and indirectly from spectra, see Lovejoy (1982)).

It is therefore of considerable interest to investigate the properties of straight-line structures in a more direct manner. These fronts have two main characteristics: (a) their length (l), and (b) their average intensity (i). The probability distributions of l,i were determined in the following manner. Rain maps were divided into two by randomly chosen straight lines. The total length of these lines that were within one pixel or a rain perimeter was taken as the length. The intensity was simply determined as the mean gradient. Data were separated into left and right hand sides, depending on which side of the line the rain part happened to be.

The results of such an analysis for radar rain data, and satellite cloud top temperature data over France, are shown in Fig.6. Also shown are the results for computer simulations of the sort shown in Fig.3, as well as for classical shapes such as circles and squares. The data and the simulations are well approximated by

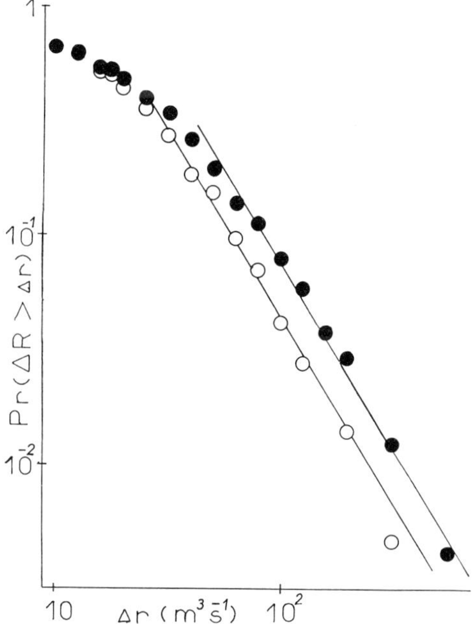

FIG.5 The probability ($Pr(\Delta R > \Delta r)$) of a random change in rain flux over 5 minutes (ΔR), exceeding a fixed Δr; ●, positive changes; ○, negative changes. Data are from the tropical Atlantic; rain areas were selected as described in the text.

the straight lines representing $Pr(L > l) \sim l^{-3.6}$. If alternative methods of defining l are used, the width of the distribution is changed, but not the slope (i.e. the $l^{-3.6}$ behaviour is unaffected).

If two different physical mechanisms were responsible for the curved sections of the rain perimeter and for the straight "frontal" sections, then we would expect a kink in Fig.6 separating the short lengths (from the curved sections), from the longer "frontal" sections. This would indicate a bimodal probability density of l, and thus allow an objective distinction to be made between the small and large l regimes. To illustrate this separation, the probability distribution has been determined for two cases with "fronts" of well defined size - a square and a series of parallel "stripes", and for a case with no "fronts" - the circle. The distributions in the former case are clearly characterized by a kink at a length corresponding to the size of the square and stripes. For the circle, we have only an extremely rapid fall-off with no lengths greater than a fraction of the circle radius. This is quite unlike the hyperbolic distributions found in the data which have no characteristic value. Also of interest is the close agreement between the distribution of l from both satellite and radar data with the Monte-Carlo simulations of the type shown in Fig.3. Since the simulations were designed to exhibit the Noah effect with $\alpha = 5/3$, and thus only indirectly produce straight-line structures, this agreement is significant. Figure 7 shows the distribution of i; it also shows agreement between the simulations

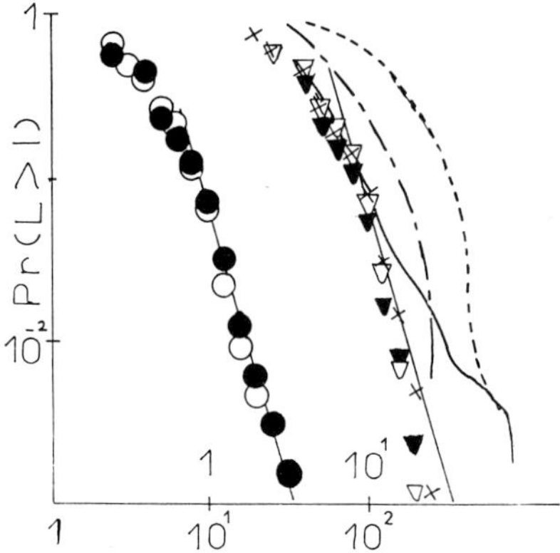

FIG.6 The probability (Pr(L > l)) of a randomly sampled front, length L exceeding a fixed l. Units are in pixels, the lower scale is only for the open circles (satellite cloud top temperature data over France), and for the closed circles (radar rainfall data also over France). The straight lines represent the function $l^{-3.6}$. *The triangles and X's are from simulations of the sort shown in Fig.3. The solid (curved) line is for a square of 80 pixels on a side, and the regular dashed line, for a series of 20 parallel rectangles, each 2 x 80 pixels, separated by a distance of 2 pixels. Note the kink before the sudden fall-off at l = 80. The stipled line is for a circle, radius 50 pixels.*

and the data (see Lovejoy *et al.*, 1983).

FRACTAL RAINFALL SIMULATIONS

It is possible to construct stochastic processes that reproduce the basic characteristics of the rain field - the hyperbolic exponent α, and the scaling exponent H. However, here, unlike the case of Gaussian fluctuations (for example, Mandelbrot's (1977) fractal mountains and planetscapes), the scaling is insufficient to uniquely specify the field. The existence of the Noah effect in rain is fortunate in that it allows for a wide variety of possible rainfall shapes in accord with the richness of actual rainfall geometries. This multiplicity of possibilities may be understood by considering the construction of random rainfields by the addition of large numbers of basic shapes - e.g. the "fronts" used in Fig.3(a),(b),(c) or the "annular eddies" used in Fig.3(d). When the intensities of these forms are distributed hyperbolically with $\alpha < 2$, the strongest dominates the others, and thus the geometry of the basic shape is important no matter how many of these basic shapes are added together (see Fig.3(e) for an illustration of an intermediate stage in the construction of the "annular eddy" model [see Lovejoy & Mandelbrot (1985) for the details - mathematical and otherwise - of these models]).

A more realistic rain model would clearly require a better

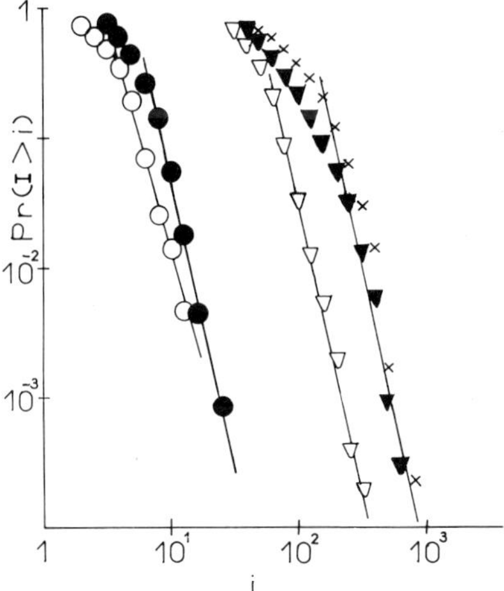

FIG.7 The probability (Pr(I > i)) of a random intensity I exceeding a fixed i, arbitrary units. The straight lines indicate the function $i^{-4.5}$ *(except for the open circles) where it represents* $i^{-3.5}$*). Note the close agreement between the simulations and the radar data.*

empirical knowledge of the rain field - including other geometric parameters (such as the "lacunarity", see Mandelbrot (1982)). A physical interpretation of the fundamental shapes involved would also be important. For the moment, the annular eddy model is preferred because of its simplicity. The example shown in Fig.3(d) has $\alpha = 5/3$, $H = 3/5$ and roughly correct values for the "complexity" of the shapes (fractal dimension), the distribution of the fronts, areas of rain, etc. This model may therefore already be suitable to certain types of hydrological simulations.

The generalization of the model to the time domain (Fig.3(a),(b),(c)) was effected by making the Taylor hypothesis of "frozen turbulence". An isotropic shape in the three-dimensional x,y,t space was constructed, and the three slices shown in Fig.3(a),(b),(c) were taken parallel to the x,y plane. Generalizations to the vertical coordinate can be made in a similar manner if the strong anisotropy of the vertical direction was taken into account, as described in Schertzer & Lovejoy (1985a,b). Other improvements include taking into account the Coriolis force (see Lovejoy & Schertzer, 1985a,b).

CONCLUSIONS

Based on data from Spain, Canada, the tropical Atlantic and France, it has been established that rainfall fluctuations are indeed erratic, and can be characterized by the parameter $\alpha = 5/3$. In addition, evidence here as well as elsewhere indicates the rain field to be scaling, i.e. rain areas are bounded by fractals. Combining these two results leads us to conclude that rain areas are bounded by a hierarchy of straight-line structures (a necessary consequence of discontinuity in two dimensions), the largest of which we identify as bands or fronts. Finally, this conclusion was directly verified by showing that the empirical distribution of both rain and cloud front lengths was not bimodal, but hyperbolic, of the form Pr(L > l) ~ $l^{-3.6}$. This direct argument establishes that rain and cloud areas are indeed bounded by a hierarchy of straight structures, and that the longest of these, often identified with fronts or bands, are simply the largest of a continuous hierarchy of such structures.

REFERENCES

Lovejoy, S. (1982) Area-perimeter relation for cloud and rain areas. *Science* 106, 185-187.

Lovejoy, S., Tardieu, J. & Monceau, G. (1983) Etude d'une situation frontale - analyse météorologique et fractale. *La Météorologie* 4 (29-30), 111-118.

Lovejoy, S. & Mandelbrot, B. (1985) Fractal properties of rain and a fractal model. *Tellus* (in press).

Lovejoy, S. & Schertzer, D. (1985a) Generalized scale invariance in the atmosphere and fractal models of rain. *Wat. Resour. Res.* (in press).

Lovejoy, S. & Schertzer, D. (1985b) Scale invariance, symmetries, fractal and stochastic simulations of atmospheric phenomena. *Bull. Am. Met. Soc.* (in press).

Mandelbrot, B. (1960) The Pareto-Levy law and the distribution of income. *J. Business* 36.

Mandelbrot, B. (1973) Formes nouvelles du hasard dans les sciences. *Economie Appliquée* 26, 307-319.

Mandelbrot, B. (1977) *Fractals: Form, Chance and Dimension.* Freeman and Co., San Francisco.

Mandelbrot, B. (1982) *The Fractal Geometry of Nature.* Freeman and Co., San Francisco.

Mandelbrot, B. & Wallis, J.R. (1968) Noah, Joseph and operational hydrology. *Wat. Resour. Res.* 4, 909-918.

Schertzer, D. & Lovejoy, S. (1985a) The dimension and intermittency of atmosperhic dynamics. In: *Turbulent Shear Flow*, vol. 4 (ed. by B.Launder), 7-33. Springer, Berlin.

Schertzer, D. & Lovejoy, S. (1985b) Generalized scale invariance in turbulence phenomena. *J. of PCH* (in press).

Tsonis, T. & Austin, T. (1981) An evaluation of extrapolation techniques for the short-term prediction of rain amounts. *Atmos.-Ocean* 19, 54-65.

Hydrological Applications of Remote Sensing and Remote Data Transmission (Proceedings of the Hamburg Symposium, August 1983). IAHS Publ. no. 145.

Quantitative measurements of snowfall using unattended mountain top radar

J. A. KLEPPE
Scientific Engineering Instruments, Inc., Sparks, Nevada, USA
S. L. LIU
College of Engineering, University of Nevada at Reno, Reno, Nevada, USA

ABSTRACT There has been long term disagreement in the scientific community as to whether or not radar could be used to provide quantitative measurements of snowfall. Most work accomplished to date in radar meteorology has been concerned with rain, hail and severe storms, but there has been very little comprehensive research involving snow. This paper reports on a research project that involves an investigation into a new method whereby unattended, calibrated weather radars could be used to provide wide area precipitation measurements of snowfall. Mountain top radars would provide valuable data in mountainous regions where snowfall is of major importance to flood control, cloud seeding, vehicular and aircraft traffic, and general watershed operations and/or management. During the winter season of 1981 and 1982 in the Sierra Mountains, experimental results support the existance of a "correction factor" that could be of major importance to radar meteorology in snow regions. Continued field sampling of snow storms is proposed in conjunction with the operation of a vertically pointed Doppler sodar.

Mesure quantitative de la chûte de neige à l'aide d'un radar isolé situé en haut d'une montagne
RESUME Depuis longtemps on discute de la possibilité pour le radar de fournir des mesures quantitatives des chûtes de neige. Jusqu'à présent, l'emploi du radar en météorologie s'est limité généralement à l'étude de la pluie, de la grêle et des orages importants, mais il y a eu peu de recherches soutenues en ce qui concerne la neige. La présente communication décrit l'application d'une nouvelle méthode dans laquelle des radars météorologiques isolés et étalonnés pourraient être utilisés pour mesurer la chûte de neige dans une région assez étendue. Ces radars en haut des montagnes seraient importants dans les régions montagneuses où la chûte de la neige joue un grand rôle dans le contrôle des inondations, la pluie provoquée, la circulation sur la terre et dans l'air, et en général tout ce qui concerne l'écoulement de l'eau. Des recherches préliminaires menées par Scientific Engineering Instruments, Inc. (SEI) en hiver 1981 et 1982

dans les montagnes de la Sierra Nevada suggerènt qu'il y aurait un "facteur de correction" qui serait d'une importance capitale pour l'application des radars météorologiques dans les régions montagneuses. On propose de continuer les recherches sur place en combinaison avec un sodar Doppler orienté verticalement.

INTRODUCTION

Radar has been used for years in various weather measurement applications (Smith *et al.*, 1974). There has recently been an increased interest in developing radars for use as a tool in bringing the "art and sciences" of weather forecasting down to "the man on the street" (Salisbury, 1982). Weather pictures, as seen on the nightly news, do help weather watchers and meteorologists obtain an overall picture - atmospherically speaking, but they do not provide much information about the local weather conditions that an area might experience. One major limitation of existing valley based radar systems, in mountainous areas, is the effect of ground clutter as the radar "looks" up over the foothills and into the mountainous areas. In Sierra-type snowstorms, for example, much of the precipitation of interest can occur at levels well under the radar beam of a valley based radar. Therefore, unless each valley has a radar, little or no local information on the storm can be obtained as it tracks over the mountains.

There are many basins that derive their influx mostly from snowfall with the resulting snowpack serving as the basic water reserve. In the Sierra Range, snowpack becomes a critical storage means for annual precipitation. Also, there are extensive cloud seeding operations planned and in progress in several snow regions throughout the United States, as well as in the Sierra. Such programs could use mountain top radar information during both seeding operations and down-wind studies. Precipitation patterns and cell movements would provide valuable targeting information for both ground based and airborne cloud seeding projects. Mountain top radar data would also be of great value for flood forecasting and wide area water resource management.

The major portion of work accomplished to date in quantitative radar meteorology has been mostly concerned with rain, hail, and severe storms, but very little has been done with snowfall. It is not that researchers haven't attempted to use radar for quantitative snowfall measurements, but rather that most of the work to date has led to inconsistent results (Ohtake, 1969; Carlson & Marshall, 1972; Punakka, 1975; Passarelli, 1978). The feasibility of being able to relate radar reflectivity of snowfall to meteorological parameters such as water content and equivalent rainfall rate continues to be quite a controversial subject. Some researchers even argue that there are too many basic problems associated with radar measurement in snow to warrant further investigation. The most common problems cited have been:

(a) Snow can be easily blown over large regions rather than being deposited directly under the measured precipitative area.

(b) Different temperatures and moisture contents of snow can result in relative dielectric constants ranging from about 1 to 81, hence creating measurement errors.

(c) The terminal fall velocity of snowflakes is a function of the snowflake shapes and drag coefficients, hence leading to additional measurement errors.

Such arguments do represent valid concerns; however, in most cases they have not been supported by a careful planned set of experiments or actual radar snowfall measurements. For example, it is obvious that if one were to measure snowfall having mixed phases, quantitative results could not be expected. Boucher (1978, 1981) reports correctly that when the hydrometeors are all in the ice phase (dry snow) strong correlations can be found between the radar reflectivity and snowfall rate. This is one reason for using mountain top radars since they can be located such that the radar beam is above the melting layer. The system (Fig.1) reported by Kleppe, 1974; Chisholm *et al.*, 1975) was operated high on a 2743 m peak for just this reason. Also, this radar was pointed horizontally and hence minimized errors due to spatial differences between the radar observed precipitation and where it was finally deposited.

The development of mini and microcomputer technology may be effectively applied to support the operation of such remote mountain top radar systems. The work reported herein is based, in part, on the discovery of a radar reflectivity "correction" factor, the use of a remote unattended mountain top radar and the application of a standard target for routine system calibration.

TECHNICAL DISCUSSION

It is instructive to briefly review some weather radar fundamentals in order to understand the detailed research plan being implemented. The equation for a distributed target can be written in the form:

$$P_r = \frac{cP_t\tau\lambda^2\theta^2\eta_{av}g^2}{(1024)\pi^2[\ln(2)]r^2\ell}$$

where
P_r = received power (W),
P_t = peak transmitted power (W),
τ = pulse width (s),
λ = wavelength (m),
g = antenna gain
θ = beam width (radians)
c = 3×10^8 (ms^{-1})
r = range (m)
ℓ = system losses
η_{av} = backscatter coefficient (m^2m^{-3})

The factor η_{av} can be related to the "reflectivity factor", Z by

$$\eta_{av} = \frac{\pi^5|K|^2Z}{\lambda^4}$$

where λ = wavelength (m), $|K|^2$ = constant for snow = 0.197, and Z = reflectivity factor (m^6m^{-3}).

The parameters K and λ are fixed for any given radar, thus making Z the variable measured by a stable technically calibrated radar system. One of the main relationships of interest is that between Z and the rainfall rate R (hereafter the term "rainfall rate" will refer to the equivalent melted snowfall rate).

The radar reflectivity factor, Z, assuming Rayleigh scattering, can be shown to be given as:

$$Z_\infty = \int_o^\infty N_D \; D^6 \; dD \tag{1}$$

where $N_D = N_o \exp\,[-\Lambda\, D]$ with N_o and Λ as the distribution parameters.

$N_D\,\Delta D$ is the concentration of raindrops (equivalent melted snowflakes) having diameters in the range D to D + ΔD.

The subscript on Z denotes that the limit of the integral is 0 to ∞.

The rainfall rate, R, can be expressed as:

$$R_\infty = \frac{\pi}{6} \int_o^\infty V_D \; D^3 N_D \; dD$$

where V_D = particle (snowflake) fall speed, D = diameter, and N_D = as described for Z.

The main point of interest here is with the limit of these integrals. It is interesting to consider truncation of these integrals and study the effect that truncation has on the values R_∞ and Z_∞.

Following the work of Sekhon & Srivastava (1970), it can be shown that truncation can have a major effect on the values of Z and R thus obtained.

Consider the median volume diameter as given by:

$$\int_o^{D_o} D^3 e^{-\Lambda D} \; dD = \int_{D_o}^{D_m} D^3 e^{-\Lambda D} \; dD$$

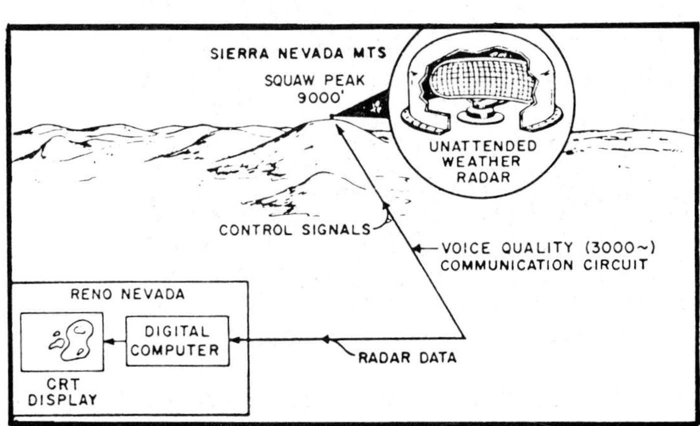

FIG.1 (a) Experimental remotely operated mountain top weather radar system that was located on Squaw Peak (2743 m).

Hydrological Applications of Remote Sensing and Remote Data Transmission
(Proceedings of the Hamburg Symposium, August 1983). IAHS Publ. no. 145.

Remote sensing of snow cover with passive and active microwave sensors

H. ROTT
Institut für Meteorologie und Geophysik, Universität Innsbruck, A-6020 Innsbruck, Austria
K. F. KÜNZI
Institut für angewandte Physik, Universität Bern, CH-3012 Bern, Switzerland

ABSTRACT Investigations using data from the Scanning Multichannel Microwave Radiometer (SMMR) on Nimbus-7 revealed the great potential of passive microwave sensors to monitor snow cover parameters, such as areal extent, water equivalent and onset of snowmelt, both on a global scale and for large drainage basins ($\geq 10^5 km^2$) virtually unaffected by cloud cover. Active microwave sensors (e.g. synthetic aperture radar, SAR) offer a much higher spatial resolution from space and aircrafts than can be achieved with passive microwave sensors. Data from an airborne SAR-experiment (X- and C-band) show, that snow extent during the runoff phase can be mapped even in rugged terrain.

Télédétection de la couverture neigeuse à l'aide de détecteurs passifs et actifs à hyperfréquences
RESUME Des recherches à partir de données obtenues par le radiomètre à balayage à multi-hyperfréquences (SMMR) sur Nimbus-7, ont révélé le grand potentiel des détecteurs passifs à hyperfréquences dans la détermination des paramètres de la couche de neige, tels que l'étendue spatiale, l'équivalent en eau et l'amorçage de la fonte, sur une échelle globale et pour des bassins étendus ($\geq 10^5 km^2$). Les mesures ne sont virtuellement pas affectées par la couverture nuageuse. Les détecteurs actifs à hyperfréquences (par exemple, radar à synthèse d'ouverture, SAR) offrent une beaucoup plus grande résolution spatiale dépuis l'éspace et les avions, que celle qui sera jamais atteinte avec les détecteurs passifs. Les résultats obtenus à l'aide d'un SAR aéroporté (dans les bandes X et C) montrent qu'une étude de l'étendue de neige pendant la phase d'écoulement, peut être réalisée même en terrain accidenté.

INTRODUCTION

Satellite remote sensing of snow areal extent in the visible spectrum is operationally used for hydrological modelling and forecasting and for climatological applications. However, in many regions the use of visible and infrared satellite data is severely restricted due to frequent cloudiness. With sensors in the microwave region snow cover observations are possible under almost all weather conditions. In addition, microwaves are able to penetrate the snow layer and thus to provide information on snowpack properties not available from other sensors.

This paper reports on ongoing research with microwave remote sensing data to monitor snow parameters on global and regional scales. Investigations with data of the Nimbus-7 Scanning Multichannel Microwave Radiometer (SMMR) resulted in algorithms for mapping snow parameters on a global scale, which are also useful for snow mapping in individual drainage basins. Synthetic aperture radar (SAR) systems on satellites offer significantly better areal resolution than microwave radiometers, however, more experiments are needed to determine the optimum active system for operational snow monitoring. As an example we report on a snow mapping experiment conducted in July 1981 at a test site in the Austrian Alps with an airborne X- and C-band SAR.

MICROWAVE CHARACTERISTICS OF SNOW

Microwave emission of snow

The observed microwave emission of a surface can be expressed as brightness temperature T_B, which is the product of the effective emissivity e $(0 < e < 1)$ and absolute temperature T:

$$T_B(\nu) = e(\nu)\, T \qquad (K) \tag{1}$$

In the case of dry snow both the snow volume and the underlying ground contribute to T_B. Scattering within the snow volume reduces T_B in dependence of frequency, enabling the discrimination of snow-covered and snow-free ground. Scattering losses are correlated with the total snow volume (water equivalent) at higher microwave frequencies. Grain size and stratigraphy, however, have also some effect on scattering. Liquid water drastically changes the emission and scattering properties of snow. The emissivity of a wet snow pack is almost one, therefore wet snow cannot be discriminated from snow-free ground in many cases.

Microwave backscattering from snow

Contributions to radar return from snow-covered ground originate from the air-snow boundary, from scattering within the snow volume, and from the snow-ground boundary. The radar return is described by σ^0, the scattering cross section per unit area, which is for a given target a function of frequency ν, polarization p, incidence angle θ, and azimuth angle ϕ:

$$\sigma^0 = \sigma^0(\nu, p, \theta, \phi) \tag{2}$$

In C-band (4-8 GHz) and X-band (8-12.5 GHz) volume scattering losses in a dry snow pack are small, reducing σ^0 relatively to snow-free ground only slightly. Therefore dry snow often cannot be detected with radar (Mätzler & Schanda, 1983). The penetration depth of wet snow is in the order of a few centimetres. For radar return from wet snow, volume scattering of the top few centimetres is dominant, with some contribution by scattering from the rough surface. This results in low σ^0-values for wet snow (Stiles & Ulaby, 1980). Therefore in contrast to passive microwave sensors, wet snow and snow-free ground can be clearly distinguished with active sensors.

SNOW MAPPING WITH THE NIMBUS-7 SCANNING MULTICHANNEL MICROWAVE RADIOMETER (SMMR)

The SMMR experiment on board Nimbus-7, launched into a sun-synchronous orbit on 24 October 1978, is scanning the earth's surface at five frequencies (6.6, 10.7, 18.0, 21.0, 37.0 GHz) in two polarizations under a constant incidence angle of ~50°. SMMR covers a swath width of 780 km. Due to power limitations SMMR operates only on alternate days. The T_B-values of the standard data product, as processed by NASA, are given for cells of 30x30 km^2 (37 GHz) to 156x156 km^2 (6.6 GHz). The original antenna temperature data have somewhat higher resolution, ranging from 28x17 km^2 to 152x97 km^2.

The algorithms for retrieval of snow parameters

The algorithms for snow mapping with SMMR data were derived by statistical analyses and correlation with ground truth data; a detailed description is given by Künzi *et al.* (1982). The main results are briefly summarized in the following.

The brightness temperature gradient

$$GT = [T_B(\nu_1) - T_B(\nu_2)]/(\nu_1 - \nu_2) \qquad (K\ GHz^{-1}) \tag{3}$$

with $\nu_1 = 37$ GHz and $\nu_2 = 18$ GHz, and both T_B values in horizontal polarization, revealed the best results for discriminating snow-covered from snow-free ground and also for calculating the snow water equivalent. The errors in GT due to atmospheric extinction and emission can be neglected for snow studies under most meteorological conditions. The decision rule, which enables automatic mapping of snow areas on a global scale, is

$$\text{dry snow is present, if } GT \leqq D \tag{4}$$

The decision boundary D was determined empirically from the SMMR data of the first year as $D = -0.1$ K GHz^{-1} (Rott & Künzi, 1983), in the case of repeated coverage of the same pixel the minimum GT value is taken. Figure 1 shows examples for frequency distributions of minimum GT in winter and summer for the European continent. The GT-distribution of the snow free continent shows little dispersion with a marked peak at +0.1 K GHz^{-1}. The bimodal GT-distribution in winter illustrates the separation between snow-free land with positive GT values and snow-covered land on the negative side. The negative GT values are inversely correlated with snow depth or water equivalent. GT-values $\gtrsim 0.3$ K GHz^{-1} originate from very humid soil.

For calculating the water equivalent w_n from SMMR measurements

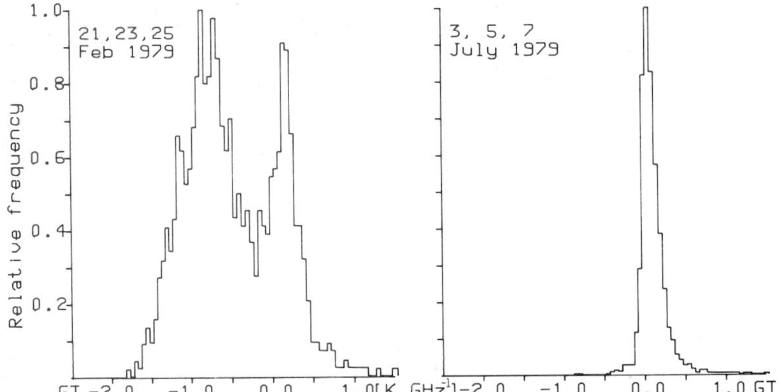

FIG.1 Frequency distribution of the minimum brightness temperature gradient GT (equation (3)) for Europe, normalized to maximum frequency.

the following relation was found by comparison with ground truth data from Canada, Russia, and Finland in the 1978/1979 winter season (Künzi *et al.*, 1982):

$$w_n = A(GT - D) \qquad \text{(mm)} \tag{5}$$

This relation is valid for dry snow layers <50 cm, the empirical determined coefficient A varies for substantially different climatic regions, because of different snowpack scattering properties. For the investigated test areas a one sigma error of w_n = 2 mm was found for equation (5) with an average coefficient A = -7.5 (mm GHz K^{-1}). The onset of snowmelt can be detected by observing the temporal change in GT of wet snow (GT ≈ 0) and dry snow (GT < 0) due to the melt and refreeze cycle.

Examples of snow mapping at three scales

Automatic snow cover mapping was carried out with the use of a digital image processing system linked to a minicomputer. For one hemispheric analysis SMMR data of three alternate days (42 orbits) are used. The computer time for mapping these data in equal area projection and for classification is less than 2 h. An example is given in Fig.2, showing the northern hemispheric dry and melting snow areas derived from SMMR data on 15, 17, 19 March 1979. The analysis is based on the SMMR standard data product in 37 GHz and 18 GHz with 60x60 km^2 cell size using the classification algorithms specified above. From the data of Fig.2 the total snow cover on land surfaces was calculated as 42.7×10^6 km^2, large melting areas were found in Europe (2.2×10^6 km^2 melting out of 5.5×10^6 km^2 total snow cover) and in North America (3.8×10^6 km^2 and 11.9×10^6 km^2 respectively). A comparison of SMMR-derived total hemispheric snow areas from all seasons with NESDIS northern hemisphere weekly snow cover data derived from visible satellite sensors showed good agreement (Rott & Künzi, 1983). In general SMMR derived hemispheric snow cover was a few percent smaller than NESDIS snow cover, because very thin snow and continuously melting areas cannot be detected

FIG.2 Hemispheric snow cover derived from SMMR data on 15, 17, 19 March 1979. Code for ice-free land surfaces: dark grey = snow free; light grey = dry snow; white = melting snow.

with SMMR. Larger discrepancies due to wet snow were found only in late spring and summer.

The two following examples indicate the potential of spaceborne microwave radiometers for hydrological applications. To take advantage of the full spatial resolution the SMMR antenna temperature data were used, processed by NASA on special request for a number of days. The footprints are ellipses with the dimensions 56 km x 35 km at 18 GHz, and 28 km x 17 km for the 37 GHz channel.

Figure 3 shows a map of the snow extent in Central Europe derived from SMMR data on 19, 21, 23 February 1979; the snow boundaries correspond well to ground truth data. The snow covered mountain ranges of the Alps, the Carpathians, and the comparatively small Massif Central are evident.

Figure 4 shows snow extent in the drainage basin of the Danube above Vienna with a total area of 104×10^3 km^2, automatically mapped and enlarged from SMMR snow maps. Snow depth is given in two steps, the SMMR-derived snow area in the basin amounted to 61% on 21 February, to 71% on 27 February, to 28% on 13 March, and to 27% on 17 March 1979. The snow extent agrees with ground observations, snow cover first increased due to snowfall on 26 February, after 5 March the snow cover melted in lower altitudes.

From the global SMMR snow maps similar analyses can be made for any drainage basin $\gtrsim 1 \times 10^5$ km^2. For deriving w_n from SMMR data for basins with various surface types, additional information on emission characteristics of the surface can improve the results (Tiuri & Sihvola, 1982).

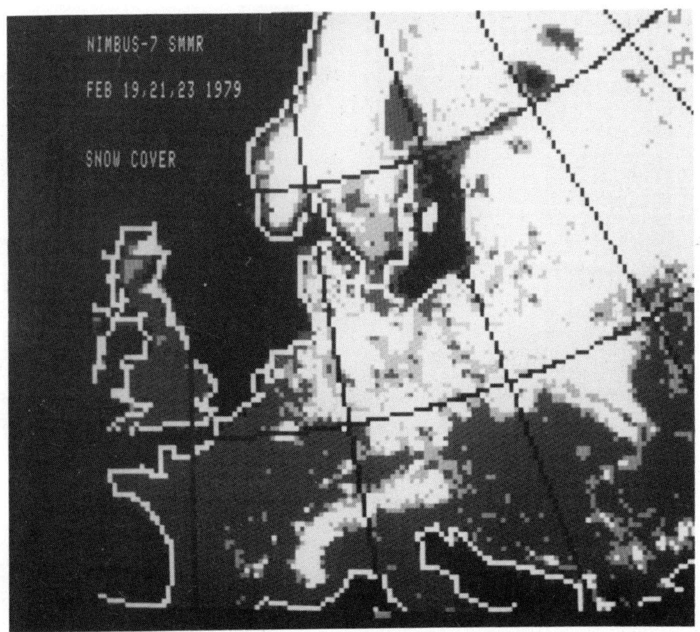

FIG.3 Snow cover in Central Europe derived from full resolution SMMR data on 19, 21, 23 February 1979. Dark grey = snow free; light grey = snow ≲ 10 cm or broken snow cover; white = dry snow > 10 cm.

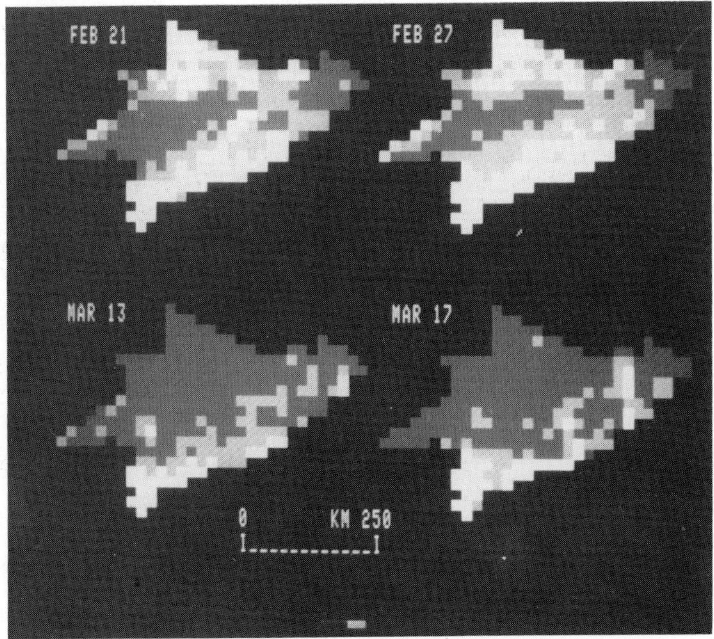

FIG.4 Snow extent from SMMR data for the drainage basin of the Danube above Vienna on four days in late winter 1979. Grey level code as in Fig.3.

THE SAR SNOW MAPPING EXPERIMENT

On 7 July 1981 a test site in the Ötztaler Alps (Austria) was mapped during the European SAR-580 Campaign with X-band (9.3 GHz) and C-band (5.3 GHz) SAR from an aircraft flying at 6100 m a.m.s.l. The partly glacierized site covers altitudes from 2000 to 3600 m; most parts of the glaciers and some ice-free areas were covered with wet snow during the SAR overflight. Due to the high liquid water content (4% to 7% volume) the penetration depth in snow was on average only 2 cm in X-band and 4 cm in C-band, the snow surface was comparatively smooth with r.m.s. heights between 0.3 and 0.8 cm.

Figure 5 shows part of the digitally processed SAR data in X-band, horizontal polarizations (HH). The full resolution of a pixel is about 3 x 3 m; in Fig.5 the data were averaged over 4 x 4 pixels and enhanced by a square root function, to increase the range of the low brightness values. Areas with high radar return, mainly rock covered slopes and moraines, appear bright, low grey values correspond to low return. A grey level profile is given in the look direction, covering radar look angles from 45° to 72° off normal. Topographic features are enhanced, because the backscattering intensity is dependent on the local incidence angle, given by the look angle and the surface slope angle, and because the coordinates in look direction are proportional to the distance of the surface elements to the radar antenna. Therefore slopes inclined towards the antenna appear shortened and give a strong return. No information is

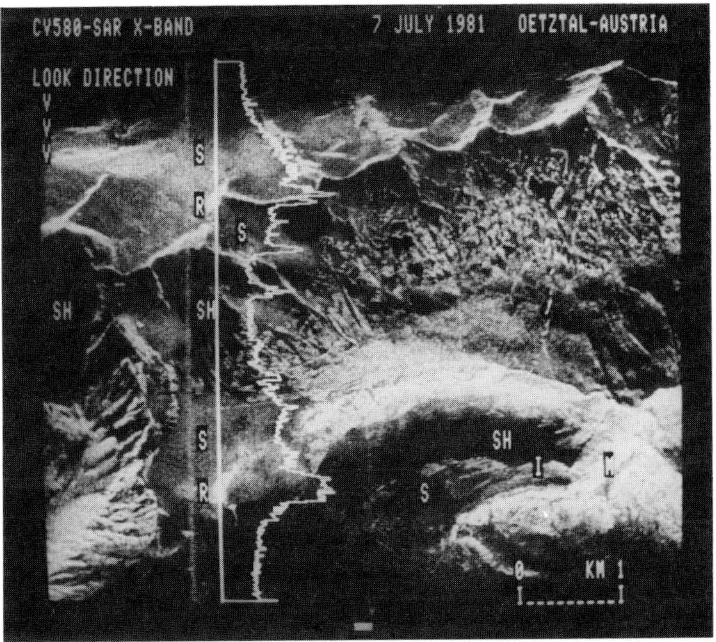

FIG.5 Enhanced airborne SAR image in X-band, HH polarizations, from a test site in the Austrian Alps. The grey values at the white line are plotted to the right in a relative scale. Major surface types: S = snow, R = rock, I = glacier ice, M = moraine; SH = radar shadow.

received from the zones in the shadow of the radar beam. The snow areas show low return and can be discriminated by tone from the surrounding areas in most parts of the test site. Because of the angular dependence of the radar return, topographic information has to be included for automatic snow mapping. The differences in the backscattering can be seen in the mean values of the scattering cross section σ^0, which were derived on a relative scale at 60° incidence angle in X-band (HH):

	Rock	*Grassland*	*Wet snow*	*Noise*	
σ^0(relative)	0	-3	-8	-19	dB

Qualitatively similar results were obtained from C-band data, though quantitative analysis did not appear useful due to the poor signal to noise ratio related to sensor problems. Only a small area of the glaciers was snow free during the experiment; in X-band σ^0 of the glacier ice with its rough surface was about 5 dB above σ^0 of the snow cover. Glacier ice and snow could also be separated in C-band, and similar results were obtained with Seasat SAR in L-band (1.3 GHz) (Rott, 1980). The investigations have shown the capability of radar systems to monitor the snow cover during the runoff phase.

CONCLUSIONS

Spaceborne microwave sensors have the potential to provide worldwide valuable data on the snow cover under all weather conditions. For applications in hydrology such as long-term and short-term runoff forecasts, a combination of passive sensors for mapping dry snow, water equivalent, and onset of snowmelt and active sensors for mapping wet snow with high areal resolution could guarantee the optimum information. The further improvement of the sensors, such as increasing surface resolution of the passive sensors, will increase the number of applications. But also with present sensor technology many users can be satisfied, however, for an operational microwave satellite system close to real time data transmission and analysis is required.

ACKNOWLEDGEMENTS This work was supported in part by the Austrian Fonds zur Förderung der wissenschaftlichen Forschung and by the Swiss National Science Foundation; the SMMR data were made available by the NASA Goddard Space Flight Center. The SAR-580 Campaign was conducted by the European Space Agency and by the Joint Research Centre of the European Communities.

REFERENCES

Künzi, K.F., Patil, S. & Rott, H. (1982) Snow cover parameters retrieved from Nimbus-7 Scanning Multichannel Microwave Radiometer (SMMR) data. *IEEE Trans. Geosci. Remote Sens.* GE-20 (4), 452-467.

Mätzler, C. & Schanda, E. (1983) Snow mapping with active microwave sensors. *Int. J. Remote Sens.* 4 (in press).

Rott, H. (1980) Synthetic aperture radar capabilities for glacier monitoring demonstrated with Seasat SAR data. *Z. Gletscherkunde Glazialgeol.* 16 (2), 255-166.

Rott, H. & Künzi, K.F. (1983) Properties of the global snow cover and of snow free terrain from the Nimbus-7 SMMR first year data set. In: *Proc. of the Specialist Meeting on Microwave Radiometry and Remote Sensing Applications* (Rome, March 1983) (in press).

Stiles, W.H. & Ulaby, F.T. (1980) The active and passive microwave response to snow parameters. 1. Wetness. *J. Geophys. Res.* 85 (C2), 1037-1044.

Tiuri, M. & Sihvola, A. (1982) Remote sensing of snow depth by passive microwave satellite observations. In: *Proc. of IEEE Geosci. and Remote Sensing Symp* (Munich, June 1982).

Hydrological Applications of Remote Sensing and Remote Data Transmission
(Proceedings of the Hamburg Symposium, August 1983). IAHS Publ. no. 145.

Resolution in operational remote sensing of snow cover

A. RANGO
Hydrology Laboratory, Agricultural Research Service, Beltsville, Maryland 20705, USA
J. MARTINEC
Federal Institute for Snow and Avalanche Research, CH-7260 Weissfluhjoch/Davos, Switzerland
J. FOSTER & D. MARKS
NASA-Goddard Space Flight Center, Greenbelt, Maryland 20771, USA

ABSTRACT Recent advances in remote sensing have greatly improved capabilities for mapping the areal extent of seasonal snow cover, an important variable used in modelling of snowmelt runoff from mountain basins. Aircraft orthophotographs with a resolution of 3-15 m can be used to map snow extent on basins from 1 to 100 km^2 in area. When using Landsat, the recently available thematic mapper resolution of 28.5 m is adequate for basins larger than 2.5 km^2, whereas the multispectral scanner data (resolution 57 m) should be used on basins larger than 10 km^2. Landsat is more cost effective than aircraft for areas larger than 25 km^2. For basin or zonal areas greater than 200 km^2, the resolution of NOAA satellites, 1.1 km, is satisfactory for the evaluation of snow-covered areas. When photo-interpretation is used instead of digital analysis, the minimum basin sizes should be approximately doubled. The importance of temporal resolution for the interpretation of snow-covered area is also illustrated. Examples of discharge simulations using various types of snow cover data on different size basins are given, and procedures are outlined for operational forecasts which could produce a considerable economical benefit.

Résolution dans la télédétection opérationnelle de la couche de neige

RESUME Les progrès récents dans la télédétection ont améliorés de façon décisive les possibilités de mesurer la surface enneigée. Cette grandeur variable est très importante pour calculer l'écoulement dû à la fonte des neiges dans les bassins montagneux. Les orthophotos aériennes avec une limite de résolution de 3-15 m peuvent être utilisées dans les bassins de 1 à 100 km^2. Avec Landsat, la résolution de 28.5 m obtenue récemment suffit pour les bassins plus grands que 2.5 km^2, tandis que les données fournies par le radiomètre multispectral avec une résolution de 57 m sont utilisables dans les bassins plus grands que 10 km^2. Landsat est plus économique que l'avion à partir de 25 km^2. Pour les surfaces terrestres plus grandes que 200 km^2, la limite de résolution de 1.1 km, obtenue par les satellites de la série NOAA, est suffisante pour mesurer la surface enneigée. Si l'exploitation des données est réalisée par analyse visuelle au lieu de l'analyse digitale, il faut doubler les surfaces terrestres minimales. Le rôle de la résolution temporelle (la répétitivité) en interprétant la surface enneigée est aussi démontré. Les simulations des débits en utilisant des observations diverses de la couche de neige sont illustrées par quelques exemples. Les possibilitiés des prévisions opérationelles avec un bénéfice économique considérable sont indiquées.

INTRODUCTION

Snowmelt is the source for a large portion of the streamflow generated in many mountainous basins. In excess of 50% of the annual total discharge typically results from snowmelt in areas like the Rocky Mountains of the USA, the Alps of Switzerland, and the Himalayan Mountains of Asia. The snowpack that accumulates during winter is primarily important as a major source of stored water, but it also serves as an insulating blanket for the soil and agricultural crops. In the growing trend toward improved water management through the use of hydrological models, knowledge about the snow cover is becoming more critical. In all models with snowmelt subroutines, the procedure for melting the snowpack, whether based on radiation balance or degree-day approaches, should only be applied to the area of the basin covered by snow.

Early work on using snow-covered area data to improve hydrological modelling was conducted on small basins because data collection over large basins was either extremely difficult or impossible. As a result, snow cover for modelling was obtained by either ground-based observations or low-altitude aircraft flights (Leaf, 1969). With the advent of satellite observations snow-cover data could be obtained over large basins as well. Because a wide range of resolutions for snow cover data is now available, use of snow cover in runoff modelling for a variety of basin sizes is possible. This should allow replacement of surrogate algorithms in existing models by the currently available actual snow cover information. Indeed, this should be instituted in all possible situations since confidence in models is reduced when snowmelt is calculated by a model for areas of a basin actually snow free.

METHODS OF SNOW MAPPING IN RELATION TO BASIN SIZE

Ground-based observations

The areal extent of snow cover on basins less than 10 km^2 in size can be determined by visual observations and from snow course data. Figure 1 shows the snow cover in the Modrý Důl basin (2.65 km^2) in Czechoslovakia on two different dates. The terrain is not rugged so

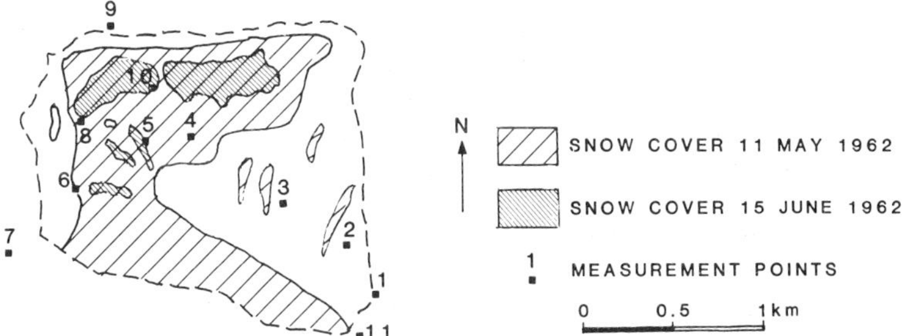

FIG.1 Visual ground-based observations of snow extent in the Modrý Důl basin.

that the boundaries of snowfields can be drawn as seen from one or two observation points. The total snow coverage as a percentage of the surface area of the basin can be determined by planimetering. An approximate percentage can even be obtained by observing the number of points of the snow measurement network which are inside or outside the snow-covered area. To this effect, the measurement points should be located in a representative way with regard to the elevation range and the area-elevation curve of the basin. In the described example (Fig.1), there are 11 measurement points spread over the elevation range 1000-1560 m. On 11 May 1962, five points were still under snow (point no. 6 was at the boundary), which indicates a snow coverage of 40-50%. On 15 June 1962, two points were at the boundary of the remaining snowfields so that a snow coverage of less than 10% could be estimated. A drawing of the snow line is more accurate. However, if such drawings are not available, as was the case with the W-3 basin (8.42 km^2) in Vermont, USA, when it was used for model tests described by the World Meteorological Organization (1982), an estimate of the snow coverage from single points or snow courses can still be helpful. Low altitude aircraft observations or higher altitude orthophotos, of course, give results superior to the methods mentioned here.

Aircraft orthophotographs

Basins exceeding 10 km^2 in area are too large for visual, ground-based snow mapping, and an aircraft observing capability is the next logical step. Another consideration in moving to larger basins is that the snow cover in rugged terrain (particularly in the Swiss Alps) can be scattered in numerous patches so that it is practically impossible to draw a single snow line for planimetering the snow-covered area. Comprehensive coverage of basins ranging from 1 to 100 km^2 in area is needed so that automated calculation of the discontinuous snow-covered area is possible. Figure 2 shows the snow-covered area in the Dischma basin, Switzerland (43.3 km^2, 1668-3146 m) at different resolutions. Due to the large elevation range, hydrological applications of the snow cover data necessitate a division into three elevation zones so that the required resolution relates to the smallest partial area and not to the total area of the basin. In Fig.2(a), the orthophoto, taken from an altitude of 9.8 km, has a resolution of about 1-3 m. When subsequently evaluated

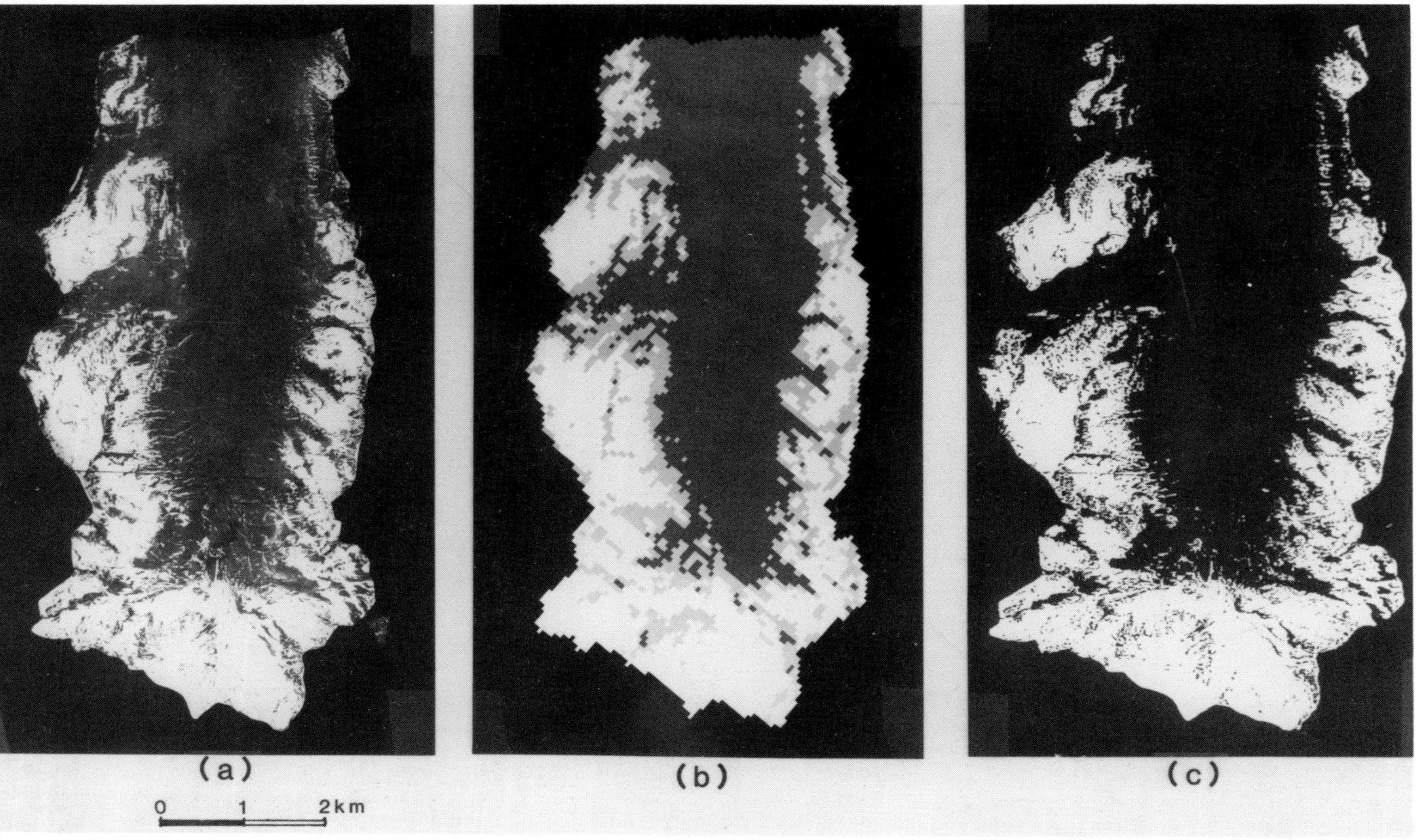

FIG.2 Snow cover in the Dischma basin, 8 June 1976, displayed at different resolutions from (a) aircraft orthophoto (1-3 m), (b) Landsat MSS classified image (80 m), and (c) computer printout from orthophoto after edge-enhancement preprocessing (10 m).

by a Quantimet computer (Martinec, 1973), about 200 000 points are counted as being snow-covered or snow-free, so that the effective resolution is reduced to about 15 m. The Landsat digital image, (Fig.2(b)), taken at 920 km, has a resolution of about 57 m which is still sufficient for evaluating snow cover. In the given example, the snow coverage is determined by counting and weighting the white pixels (snow-covered), the grey pixels (partially snow-covered) and the black pixels (snow-free). The third image, Fig.2(c), is a computer printout obtained from the orthophoto in Fig.2(a), which has a resolution of about 10 m after edge enhancement preprocessing. The width distortion is caused by the horizontal and vertical spacing of the printer. Again, the snow-covered and snow-free points are counted in order to obtain the snow coverage. However, the main purpose of this processing of orthophotos is to study the patterns of snow fields in an attempt to estimate not only the areal extent but also the volume of snow from two-dimensional orthophotos (Good, 1983).

Multispectral satellite sensors

The most recent multispectral observing capability in space is the thematic mapper (TM) on Landsat 4. Several improvements have been made on the TM in comparison to its predecessor the multispectral scanner subsystem (MSS) the foremost of which is an increased spatial resolution from 57 m (MSS) to 28.5 m (TM). This improved resolution alone should allow mapping of snow cover at a greater accuracy than possible with the MSS. In addition, the TM spectral bands are narrower than on the MSS which may allow textural analysis leading to possible information on snow volume. More immediate is the newly-added TM band 5 (1.55-1.75 μm) which can be used to discriminate automatically between snow and clouds. Although only preliminary tests have been conducted, it appears that the TM digital data can be used for mapping snow cover on basins as small as 2.5 km^2. Analysis of TM snow data over the Owens Valley in California, USA, is continuing in order to establish the limits of the TM data.

Even though the TM intuitively provides a capability for more accurate mapping of snow cover than the MSS, it should not be used in place of the lower data rate MSS unless necessary. In digital analysis of MSS data the minimum basin size for snow cover determination is about 10 km^2. When photo-interpretation of MSS data is used, this minimum basin size increases to about 20 km^2. From related studies on land cover, it has been determined that MSS data can be used cost effectively on basins larger than 25 km^2 (Rango *et al.*, 1983). As a result use of TM data for most snow-cover related analyses should be limited to a basin size range of 2.5-25 km^2. Since there are very few basins of this size that will require operational snow mapping, the TM will mostly be limited to use as a research sensor. In operational snow-cover analysis, orthophotographs may be preferable to the TM data for the 2.5-25 km^2 range because they can be requested when the basin is cloud free, a capability not available with the TM or the MSS. The return beam vidicon (RBV) system on Landsats 1-3 provides some additional data for snow mapping at an intermediate resolution of 40 m.

The best satellite for providing highly repetitive coverage of a basin is NOAA with imagery from the advanced very high resolution radiometer (AVHRR). In the visible channel, 0.56-0.72 μm, the resolution is about 1.1 km near nadir. Although the resolution is much lower than Landsat, NOAA provides one daytime and one night-time overpass every 24 h. Standard photo-interpretation can be done effectively with the AVHRR data, however, because of the poor resolution, digital analysis permits applicability to much smaller basins or zonal areas (200 km^2 *vs.* 500 km^2). Although a typical supervised classification of the snow is possible, an alternate digital approach described by Andersen (1982) seems to be more applicable to operational situations. This method involves comparison of reflectance in areas of known snow coverage with the reflectance of pixels covering an entire drainage basin. In areas of known snow coverage the reflectance range between snow-free pixels and completely snow-covered pixels is calculated. A linear relationship between pixel reflectance or brightness level and snow coverage is then derived and used to calculate the snow cover over the entire basin (Andersen, 1982). In heavily forested basins the relationship between reflectance and snow coverage is considerably more complicated, and major modification of the technique may be necessary.

When data are required more frequently than daily, the only available satellite and sensor is in geosynchronous orbit, namely, the GOES visible and infrared spin scan radiometer (VISSR). The characteristics and operation of this sensor are very similar to the AVHRR with the exception that the over-the-equator orbit permits data acquisition whenever the target area is cloud free, and that the imagery becomes increasingly distorted as the target area is located further and further from the equator. Table 1 briefly summarizes the characteristics and costs of the various remote sensing data applicable for mapping snow cover. From data handling considerations, it is recommended to use the lowest resolution data possible while at the same time considering basin size, repeat period, and cost factors.

TABLE 1 Characteristics of various remote sensing data used for snow-cover mapping

Platform sensor/data	*Nominal resolution (visible)*	*Minimum basin size (digital/photo)*	*Repeat period*	*Cost in US $ (tape/photo)*
Aircraft				
Orthophoto	*3 m*	*1 km^2*	*as needed*	*variable*
Landsat				
TM	*28.5 m*	*2.5/5 km^2*	*16 days*	*2800/33*
RBV	*40 m*	*5/10 km^2*	*18 days*	*1300/30*
MSS	*57 m*	*10/20 km^2*	*16 days*	*650/30*
NOAA				
AVHRR	*1.1 km*	*200/500 km^2*	*12 h*	*99/8.5*
GOES				
VISSR	*1.1 km*	*200/500 km^2*	*as needed*	*99/8.5*

APPLICATION OF SNOW COVER IN A SNOWMELT-RUNOFF MODEL

Figure 3 shows day-by-day computations of discharge from the W-3 basin compared with the measured values for the snowmelt season of 1971. Besides air temperature and precipitation, snow-covered area is the main information necessary for this snowmelt-runoff model, as explained elsewhere (Martinec *et al.*, 1983). In another example (Fig.4) the runoff simulation for the Dischma basin is extended from the snowmelt season to the entire year. The areal extent of the snow cover is obtained from orthophotos taken roughly at monthly

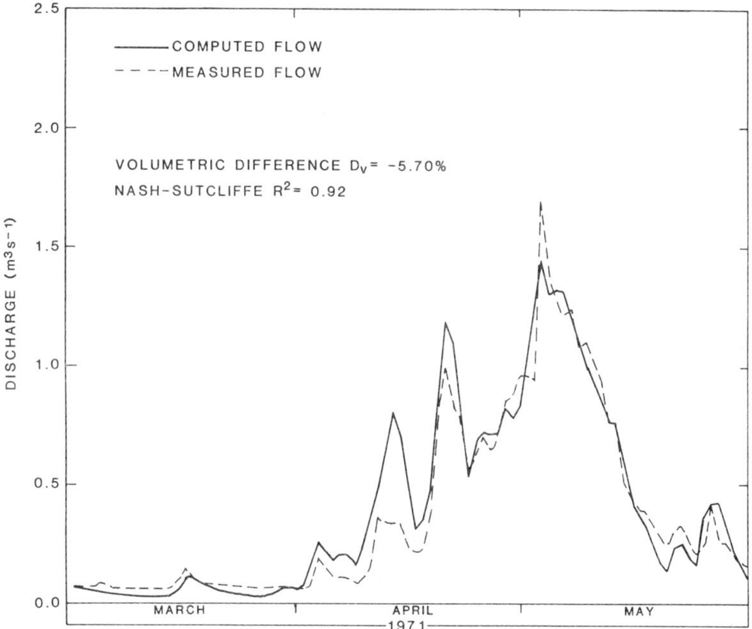

FIG.3 Snowmelt runoff simulation for the W-3 basin based on the variable areal extent of the snow cover.

intervals. Landsat data would be equally suitable but in view of the overflight interval of 16-18 days and of a frequent cloud interference in the Alps, it is hardly possible to obtain sufficient data for the depletion curves of snow coverage. This situation has been recently improved by introducing a "jumping orbit" for Landsat. This means that if, for example, the Dischma basin was previously seen on two consecutive overflight days because of overlapping coverage, it is now seen on the first and the ninth day. Thus the chance of observation with minimal cloud cover is slightly better than before. In addition, the overflight interval has been shortened to 16 days with the launch of Landsat 4.

In large basins like the Kings River in California (4000 km^2), both Landsat and NOAA satellites are suitable for snow cover mapping. While Landsat has a better spatial resolution (57 m against 1.1 km for NOAA), the NOAA satellites have a better time resolution of one visible image per day. The NOAA spatial resolution deteriorates

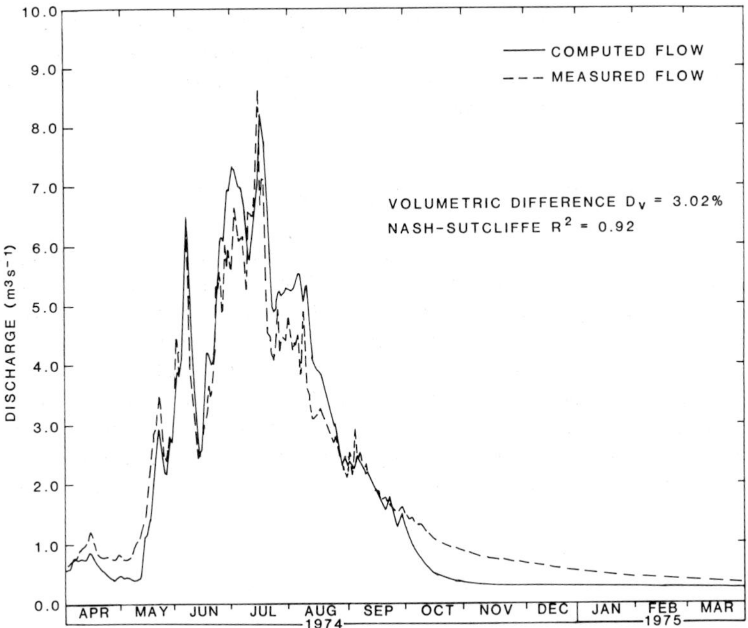

FIG.4 Runoff simulation in the Dischma basin extended to 365 days.

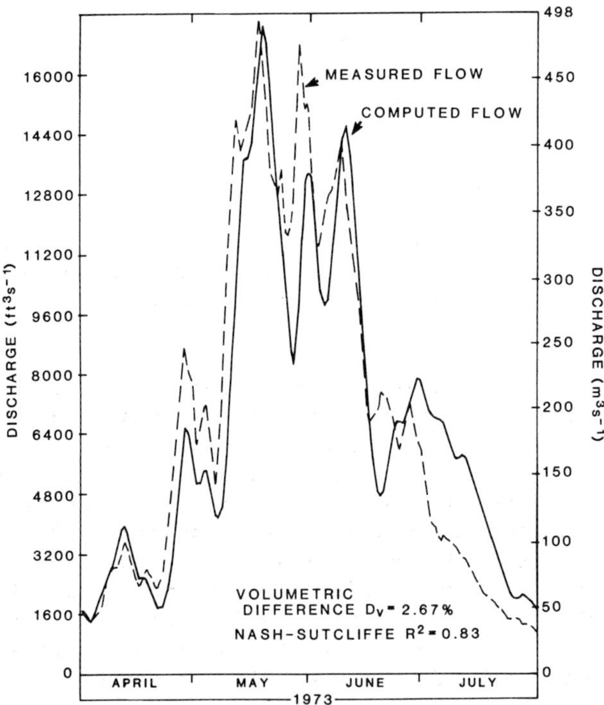

FIG.5 Snowmelt runoff simulation in the Kings River basin. The areal extent of the snow cover for day-to-day computations of snowmelt was determined from Landsat and NOAA data.

with the distance of the basin from the centre of the image. Figure 5 shows a runoff simulation on the Kings River basin using depletion curves of snow cover which are based on combined data from the Landsat and NOAA satellites.

TEMPORAL RESOLUTION IN SNOW-COVER MONITORING

While a sufficient spatial resolution for snow-cover mapping is necessary with regard to the size of the basin and the accuracy of results, the frequency of periodical measurements must be sufficient to interpolate the depletion curves of snow coverage. Figure 6 illustrates a possible error which can occur if the interval between useable Landsat images becomes too long. Following a summer snow-storm on about 7 June, the snow-covered area can temporarily increase back to 100% as shown in Fig.6. Before this thin snow cover is entirely melted, Landsat monitors an anomalously large snow-covered

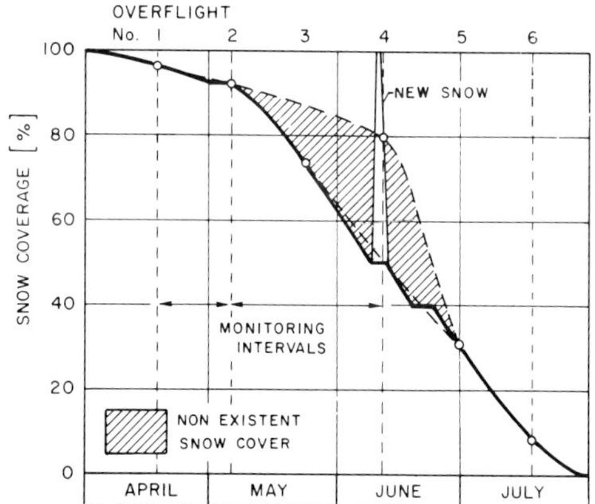

FIG.6 Hypothetical distortion of a seasonal snow-cover depletion curve resulting from a summer snowstorm and an inadequate frequency of observation.

area on 10 June. If this measurement is not identified as false (in reference to the seasonal snow cover), it is connected with the previous and subsequent points, thus distorting the true depletion curve. As a result, the model would compute excessive meltwater from a partially nonexistent snow cover. The risk of such errors is reduced if the interval between the satellite overflight is short, as for example with the NOAA satellites. In this case, however, the spatial resolution of about 1 km limits the application to areas larger than about 200 km^2 (Andersen, 1982). In the given example (Fig.6) the risk of error in drawing the depletion curves is increased by a missing Landsat image before the snowstorm.

UPDATING DEPLETION CURVES FOR DISCHARGE FORECASTS

For runoff simulations, historical data are used and obtained by

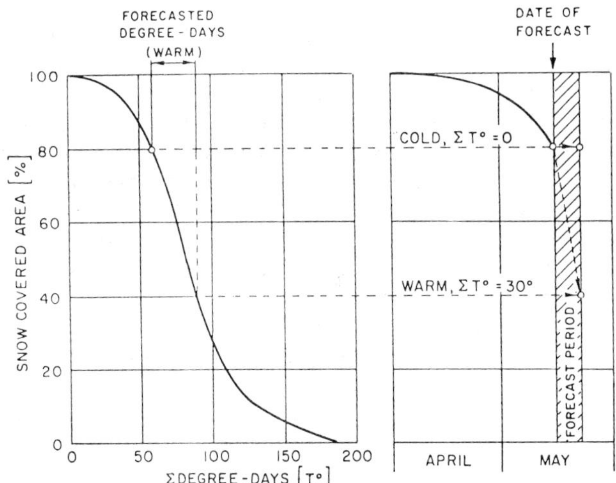

FIG.7 Extrapolation of a depletion curve of snow cover using a modified depletion curve and temperature forecasts.

interpolating between the measured points of the snow-cover depletion curves. For operational discharge forecasts, the depletion curves are known only up to the last measurement before the date of forecast. They must be extrapolated forward for any future forecast period and then updated with the next available satellite or aircraft observation. To this effect, modified depletion curves have been introduced (Martinec, 1980) in which the snow coverage is related to accumulated degree-days instead of the elapsed time. For a given accumulation of snow in a basin, the slope of the depletion curve is related to the energy input which can be represented by the air temperature. Figure 7 illustrates the extrapolation of a hypothetical depletion curve using a temperature forecast. If temperatures below 0°C are forecast for the next week, the snow coverage of 80% will remain undiminished. If, for example, a total of 30 degree-days is

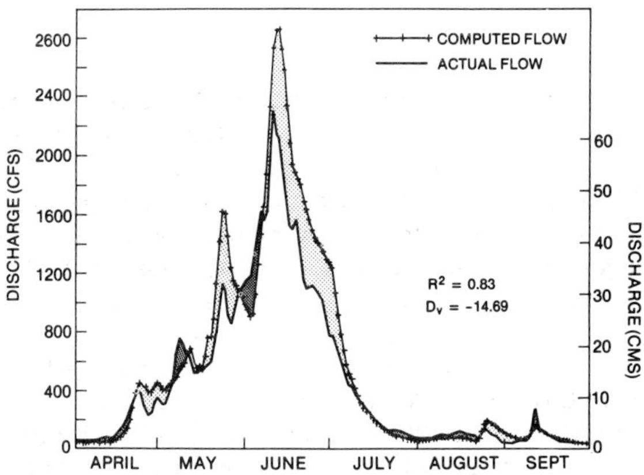

FIG.8 Operational discharge forecast in the South Fork basin, Colorado, USA (559 km^2) with partially simulated real time conditions.

forecast, as indicated in the left portion of Fig.7, the snow coverage will drop to 40% and the depletion curve on the right side can be extrapolated accordingly. Thus the forecast temperatures are used for (a) extrapolating the depletion curve, and (b) computing the snowmelt from snow-covered areas indicated by these curves. In Fig.8 (Shafer *et al.*, 1982) the runoff was computed using conditions similar to those associated with a real time forecast; the depletion curves, although available, were disregarded and replaced by curves extrapolated week by week in the described manner. Actual and not forecast temperatures were used, however. For an efficient updating of depletion curves in real time, the evaluation of satellite or aircraft data should not take more than a few days.

CONCLUSIONS

The changing areal extent of the seasonal snow cover appears to be important information for snowmelt-runoff computations in basins ranging in size from several km^2 to several thousand km^2. The upper limit of the basin size has not yet been established by testing. The required spatial resolution of the snow cover mapping depends on the size of the respective partial areas of a basin for which the snowmelt is computed. The method of evaluating the data depends also on other basin characteristics, like ruggedness of the terrain and vegetation conditions. Apart from the spatial resolution, the time resolution enters the picture in two ways: (a) the interval of the observation cycle should be short enough for interpolating the depletion curves of the snow coverage between the measured points. An adequate monitoring frequency also reduces the risk of misinterpreting a temporary snow cover from occasional snow storms; (b) the time delay between the date of measurement and the delivery of result is not important for the simulation mode of runoff models since historical data are used. For real-time discharge forecasting, however, rapid data processing is essential for the extrapolation and updating of the depletion curves of snow-covered areas.

REFERENCES

Andersen, T. (1982) Operational snow mapping by satellites. In: *Hydrological Aspects of Alpine and High-Mountain Areas* (Proc. Exeter Symp., July 1982), 149-154. IAHS Publ. no. 138.

Good, W. (1983) Estimation par des méthodes de traitement d'images de la quantite d'eau stockée dans un bassin versant (Estimation of the water quantity stored in a basin by the methods of image processing). *Internal Report, Federal Institute for Snow and Avalanche Research, Weissfluhjoch/Davos, Switzerland.*

Leaf, C.F. (1969) Aerial photographs for operational streamflow forecasting in the Colorado Rockies. In: *Proc. 37th Annual Western Snow Conference,* 19-28. Salt Lake City, Utah, USA.

Martinec, J. (1973) Evaluation of air photos for snowmelt-runoff forecasts. In: *The Role of Snow and Ice in Hydrology* (Proc. Banff Symp., September 1972), 915-926. IAHS Publ. no. 107.

Martinec, J. (1980) Snowmelt-runoff forecasts based on automatic temperature measurements. In: *Hydrological Forecasting* (Proc. Oxford Symp., April 1980), 239-246. IAHS Publ. no. 129.

Martinec, J., Rango, A. & Major, E. (1983) The snowmelt-runoff model (SRM) user's manual. *NASA Reference Publ. 1100, Washington, DC, USA.*

Rango, A., Feldman, A., George III, T.S. & Ragan, R.M. (1983) Effective use of Landsat data in hydrologic models. *Wat. Resour. Bull.* 19 (2), 165-174.

Shafer, B.A., Jones, E.B. & Frick, D.M. (1982) Snowmelt runoff modeling in simulation and forecasting modes with the Martinec-Rango model. *NASA Contractor Report 170452, Washington, DC, USA.*

World Meteorological Organization (1982) WMO project for the intercomparison of conceptual models of snowmelt runoff. In: *Hydrological Aspects of Alpine and High-Mountain Areas* (Proc. Exeter Symp., July 1982), 193-202. IAHS Publ. no. 138.

Hydrological Applications of Remote Sensing and Remote Data Transmission
(Proceedings of the Hamburg Symposium, August 1983). IAHS Publ. no. 145.

Snow mapping in Greenland based on multi-temporal satellite data

HENRIK SØGAARD
Geographical Institute, University of Copenhagen, Haraldsgade 68, 2100 Copenhagen Ø, Denmark

ABSTRACT A snow-mapping procedure based on digital NOAA-satellite data has been developed for use in Greenland. By means of spatial correlation, the data are registered with an accuracy down to a sub-pixel level. The data from the visible channel are corrected for topographic effects and recomputed to albedo values. By combining images from different stages during the melting season, the snow cover corresponding to each scene can be classified. The procedure is demonstrated on data from the Taserssuaq basin, West Greenland, and the results have been tested against measured snow cover. Together with data from field surveys, the snow-cover maps have been used for computing the depletion of the snowpack water equivalent. The computed volume of meltwater is shown to agree well with runoff measurements.

Une cartographie des neiges au Groenland basé sur données de satellite multitemporelles
RESUME Un procédé de cartographie des neiges basé les données du satellite NOAA a été mise au point pour être appliquée au Groenland. En utilisant une correction spéciale, les données sont enregistrées avec une précision inférieure aux pixels. Les données du canal visible ont été corrigées de l'effet topographique et calculées à la valeur de l'albedo. En combinant des vues de différentes phases de la période de fonte la couverture de neige correspondant à chacune des phases a été classifiée. La méthode a été testée sur des données du bassin de Taserssuaq, Groenland Ouest, et les résultats ont été testés comparativement à la couverture neigeuse observée. Les données observées et les cartes de couverture neigeuse ont permis de calculer la réduction de la masse équivalente d'eau de la couverture neigeuse. Le volume d'eau calculé s'est avéré correspondre à l'écoulement mesuré.

INTRODUCTION

In order to develop an operational procedure for snow-mapping in Greenland a pilot study has been running since 1981 in the Taserssuaq basin, northeast of Holsteinsborg, West Greenland. The present study summarizes parts of the results from the 1982 data, while the results from 1981 are found in Søgaard (1982a). In the latter report it was stated that the NOAA-satellite data were preferable, especially because of the high frequency of data collection for a specified area. In the present study only NOAA satellite data have been used.

In mapping the snow cover in 1981 the routine developed by Anderson & Ødegaard (1980) was used, i.e. calibration of pixel values in channel 1 on data from areas with known snow cover, snow cover in the rest of the area being found by linear interpolation. In general, this routine works quite well, although it will cause an underestimate of the snow cover in areas with little input of solar radiation, e.g. north-facing slopes, and a corresponding overestimate on south-facing slopes. In studying the depletion of the snow cover, the need for ground-truth data throughout the melting season is seldom met. An attempt at solving this problem has been made with the procedure presented.

The data analysis was carried out at the computer unit DK.IDIMS at the Electromagnetics Institute, Technical University of Denmark. This unit has the ESL.IDIMS software package, supplemented with software developed by staff members at the Institute, which facilitates testing of a great number of different functions and procedures. The present study was aimed at concentrating on procedures which might also be implemented on minicomputers.

The study is still going on, and at present the 1983 and 1984 investigations in the basin are being planned.

THE AREA OF STUDY

With its area of 865 km^2, the Taserssuaq basin is one of the largest drainage basins in Greenland outside the Inland Ice. The basin, determined by the waterdivide, is shown in Fig.1. Physiographically, it has an alpine relief in its western part, whereas its eastern part is mainly a plateau lying 700-800 m above sea level. In Table 1 the area-elevation distribution is shown.

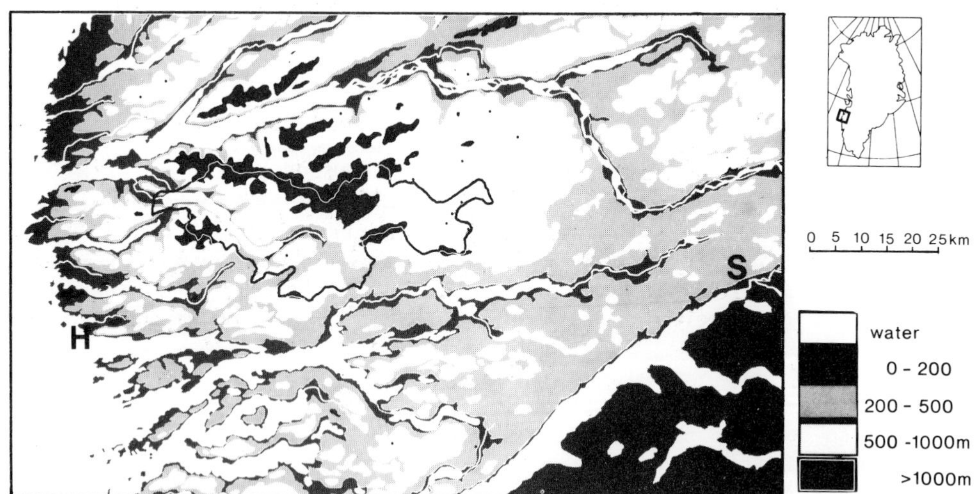

FIG.1 The Taserssuaq basin, West Greenland, indicated by black-white line. H: Holsteinsborg/Sisimut; S: Søndre Strømfjord Airport.

TABLE 1 Area-elevation and glacier/lake distribution in the Taserssuaq basin

Elevation	*Area (km^2)*	*% of area*	*Cum. area (%)*	*Glaciers (%)*	*Lakes (%)*
1400-1600	*2.2*	*0.3*	*100.0*	*17.0*	*0*
1200-1400	*35.8*	*4.1*	*99.7*	*16.0*	*0*
100-1200	*122.0*	*14.1*	*95.6*	*16.0*	*0.4*
800-1000	*166.2*	*19.2*	*81.5*	*3.0*	*2.0*
600-800	*267.6*	*30.9*	*62.3*	*0.2*	*6.0*
400-600	*110.6*	*12.8*	*31.4*	*0.0*	*2.0*
200-400	*80.3*	*9.3*	*18.6*	*0.0*	*10.0*
0-200	*80.3*	*9.3*	*9.3*	*0.0*	*55.0*
Total	*865.0*	*100.0*		*3.6*	*5.1*

A DIGITAL TERRAIN MODEL OF THE AREA

As representation of the area for digital data processing, a digital terrain model (DTM) of the municipality of Holsteinsborg has been constructed on the basis of a local grid with 0.5 km of horizontal resolution. The north-pointing axis has been selected as parallel to the longitude of 52°W, while the east-pointing is perpendicular to this at the intercept of latitude 67°N. The grid is shown in Fig.2.

Maps of 1:250 000 from the Danish Geodetic Institute have been transformed into the grid by digitizing the 200-m equidistance contours. The niveaus of larger lakes were then added, while in areas with little topographical variation, supplementary 100-m contours were drawn.

From this contour map an elevation model has been computed

FIG.2 Elevation model for the Taserssuaq basin. Letters indicate measuring points in the field surveys, cf. Table 2. Grid coordinates are also shown.

according to the method outlined by Carlé (1982). By adding physiographical parameters such as lakes and glaciers, a regular DTM was constructed. For use with the satellite data, a reduced version with 1 x 1 km resolution has been computed. In Fig.2 the elevation model for the basin is shown.

FIELD SURVEYS

Programme and sampling technique

Snow surveying was carried out in two periods. The first, from 22 to 29 April, was selected as representative of the maximum snow cover, while the second period, from 27 May to 6 June, was planned to cover part of the melting season. The field investigations comprised:

(a) photographing the snow cover in the basin from a low-flying plane or helicopter, with standard 35 mm camera,

(b) field measurements of depth, density, and temperature of the snowpack at the locations indicated on Fig.2.

The snow surveying was carried out as a stratified, systematic random sampling in places selected according to the criteria of not too difficult access and of representative landforms, in accordance with Hasholt (1972), and Søgaard (1982a). In the course of each sampling, a snow route was laid out, and the snow depth was measured at 50 m intervals by a graduated rod. Along the line the density was determined at two or three points.

RESULTS OF THE FIELD STUDY

Structure of the snowpack

At selected measuring points the structure and stratification of the snowpack were investigated, i.e. the density and hardness of the snow layers, shape and size of snow crystals, and in most cases the varying temperatures of the snowpack.

In the April survey, which was carried out at temperatures around -20°C, the structure of the snowpack showed features typical for continental, arctic climates: bottom layers with well developed depth-hoar crystals, densities around 270 kg m^{-3}, which clearly indicate strong snow drifting. Only in a few places in the lowest part of the basin did ice lenses indicate that earlier melting had occurred.

In the May-June survey the melting had started, and the snowpack structure in the lowest part, below 400-500 m a.s.l., showed equithermal metamorphosis of the snowpack; in the upper part the structure had been maintained, indicating that no significant through-flow of meltwater had occurred. The overall density increased from a mean value of 0.30 in April to 0.36 in June.

Comparison between snowpack water equivalent (wn) values from the common point in the two surveys showed only minor changes for areas above 500 m and with snow depths greater than 30 cm. In lower-lying areas with a thin snowpack, melting was evident, and at location f (Fig.2) melting rates of 25 mm a day were recorded.

TABLE 2 Measured and estimated snowpack water equivalent for plateaus and broader valley bottoms, Taserssuaq 1982

Points	*Coordinates*	*Altitude (m)*	*No. of points*	*Mean wn (mm)*	*Standard deviation on wn (mm)*	*Estimated wn (mm)*	*Measured on survey no.*
a	81,38	110	29	230.0	64.0	235.0	1
b	82,58	685	25	260.2	114.4	259.6	1
c	90,59	275	14	171.0	137.6	162.1	1
d	90,67	125	33	75.2	41.6	86.4	1
e	95,67	630	17	223.4	112.9	200.4	2
f	91,71	270	-	-	-	-	2
g	81,72	1120	21	292.3	100.2	284.0	2
h	81,73	1150	13	282.0	142.7	285.5	2
i	93,73	610	47	204.8	217.4	164.0	2
j	80,75	950	47	205.2	74.8	230.0	2
j	82,75	1100	10	298.1	34.0	264.0	2
l	86,77	680	30	154.3	127.1	158.8	1
m	79,84	920	17	165.3	109.9	176.0	1
n	81,84	700	24	120.0	34.2	126.5	1
o	84,85	640	15	97.6	48.1	107.8	1
p	80,87	710	20	108.7	36.2	113.0	1
q	83,87	690	17	122.3	61.6	108.5	1
r	85,89	670	29	103.0	68.4	93.5	1

In Table 2, typical values of water equivalent are given. All locations with a depth-hoar bottom layer in the May-June survey were interpreted as representative of the maximum wn and used together with data from April for construction of the following wn-model.

Modelling the observed snowpack water equivalent (wn)

From meteorological data is is known that in the coastal zone of Greenland the yearly precipitation decreases from the south towards the north. At the same time, a west-east decrease is observed; thus, the precipitation in Søndre Strømfjord is only half of the amount recorded for Holsteinsborg. In earlier studies (Søgaard, 1982a) a clear altitude-dependent variation in wn has been demonstrated as far as the central part of the basin is concerned. When ignoring other effects such as precipitation shadow, snow drifting etc., it seems that three variables have to be taken into account when modelling the wn-distribution.

In order to evaluate the significance, a stepwise multiple regression analysis was carried out. All measuring points within a range of ±100 m of the median altitude of 700 m were selected. For these 12 points a linear-trend surface analysis was carried out on the wn-values with northing and easting as independent variables. It proved that more than 94% of the total variance could be explained by this model, but that the easting component was by far the most powerful term. In order to reduce the number of variables, the model was then reduced to the following expression for the variation in wn at the altitude of 700 m:

$$wn_{700} = 568.0 - 5.25x \text{ (mm)}$$

with x in km as the easting component as indicated on Fig.2. The model still accounts for more than 90% of the total variance.

The vertical variation, investigated at four points, showed a lapse rate of 12% per 100 m in the central and 16% in the eastern part of the basin, while a value of 6% would be demanded if the lake-level values in the western part should be incorporated.

With little loss of information, this could be rearranged in the following simple model of the maximum water-equivalent:

$$wn_h = 410.0 + 0.225h - 5.25x \text{ (mm)}$$

with h = altitude in m, x = easting in km.

The standard error of estimate on data from Table 2 is only 16.9 mm.

UTILIZATION OF NOAA-DATA FOR SNOW MAPPING

The satellite data

During the actual period of study two NOAA satellites were in operation (NOAA-6 and NOAA-7). All satellite data were received by the ground station in Søndre Strømfjord. From a collected total of data from 20 orbits, ranging from April to September, eight images were selected based on the following criteria:

(a) maximum cloud cover over the basin of 10%;
(b) near nadir passages, i.e. scan-angles less than 15°;
(c) equal spacing throughout the melting season.

Aside from a gap in July caused by bad weather conditions, a fairly equal spacing of data has been obtained.

Processing of the satellite data

For studying the depletion of the snow cover a time series of satellite data has been built up so, instead of analysing each image, the whole series can be treated at a time, i.e. a multi-temporal analysis. This necessitates of course a standardization of the data. During the period of study, the satellite orbit parameters will change, including the scan angle to the specific area and the geometrical distortion.

In the initial stage each image has to be rectified, and before the analysis a radiometric transformation has to be applied to correct for changes in illumination level during the data collection run. The data analysis is thus composed of the following stages:

(a) preprocessing, including geometric and radiometric transformation of data and correcting for topographical effects; and,

(b) image analysis, including classification of the snow cover testing the results against results from other methods and computation of the water equivalent distribution.

Geometric transformation

All images in the data series have been geometrically transformed into the indicated grid by second-order polynomial regression. In computing the pixel values from the original resolution of approx.

1.1 x 1.1 km to the 1 x 1 km of the grid, a cubic convoluting interpolation routine has been used. In the selection of control points for determining the constants of the transformation equation, two methods have been applied:

(a) the corresponding coordinates of 15-20 points, easily identifiable in both model and image, are selected visually. The topographical maps, overlain by the grid, are used as the model. When reading the coordinates in the image directly from the screen, an accuracy of ± 1 pixel is obtained, at best; the residuals typically turn out to have a r.m.s.-value (root mean square) of about 1 to 2 pixels so the method is rather coarse.

(b) by a spatial cross-correlation, the corresponding coordinates of the same number of points are identified in image and model (with a displacement of 0.2 pixels), using a method developed by Hansen (1982). The method operates on a sub-pixel level, applying interpolation techniques. The model used here was the DTM. This method gives a significantly higher accuracy than (a), with r.m.s.-values for most images within the range of 0.2-0.4 pixels.

Radiometric corrections

The output in channel 1 (0.58-0.68 μm) and 2 (0.7-1.1 μm) is recomputed to albedo values. Here the standard linear expressions, given by Schwalb (1978), divided by the sine of the sun elevation are used. When computing albedo values, it is assumed that snow is a good diffuse reflector, i.e. the intensity of reflected light is independent of the angle of the incident beam.

When correcting for the varying input of solar radiation at the surface, depending on slope and aspect, a trend surface has been computed around each point in the terrain model. By taking the cosine of the angle between the normal to the surface and the incident beam, the correction factor is found. The diffuse radiation's share of the total radiation is estimated to be 20%.

The output from channel 4 (10.5-11.5 μm and 10.3-11.3 μm, NOAA-6 and 7, respectively) is converted into temperatures by using the standard calibration adjusted with temperature samples.

COMPUTATION OF THE SNOW COVER

If we consider a unit area on the ground with a fraction of snow cover (A_n) with known albedo (r_s) and a background with the albedo (r_b), then A_n can be given the following expression:

$$r_t = A_n r_s + (1 - A_n) r_b$$

where r_t is the total satellite measured albedo, and r_b can be estimated from data series when the area is snow-free. As this expression holds for both channel 1 and 2, it should be possible to solve the equations for A_n, if r_s had the same value in the two channels. This is by no means correct, however, the ratio r_{s1}/r_{s2} being strongly dependent upon the state of the snowpack. Instead of trying to use data from both channels, only channel 1 is used, based on estimations on r_s.

By using the r_b -values we avoid classifying areas with a natural high albedo as snow, e.g. braided rivers. This is in conformance with Lillesand *et al.* (1982) who demonstrated that the general classification accuracy is thereby improved.

DETERMINATION OF THE SNOWPACK ALBEDO

In order to evaluate the albedo for the fully snow-covered area r_s, the state of the snowpack has to be known, as the spectral characteristics of the snow change quite clearly when the melting of the snow starts. O'Brien & Munis (1975) showed that a sharp decline in reflectivity occurs when melting starts, especially in the 0.7-1.4 μm spectral range. This can be demonstrated from satellite data by comparing data from channel 1 with channel 2, either by the ratio ch1/ch2, or by principal component analysis of the two channels. In the latter the second principal component has the highest values in areas with undisturbed snow, as also found by Haefner (1980). Both methods, are, however, affected by changes in the snowfree areas, since the ch1/ch2 ratio is strongly dependent on state of vegetation cover.

Instead of using ch1/ch2 to determine the state of the snow, the emittance temperature from ch4 was used with 0°C as threshold value. By separating the area in a melting and a non-melting part, albedo

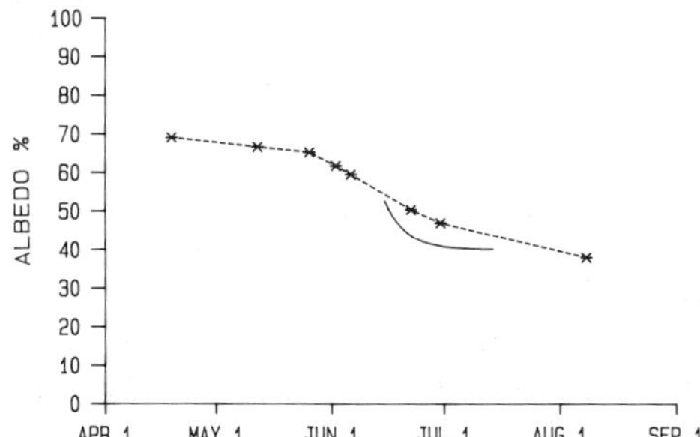

FIG.3 The decrease of albedo for 100% snow cover in areas lying about 1100 m a.m.s.l. The asterisks indicate the used satellite data. The black line indicates decrease, according to Corps of Engineers (1956), from estimated start of melting.

can be estimated from the data series. In Fig.3 the snowpack albedo is shown as a function of time. Compared with data from Corps of Engineers, US Army (1956), the data here show a somewhat slower rate of decline.

CLASSIFICATION OF THE SNOW COVER

By using the equation with r_s -values indicated in Fig.3 it is now possible to classify the snow cover of the basin. In Fig.4 the distribution is shown on 25 May 1982, and in Fig.5 the snow cover

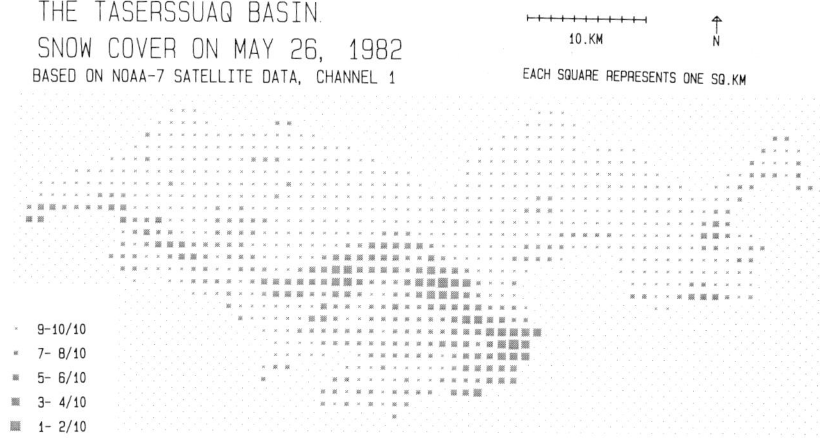

FIG.4 Outprint of the snow cover map for 26 May 1982.

depletion can be seen as a heavy melting which occurs within the period from the end of May to the end of June.

The snow cover distribution based on air photographs and data from the field-survey snow cover maps have been produced for 22 April and 26 May in Søgaard (1982b).

When testing the computed snow cover maps it must be borne in mind that those produced from air photographs are by no means absolute "ground truth", but optimally will have an accuracy of ±10%. The original has therefore been rearranged with a resolution of 20% such as seen in Fig.4.

When comparing the maps from April it appears that 87% of the pixels have equal snow cover and that the mean error on the rest is only 1.1 unit.

For the May data the comparison is only made for the eastern part of the basin, crossed by skiing. Here 55% of the pixels have identical values, and the mean error on the rest is 1.7 unit. When applying the linear-scaling method (Andersen & Ødegård, 1980) on

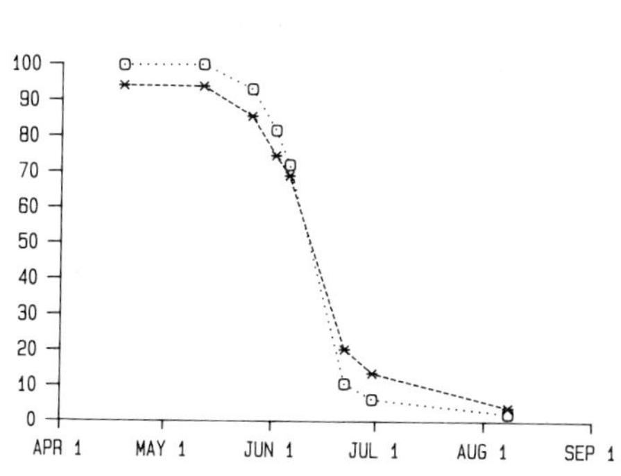

FIG.5 Snow cover depleton,Taserssuaq 1983. --x--- total snow cover,.⊡...⊡ area with snow cover greater than 50%.

the same data, it was found for April that 61% of the pixels had values equal to those mapped from air photographs against 54% for May.

Computing of total water equivalent

The drawback that the wn model is only valid for topographic features such as valley bottoms and plateaus is overcome by multiplying the wn model by the snow-cover map and thereby including other landforms with different snow patterns, e.g. slopes. Moreover, the general wn-distribution has to be adjusted in two ways. The first one is to cut off the model at 40 mm, which means that all possible values below this limit will be put to 40 mm. Aside from snowpacks on ice, wn-values of less than 40 mm have not been observed because of the effect of edge-melting.

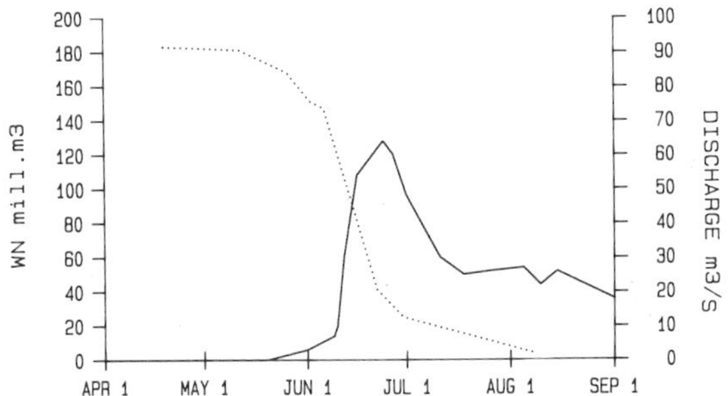

FIG.6 Depletion of total snowpack wn (......) and simplified discharge (———). The discharge is being recorded by Greenland's Technical Organization, Dept of Hydro Power Investigations.

Melting from the top of the snowpack necessitates the second adjustment, i.e. the values in the wn model have to be reduced from mid-June and throughout the melting season. By giving the wn-maps albedo as indicated in Fig.3, it is possible to compare this picture with the satellite image. By repeated comparisons this melting has been estimated to be 60 mm in the last part of June and 50 mm in July. Figure 6 shows the depletion of the total snowpack, wn, together with the recorded discharge for the whole basin. From the water balance it appears that the maximum wn, with a standard error of estimate of 15%, is in general agreement with the accumulated runoff. With respect to the timing, the accordance is obvious, as the high discharge in July-August was due to heavy rainfall.

CONCLUSION

By using geometric transformation with an accuracy at sub-pixel level the presented procedure makes it possible to combine several satellite pictures throughout the melting season and to integrate field survey data. This method is more time-consuming than the linear-scaling method, but since it includes other surface parameters, such as albedo and emittance temperatures, it will be a rewarding method for wider scopes, e.g. energy budgets.

With respect to accuracy, it seems reasonable to conclude that with low angles of sun elevation in April, the shadow effect will strongly influence the results from the linear-scaling method. With higher angles and careful selection of the points for linear-scaling, there is no significant difference between the two methods.

ACKNOWLEDGEMENTS The project was funded by the Commission for Scientific Research in Greenland, to whom the author wishes to express his gratitude. Thanks are also due to MScs Niels Thingvad and Senior Lecturer Bent Hasholt for valuable discussions, and to Secretary Kirsten Winther for linguistic assistance. Finally, the Greenland Technical Organization deserves many thanks for their useful practical advice and help.

REFERENCES

Andersen, T. & H. Ødegaard (1980) Application of satellite data for snow mapping. *Report no. 3, Norwegian National Committee for Hydrology, Oslo.*

Carlé, C. (1982) Satellite mapping. *Medd. no. 12, Inst. for Landmåling og Fotogrammetri, Tech. Univ. of Denmark.*

Corps of Engineers, US Army (1956) *Snow Hydrology.* US Dept of Commerce, Office of Technical Services.

Haefner, H. (1980) Snow cover monitoring from satellite data under European conditions. In: *Remote Sensing Applications in Agriculture and Hydrology* (ed. by G.Fraysse). Rotterdam.

Hansen, P. (1982) Image to image registration on a subpixel level using cross correlation. *R264 Electromagnetics Inst., Tech. Univ. of Denmark.*

Hasholt, B. (1972) Random sampling techniques applied in measuring snow water equivalent in a drainage basin. Internat. Symp. on Measurement and Forecasting, Session WMO-1.

Lillesand, T.M., E.D.Meisner, A.Downs la Mois & Deuell, L.R. (1982) Use of GOES and TIROS/NOAA satellite data for snow-cover mapping. In: *Photogram. Engng and Remote Sens.* 48 (2).

O'Brien, H.W. & R.H. Munis (1975) Red and infrared spectral reflectance of snow. In: *Operational Applications of Satellite Snowcover Operations* (ed. by A.Rango). Workshop Proceedings, NASA Special Publ. SP-391, Washington.

Schwalb, A. (1978) The TIROS-N/NOAA A-G satellite series. *NOAA Tech. Memo. NESS 95.*

Søgaard, H. (1982a) Snow mapping in the Taserssuaq basin, West Greenland, based on satellite data and field measurements. Fourth North. Research Basin Symp. Norway. *Report no.12, Norwegian National Committee for Hydrology, Oslo.*

Søgaard, H. (1982b) Snow hydrology studies in the Taserssuaq basin, West Greenland. *Newsletter no. 7, Copenhagen.*

Hydrological Applications of Remote Sensing and Remote Data Transmission
(Proceedings of the Hamburg Symposium, August 1983). IAHS Publ. no. 145.

Snow cover on the Stanovoe Upland determined by satellite imagery

V. G. PROKACHEVA
State Hydrological Institute, 2 Linija 23, 199053 Leningrad, USSR

ABSTRACT The snow cover boundary for three mountain (up to 3000 m high) river basins with dimensions 4000-21 000 km^2 was determined from all the cloudfree images obtained from the satellite "Meteor" during the period 1969-1981. The results were used when analysing hydrographs according to types of recharge for determining altitudes of zones of snow deficit and snow excess in basins for revealing correlations between degrees of snow cover on various basins. The purpose of this work was to obtain long-term information on the periods of snow cover formation and disappearance at different altitudes in order to develop forecast correlations between snow-line dynamics and the volume of snowmelt runoff.

Couverture neigeuse du Plateau Stanovoé d'après les données des satellites

RESUME La limite de la couverture neigeuse pour trois bassins versants montagneux (l'altitude allant jusqu'à 3000 m) ayant la superficie de 4000 jusqu'à 21 000 km^2 a été déterminée à l'aide de toutes les images sans nuages fournies par le satellite artificiel "Meteor" pour la période 1969-1981. Les résultats obtenus ont été utilisés pour l'analyse des hydrogrammes selon les différents types d'alimentation pour préciser la position sur les bassins versants des zones présentant un déficit ou un excès de neige, pour la détermination de corrélations entre les diverses épaisseur de la couverture neigeuse des bassins versants différents. Le but de cette étude était d'aboutir à des conclusions à long terme sur les périodes de formation et de fusion du couvert de neige à différentes altitudes en vue de la mise en évidence de liens de prévision entre la dynamique de la ligne de neige et le volume d'écoulement de l'eau de la fusion nivale.

INTRODUCTION

Surveys from satellites give information on existing snow cover distribution over the Earth's surface. Using satellite imagery, snow cover boundaries for the moment of time when the image was obtained can be determined. For revealing general regularities and obtaining systematic data on the dynamics of the snow boundary, regular surveys during different seasons over a long-term period are needed.

Soviet meteorological satellites "Meteor" provide information for studying the snow cover boundary regime. They carry out daily surveys of the Earth's surface with the resolution of about 1000 m. Using these images, information on snow cover dynamics can be obtained for remote and difficult-to-access territories where the surface hydrometeorological observational network is sparse. One of these territories is the Stanovoe Upland.

SNOW COVER ANALYSIS - STANOVOE UPLAND

Image interpretation

Using TV imagery from "Meteor", the dynamics of snow cover for three river basins in the territory of the Stanovoe Upland for a 13-year period (1969-1981) were determined. Areas of the river basins under study are as follows: the River Chara - village Chara - 4150 km^2; the River Muya - village Taximo - 9900 km^2; the Upper River Angara - village Verkhnaya Zaimka - 20 600 km^2. The altitude of this territory ranges from 500 to 3000 m. Hydrometeorological observations in each basin are carried out at the outlets. For the region, stable snow cover in winter (November-March) and a short snowfree period in summer (July-August) are characteristic. Melting of snow produces 80% of the flood flow volume and about 40% of the annual river flow.

From the whole set of satellite imagery, cloudfree TV images were selected for each basin for the period in spring and in autumn when the cover boundary was changing. From these images, the snow cover boundary was extracted and the extent of snow coverage (i.e. ratio of the area covered with snow to the whole basin area) was determined. Then, using hypsographic curves, the equivalent snow line altitude was determined. Methodology of the extraction and mapping of snow cover boundary is described in *Vremennye Metodicheskie Rekomendatsii...* (1980). The extent of snow cover of a basin is determined from images with an error of about 6% and the equivalent snow line elevation with an error of about 200 m. Using the results from imagery analysis, by interpolating actual values for each year, the chronological variation of snow line elevation and snow cover extent in the basin were determined. During the spring period for plotting the graphs 5-26 point (satellite images) were used, and in autumn 5-10 were used. These graphs usually show good agreement with variations of other hydrometeorological elements.

Use for hydrological analysis

As a result of this work valuable information on snow line dynamics in river basins was obtained. It is impossible to obtain such information using routine methods of surface observations. The results were used for the hydrological purposes listed below:

(a) *Adjustment of the time of beginning and ending of flooding and the analysis of hydrograph by types of recharge.* As a result of the analysis snowmelt runoff characteristics (volume, layer, normal flow, mean and extreme discharges, snowmelt runoff duration in spring, the portion of snowmelt flow in annual flow) for each of the 13 years under study were determined. Statistical treatment of the results gave design hydrological characteristics for the three basins under study typical of the Stanovoe Upland.

(b) *Determination of altitudinal position of zones of snow excess and snow deficit within the basin.* For this purpose, using the results of imagery analysis, the rate of change in snow-line elevation with the increase of mean daily air temperature by 1°C was calculated. This relative value fairly well reflects variations of snow storage. For example, for years of high snow storage in the basin of the River Chara mean relative rate of snow-line rise was 2-3 m/(°C day), and for years of low snow storage it was 5-9 m/(°C day). Besides, for each year the regularity in variations of the relative snow-line rise with altitude was revealed. For low altitudes (up to 1300 m) a gradual decrease of this value is observed, then, for higher altitudes up to 2000 m, the rate of rise stabilizes, and for altitudes more than 2000 m it increases sharply again. Altitudinal interval, for which the least values of snow-line rate of rise are observed, is the same for each year, but it varies for the individual basins: River Chara - village Chara - 1600-2000 m; River Muya - village Taximo - 1500-1900 m; Upper River Angara - village Verkhnaya Zaimka - 1400-1800 m. These altitudes correspond to zones of maximum snow accumulation which produce up to 70% of the total snowmelt volume during the spring flood period.

(c) *Revelation of relationships between the degree of snow coverage and snow-line rise for adjacent and distant basins.* Sufficiently close annual and long-term correlations were determined between the extent of snow coverage for adjacent basins situated in the Stanovoe Upland (correlation coefficients 0.94-0.98), between snow-line elevation for the same date in basins situated in the Altai Mountains and the Stanovoe Upland, between the extent of snow coverage in river basins situated in the Stanovoe Upland (Siberia) and Rocky Mountains (North America).

(d) *Determination of periods of snow cover formation and melting at different altitudes in mountains.* From chronological graphs of the variation in snow-line elevation during autumn and spring for each year, dates of snow-line appearance at the pre-selected altitudes with the interval of 200 m were read. Conclusions on mean values were made for 11-12 years for periods of snow cover disappearance and for 8-9 years for the periods of stable snow cover formation. Using these results averaged curves of time variations of snow-line elevation for each of the three basins were plotted (Fig.1).

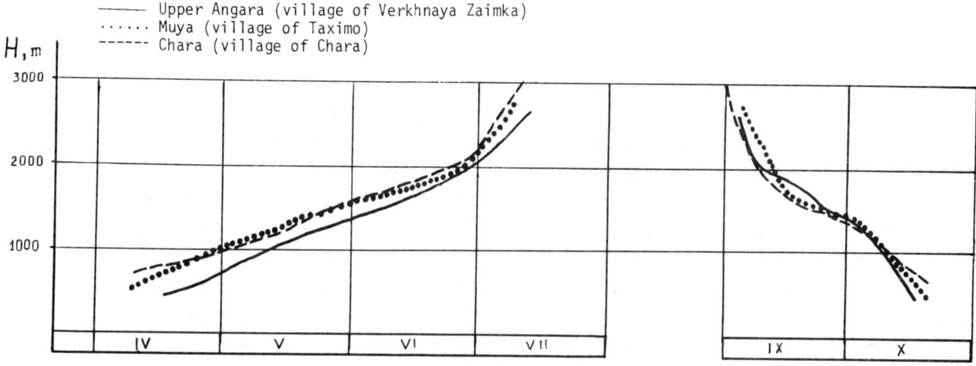

FIG.1 Temporal variations of average snow-line altitude (H) for basins of three rivers.

After the analysis of survey imagery it was stated that the isochrones obtained gave the mean snow-line position at the corresponding altitude with a variation ±70 m.

(e) *Determination of forecast correlations between snow-line dynamics and snowmelt volume.* Data on the extent of snow coverage in the basin at particular moments of time or on the rate of snow-line rise for specific time intervals, or on the relative snow-line rise by 1° of mean positive daily air temperature, obtained as a result of satellite imagery interpretation, were indicative of snowpack accumulation in the basin and of the rate of its depletion. These characteristics were used as predictors when searching for correlations between snowmelt runoff volume, mean monthly water discharges during spring floods and maximum spring flood discharges. Correlations of various quality and reliability were obtained. In Figs 2 and 3 two such correlations are given; test forecasts for three years (1979, 1980, 1981) were made using this relation and achieved good results.

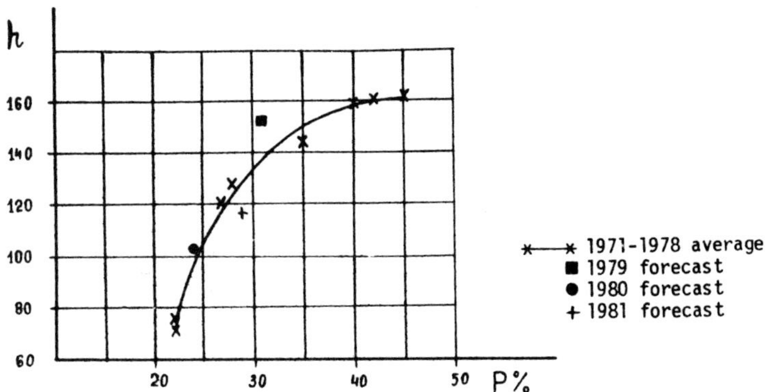

FIG.2 Snowmelt runoff (h) vs. snow coverage extent (p) for the River Chara (village of Chara) basin at the end of May.

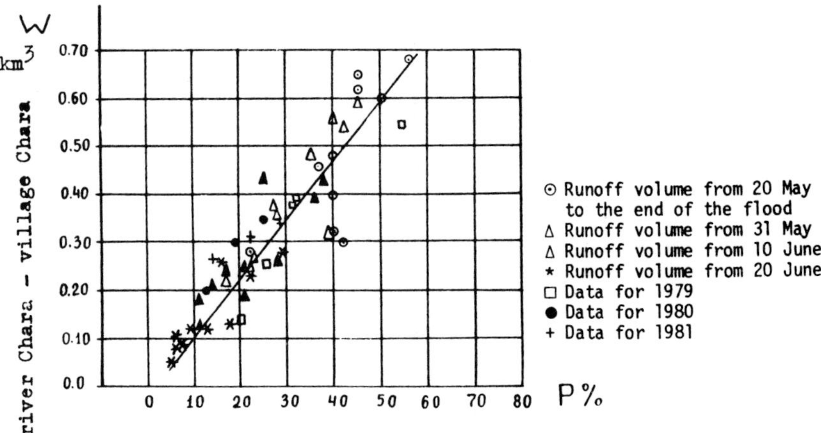

FIG.3 Snowmelt runoff volume (W) for the rest of a flood compared to snow coverage extent (p) in the River Chara (village of Chara) basin during the previous day.

REFERENCES

Prokacheva, V.G., Snishchenko, D.V. & Usachev V.F. (1982) *Distantsionnye Metody Gidrologicheskogo Izuchenia zony BAM'a* (Remote sensing methods of hydrological studying of the Baikal-Amur Railaway zone). Gidrometeoizdat, Leningrad.

Prokacheva, V.G. & Chmutova, N.P. (1982) O prognozirovanii obyema vesennego polovodia s pomoshchiu sputnikovoi informatsii (na primere r. Chara) (On the forecasting of the volume of spring flood using satellite imagery (exemplified by the river Chara). In: *Issledovanie Zemli iz Kosmosa (Investigation of the Earth from Space)*, vol.2.

Vremennye Metodicheskie Rekomendatsii po Ispolzovaniu Sputnikovoi Informatsii v Operativnoi Praktike. Kartirovanie Snezhnogo Pokrova (Temporal methodological recommendations on the use of satellite information in operational practices. Mapping of snow cover) (1980). Gidrometeoizdat, Leningrad.

Hydrological Applications of Remote Sensing and Remote Data Transmission
(Proceedings of the Hamburg Symposium, August 1983). IAHS Publ. no. 145.

Studies of Himalayan snow cover area from satellites

M. S. DHANJU
Space Applications Centre (ISRO),
Ahmedabad 380053, India

ABSTRACT Studies were carried out on the variations in the snow-covered areas of the Himalayas for the period June 1979 to June 1982, using weekly charts of northern hemisphere snow and ice boundaries prepared by NOAA/NESDIS of the United States, based on data of the visible band sensors aboard TIROS-N and GOES satellites. The seasonal changes of the area under snow cover for the three classes shown as most reflective, moderately reflective and least reflective are studied. Comparison is made of the ambient temperature of certain areas with the accumulation and ablation periods. The extent of snow cover plays an important role not only in the climate of the Indian sub-continent, but also with its supply of water resources providing meltwater for rivers that rise in the Himalayas. The relationship between the changes in snow cover area and the corresponding meltwater contribution is investigated.

Etudes par satellites des superficies couvertes de neige dans les Himalayas
RESUME Des études ont été effectuées sur les variations des superficies couvertes de neige dans les Himalayas pour la période de juin 1979 à juin 1982. On utilise ici des cartes hebdomadaires des limites de la neige et des glaces préparées par NESDIS de NOAA, USA, pour l'hémisphère nord, cartes basées sur les données de la bande visible à bord des satellites TIROS-N et GOES. Les changements saisonniers des superficies couvertes de neige sont étudiées pour trois classes: les plus réflectives, modèrement réflectives et les moins réflectives. On procède à une comparaison entre la température ambiante de certaines superficies avec l'accumulation et l'ablation de la neige. L'étendue de la couverture neigeuse joue un rôle important dans le climat de l'Inde et aussi dans les caractéristiques des ressources en eau, en fournissant de l'eau de fonte dans les grands fleuves qui sont issus des Himalayas. Les relations entre les variations des superficies couvertes de neige et la contribution d'eau de fonte de neige sont étudiées.

INTRODUCTION

The use of satellite data for the study of terrestrial resources has opened new vistas in the area of applications where ground methods in general are inadequate. In imagery from the first meteorological satellites of the sixties, the areas of snow cover were the first to be discerned and was thus one of the first terrestrial resources to be observed from space. The study of snow-covered areas from satellites can provide important information for the estimation of snowmelt water that flows into rivers having reservoir system built for power generation and irrigation (Rango & Salomonson, 1975; Dhanju, 1982).

The Himalayan mountains are the world's largest and highest and the changes in their seasonal snow-cover area plays an important role in the hydrology and meteorology of the surrounding countries. In this paper, some of these aspects are investigated based on snow-cover data derived from satellite imagery of TIROS-N and GOES.

DESCRIPTION OF THE HIMALAYAS

The Himalayas extract respect from everyone, whether one is planning to scale the highest peak of the world or lesser peaks, trying to capture their grandure and beauty in photographs or trying to find the abundance of their various resources.

The world's highest mountains are still becoming higher, rising at an annual rate of 7.5-10 cm. One of the peculiar characteristics of Himalayan rivers is that several of these rising in Tibet flow between the soaring ridges. These rivers have cut deep valleys across the range from north to south. In many cases they rise as high as 5000 m above the river bed. The Kali River (named Gandak in India) which flows between the peaks of Annapurna and Dhaulagiri, has its bed at a height of 1500 m, but the peak only 6 km away has a height of 8172 m. Nanga Parbhat, at an elevation of 8125 m, is only 22 km away from the Indus River located in a valley at an elevation of 1500 m. This makes the Himalayas one of the most rugged mountain ranges of the world and one of the most inaccessible. The present study includes the general range of mountains skirting the Indian sub-continent and lying between 70° and 100°E and south of 40°N. For various contour heights, the area of the Himalayas is given in Table 1.

The Himalayas control the climate and water resources of the Indian sub-continent. The major rivers Indus, Ganga and Brahamaputra originate from its vast snow fields. The snow line during the winter

TABLE 1 Himalayan area above various contour heights

Contour height (m)	*Area ($km^2 \times 10^6$)*	*%*
1500	*4.60*	*100*
2100	*3.90*	*85*
3000	*3.20*	*69*
3600 and 4500	*2.10*	*45*
5400 and 6000	*0.56*	*12*

months, December to March, can descend to altitudes as low as 2100-3000 m, and by June recedes to about 5000 m. It is important to note that precipitation during the snow accumulation period, as part of the total yearly precipitation, progressively decreases from the western part to the eastern part. It is 22% in Kashmir, 11% in Himachal, 6% in Garwal, 4% in Nepal and 2% in Assam (Gulati, 1972).

SEASONAL CHANGES IN HIMALAYAN SNOW COVER FROM NORTHERN HEMISPHERE SNOW CHARTS

In recent years a new data set has been generated for the monitoring of snow-cover areas as observed from satellites. The northern hemisphere snow and ice cover charts produced on a weekly basis by NESDIS of the National Oceanic and Atmospheric Administration, USA, make use of the visible band imagery from TIROS-N and GOES satellites. The spatial resolution lies in the range 1-7.4 km. The charts have been found to be extremely useful for the study of the seasonal changes of large snow-cover areas (Matson & Wiesnet, 1981). In these charts the Himalayan snow-cover area can be fairly well identified. The three categories of snow cover in which the area has been divied pertain to the most reflective, moderately reflective and least reflective.

The study area lying east of 70°E and south of 40°N encompasses an area of 4.6 x $10^6 km^2$ if the 1500 m contour is considered as the boundary line. In the present analysis, weekly maps for the period from the third week of June 1979 to the second week of June 1982, i.e. 156 weeks, are used. From each weekly chart the areas for each of the three categories of snow cover are determined by dot grid method. The total snow-covered area for each week is also determined. This process is carried out for all 156 charts. Taking the maximum weekly value from among all the values as 100%, the values in each category are normalized. It may be noted that the area of maximum snow cover observed is about 80% of the total area of the Himalayas. The normalized values of the snow-covered area for each week are plotted in Fig.1. The graphs indicate the snow area for total, most reflective, moderately reflective and least reflective areas.

Considering the ruggedness of the Himalayan terrain, it is possible to assume that the area of snow cover shown as most reflective is the area of heavy snow, moderately reflective as of moderate snow and least reflective as of least snow. The bottom graph in Fig.1 shows total snow-covered area for each week for three cycles of seasonal changes for the 1979-1982 period. The various values of the maximum and the minimum area of snow cover observed are given in Table 2.

The contours given in column 4 of Table 2 are derived by comparing the area under snow cover with the area for contour heights given in Table 1. This gives the height and the fluctuations of the snow line at the time of maximum or minimum snow cover. The large degree of variability in the maximum area of snow cover observed in January 1980, March 1981, and January 1982 depends upon the strength of the western disturbances that are active in the months of October-May resulting in snowfall in the Himalayas. The western part of the

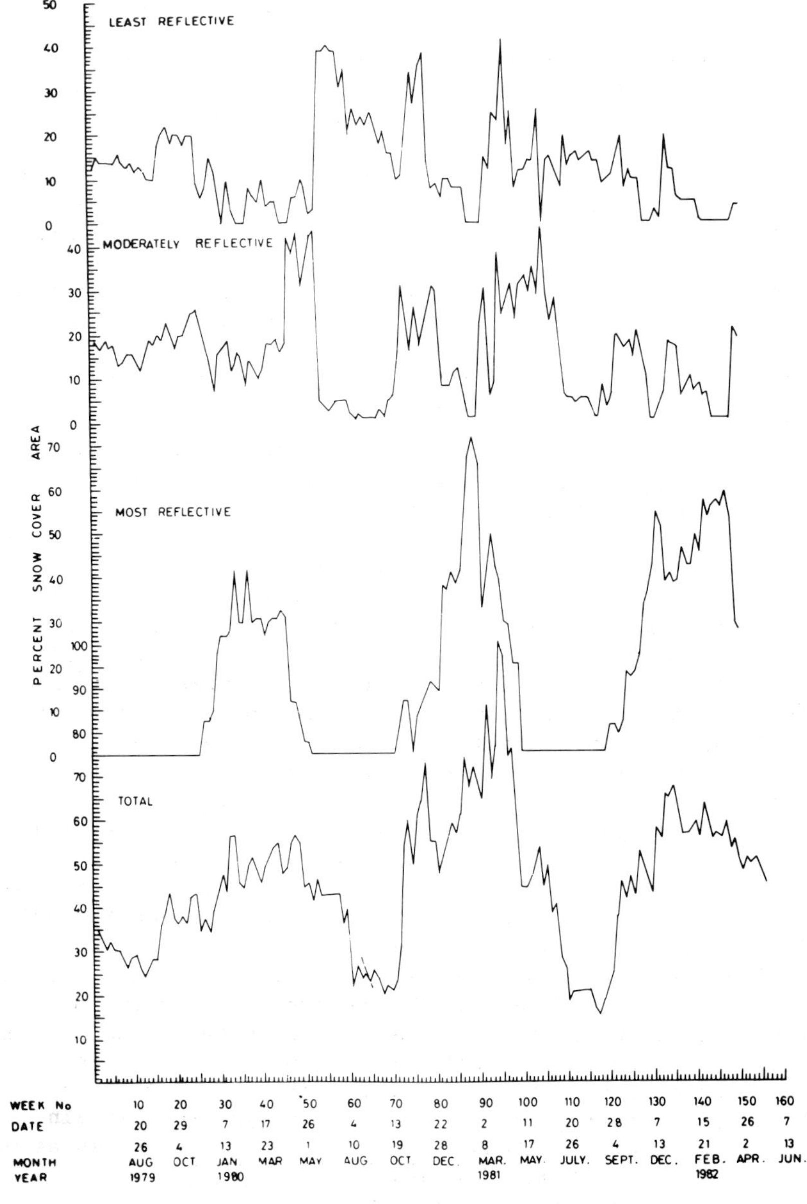

FIG.1 Seasonal snow cover in the Himalayas from June 1979 to June 1982 derived from northern hemisphere weekly snow charts.

Himalayas gets more snowfall because the disturbances are active earlier there than in the eastern part which gets snowfall later. The various meteorological factors play an important role and the orography of the Himalayas acts as a modulating factor. On the average there may be 4-10 disturbances per month beginning between October and May, ceasing in the later months (*Weather*, 1977). The process of the building up of large snow-covered areas which is

TABLE 2

Week no.	*Month*	*Area (km^2 x 10^6)*	*Approx. contour (m)*	*Remarks*
12	*Sept. 79*	*0.93*	*5400*	*minimum snow cover*
33	*Jan. 80*	*2.11*	*3600*	*maximum snow cover*
67	*Sept. 80*	*0.74*	*5400*	*minimum snow cover*
94	*Mar. 81*	*3.67*	*2100*	*maximum snow cover*
117	*Sept. 81*	*0.55*	*5400*	*minimum snow cover*
134	*Jan. 82*	*2.44*	*3000*	*maximum snow cover*

mostly related to these westerly disturbances is shown in the second graph in Fig.1. These appear in the western part of the Himalayas earlier than in the eastern part. The middle area is covered towards February or March. Table 3 summarizes the time of build-up, the peak and ending of snow-cover over the area.

It is interesting to note that for the week when the area of heavy snow shows a peak value, the corresponding area of moderate or least snow is either zero or minimum. The start of the snow accumulation period is reflected in the increase in the least snow area in the initial stage. Later the moderate snow area also starts building up. But with the start of the heavy snow area, the other areas start dropping until it reaches the peak value and the others drop to zero or are at a minimum. The decrease in the heavy snow area is accompanied by the increase in the moderate and least snow area. Later the moderate snow area also drops to zero or minimum leaving the residual in the least snow area. This is the permanent snow-covered area when the snow line has receded to 5000 m or so, leaving glaciated areas or ice.

The heavy snow-covered area plays an important role in providing the maximum of meltwater. The snowmelt hydrograph must follow the same profile as that of the heavy snow area. Hence, it may be possible to obtain estimates of the meltwater that may be expected for each season. This is done by integrating the area under the heavy snow-cover graph for each of the seasons. Some of the estimates are as follows:

1979-1980 840 000 km^2 or 84 million ha
1980-1981 1080 000 km^2 or 108 million ha
1981-1982 1344 000 km^2 or 134.4 million ha

If it is assumed that on the average the snowfall for the season

TABLE 3 Build-up, peak and end of snow cover

Season no.	*Start*	*Peak*	*End*
1	*2nd week Dec. 79*	*3rd week Feb. 80*	*1st week June 80*
2	*3rd week Oct. 80*	*3rd week Feb. 81*	*1st week May 81*
3	*4th week Sept. 81*	*4th week March 82*	*Late June 82*

is 1 m and the snow density is 100 kg m^{-3}, then the meltwater provided in each season can be calculated as:

1979-1980   8.4 million ha-m
1980-1981   10.8 million ha-m
1981-1982   13.44 million ha-m

Some of the estimates available for the snowmelt contribution from the Himalayas are in the range of 10 million ha-m (Nag & Kathpalia, 1975). This compares favourably with the estimates calculated above.

SEASONAL TEMPERATURE CHANGES IN THE HIMALAYAS

For the study of seasonal temperature changes in the Himalayas, seven stations from three representative areas have been selected, namely Kashmir (Leh, 3522 m a.s.l.; Gulmarg, 2730 m a.s.l.; Srinagar, 1582 m a.s.l.), Himachal Pradesh (Simla, 2205 m a.s.l.; Dharamsala, 900 m a.s.l.; Delhousie, 1200 m a.s.l.) and Sikkim (Gangtok, 1871 m a.s.l.), covering the western, middle and eastern parts respectively. Weekly average temperatures are compiled for each of the areas from the data given by the Indian Meteorological Department (Indian Meteorological Department, 1979-1982). For the week ending 27 June 1979 to 9 June 1982, the weekly average temperature values are plotted in Fig.2 for each area.

The maximum temperature for the season for all the three regions remains more or less in the range of 24°-28°C. However, the minimum temperature shows a marked difference. For Kashmir the minimum temperature is in the range 0.5°-2°C while for Himachal Pradesh it is 4°-6°C and for Sikkim it is 14°-16°C. The amount of energy available in the eastern region of the Himalayas is higher so the snowmelt process starts earlier making the snow-line recession faster. It will be slower in Himachal Pradesh and very slow for the Kashmir area. Since these are ambient temperatures recorded in the valley stations, where the snow-cover may be absent or present only for a short period, these may not represent the actual temperatures of the environments of the snow-covered areas; however, these do represent the profile of the seasonal variations. Moreover, snowmelt in general starts from the lower altitudes from where the snow-line recession takes place, and so initially, the valley temperature will be important to the snowmelt process.

The transfer of heat to the snow results in meltwater. The most important components of the heat budget of the snow pack are:

(a) Solar energy absorbed by the snow. It includes short-wave radiation received directly from the sun and diffuse solar radiation.

(b) The sensible heat transfer between the air and snow by convection and conduction from the atmosphere.

(c) The net long-wave radiation exchange between the snow and its environments.

In the snowmelt period solar radiation plays a dominant role. In fact the increase in the incident solar radiation in April heralds the snowmelt season and by that time the snow accumulation process has also reached the maximum. The snowmelt is accelerated due to the increase in the incident radiation in the subsequent months. Table 4 gives the incident solar radiation values for the different

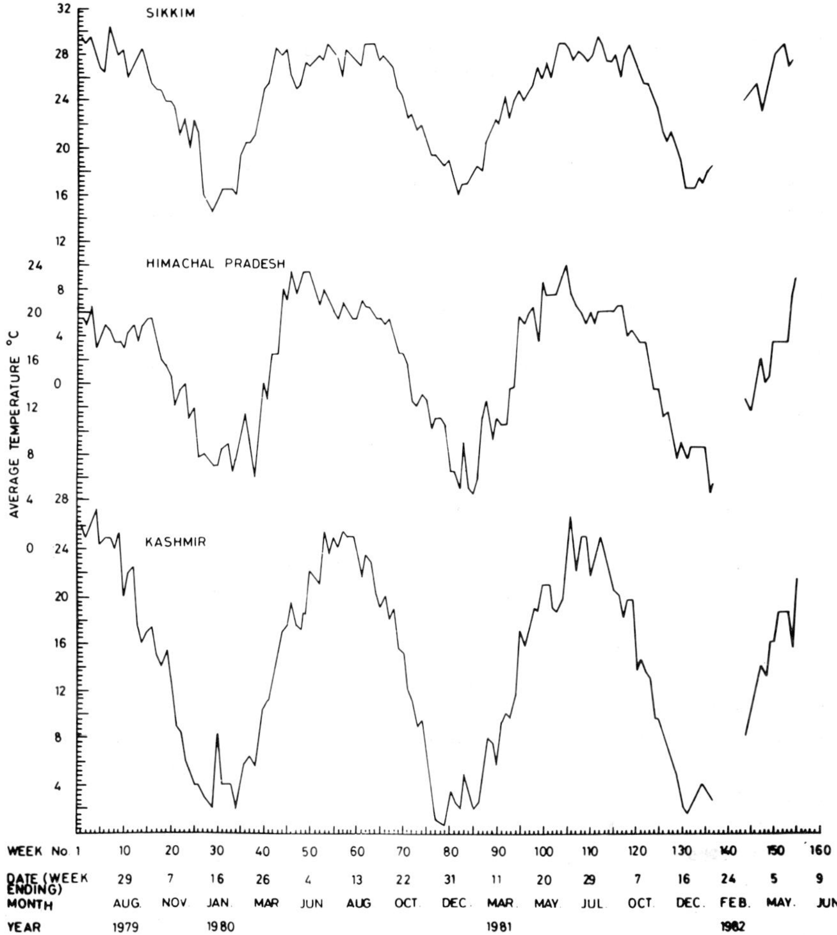

FIG.2 Seasonal temperature variations for some areas of the Himalayas for the period from June 1979 to June 1982.

months of the year at 31°N latitude (*Climatological and Solar Data for India*, 1969).

At higher altitudes the air temperature decreases, but the intensity of incident radiation remains the same so that for large areas the major heat energy is provided by solar radiation. The east west ranges of the Himalayas have prominent southern slopes which will receive comparatively more radiation thereby hastening the melting process. On the northern slopes the snow will melt later.

CONCLUSIONS

The study of the Himalayan snow-covered area from the northern hemisphere weekly snow and ice charts shows that the gross seasonal changes in the snow area can be fairly well identified. The profile for the snow accumulation and melt season can indicate the changes

TABLE 4 Mean daily incident solar variation at 31°N latitude

Month	*Mean daily value (cal cm^{-2}): Horizontal*	*South*	*North*
January	*264*	*395*	-
February	*343*	*371*	-
March	*445*	*295*	-
April	*545*	*178*	*9*
May	*612*	*87*	*40*
June	*641*	*41*	*72*
July	*630*	*57*	*59*
August	*584*	*128*	*22*
September	*497*	*237*	*2*
October	*394*	*340*	-
November	*297*	*388*	-
December	*247*	*397*	-

from one season to another and corresponding changes in the meltwater available. Ambient temperature and incident solar radiation profiles indicate the important processes that are responsible for the snowmelt condition in the Himalayas. The data in the form of three categories of snow cover as identified in northern hemisphere snow and ice charts are extremely useful and it is suggested that this process should be continued in the preparation of the current charts. It is evident that a longer series of such data can greatly help in comparing seasonal changes in snow cover for a longer period thereby identifying their behaviour pattern.

ACKNOWLEDGEMENTS The author is thankful to NOAA/NESDIS for the supply of northern hemisphere snow and ice charts for the period under study. Thanks are also due to Prof.P.D.Bhavsar, Chairman, Remote Sensing Area, Space Applications Centre, for his interest in the present study.

REFERENCES

Climatological and Solar Data for India (1969) Published by Sarita Prakashan, Meerat, India.

Dhanju, M.S. (1982) Investigations in the application of remote sensing techniques for monitoring snow cover Himalayan catchments contributing meltwater to Bhakra reservoir. *Technical Report, Remote Sensing Area, Space Applications Centre, Ahmedabad - India.*

Gulati, T.D. (1972) Role of snow and ice hydrology in India. In: *Role of Snow and Ice in Hydrology* (Proc. Banff Symp., September 1972), vol. 1, 610-623. IAHS Publ. no. 107.

Matson, M. & Wiesnet, D.R. (1981) New data base for climate studies. *Nature* 289 (no. 5797), 451-456.

Nag, B.S. & Kathpalia, G.N. (1975) Water resources of India. In:

Proceedings of the Second World Congress on Water Resources (New Delhi, India, December 1975), vol. II, 373-382.

Rango, A. & Salomonson, V.V. (1975) Employment of satellite snow-cover observations for improving seasonal runoff estimates, in operational applications of satellite snowcover observations. *NASA-SP-391*, 157-174.

Weather (1977) Indian Journal of Met. Hydrol. Geophys., no. 28, 283-290, 407-416 and 528-532.

India Meteorological Department (1979-1982) *Weekly Weather Reports*, IMD, New Delhi.

Hydrological Applications of Remote Sensing and Remote Data Transmission
(Proceedings of the Hamburg Symposium, August 1983). IAHS Publ. no. 145.

The use of aerial gamma surveys of snowpack for spring snowmelt runoff forecasts

L. K. VERSHININA
State Hydrological Institute, 2 Linija 23,
199053 Leningrad, USSR

ABSTRACT Basic methodological principles of aerial gamma-surveys and total errors of determining snowpack water equivalent in the basin are considered. The method of aerial gamma-survey is widely used for forecasting spring snowmelt runoff in regions with stable snow cover such as in the north of the European USSR, in Siberia and in the Far East. The error of determining snow storage by the method of aerial gamma survey in these regions doesn't exceed 10% in 80-90% of cases. Reliability of determining snow storage by gamma surveying is estimated by the precision and timeliness of measuring the initial level of the gamma field. For basins of the Rivers Sukhona and Yug the computational forecasting correlations based on aerial gamma survey data were obtained. The mean square error of forecasting snowmelt runoff doesn't exceed 20 mm or 10%. A knowledge of the spatial distribution of snowpack made it possible to adjust forecasts in difficult conditions of interrupted snowmelt.

Utilisation des relevés gamma aéronautiques de la couverture neigeuse dans les prévisions de l'écoulement de la crue de printemps
RESUME On examine les principes méthodologiques de base des relevés gamma aéronautiques et les erreurs totales de l'estimation des valeurs de l'équivalent en eau de la couche de neige sur la surface du bassin versant. La méthode du relevé gamma aéronautique est largement pratiquée pour la prévision de l'écoulement de la crue de printemps dans les régions ayant une couverture neigeuse stable - au nord du territoire européen de l'URSS, en Sibérie et en Extrême-Orient. L'erreur de l'estimation de l'équivalent en eau de la couche de neige par la méthode du relevé gamma aéronautique ne dépasse pas dans ces régions 10% pour 80-90% de cas. La fiabilité de l'estimation de l'équivalent en eau de la couche de neige par le relevé gamma est déterminée par la précision et l'époque de la mesure du niveau initial du champ gamma. Pour les bassins versants des rivières Soukhona et Youg on a obtenu des corrélations de calcul de prévision, basées sur les données du relevé gamma aéronautique. L'erreur moyenne quadratique de prévision de l'écoulement d'eau de la fusion nivale ne dépasse pas 10 mm ou 10%. La connaissance de la répartition spatiale de la couverture neigeuse a permis de réaliser la

correction de prévision dans les conditions complexes de la fusion nivale interrompue.

INTRODUCTION

Precision of determining snowpack water equivalent when forecasting spring snowmelt runoff is of great importance. However, in some regions of our country because of an insufficient observational network density or the difficulty in obtaining reliable measurements of snowpack characteristics, for example, during winter thaws, errors of estimate of snow storage can exceed permissible values.

Therefore, since 1964 much attention has been paid to a new remote-sensing method for measuring snowpack water equivalent - the method of aerial gamma survey (Kogan *et al.*, 1964, 1965). The method is based on the effect of the weakening the gamma radiation of natural radioactive elements of soil and mountain rocks by a snowpack. Nowadays the method of aerial gamma survey is widely used in regions with a stable snowpack.

THEORY OF THE GAMMA RADIATION METHOD

The main sources of soil gamma radiation are radioactive elements of the families of uranium-238, thorium-232 and isotopes of potassium-40. Natural radioactive elements in soils and mountain rocks are present everywhere. Spatial variability of concentrations of the above elements is determined by the genetic type of soils, their mechanical composition, climatic conditions and soil moisture variations. The greatest concentration of these elements is found in serozems, grey-brown and chestnut soils of the steppe zone, and the least in podzolic and swamp soils which are characteristic of the forest zone. Chernozem, grey forest and sod-podzolic soils of the forest-steppe zone and southern part of the forest zone have medium concentrations of radioactive elements.

The degree of concentration of radioactive elements in soils predetermines the objective estimation of the applicability of the gamma method to various regions.

Snow cover causes deformation of the gamma field in the near-earth layer of the atmosphere. The degree of deformation depends on snowpack water equivalent (W_n), i.e. the distribution of gamma-quanta according to energy and angles is a function of W_n. Since the absorption and scattering of gamma quanta practically doesn't depend on the state of aggregation of the matter, then W_n reflects the full water storage in the form of snow, ice cover and melt-water.

Methods of determining snow storage by aerial gamma surveys are conventionally sub-divided into two groups: direct methods and methods of increments (Dmitriev & Fridman, 1979). By direct methods snow storage is determined directly by measuring gamma-field parameters. By methods of increments the change in snow storage during the time between two successive measurements can be determined. The latter method is the basic one used when conducting aerial gamma surveys of snow cover.

The intensity of gamma radiation in the near-earth layer of the atmosphere (I) at an altitude (Z) above the soil level directly depends on the weighted soil moisture U_s and water storage on the soil surface W_n. This dependence is described by the equation (Kogan *et al.*, 1969):

$$I = \frac{I_o}{1 + kU_s} \exp[-\alpha(W_n + \frac{Z}{k_1})] \qquad (1)$$

where $I = I_o$ in the case $U_s = 0$, $Z = 0$ and $W_n = 0$, i.e. the value, determined by the concentration of radioactive elements in absolutely dry soil; W_n and Z are expressed in g cm^{-3}; k_1 and k are coefficients describing differences of absorptive properties of soil, water and air; $\alpha = 0.0062$ is a coefficient which depends on the spectro-angular characteristics of gamma radiation.

For aerial surveys at altitudes of 20-100 m, $k_1 = k = 1.11$ (Dmitriev & Fridman, 1979). Expression (1) is true in the case of an even and homogeneous distribution of moisture in the top 30-40 cm of the soil as well as of the concentration of radioactive elements in it.

METHOD OF AERIAL GAMMA SURVEY

The basic method of aerial gamma survey of a snowpack is based on two gamma radiation measurements: in the absence of snow cover, I_1 ($W_n = 0$ and $U_{s,1}$), and with snow cover, I_2 (W_n and $U_{s,2}$).

In the case $U_{s,1} \simeq U_{s,2}$ the ratio I_1/I_2 allows the estimation of snowpack water equivalent, W_n.

Gamma surveys of snow cover are carried out on plain territories from airplanes and in mountain regions from helicopters.

A record of gamma radiation is kept by two scintillation detectors with crystals of sodium iodide having dimensions 150 x 100 mm and with photoelectronic multipliers FEC-49 (Dmitriev & Fridman, 1979). Both detectors have different characteristics of sensitivity for effective and impeding radiation which is caused by various diagrams of directions produced by steel screens.

By gamma survey the following values are registered:

(a) mean velocity of counting gamma quanta for the whole route and its individual components (forest, field, bushes);

(b) mean velocity of counting for 3-s time intervals;

(c) mean for the route of experimental spectrum of gamma quanta with the purpose of controlling gamma radiating isotopes;

(d) altitude of the flights, recorded on tape by the radio altimeter.

Simultaneously, main landscape types are photographed and snow cover depth is visually estimated. The altitude of flight, depending on the relief, vegetation, type of buildings over the territory, may vary within the limits of 25-100 m. Depending on the height of a flight, the swath width on the ground of continuous measurements of snow storage varies from 150 to 300 m (the sensing band of gamma radiation).

The system of aerial gamma survey routes consists of separate bands each of which embraces small sub-basins with an area of 15-20 000 km^2. Surveying of one band consisting of 40-50 routes, each

15-30 km long, is generally carried out during one day of flights.

When analyzing and estimating the system of aerial routes, the main factor is that routes should not pass close (closer than 500 m) to forest borders, ravines, flood plains, swamp edges, lakes or roads, but cross them at an angle close to 90° (Vershinina & Uryvaev, 1969). This condition is explained by the fact that at such places there can be high spatial variability of gamma field levels and the slightest deviation from the route can cause great errors.

Total error of determining snowpack water equivalent within the basin is a function of:

(a) instrumental error;

(b) methodological error caused by weather conditions or deviations from following the survey method developed;

(c) statistical error in determining mean values along the route;

(d) statistical error of averaging over the basin area.

Instrumental random errors of the aerial gamma method are connected with the registration of radiation and the non-stable functioning of instruments. When estimating errors in determining snow storage, errors in the measurement of the velocity of counting on the route with and without snow, and the errors of measuring impeding radiations are taken into account. When measuring the total velocity of counting impulses from the scintillating detector for routes of more than 15 km, these errors are small, while in the case of measuring velocities of counting impulses along short distances, they can be considerable.

Sensitivity of the equipment used is extremely important when estimating errors, since the same intensity of radiation is accounted to a different extent by different detectors (even in the case of equal dimensions of crystals). It should be mentioned that these errors can be systematic, and when transformed into water volumes, they can reach 8-15 mm.

Variations of space radiation and air radioactivity can be related to methodological errors. Nowadays, when performing aerial gamma survey the impeding radiations are controlled by measuring above water surfaces 1-3 times during the day of flight at the survey altitude or at an altitude about 1000 m above soil level (Dmitriev & Fridman, 1979). The greatest errors should occur on account of non-controlled changes of air radioactivity. Radon comes to the atmosphere from the soil and mountain rocks, and during the time of its existence (more than 3 days) can be carried over many hundreds of kilometres. This can cause an error in determining snow storage by up to 5 mm. The influence of air radioactivity is most greatly manifested in many mountain valleys where the gamma field level sharply increases during cold days with temperature inversion.

The increase of air radioactivity is observed, also, during precipitation falls, especially during heavy snowfall. Therefore, gamma survey is carried out only when some time has passed (3-4 h) after the precipitation has ceased.

Among methodological errors are those by navigation problems with survey routes. The greatest amount of error of this type (up to 10 mm) can take place in regions with great non-homogeneity of the mechanical composition and radioactivity of the soils, although on the average the value of error caused by navigation is only 3-4 mm.

Investigations carried out (Uryvaev & Vershinina, 1969) show that the greatest difficulties in estimating water storage on the surface of basins using data from the main method of gamma survey by increments, are caused by moisture variations in the top 30-40 cm soil layer for the period between the initial survey of the gamma field (without snow cover) and the snow cover surveys. In the case of an even distribution of radioactive elements, the relative increment of gamma radiation intensity (ΔI) due to soil moisture storage increment U_s at the depth Z approximately equals:

$$\frac{\Delta I}{I} = \alpha \Delta U_{s,Z} \exp(- \frac{\alpha Z}{1.11} - \alpha \int_o^Z U_s dZ) \qquad (2)$$

where α is the coefficient of damping of the velocity of counting impulses (Dmitriev & Fridman, 1979).

As scientists of the State Hydrological Institute have shown (Vershinina & Uryvaev, 1969; Uryvaev & Vershinina, 1969; Vershinina, 1979), these errors, as a rule, are systematic and not random. It was also found that changes of moisture content by weight in a 30-cm soil layer of 1% are equivalent to 2-2.5 mm in terms of differences between the results of aerial and surface surveys in regions where winter thaws occur. Estimations made by Sh.D.Fridman and A.V.Dmitriev also show that great errors are possible (30 mm and more) when estimating snow storage when changes of soil moisture are not taken into account. Therefore, in regions with unstable snow cover (i.e. where there are frequent thaws) the use of data on snow storage, obtained by the gamma survey method, can create great difficulties (Vershinina, 1979).

Among methods allowing the computation of snowpack water equivalent on the surface of basins only, is the determination of gamma radiation intensity for absolutely dry soils, I_o, and their moisture-content U_s at the moment of snow cover gamma survey. Gamma radiation from dry soils is rather stable and only depends on the mechanical composition of the soil. This allows for the determination of gamma radiation of homogeneous soils in the dry state, in case they prevail in the basin, at a limited number of observational sites, and to spread these data over large distances. For example, in the River Don basin where clayloam chernozems occupy about 90% of the area, it was sufficient to determine I_o for 25 routes. The knowledge of the intensity of radiation of dry soils allowed for the determination of water storage on the soil surface at the end of winter independently from the presence of deep thaws by equation (1):

$$W_n = P_o - P_\gamma - \{\frac{1}{\alpha}[\ln(1 + kU_s)] + 26.4\} \qquad (3)$$

where, P_o and P_γ are levels of the gamma field of dry soils and those at the moment of the survey of snow cover, reduced to a common flight altitude of Z = 25 m; and U_s is the moisture content by weight of the 30-cm soil layer, in %, determined from the basic agrometeorological network.

Correction of data of the aerial measurement of the water equivalent of the snow cover by the actual moisture content of the upper soil horizons made it possible to eliminate systematic divergencies between values of snow storages measured by the gamma method and by usual surveying (Fig.1(b)), and to determine water storage on the soil surface sufficiently reliably.

As a result of the use of corrected gamma survey data for snow

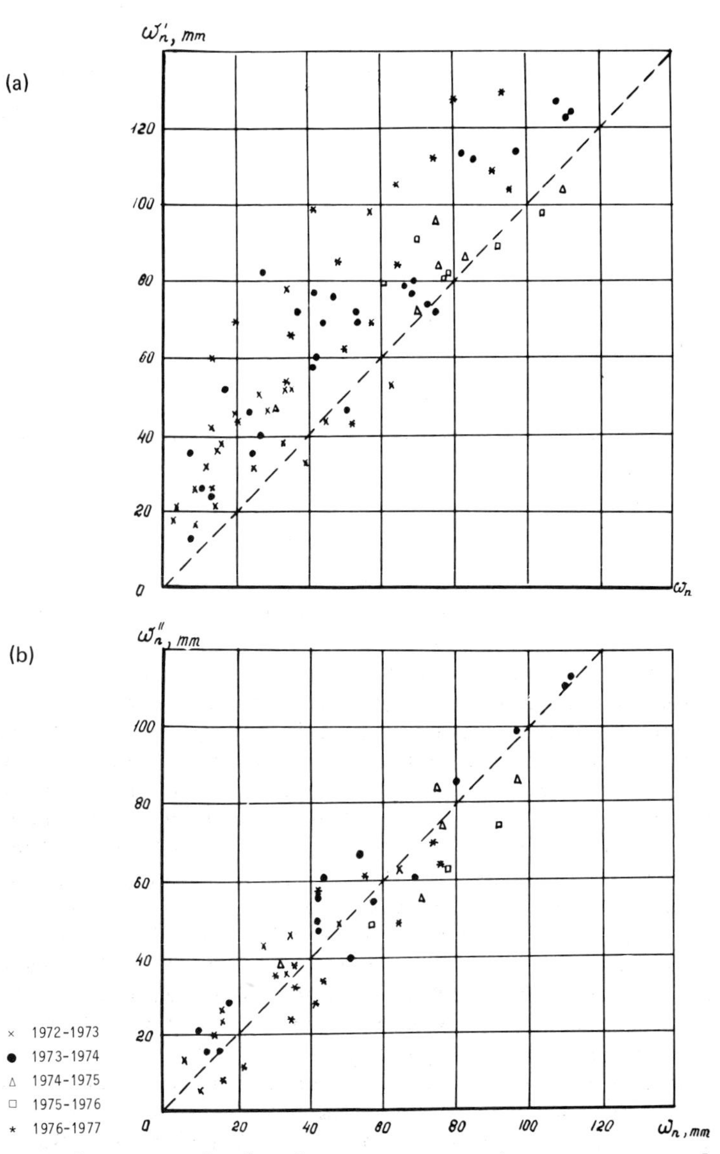

FIG.1 Correlation between snow storage measured by surface (W_n) and aerial gamma surveys (W'_n).
(a) according to actual data of measurements from the aircraft W'_n; (b) according to data of aerial measurements, corrected for actual soil moisture content.

storage during winters with considerable thaws, the quality of forecasts of spring flood runoff improved (Table 1).

TABLE 1 Errors of forecasting spring snowmelt runoff (in mm) in the River Don basin for surface and aerial (gamma survey) methods of determining snow storage (W_n)

River basin	Drainage area (km^2)	1972 S	1972 A	1973 S	1973 A	1974 S	1974 A
Sosna	16 300	-25	- 3	0	-19	12	- 6
T.Sosna	2 060	- 7	-11	-	-	-15	- 6
Bitiug	7 340	-25	0	6	2	7	10

River basin	Drainage area (km^2)	1975 S	1975 A	1976 S	1976 A	1977 S	1977 A
Sosna	16 300	2	2	3	1	-13	28
T.Sosna	2 060	- 4	-15	- 5	- 5	- 1	- 2
Bitiug	7 340	0	14	-17	-16	-57	-17

S Surface measurement
A Aerial measurement

The method of aerial gamma survey has become most popular in regions with stable snow cover - in the north of the European USSR, in Siberia and in the Far East, i.e. in those regions where the surface observational network was inadequate or did not exist. The error of determining snow storage in these regions by the gamma survey method does not exceed 10% in 80-90% cases. Correlation coefficients between values of snowpack water equivalent measured by usual surface methods and the aerial gamma method, exceed 0.80.

Reliability of results of snow cover gamma survey depends to a large extent, on the precision and timeliness of measuring initial levels of the gamma field $P_{\gamma o}$. The most optimum period for determining the latter is a 5-day period before the formation of stable snow cover. Since the temporal variability of $P_{\gamma o}$ depends mainly on the variations of moisture content in the upper layers of the soil, then initial levels of the gamma field can characterise the pre-winter state of the moisture content of basins (Fig.2). Therefore, they can be used when plotting computational-forecasting dependences and forecasting snowmelt runoff depth as one of the runoff producing factors (Vershinina & Krestovsky, 1980).

For example, for the Sukhona and Yug River basins (Severnaya Dvina River basin) new quantitative computational forecasting correlations have been obtained, which are based on aerial gamma survey data only: water storage in snow cover, W_n, and initial levels of gamma field, $P_{\gamma o}$ (see Fig.3).

Figure 4 illustrates the correlation between depth of snowmelt

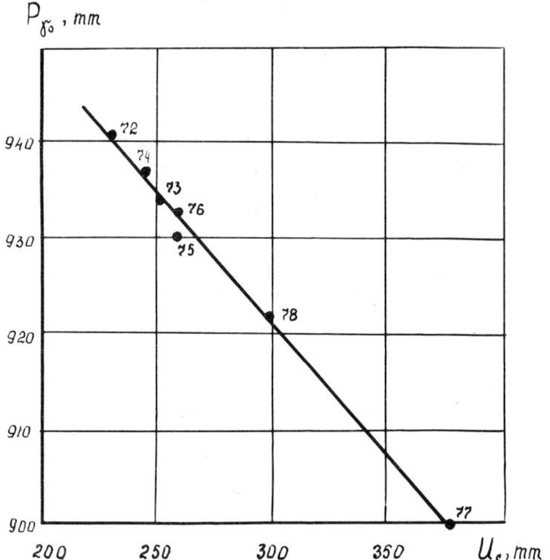

FIG.2 Correlation between the initial levels of gamma field $P_{\gamma o}$ and moisture storage in the top 1 m soil layer, $U_{s,0-100}$, for the Sukhona River basin.

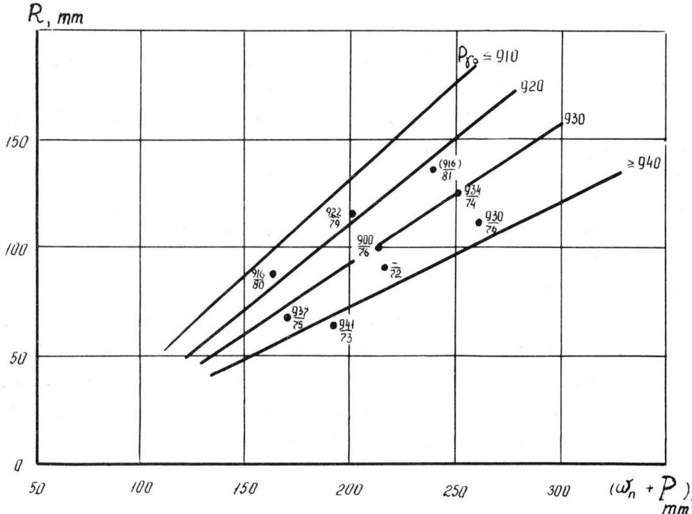

FIG.3 Correlation between snowmelt runoff depth of the River Sukhona (R) and snow storage (W_n) measured by aerial gamma survey method, summed with spring precipitation before flood maximum (P) and values of initial levels of the gamma field $P_{\gamma o}$.

runoff from the Sysola and Vychegda River basins and the volume of snow storage as measured by aerial gamma survey alone.

The assessment of the quality of the computational forecasting correlations, based on the use of aerial gamma surveys of the snow cover in regions with stable snow cover showed that mean square errors of forecasting snowmelt runoff do not exceed 20 mm, or 10%, and reliability of methods is 85-100%. As well, it should be pointed

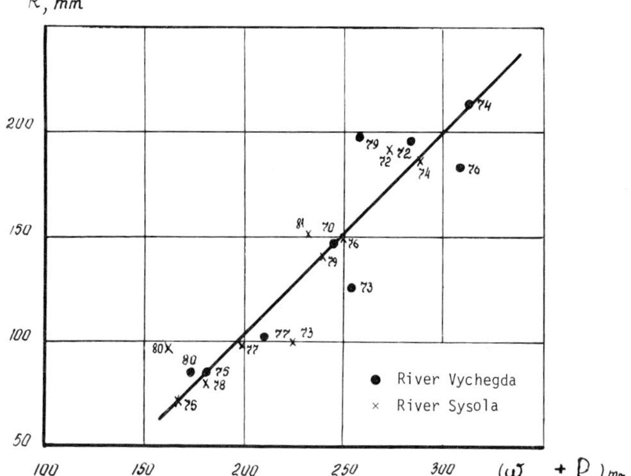

FIG.4 Generalized correlation between snowmelt runoff layer (R) and snow storage (W_n), measured by aerial gamma survey method, together with spring precipitation before flood maximum (P).

out, that in these regions, results of gamma surveys may be used instead of data from surface observations when making forecasts using existing dependences based on long-term series of observational data on runoff and snow cover.

Knowledge of the spatial distribution of snow cover (especially in forests) using gamma survey data makes it possible to make a correction to forecasts of flood characteristics in extremely severe conditions of interrupted snowmelt.

Investigations carried out showed that aerial gamma surveys of snow cover in the future should become the main method of determining water storage on the surface of basins in all regions of the country including the zone where winter thaws occur, since these surveys give considerably more complete and reliable information on water volumes producing spring snowmelt runoff.

REFERENCES

Dmitriev, A.V. & Fridman, Sh.D. (1979) *Osnovy Distantsionnykh Metodov Izmerenia Vlagozapasov v Snege i Vlazhnosti Pochv po Gamma-Izlucheniu Zemli* (Principles of Remote Sensing Methods of Measurements of Snowpack Water Equivalent and Soil Moisture Content by Gamma Radiation of the Earth). A. Gidrometeoizdat.

Kogan, R.M., Nikiforov, M.V. & Uryvaev V.A. (1964) Sposob opredelenia vodnykh zapasov v verkhnem sloe pochvy i na ee poverkhnosti (Method for determining water accumulation in the upper soil layer and on its surface). Auth. certificate no. 160876, 28.02.1963. *Bull. no. 5,26.02.*

Kogan, R.M. Nikiforov, M.V., Fridman, Sh.D. *et al.* (1965) Opredelenie vlagozapasov v snezhnom pokrove metodom samoletnoi gamma syemki (determining water storage in snowpack by aerial gamma survey method). In: *Meteorology and Hydrology,* No. 4.

Kogan, R.M., Nazarov, I.M. & Fridman, Sh.D. (1969) *Osnovy Gamma Spektrometrii Prirodnykh Sred* (Foundations of Gamma Spectrometry of Natural Environments). Atomizdat, Moscow.

Uryvaev, V.A. & Vershinina, L.K. (1969) Rezultaty eksperimentalnykh issledovanii samoletnogo gamma-metoda izmerenia zapasov vody v snege (Results of experimental investigations of aerial gamma survey methods of measuring snowpack water equivalent). *Trans. GGI* 178.

Vershinina, L.K. (1979) Otsenka vozhmoznostei opredelinia zapasov vody v snege samoletnym gamma metodom v raionakh s neustoichevym zaleganiem snezhnogo pokrova (Estimation of possibilities of determining snowpack water equivalent by aerial gamma survey method in regions with unstable snow cover). *Trans. GGI* 259.

Vershinina, L.K., & Krestovsky, O.I. (1980) Uchet vodopoglotitelnoi sposobnosti vodosborov pri prognozakh stoka vesennego polovodia (Account of water consumption capacity of basins when forecasting spring flood runoff). *Trans. GGI* 265.

Vershinina, L.K. & Uryvaev, V.A. (1969) Osnovnye pravila vybora i prokladki marshrutov dlia proisvodstva samoletnykh izmerenii zapasov vody v snege (Basic laws for choosing and plotting routes for making aerial measurements of snowpack water equivalent). *Trans. GGI* 178.

Hydrological Applications of Remote Sensing and Remote Data Transmission (Proceedings of the Hamburg Symposium, August 1983). IAHS Publ. no. 145.

Snow mapping and hydrological forecasting by airborne γ-ray spectrometry in northern Sweden

STEN BERGSTRÖM & MAJA BRANDT
Swedish Meteorological and Hydrological Institute, Box 923, S-60119,Norrköping, Sweden

ABSTRACT The Kultsjön basin in northern Sweden has been the subject for detailed studies of the potential of airborne γ-ray spectrometry for snow mapping and hydrological forecasting since the spring of 1980. A brief introduction to the theory behind this technique is given. Results from the three melt seasons are presented, and problems and uncertainties are discussed. A verification against ground "truth" based on conventional snow courses is shown together with examples of the variability in the snow-accumulation pattern. Finally, it is shown how the data can be used for updating and improving more conventional forecasting models.

Cartographie de la couche de neige et prévision hydrologiques à l'aide de la spectrométrie rayons-γ, par voie aérienne

RESUME Depuis le printemps 1980, le bassin du lac Kultsjön est minutieusement étudié pour connaître le potentiel de la spectrométrie rayons-γ en vue de mesurer la couche de neige et prévoir les conditions hydrologiques. Une brève introduction décrivant la théorie de cette méthode et les résultats obtenus au cours des trois saisons printanières sont présentés et les problèmes et les incertitudes de la méthode sont discutés. En plus l'exactitude de cette méthode est prouvée à l'aide de la méthode traditionnelle, et les exemples prouvant les variations de la couche de neige sont donnés. Finalement, il est montré comment les données peuvent être employées pour améliorer les méthodes traditionnelles de prévisions hydrologiques.

BACKGROUND

Natural radioactive elements in the ground are the sources of gamma radiation from the surface. The attenuation of this radiation due to the water equivalent of the snowpack is the foundation of the use of γ-ray spectrometry for hydrological forecasting. Normally the two-flight method is used, i.e. one flight shortly before the beginning of snow accumulation to measure ground activity, and one when the snowpack is at its maximum.

The theory and the technical aspects of γ-ray spectrometry were discussed in great detail at the Workshop on Remote Sensing of Snow and Soil Moisture by Nuclear Techniques arranged by the WMO in 1979

(WMO, 1979), where a number of applications were also shown. The major problems, excluding the instrumentation, can be summarized as follows:

(a) *Navigation precision:* particularly in areas with variable geology and radiation it is important to keep to the original flight lines, where ground activity under snow-free conditions is measured.

(b) *Wet areas:* these reduce the ground activity and have to be excluded in the analysis.

(c) *Contribution from radon and cosmic radiation:* the radon problem is not as important in a climate with good ventilation.

(d) *Low ground activity in relation to the snowpack:* if the ground activity is low, the instrument will register very few counts, which will strongly affect the precision or make the analysis impossible.

(e) *Irregular snowpack:* due to nonlinearity of the attenuation caused by snow, irregularities in the snowpack and bare patches will cause an underestimation of the snowpack.

(f) *Weather conditions:* these may make flying at low altitudes hazardous and therefore delay the measurements. They may also affect the navigation precision and flight elevation.

APPLICATION OF THE TECHNIQUE TO THE KULTSJÖN BASIN

Since the spring of 1980, γ-ray spectrometry has been applied to the Kultsjön basin in upper Åseleälven in northern Sweden in order to explore its potential for hydrological forecasting. The work has been carried out on contract from the Swedish Association of River Regulation Enterprises with support from Studsvik Energy Techniques. The Swedish Geological Survey has been responsible for instrumentation and flights, and the Swedish Meteorological and Hydrological Institute has acted as project leader.

The instrument is the same as the one used for geological mapping and prospecting by the Swedish Geological Survey. It is installed in an Aero Commander 680 E airplane. Flying height is approximately 50 m above ground level. The energy band 400-3000 keV is used for the snow measurements.

The project started with 14 flight lines covering the basin in a pattern that was possible to fly at very low altitude. These lines are shown in Fig.1. The total length of the lines is approximately 220 km, and the basin area is 1109 km^2. The number of lines has been reduced, as some of them proved to be unsuitable as the project proceeded.

The water equivalent of the snowpack was calculated by a moving average technique based on the number of pulses registered over a given distance.

The dates for the flights were 27, 25 and 29 March for 1980, 1981 and 1982 respectively.

VERIFICATION AGAINST SNOW COURSES

In 1980 the airborne measurements were verified against a total of

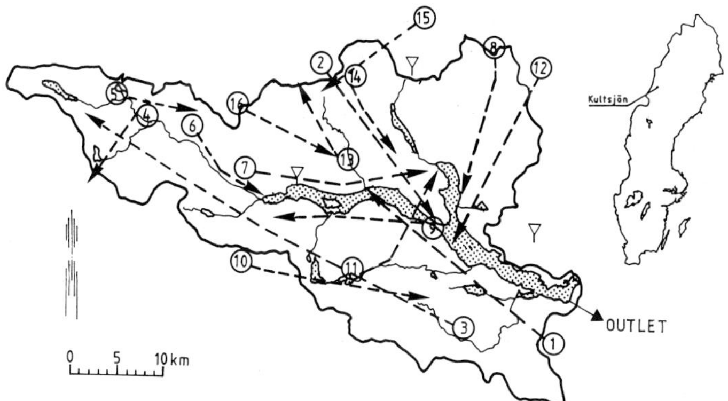

FIG.1 The original set of flight lines covering the Kultsjön basin.

17 km of conventional snow courses spread over eight short stretches with snow samples being taken every 50 m using snowtubes. The result in Fig.2, which was first presented by Nilsson *et al.* (1980), shows good agreement between the two methods except for one stretch (10b). This deviation is caused by a very irregular snowpack with rocks frequently penetrating the snow. Thus, it causes an underestimation of the total snowpack as discussed earlier.

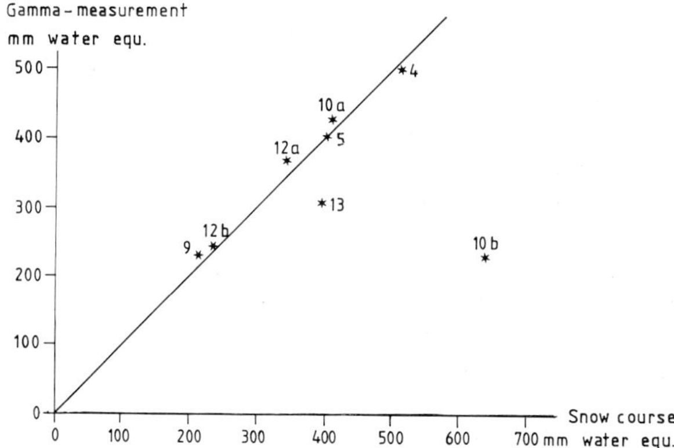

FIG.2 Comparison between conventional snow courses and results from airborne γ-ray spectrometry. Each point represents approximately a 2 km flight line with one sample every 50 m (the numbers refer to the lines in Fig.1).

REPRODUCTION OF A REGISTRATION

In 1980 line number 1 was flown twice. The total snowpack estimates of water equivalent were 359 and 389 mm, respectively, which is a deviation of 8%. Plottings of the registrations with 1000 m integration intervals and 500 m overlap are shown in Fig.3. As can be seen, local deviations are sometimes considerable. Some of the

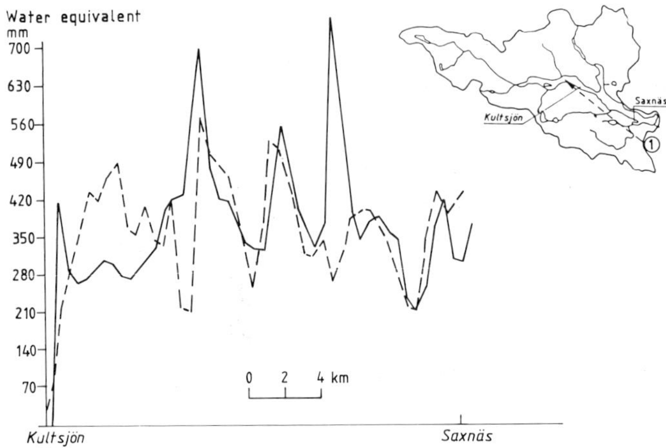

FIG.3 Example of reproduction of the snow registration on line 1 when flown twice in 1980.

peaks are caused by weak ground activity due to wet areas. These will automatically be excluded in future work.

SNOW ACCUMULATION AND ELEVATION

The relation between snow accumulation, as recorded from the airborne measurements, and elevation above sea level is analysed in a joint plotting for lines 2, 8, and 16 north of Lake Kultsjön (Fig.4) and individually for line 1 (Fig.5) and line 9 (Fig.6) south of Lake Kultsjön. The results show that it is possible to determine a gradient or increase of snow accumulation below the timber line, while there is no significant relation between snow accumulation and elevation above this line. The latter is of course an effect of the strong redistribution of the snowpack above the timber line. When analysing Figs 4-6 it is important to bear in mind that there is also a west to east gradient in the snow accumulation pattern, which is superimposed on the effect of elevation. This is discussed in the following section.

LARGE SCALE VARIATIONS OF THE SNOWPACK

The west-east gradient in the snow accumulation pattern was analysed by registrations from lines 7 and 3. They are plotted separately for the three years in Figs 7 and 8, where the topography of the landscape is also shown schematically. The figures clearly show a strong west-east gradient for all three years, which is normal under the climatic conditions in northern Sweden, although the gradient is less pronounced in 1982.

If data from all the lines are used, it is possible to map the snow conditions in the major part of the basin. This is shown in Fig.9 for the three years. The years differ considerably in regard

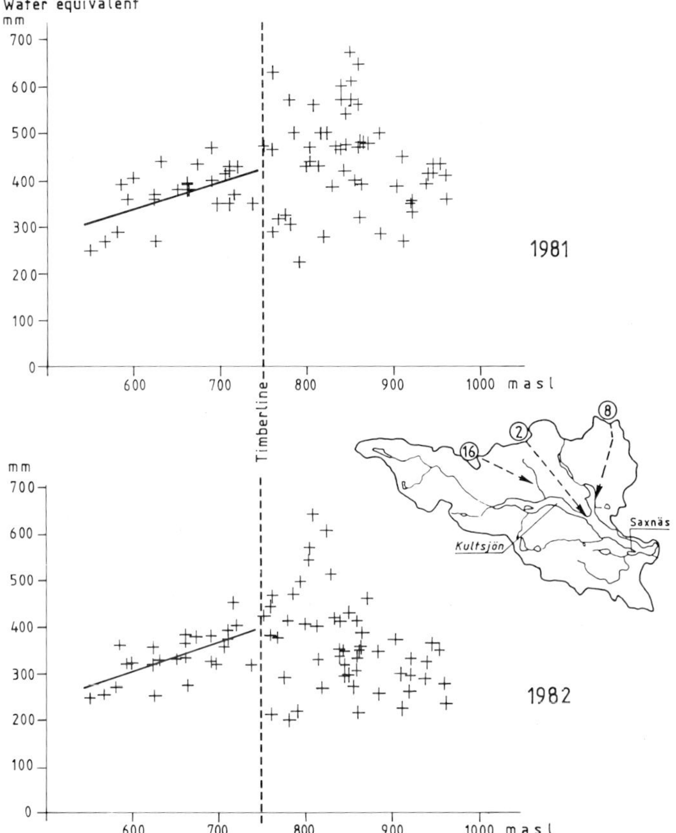

FIG.4 Relation between ground elevation above sea level and snowpack as registered on flight lines 2, 8 and 16 in 1981 and 1982.

to total snow storage and its geographical distribution.

In Table 1 the total estimated basin snow storage measured by airborne γ-spectrometry is compared to the snow storage calculated by a conceptual runoff model (the HBV-model, Bergström, 1976), which is used regularly for forecasts of remaining inflow to Lake Kultsjön.

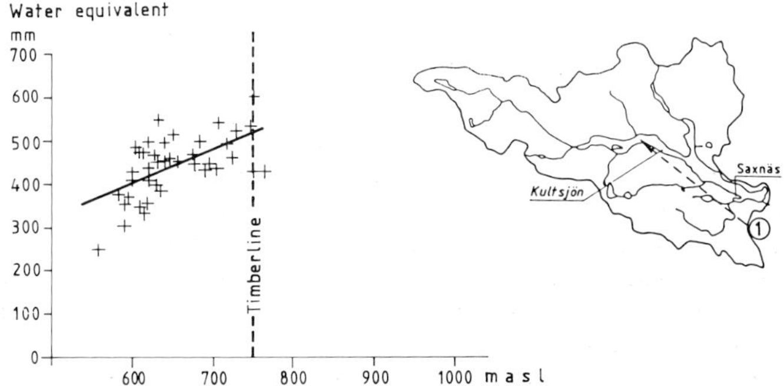

FIG.5 Relation between ground elevation above sea level and snowpack as registered on flight line 1 in 1981.

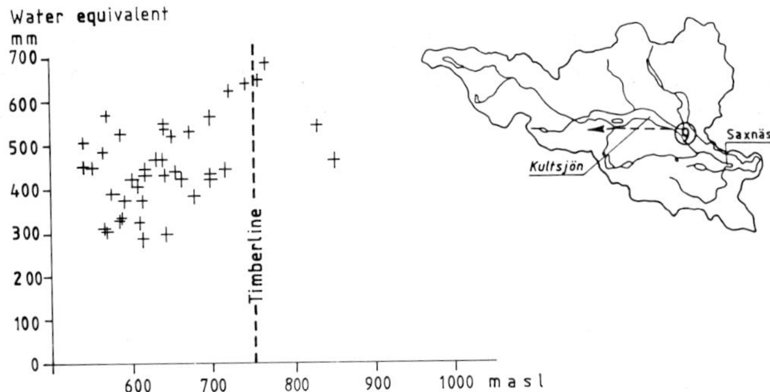

FIG.6 Relation between ground elevation above sea level and snowpack as registered on flight line 9 in 1981.

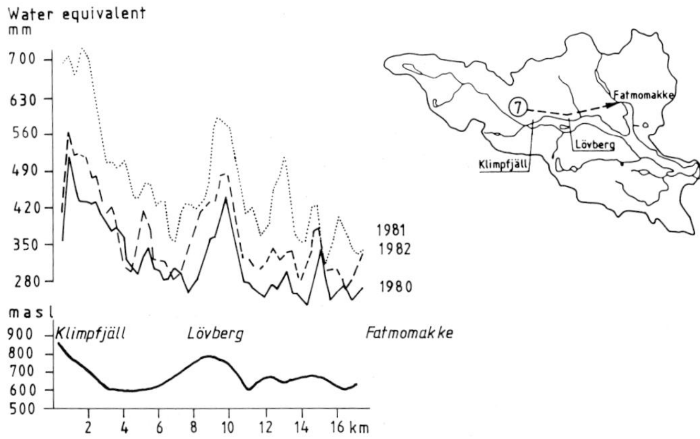

FIG.7 The west-east gradients on the snow accumulation as registered on flight line 7.

The table also contains the modelling errors when the model was run over the melt seasons with actual precipitation and temperature data. Most of these errors are likely to have their origin in the snow accumulation calculations of the model, which are based on precipitation observations at the three stations shown in Fig.1.

The interpretation of Table 1 is that the two methods are

TABLE 1 Comparison between basin snow storage measured by γ-ray spectrometry and the HBV conceptual model in relation to the modelling error (expressed in mm water equivalent)

	1980	1981	1982
HBV-model	350	460	331
γ-ray spectrometry	353	457	406
Difference	-3	+3	-75
Modelling error for the melt period	+35	+5	-80

surprisingly close for 1980 and 1981, and that the disagreement for 1982 is of the same order of magnitude as the modelling error. This means that the use of the γ-method to support the conceptual model

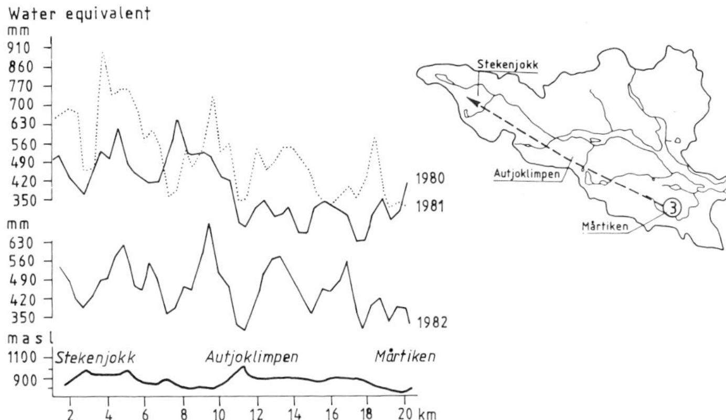

FIG.8 The west-east gradients of the snow accumulation as registered on flight line 3. Note that the 1982 plot is separated from 1980 and 1981.

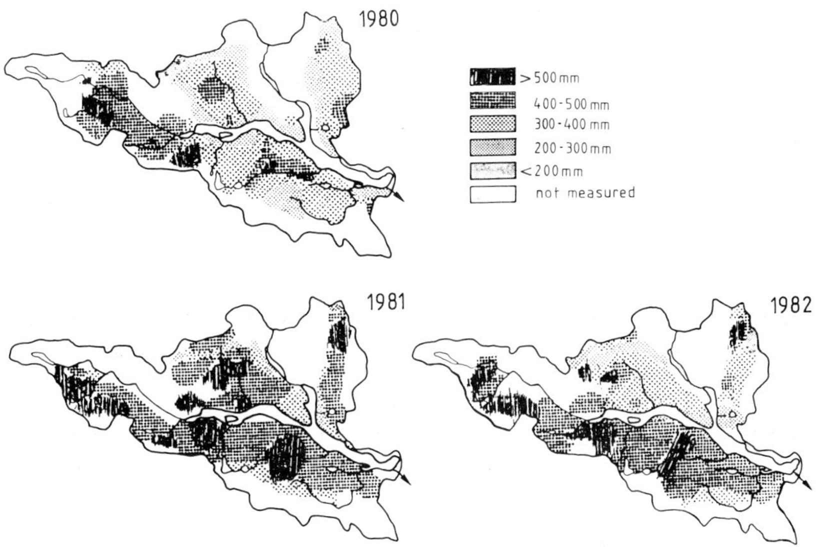

FIG.9 Schematic snow mapping in the Kultsjön basin based on airborne γ-ray spectrometry.

would have improved the forecasts. The reason for the improvement is simply that three precipitation stations (shown in Fig.1) are insufficient to cover the biased snow distribution in 1982 (see Fig.9).

FUTURE WORK

The project is planned to continue over two more melt periods before a final evaluation is made. In the spring of 1983 only half of the lines will be flown, but every line will be flown twice. Better and quicker routines for data processing will be developed to shorten the timelapse between measurement and forecast, and parts of lines, which have been shown to confuse the results, will be excluded. Efforts will be made to find the maximum snow-water equivalent, which can be observed with any certainty.

REFERENCES

Bergström, S. (1976) Development and application of a conceptual runoff model for Scandinavian catchments. *Report no. RHO 7, The Swedish Meteorological and Hydrological Institute, Norrköping.*

Nilsson, J., Landstrom, O., Lindén, A. & Melander, A. (1980) Mätningar med flygburen gammastraleutrustning for avrinningsprognosverksamhet (Measurements by airborne γ-ray spectrometry for runoff forecasting). In: *Problems in Water Power Exploitation* (Proc. Nordic Hydrologic Conference 1980). UNGI Report no. 53, Uppsala University, Uppsala.

WMO (1979) Workshop on Remote Sensing of Snow and Soil Moisture by Nuclear Techniques. Technical papers presented at the workshop convened by WMO and organized in cooperation with IAHS and the Norwegian National Committee for Hydrology, Voss, Norway.

Hydrological Applications of Remote Sensing and Remote Data Transmission
(Proceedings of the Hamburg Symposium, August 1983). IAHS Publ. no. 145.

Field experiments on propagation of 10 and 30 GHz waves through a snow cover

TADASHI MATSUMOTO, MASAHIRO SUZUKI,
DAISUKE KUROIWA
Hokkaido Institute of Technology, Teine-Maeda, Nishi-ku, Sapporo 061-24, Japan
KAZUO FUJINO & GOROW WAKAHAMA
The Institute of Low Temperature Science, Hokkaido University, Kita 19, Nishi 8, Kita-ku, Sapporo 060, Japan

ABSTRACT Relative attenuation of microwaves was measured as a function of the thickness of the snow pack when propagated through a snowpack in a horizontal and a vertical direction, using waves of 30 and 10 GHz in frequency. The rate of attenuation of the former wave was found to be 2-3 and 6.3 dB.10 cm^{-1}, respectively, for the horizontal and the vertical propagation through coarse granular snow containing ice plates. The attenuation of the 10 GHz wave was not simple, however, because of the phenomena of dielectric coupling of interlayers or resonance or both. Consequently, a diurnal variation on rate of attenuation of this wave was observed by burying the emitter and the receiver of the wave in the snowpack. It was found that the rate increased with rising air and snow temperatures.

Expériences sur le terrain sur la propagation des ondes de 10 et 30 GHz à travers la couverture neigeuse

RESUME L'atténuation relative des micro-ondes a été mesurée comme une fonction de l'épaisseur de la couche neigeuse lorsqu'elles se propagent dans une direction horizontale et verticale en utilisant des ondes de fréquence 30 et 10 GHz. Les taux d'atténuation pour la première longueur d'onde ont été trouvés respectivement égaux à 2-3 et 6.3 dB.10 cm^{-1} pour les propagations horizontales et verticales à travers de la neige à granulométrie grossière avec des plaques de glace. L'attenuation des ondes de 10 GHz n'était pas un phénomène simple cependant par suite du phénomène de couplage diélectrique entre couches intermédiaires ou de résonance ou les deux à fois. Par conséquent on a trouvé une variation diurne du taux d'atténuation concernant cette longueur d'onde en enfouissant l'émetteur et le récepteur des micro-ondes dans la couche de neige. On a trouvé que ce taux croîssait avec une élévation des températures de l'air et de la neige.

INTRODUCTION

The propagation of microwaves in snowy districts of Japan has been the subject of extensive studies by the Research Institute of Applied Electricity of Hokkaido University in conjunction with television broadcasting and microwave communications (Asami, 1958). Among those studies the ones made by Asami (1958) were devoted to investigating interference phenomena between transmitting waves and reflected waves from the snowpack.

Recent studies on the interaction between snowpack and microwaves ranging from 10^3 to 10^5 MHz in frequency have been stimulated by the potential for remote sensing of seasonal snow cover from aircraft and spacecraft (Ulaby, 1982). However, it appears that ambiguities abound in the mechanism of interaction between microwave frequencies and the snowpack. They may arise from the complexities of the dielectric properties and structure of the snowpack. Snow that has deposited on the ground stratifies horizontally as the result of the consecutive densification and metamorphism, which alters the shape, size and configuration of snow grains with the lapse of time. If the surface of snow is exposed to strong sunlight, slight melting of the snow grains can occur even when the air temperature is maintained well below 0°C; an ice plate or layer is then formed because of the subsequent refreezing. Therefore, if a microwave is propagated through the natural snowpack composed of multilayers with different dielectric properties, the characteristics of horizontal propagation must be different from those of vertical propagation. The present authors attempted to measure the rate of relative attenuation of a microwave through the snowpack at Kita Moshiri and Toikanbetsu Forest Experimental Stations of Hokkaido University during the winters of 1981 to 1983, using waves of 10 and 30 GHz in frequency.

ATTENUATION OF A MICROWAVE PROPAGATED THROUGH HORIZONTAL LAYERS OF THE SNOWPACK

Experiments were conducted on the propagation of a microwave through the snowpack at Kita Moshiri Forest Experimental Station near the end of March 1981. Figure 1 shows the stratigraphic structure and profiles of the density and grain size of the snow. The depth of the snowpack is approximately 135 cm and the upper layers near the surface consist of new snow. Several thin ice plates and two thick ice plates exist within coarse granular snow located 90-125 cm from the ground surface. The lower layers of the snowpack near the ground surface are composed of depth hoar. The density of snow ranges between 300 and 400 kg m^{-3}, although the new snow near the surface has a density of 100 kg m^{-3}.

For measuring the rate of relative attenuation of a microwave through horizontal layers of the snowpack, two pits were dug in the snow cover, with the body of snow between them about 170 cm in horizontal thickness. Two emitters were set horizontally side by side at a definite height from the ground surface against the vertical wall surface of the one pit; the two receivers were placed in the other pit in a similar manner. One of the emitters was for a

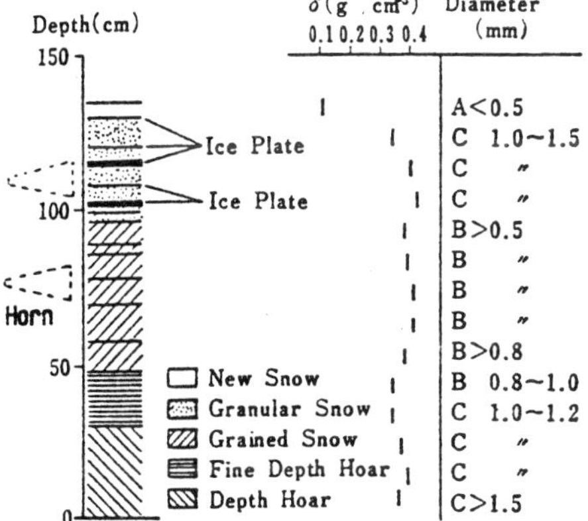

FIG.1 Structure of snowpack (Kita Moshiri, 1981).

10-GHz wave and the other was for a 30-GHz wave; their apertures were 11 cm x 15 cm and 7 cm x 8.5 cm, respectively. The receivers had the same specifications. The direction of polarization of an emitted wave was vertical to the ground surface. Each of the receivers was to receive an electromagnetic wave coming out through horizontal snow layers. To measure the rate of relative attenuation of a microwave as a function of the length of the propagation path, L, the horizontal thickness of the body of snow between the two pits was successively reduced by removing snow vertically along the wall of each pit.

The relation between the relative attenuation, measured in decibels, and the thickness (L) of the body of snow between the two pits is shown in Fig.2. As seen from the figure, L was approximately

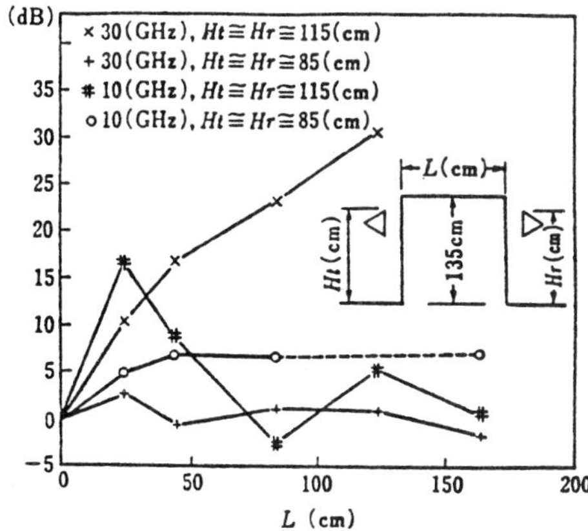

FIG.2 The experimental results of horizontal propagation of microwaves through a snowpack.

170 cm at first, and it was reduced successively to the final thickness of 25 cm. Since the temperature of snow was maintained at -3 to -1°C, the whole snowpack was kept in a dry condition. The location of an emitter to measure horizontal propagation is shown by

dotted lines in Fig.1. When it was set at the height of 115 cm from the ground surface, the electromagnetic wave propagated horizontally through layers of coarse granular snow which contained two thick ice plates and consisted of grains larger than 1.0 mm in diameter. However, when it was set at the height of 85 cm, the electromagnetic wave travelled through homogeneous layers composed of fine grained snow 1.0-0.5 mm in diameter.

Upon comparison of attenuation characteristics between those values which were obtained by the above experiments using waves of 10 and 30 GHz (Fig.2), it can be said that the attenuation rate of the 30 GHz wave decreased with a decrease in L at approximately 2-3 dB.10 cm^{-3}. This result implies that the 30-GHz wave was significantly scattered by coarse granular snow grains and ice plates. Meanwhile, the attenuation characteristics of the 10-GHz wave was not simple, as it fluctuated with a successive decrease in L. The mechanism of the occurrence of the fluctuation is not obvious, but it may be assumed that, inasmuch as the layers of granular snow containing ice plates constitute "multipropagation paths" having different dielectric properties, the fluctuation is caused by phenomena of coupling of interlayers or interference of the electromagnetic waves which travel through individual paths of propagation, or both.

Secondly, upon comparison of attenuation characteristics of two waves propagating through homogeneous layers of fine grained snow located at the height of 85 cm (Fig.2), it was found that the rate of relative attenuation at the 30-GHz wave was very low and was even over the whole range of the propagation path. This means that the 30-GHz wave travelled through homogeneous layers of fine-grained snow without being subjected to any severe attenuation. The rate of relative attenuation of the 10-GHz wave propagating through the same homogeneous layers of fine-grained snow was slightly higher than that of the 30-GHz wave. However, it should be noted that the relative attenuation curve measured between L = 85 and 170 cm, is not plotted in Fig.2 and is instead represented by a broken line; this is because the rates of relative attenuation measured at this range of the propagation path were extremely large. The cause of the large deviation is not clear, but it may be attributable to the phenomena of coupling of interlayers or interferences of multi-propagation paths in snowpack, or both.

VERTICAL PROPAGATION OF A MICROWAVE THROUGH THE SNOWPACK

In order to examine the attenuation characteristics of a microwave emitted vertically to the horizontal snow layers, a horizontal pit was dug in the snowpack near the ground, leaving layers (approximately 80 cm in thickness) between the ceiling of the pit and the upper surface of the snowpack. Then the thick snow layers were sandwiched vertically by the microwave emitter and the receiver so that an electromagnetic wave would travel perpendicularly through the horizontal snow layers. A sketch of the experimental arrangement is shown in Fig.3.

Figure 3 shows the experimental results of vertical propagation of a microwave through the snowpack. In order to measure the rate

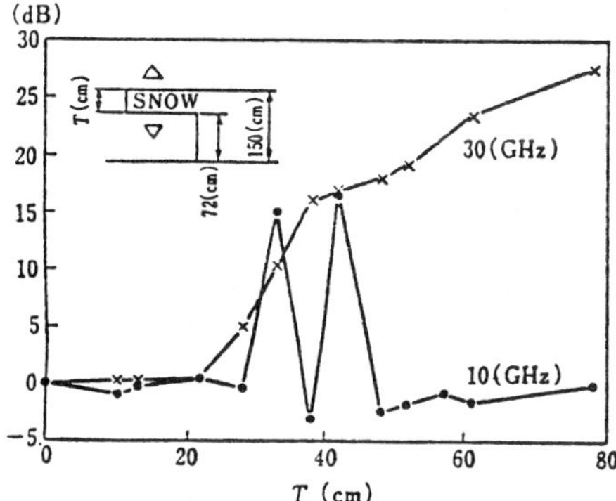

FIG.3 The experimental results of vertical propagation of microwaves through a snowpack.

of relative attenuation as a function of the thickness of the snowpack, the snow thickness was reduced by successive removal of the surface snow. As seen in Fig.3, when the thickness of snow was successively reduced from 80 to 50 cm by removal of the surface new snow, the corresponding values of relative attenuation of the 30-GHz wave decreased gradually from 27 to 19 dB. Hence, the approximate rate of attenuation in new snow came to be 2.6 dB.10 cm^{-1}. The thickness of snow was reduced further from 50 to 20 cm by removal of the layers of coarse granular snow containing several ice plates; then the value of relative attenuation decreased steeply from 19 to nearly 0 dB. Consequently, the approximate rate of attenuation in the coarse granular snow came to be 6.3 dB.10 cm^{-1}. Finally the 30-GHz wave was allowed to propagate through the homogeneous fine grained snow having the thickness of 20 cm, then no discernible attenuation was observed.

However, the characteristics of propagation of the 10-GHz wave was not simple, as shown in Fig.3. When the thickness of new snow was successively reduced from 80 to 50 cm, no discernible attenuation was obtained. After the complete removal of the new snow, the 10-GHz wave was allowed to propagate across many layers of coarse granular snow containing ice plates. With the successive removal of this part of snowpack, two distinct peaks of relative attenuation (15 and 17 dB) were observed. These two peaks are probably attributable to the resonance phenomena occurring between certain two boundaries of snow layers whose physical and dielectric properties are different. After the removal of the layers of coarse granular snow, the 10-GHz wave was allowed to propagate into the homogeneous fine grained snow, and then no discernible attenuation was obtained.

DIURNAL VARIATIONS IN ATTENUATION OF MICROWAVE PROPAGATION THROUGH SNOWPACK OBSERVED AT TOIKANBETSU

It has been accepted that the real part of the dielectric constant of ice measured in a high frequency range is independent of temperature and frequency. However, concerning the imaginary part, its dependence upon temperature and frequency seems to be ambiguous in a high frequency range. If the imaginary part depends upon temperature in the frequency range of the microwave, the attenuation characteristics of microwave propagation through the snowpack, must be influenced by the temperature of snow.

In order to investigate the temperature dependence of microwave attenuation through the snowpack, a diurnal variation in attenuation was measured at Toikanbetsu Forest Experimental Station of Hokkaido University in 1983. Both the emitter and the receiver of a 10-GHz wave were buried at a depth of 30 cm below the snow surface so that the electromagnetic wave could travel horizontally through the snow layers. The length of the propagation path maintained between the emitter and the receiver was 5 m in this experiment. Measurements were also made of air temperature at a height of 1 m above the snow surface and snow temperatures at depths of 10, 24 and 54 cm below the snow surface.

Figure 4 shows a sketch of the strata and profiles of the density

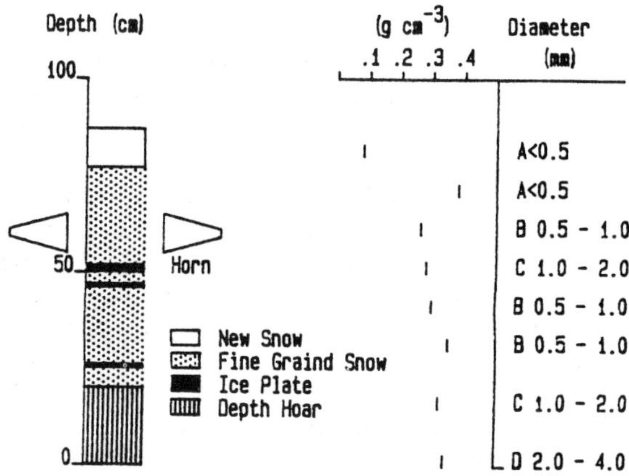

FIG.4 Structure of a snowpack (Toikanbetsu, 1983).

and grain size of the snowpack and shows the location of the emitter and receiver buried in the snowpack. The total thickness of the snowpack was approximately 87 cm, and the 10-cm thick surface layer was composed of new snow having a density less than 100 kg m^{-3}. A 1-cm thick ice layer was located at a height of 50 cm from the ground surface. Layers between the surface new snow and the ice layer consisted of fine grained snow, but their stratigraphy and density distribution were not uniform as shown in Fig.4.

Figures 5(a) and (b) show, respectively, diurnal variations in relative attenuation of the 10-GHz wave and the air and snow temperatures measured from 2155 h on 21 February to 0955 h on 23 February 1983. A sketch of the experimental arrangement is given in the lower part of Fig.5(a). As seen in Fig.5(b), the air temperature indicated its minimum, -25°C, around 0655 h, and rose to it's maximum, -1°C, around 1355 h, 22 February. After passing the maximum, it gradually decreased. However, when the air temperature approached the maximum, the surface snow began to melt slightly because of the strong irradiation of the sunlight. The variation in snow temperature measured at depths of 10 and 24 cm

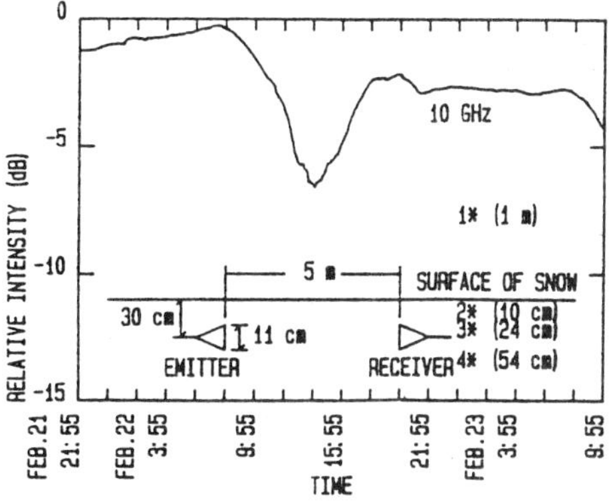

(a) Diurnal variation in propagation of a 10 GHz wave

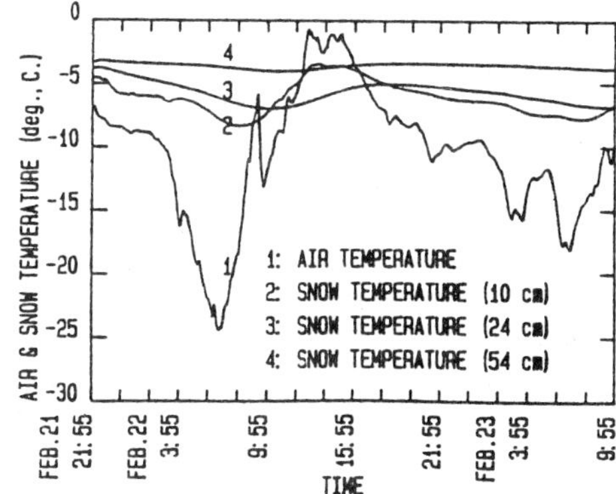

(b) Diurnal variations in air and snow temperatures

FIG.5 Experimental results of diurnal variations in horizontal propagation characteristics and temperatures of air and snow.

below the surface followed the variation in air temperature with time lags of about 2 and 4 h, respectively. Meanwhile the temperature of snow measured at the 54-cm depth was almost constant throughout the experiment.

As seen in Fig.5(a), the value of relative attenuation attained the maximum at the time when the temperatures of air and snow measured at the depth of 10 cm were maximum. During the period in which the air temperature was maintained at the maximum (-1 to -2°C), the structure of surface snow was significantly altered by the irradiation of the sunlight and a discernible surface depression occurred because of the change of grain configurations. The temperature of the snow measured at a depth of 10 cm rose from -8 to -3°C. The change of the structure and rise of temperature may cause an increase in the imaginary part of the dielectric constant of snow. Though the emitter of the 10-GHz wave was buried at a depth of 30 cm below the surface, it is regarded that the electromagnetic wave could partly travel through snow near the surface, because the emitted wave diverges along the propagation path. Hence, it appears that the observed maximum of attenuation of the 10-GHz wave was created primarily by the passage of the electromagnetic wave through subsurface snow being subjected to temperature variation and that the attenuation of the 10-GHz wave through snow layers located near the ice layer was not influenced by the temperature change of the snowpack.

SUMMARY

The results of our field experiment indicated the fairly complicated characteristics of propagation of a microwave through snowpack. In general, the microwave attenuation in the snowpack is governed by two factors, the scattering and absorption by snow grains. The scattering mainly depends on the grain size and shape of the snow and frequency of the microwave used, whereas the absorption mainly depends upon the wetness of the snowpack. Therefore, in the case of dry snow, it appears that the microwave attenuation is caused primarily by scattering. However, according to Stiles & Ulaby (1981), inasmuch as the value of the imaginary part of the dielectric constant of ice measured in the frequency range 10-30 GHz indicates the order of magnitude of 10^{-2} at the temperature near the melting point of ice, the effect of the absorption may not be ignored when the electromagnetic wave propagates through snow layers where the temperature is maintained near $0^{\circ}C$. Apart from the attenuation due to the physical properties of snow itself, if the direction of propagation of a microwave is deflected by the stratified structure of snowpack, it may possibly cause the attenuation to attain to a fairly large value such as observed in our experiments.

When the 30-GHz wave was propagated horizontally through coarse granular snow layers containing ice layers, it was attenuated at the rate of 2-3 dB.10 cm^{-1} along the propagation path. This result suggests that the severe attenuation was caused primarily by the scattering due to coarse snow grains. The similar characteristics of the attenuation due to the scattering of snow grains were observed in the vertical propagation of the microwave, as seen in Fig.3. The estimated rates of relative attenuation of the 30-GHz wave were 2.6 dB.10 cm^{-1} for new snow and 6.3 dB.10 cm^{-1} for the coarse granular snow containing ice plates. Since the average density of the coarse granular snow was 3-4 times larger than that of the new snow, it seems reasonable that the rate of relative attenuation in the new snow was lower than that obtained in the layers of the coarse granular snow. However, it should be noted that the rate of relative attenuation of the 30-GHz wave obtained in the vertical propagation of it through the coarse granular snow containing ice plates was larger than that measured in the horizontal propagation through the same snow. This difference can be explained by the fact that in the case of the horizontal propagation, the electromagnetic wave travelled through a single horizontal layer where the physical and dielectric properties are maintained homogeneous along the propagation path, whereas in the case of the vertical propagation the electromagnetic wave had to travel through many superimposed snow layers where the physical and dielectric properties are different from each other. When the wave passes every boundary between two adjacent layers, the wave is reflected because of the difference in relative refractive indices. Consequently, a large value of attenuation of the wave comes about in the vertical propagation.

In the experiment concerning a diurnal variation in microwave attenuation of the horizontal propagation, it was shown that the attenuation characteristics of the 10-GHz wave propagating through subsurface snow layers was significantly affected by the rise of snow temperature and alteration of the structure due to irradiation of sunlight. This experimental fact suggests that the attenuation of the 10-GHz wave was caused by the deflection of the propagation direction and increment of the imaginary part of the dielectric constant of snow.

A natural snowpack is composed of a large number of strata having different dielectric properties. Therefore, if an appropriate relationship is assumed between the thickness of a particular snow layer and the wavelength of a microwave used, a multiple reflection or resonance may occur and create the attenuation of the microwave there. The fluctuations found in the attenuation characteristics of the 10-GHz wave may be explained by the aforementioned argument, but the precise conclusion of this matter should await future studies.

REFERENCES

Asami, Y. (ed.) (1958) *Microwave Propagation in Snowy Districts*. The Research Institute of Applied Electricity, Hokkaido University, Sapporo, Japan.

Stiles, W.H. & Ulaby, F.T. (1981) Dielectric properties of snow. In: *Proceedings of a Workshop on the Properties of Snow* (Snowbird, Utah), 91-103.

Ulaby, F.T. (1982) Radar signatures of terrain: useful monitors of renewable resources. *Proc. Inst. Elect. Electron. Engrs* 70 (12), 1410-1428.

Hydrological Applications of Remote Sensing and Remote Data Transmission
(Proceedings of the Hamburg Symposium, August 1983). IAHS Publ. no. 145.

Studying aufeis by aerial and satellite survey imagery

A. E. ABAKOUMENKO & V. F. USACHEV
State Hydrological Institute, 2 Linija 23,
199053 Leningrad, USSR

ABSTRACT On the basis of aerial photographs of the Trans-Baikal region, methodological approaches to studying aufeis were developed. The relief of the aufeis bed characterized by multi-armed shape of the channel, complete or partial absence of vegetation and the contrasting phototone of the aufeis massif, are the interpretation features of aufeis in photographs made in summer and autumn. Advantages of multizonal surveys for the interpretation of the structure of an aufeis massif during the melting period are given. Mid-scale aerial surveys help to obtain long-term characteristics: area, length, width, shape, exposure. For mapping and cataloguing aufeis, space images obtained just after snow cover disappearance can also be used. From space images aufeis with dimensions more than 50 x 50 m can usually be distinguished. At present the precision of aufeis boundary interpretation from satellite imagery is not as good as that from aerial survey imagery.

Interprétation et établissement des cartes de l'aufeis d'après les données obtenues par les photographies aériennes et les satellites
RESUME A la base de photographies aériennes spécialement constituée pour la région de Zabaikaljé on a mis au point les approches d'une méthode pour l'étude de l'aufeis. Les indices pour l'interprétation de l'aufeis sur les photographies prises en été et en automne sont le relief du lit de l'aufeis caractérisé par la grande quantité de bras du lit de la rivière, l'absence complète ou partielle de végétation, le ton de contraste, de l'image du massif de l'aufeis. On montre les avantages de la photographie aérienne multizonale pour mettre en évidence la structure de l'aufeis dans la période de fonte des neiges.

INTRODUCTION

Aufeis is an accumulation of thick masses of ice formed in winter due to atmospheric, surface and subsurface water extruded onto the surface of mountain rocks, ground and ice and is also found within large cavities in the Earth's crust (Sokolov, 1975; Tolstikhin, 1974). Aufeis is widespread in mountain regions occupying the greatest portion of eastern Siberia (USSR) and occurs mainly in the channels and flood plains of river valleys, bases of debris cones, high terraces, etc. Most aufeis is formed during construction of engineering structures (railways and highways, bridges, embankments, dams, buildings, etc.) as a result of disturbances of the natural cryo-hydrological conditions.

For studying aufeis, aerial satellite survey methods are widely used (Abakoumenko & Usachev, 1980; Prokacheva *et al.*, 1982). By aerial and satellite imagery the following characteristics may be determined: quantity of aufeis, its position and basic morphometric characteristics, long-term variability of aufeis dimensions, dynamics of aufeis formation and melting during winter and spring periods.

BASIC METHODOLOGY

The basic methodological demand on aerial and satellite imagery is that it should be possible not only to distinguish aufeis but also to determine its characteristics. The experience gained during previous investigations show that the optimum period for making aerial surveys of aufeis is the second half of spring when snow has melted but aufeis dimensions are still close to the maximum for the given year (Katalog Naledei Zony BAM, 1980, 1981). However, this condition becomes complicated due to the non-synchronous melting of snow cover at different altitudinal zones.

The basic demands for aerial surveys when studying aufeis are as follows:

(a) surveys should be carried out during a strictly fixed period of time in order to obtain images of aufeis when it is highly developed for the year and contrasts with the surrounding landscape;

(b) Surveys should be made simultaneously over the whole territory of a region (river basin) under study;

(c) photographs should have necessary overlap to provide stereoscopic reproduction of the territory's surface;

(d) the quality of aerial survey imagery should be high enough for aufeis to be precisely distinguished for its extent to be determined.

Space imagery has the following advantages compared to aerial imagery:

(a) Coverage of the territory in the case of satellite survey allows practically synchronous imaging of such a dynamic natural phenomenon as aufeis within vast regions. Obtaining the equivalent volume of airborne information requires considerable time intervals during which the aufeis situation gradually changes.

(b) Optical generalization of photographs allows the estimation of main natural factors of aufeis formation due to a considerable reduction of the influence of small landscape details masking the general picture. In regions covered with friable deposits, lineaments, corresponding to large base splits, at which, through artesian-filtration, taliks and aufeis which are connected genetically, occur.

(c) A series of space photographs of the territory occupied by aufeis allows the collection of data on aufeis formation and melting.

(d) The use of materials of special types of surveys allows new qualitative information on aufeis to be obtained. Specifically, multi-temporal and multi-spectral photographs give the opportunity to determine aufeis genesis; winter-spring images can be used to estimate the character of the main contributions to aufeis formation and to study structural changes of the aufeis surface during the thermo-erosion destruction process.

The above possibilities of space information can be successfully realized when studying aufeis under properly selected scale, time and spectrum of photography (Topchiev, 1978). The use of multi-spectral airborne imagery gives new opportunities for studying aufeis of various genetic types. Using a multi-spectral space camera (MKF-6), fixed on-board the plane-laboratory An-30, aufeis photography within various spectral ranges was carried out. It was done within three spectral zones with effective wavelengths about 480, 600 and 820 nm. These bands were selected for the following reasons: images within the zone of 480 and 600 nm correspond to usual black-and-white photographs within the visible spectrum (0.4-0.7 μm), which allows comparative analysis of information content of the imagery. The near infrared spectrum (820 nm) is the most informative for the interpretation of many hydrological objects (Fig.1).

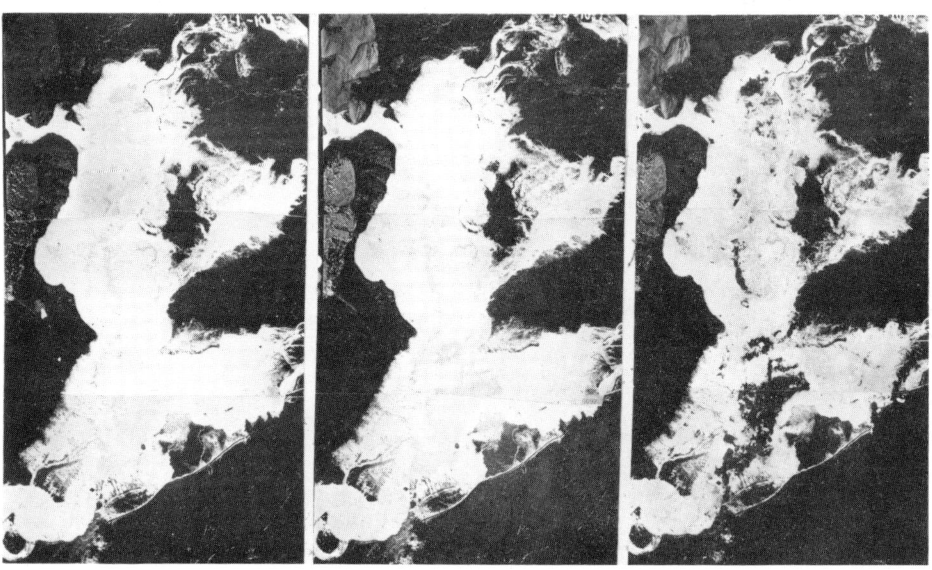

FIG.1 The change of the structure, tone and shape of the aufeis image in serial multi-spectral photographs: (a) 480 nm, (b) 600 nm, (c) 840 nm.

The main feature of the image made in the near infrared spectrum is that water and overmoistened areas have the phototone varying from grey to almost black. The structure, phototone and shape of the aufeis image are taken as basic interpretation features.

In the river basins studied with total area of more than 42 000 km^2 (Table 1) there were registered 1112 aufeis with a total area of 245.15 km^2 and total volume of 374.3 x $10^6 m^3$. The statistical analysis of basic morphometric characteristics of the aufeis revealed the following features:

TABLE 1 Characteristics of aufeis in the river basins of the Baikal-Amour Railway zone

River basin (region)	Area of basin (region)	Number of aufeis	Aufeis area (km^2)		Aufeis area (%)	Mean thickness (m)	Volume of aufeis ($m^3 x 10^6$)		Depth of aufeis water (mm)
			Mean	Total			Mean	Total	
Upper reaches of the Chara basin	9 650	220	0.454	99.9	1.04	1.71	0.777	171.0	17.7
Bottom of the Upper Chara hollow	2 100	68	0.548	42.0	2.00	1.73	1.07	72.6	34.6
River Muya basin	10 590	417	0.186	77.3	0.73	1.63	0.294	125.7	10.1
Bottom of the river Muya hollow	4 250	122	0.197	28.91	0.68	1.46	0.347	42.3	8.6
Upper Angara river basin	21 770	475	0.14	67.95	0.31	1.1	0.16	77.6	3.6
Yanchui	1 240	23	0.13	2.93	0.24	1.1	0.14	3.22	2.6
Kotera	7 370	276	0.15	40.25	0.55	1.1	0.17	45.87	6.2
Nyandoni	1 910	102	0.19	19.25	1.0	1.2	0.23	23.10	12.1
Namama	520	24	0.31	7.39	1.42	1.2	0.37	8.87	17.1
TOTAL	42 010	1112		245.15				374.3	

(a) The intensity of aufeis processes increases from the west to the east with the maximum in the basins of the River Chara (upper reaches of the Khani).

(b) Mean aufeis areas increase from 0.14 km^2 (Upper Angara) up to 0.548 km^2 (Upper Chara).

(c) The largest aufeis are concentrated in hollow bottoms and in the channels of large rivers and occur where there are discharges of artesian-filtration sub-permafrost waters (tectonic disturbances).

(d) The distribution of aufeis according to altutude is characterized by sharp asymmetry. Maximum number and total area correspond to relatively narrow altitude ranges. In the River Muya basin, 46.5% of all aufeis and 45% of their total area occur within the altitude interval 600-100 m. The maximum number of aufeis is formed within the interval of 600-800 m (25% of the total number). In the River Chara basin, within the altitudinal interval 700-1100 m, 68.8% of all aufeis and 76.4% of their total area are concentrated, with the maximum number in the interval 900-1000 m.

In the aufeis regime two periods characterizing the general process of aufeis formation can be distinguished: a period of formation and a period of destruction. Figure 2 shows the graph plotted from data of long-term surface observations (formation period) and repeated airborne survey (melting period) of the intra-annual regime of large amounts of aufeis. It should be emphasized that such a loop-like correlation between areas and volumes is characteristic of all groundwater aufeis. During the initial period, the area increases approximately 2.5 times quicker than the volume, since aufeis forming water flows widely over the aufeis glade bottom. During this period, 50% of the maximum area and 20% of the maximum ice volume found at the end of winter are formed. In the middle of cold periods the intensities of the increase of volume and area equalize. During this period the area increases by approximately 35%, and the volume by 30%. At the end of the cold period, the volume increases 3 times quicker compared to the area, since the aufeis increases, mainly, in its volume.

During warm periods the area and volume of aufeis decrease at

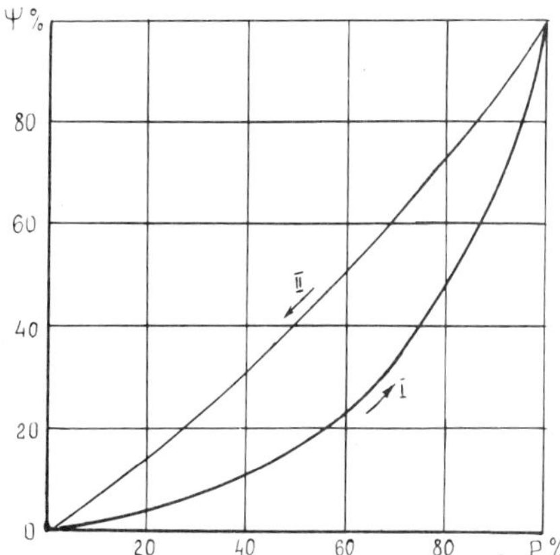

FIG.2 Relative volumes (Ψ) and areas P of aufeis during cold (I) and warm (II) year periods.

approximately the same rate (Katalog Naledei Zony BAM, 1981).

REFERENCES

Abakoumenko, A.E., Usachev, V.F. *et al.* (1980) Deshifrirovanie naladei zony BAM po materialam aerokosmicheskikh syemok (Interpretation of aufeis in the zone of the Baikal-Amour Railway by aerial and satellite survey data). *Trudy GGI* 276. Gidrometeoizdat, Leningrad.

Katalog Naledei Zony BAM (Catalogue of aufeis of the Baikal-Amour Railway zone) (1980) vol.1, Naledy verkhnei chasti basseina r. Chara (Aufeis of the upper part of the River Chara basin). Gidrometeoizdat, Leningrad.

Katalog Naladei Zony BAM (Catalogue of aufeis of the Baikal-Amour Railway zone) (1981) vol. 2, Naledy basseina r. Mui (Aufeis of the River Muya basin). Gidrometeoizdat, Leningrad.

Prokacheva, V.G., Snishchenko, D.V. & Usachev, V.F. (1982) *Distantsionnye Metody Gidrologicheskogo Izuchenia Zony BAM'a* (Remote sensing methods of hydrological studying of the Baikal-Amour Railway zone). Gidrometeoizdat, Leningrad.

Sokolov, B.L. (1975) *Naledy i Rechnoi Stok* (Aufeis and river runoff). Gidrometeoizdat, Leningrad.

Tolstikhin, O.N. (1974) *Naledy i Podzemnye Vody Severo-Vostoka SSSR* (Aufeis and groundwater of the northeast of the USSR). "Nauka" Publ., Novosibirsk.

Topchiev, A.G. (1978) Osobennosti primenenia aerokosmicheskoi informatsii pri issledovanii naledei Tsentralnogo uchastka trassy BAM (Peculiarities of the use of aerial and satellite information when studying aufeises of the central part of the Baikal-Amour Railway). *Referativny Sbornik no. 57, Cartography.* ONTI TsNIIGAIK Moscow.

Hydrological Applications of Remote Sensing and Remote Data Transmission (Proceedings of the Hamburg Symposium, August 1983). IAHS Publ. no. 145.

Studying lake ice regimes by remote sensing methods

V. V. BORODULIN & V. G. PROKACHEVA
State Hydrological Institute, 2 Linija 23, 199053 Leningrad, USSR

ABSTRACT A methodology for obtaining long-term conclusions on ice coverage of large lakes using data from remote sensing observations on ice conditions is described. The possibility of forecasting periods when a lake is clearing from ice using data from remote sensing observations of ice conditions is shown. Using information from aerial ice surveys and satellite imagery for the 37-year period (1945-1982), probabilistic characteristics of ice coverage of Lake Ladoga are calculated and a forecasting correlation between lake ice coverage at a specific moment of time and the period of its clearing of ice is obtained.

Etude du régime des glaces des lacs par les méthodes des photographies aériennes et spatiales
RESUME On décrit une méthode pour aboutir à des conclusions à long terme concernant l'extension des glaces des grands lacs d'après les données de la télédetection sur l'état des glaces. On a montré la possibilité de prévoir le délai jusqu'au moment où les lacs sont dégagés de la glace d'après les données des observations à distance de l'état des glaces. En se basant sur les données de reconnaissances aériennes et les images fournies par le satellite artificiel "Meteor" les caractéristiques de probabilité de l'extension des glaces du lac Ladoga pour une période de 37 ans (1945-1982) ont été calculées et la corrélation de prévision entre l'extension des glaces du lac à un moment particulier et les délais de son dégagement des glaces a été mise au point.

INTRODUCTION

Observations on ice conditions on large lakes and reservoirs can be made using the following remote sensing methods:

- visual observations and mapping from the shore;
- visual observations and mapping from an aircraft;
- determining ice conditions by satellite imagery.

These three sources of information are most popular and mutually supplement each other. Surface observations on the ice regime of lakes are made at shore and island hydrological sites. Information from these observations characterize the ice situation only within the field of view from hydrological stations. For determining ice conditions in central parts of lakes aero-visual observations and mapping of ice from an aircraft are carried out. During a season approximately 10 aerial surveys (1-3 each month) are performed. But observations made at this frequency do not always record all changes of ice conditions. Therefore, for this purpose satellite surveys are often used (5-20 during a season), which give more information and facilitate the analysis of changes of ice conditions on lakes.

Nowadays, it is sufficiently easy to map ice conditions on large lakes, such as Ladoga, Onego Baikal using good TV images obtained from the artificial satellites of the Earth. Methodological principles for interpreting images were developed and tested using a large amount of material (*Vremennye Metodicheskie...,* 1978).

However, the use of satellite imagery for current operational work does not fully realize such a valuable feature of it - documentation. For more than the 10-year period of surveying from space, images were obtained, at various moments, of ice conditions on lakes during the process of their natural variations within the annual ice cycle. This material, together with data from ice aerial surveys, allows one to make some generalizations and conclusions on lake ice regimes. Results of such an approach are described below using the Lake of Ladoga as an example.

EXAMPLE OF LAKE LADOGA

Time variation of ice coverage

For the period 1943-1982, more than 400 ice aerial surveys were made of Lake Ladoga. In addition, during 1971-1982, about 150 TV images were obtained from the "Meteor" satellite, from which ice conditions of the lake were determined.

For an analysis of the ice regime from long-term series it is efficient to characterize complicated ice conditions shown on images by one generalized index. An ice coverage coefficient (or simply, ice coverage, m) may be taken as such an index, showing what portion of the lake area is covered by ice (its compactness taken into account) at the moment of survey or observation. For each survey, coefficients, m, were calculated and for each winter season graphs of time variations of ice coverage of Lake Ladoga were plotted (Fig.1).

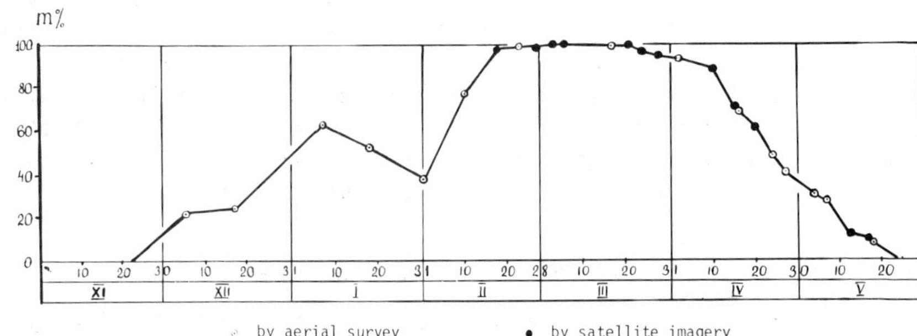

FIG.1 Time variation of ice coverage, m, for the Lake of Ladoga during winter 1980-1981.

Shapes of curves are different and change gradually from year to year. From the moment when ice cover appears in autumn, m gradually increases and reaches its maximum value in mid-March. From this point it slowly, and then rather quickly, decreases. Maximum rate of decrease of ice coverage, based on long-term means, is observed to occur during the period 5-10 May - 14% (about 3% per day). As a rule, decrease of m in spring is evidently higher than the rate of its increase in autumn. On Lake Ladoga complete ice coverage does not occur every winter, therefore, during a season, m may not always reach 100%. The periods of ice formation in autumn and of its disappearance in spring also vary widely. These periods for each season were determined by data obtained at hydrological sites and were adjusted by slight (less than 5% of m amplitude) extrapolation of surveys of ice coverage variations with time.

For obtaining computational hydrological characteristics, observational data for the 37 year period were statistically treated. From graphs of time variations, values of m for the end of each 10-day period were taken (the 10th, 20th and the last day of each month). As a result, 19 series of m values, with 37 terms in each, were obtained. Such a series may be considered as a united statistical set of random values. Further treatment of the series was made using computational methods adopted in hydrology (Rozhdestvensky & Chebotarev, 1974). Some of our series contain zero or 100% values of m. In this case for plotting theoretical frequency curves, the so-called "method of composition" proposed by A.V.Rozhdestvensky was used.

The range of m variations in a series, characterized by the coefficient of variation C_v, was different for individual series. For the period of ice cover formation and for winter (November-March) the coefficient of variation of m varied from 1.22 - 0.18, and a regular nonlinear decrease of C_v with an increase in m was observed. During the period of decreasing ice cover and clearing of ice from the lake, coefficients of variation of m increased exponentially from 0.20 (20 March) to 2.50 (20 May). Coefficients of variation for periods of ice cover formation and disappearance amount to 0.45 and 0.32, respectively.

Characteristics of ice coverage

Values of m for a definite date, as well as dates of ice cover formation in autumn and disappearance in spring for different frequency values were taken from the corresponding analytical frequency curves. As it is accepted in hydrological computations, (Lebedev, 1961), the two extremes, two intermediate and one mean characteristic (see table 1) were taken. The results of determining values of ice coverage for various probabilities are graphically illustrated in Fig.2. They can be used as probabilistic characteristics of ice coverage in scientific and design computations.

Periods of ice formation and disappearance

As well, the series of data on ice coverage of Lake Ladoga, obtained as a result of assessing information from airborne ice reconnaissance and satellite surveys, were used for the analysis of periods of ice cover formation and disappearance. These periods depend on the

TABLE 1 Characteristics of ice coverage, periods of ice cover formation and disappearance for various frequencies and probabilities

Probability	*Characteristic*			*Frequency per N years*
	Ice coverage	*Period of ice cover formation in autumn*	*Period of ice cover disappearance in spring*	
0.1	*very high*	*very early*	*very late*	*1000*
1	*very high*	*very early*	*very late*	*100*
5	*high*	*early*	*late*	*20*
10	*moderately high*	*moderately early*	*moderately late*	*10*
50	*medium*	*medium*	*medium*	*2*
75	*moderately low*	*moderately late*	*moderately early*	*4*
90	*moderately low*	*moderately late*	*moderately early*	*10*
95	*low*	*late*	*early*	*20*
99	*very low*	*very late*	*very early*	*100*

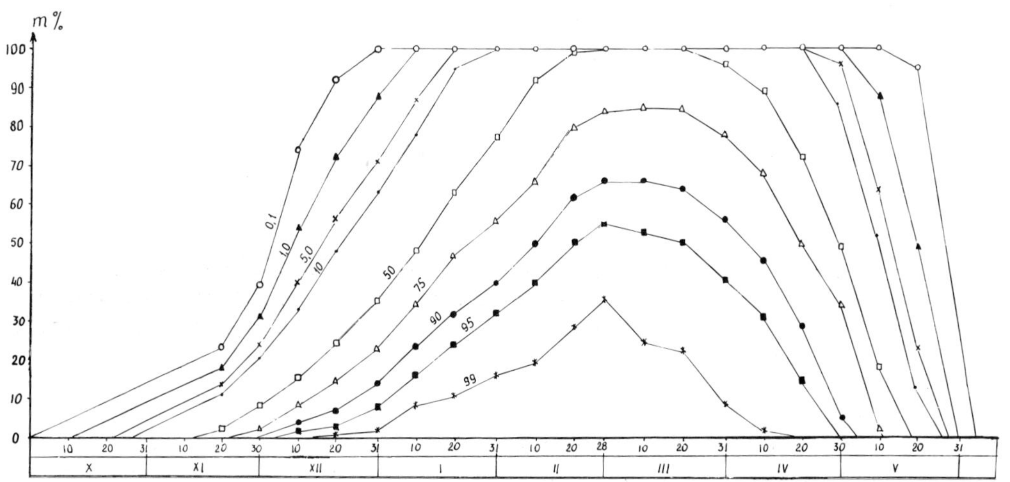

FIG.2 Graphs of chronological (October to May) distribution of ice coverage m on Lake Ladoga for various frequencies.

hydrometeorological conditions in winter and spring; therefore, the reliability of their long-term forecasts usually depends on the reliability of long-term meteorological forecasts. At the same time, the value of m itself depends on winter conditions and in turn predetermines further the process of ice clearing from the lake. The more ice that is accumulated in the lake during winter, the longer the time and the more heat it will take for the ice to disappear in spring.

It seems, that there is a moment in the lake ice regime when the amount of ice predetermined by previous meteorological conditions is a dominating factor in determining the length of a period taken for the ice to clear. And the value of m at this moment may be used as a predictor for forecasting the period of clearing lake ice. When analysing ice coverage variations during the 37-year period it was found that such a significant moment for the Lake Ladoga is observed in late March (nominally adopted as 1 April). At this time, as a rule, the process of ice cover destruction is stabilized and the amount of ice remaining will determine the length of period of its further melting. At the same time there is enough time for estimating future progress. In the long-term series, the correlation between ice coverage for 1 April, and the sums of negative air temperatures for winter with maximum ice thickness and the sums of positive air temperatures for melting period is strongly pronounced. The period of lake clearing of ice is characterized by the length of period from 1 April until the date when ice completely disappears (T,days). This value is sufficiently well connected with lake ice coverage for 1 April (Fig.3) and can be determined with the help of the latter.

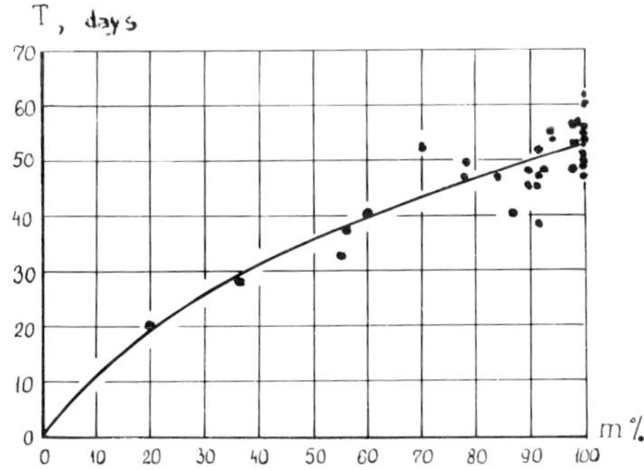

FIG.3 Correlation between the length of the period (days) from 1 April to the moment of complete clearing of the ice from Lake Ladoga (T) and ice coverage for 1 April, m, for 1945-1982.

The importance of this correlation is that it doesn't depend on meteorological forecasts. Applicability and accuracy of this forecasting methodology was estimated using $\bar{S}/\sigma$ criterium. Here $\bar{S}$ is mean square error of test forecasts. σ is the mean square deviation of the forecasted value from the normal one. When the number of test forecasts is more than 25 the methodology proves good if $\bar{S}/\sigma \leqslant 0.50$ and satisfactory if $\bar{S}/\sigma = 0.51$-0.80 (Befani & Kalinin, 1965). This dependence should be considered satisfactory for making forecasts, since $\bar{S}/\sigma$ is 0.56 and the permissible forecast error, which equals 5 days, has a probability of 80%. The normal prediction is 35-55 days, however, it can be as early as 20 days.

The account of mean maximum ice thickness measured at sites or the sum of negative air temperatures for the winter period can serve as a supplementary measure for forecast improvement. These characteristics are usually known for the moment of forecasting. Thus, it is possible to estimate periods of lake clearing from ice using the value of m for the specific moment of time without using meteorological forecast data. For the determining of this predictor it is necessary to obtain good satellite imagery of the lake for early April, or to perform aerial ice survey for this data.

REFERENCES

Befani, N.F. & Kalinin, G.P. (1965) *Uprazhnenia i Metodicheskie Razrabotki po* Gidrologicheskim Prognozam (Exercises and methodological rules on hydrological forecasts). Gidrometeoizdat, Leningrad.

Vremennye Metodicheskie recommendatsii po Ispolzovanie Sputnikovoi Informatsii v Operativnoi Praktike Gidrometsluzhby. Otsenka Ledovoi Obstanovki Ozer i Vodokhranilishch (Temporal methodological recommendations on the use of satellite data in the operational practice of the hydrometeorological service. The assessment of ice conditions of lakes and reservoirs) (1978). Gidrometeoizdat, Leningrad.

Lebedev, V.V. (1961) *Gidrologia i Gidrometria v Zadachakh* (Hydrology and hydrometry in problems). Gidrometeoizdat, Leningrad.

Rozhdestvensky, A.V. & Chebotarev, A.I. (1974) *Statisticheskie Metody v Gidrologii* (Statistical methods in hydrology). Gidrometeoizdat, Leningrad.

Hydrological Applications of Remote Sensing and Remote Data Transmission
(Proceedings of the Hamburg Symposium, August 1983). IAHS Publ. no. 145.

A study of spectral reflection characteristics for snow, ice and water in the north of China

ZENG QUNZHU, CAO MEISHENG, FENG XUEZHI,
LIANG FENGXIAN, CHEN XIANZHANG & SHENG WENKUN
Lanzhou Institute of Glaciology and Geocryology, Academia Sinica, Lanzhou, Gansu, 730000, China

ABSTRACT The spectral reflection characteristics for snow, ice and turbid water within the spectral range 380-1200 nm have been analysed. The spectral reflectance for snow decreases with increasing snow density and crystal size, and there are good correlative relationships between density and spectral reflectance. The spectral reflectance gradually decreases from 95% to 60% within the visible range while snow metamorphoses into glacier ice. The variation of spectral reflectance for turbid water is decided by the silt content in water, and when silt content is more than 5400 mg l^{-1} and the wavelength of maximum reflectance is stable near 820 nm. Based on the t-test, M_j and C_v values, the optimum remote sensing bands have been selected, that is, 420-450, 840-910, 950-1110 nm for snow, 670-760 nm for ice and 730-810 nm for turbid water, respectively.

Etude des caractéristiques de réflexion spectrale de la neige, de la glace et de l'eau dans le nord de la Chine
RESUME Les auteurs ont analysé les caractères de la réflexion des spectres 380-1200 nm de la neige, de la glace et de l'eau boueuse. La réflectance spectrale de la glace diminue avec l'augmentation de sa densité et la dimension de ses cristaux, et il y a un bon rapport de corrélation entre la densité et la réflectance spectrale. Quand la neige se change en glace des glaciers, la réflectance spectrale descends graduellement de 95% à 60% dans le domaine visible. Les variations de la réflectance spectrale de l'eau boueuse sont determinées par la concentration de limon dans l'eau et quand celle-ci dépasse 5400 mg l^{-1}, la longeur d'onde de la réflectance maximale se stabilise à près de 820 nm. Basées sur le test t, les valeurs M_j et C_v, les bandes optimales de télédétection ont été sélectionnées respectivement, c'est-à-dire 420-450, 840-910, 950-1110 nm pour la neige, 670-760 nm pour la glace et 730-810 nm pour l'eau boueuse.

INTRODUCTION

There are varied spectral reflection characteristics under different phases or different conditions with the same phase of water.

Studying the spectral reflection characteristics for natural water (solid and liquid) and its variation with some object feature parameters is very important to the selection of optimum remote sensing bands of a sensor and the interpretation of remote sensing data. Based on field measurement data collected in the north of China in 1980-1982, the spectral reflection characteristics for snow, ice and turbid water and the relationship between these characteristics and some object feature parameters have been analysed in this paper. The classification and the selection of optimum remote sensing bands for these objects are also presented.

THE METHOD OF MEASUREMENT AND EVALUATION OF DATA ACCURACY

The instrument used to make the measurements was a SRM-1200 spectral radiometer. Its wavelengths range from 380 to 1200 nm; resolution is 10 nm. The reference white plate is made of B_aSO_4 and its spectral reflectance and cosine characteristic were calibrated in the laboratory. Cloud form, cloud cover, sunshine conditions, global solar radiation and sky scattering radiation were recorded at the time of the measurement. We have also measured the object feature parameters, such as snow density, silt content in water, etc. Each measurement result of snow is the mean for three observations and that of other objects is the mean for 12 observations.

From many observations the relative error of the measured value is found to be usually less than 3%. For convenience to put the spectral reflectance data of earth objects in the field of order, to analyse and to manage them, they all have been stored in a computer. A data bank of spectral reflectance has been established in a Wang-2200 VS computer at the computation centre of Gansu province.

THE SPECTRAL REFLECTION CHARACTERISTICS FOR SNOW, ICE AND WATER, THE RELATIONSHIP BETWEEN THESE CHARACTERISTICS AND CORRESPONDING OBJECT FEATURE PARAMETERS

The basic characteristics of spectral reflection curves for snow

Figure 1 includes some typical spectral reflection curves for snow. Usually spectral reflectance within the range of 380-700 nm has little decline and the variation is less than 0.06; however, for wet snow, the spectral reflectance within range from 380 to 450 nm shows a small rise. The curves drop downwards from 700 nm and rapidly decline from 900 nm and form a wave trough at 1020-1030 nm; they then form a wave peak at 1080-1090 nm before finally declining rapidly again.

The spectral reflectance for snow varies with environment condition and time. The spectral reflectance will change especially when meltwater appears and snow crystals metamorphose to coarse grains and density increases. In Fig.1, curves A and B have been measured on the same fresh snow at an interval of about 40 h; air temperature basically is below 0°C, snow crystals coarsened slightly and density increased from 0.12 to 0.16 g cm^{-3}.

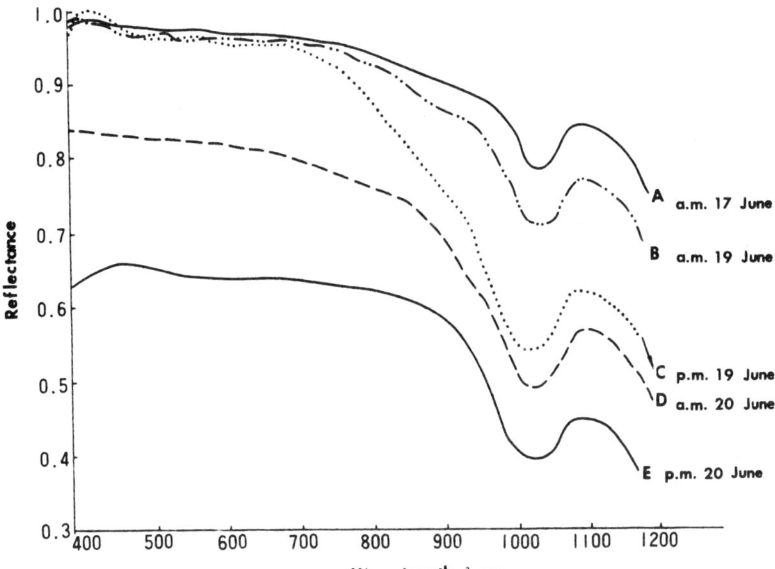

FIG.1 Spectral reflectance curves for snow showing the influence of snowmelt and metamorphism.

It will be noted that the difference between A and B is less within the visible range, but the reflectance of curve B declines about 0.05-0.09 within the infrared range. Curve D was measured about 24 h later than curve B on a clear day, with the air temperature being above +5°C, density increasing from 0.16 to 0.35 g cm^{-3} and crystals obviously metamorphosing to fine firn. Comparison between curves B and D shows that reflectance declines 0.12-0.18 within the visible range and a maximum of 0.22 within the infrared range.

Depending upon melting conditions, snow cover can be divided into dry, damp, wet and saturated snow. In Fig.1, curves B, C, D, E are the spectral reflectance curves for the above-mentioned four types of snow, respectively. It is obvious that the moisture content in snow can have an important influence on spectral reflection characteristic for snow. Comparison of curves B and E reveals that the spectral reflectance of water-wet snow within the range 380-700 nm obviously declines, but the maximum decline is still within the infrared range.

The optimal regression equations relating snow density and spectral reflectance have been established by means of regression analysis; 22 spectral reflection curves have been analysed. The result of computation shows that the linear regression equation is rather fair. The correlation coefficients between snow density and reflectance at all wavelength points from 380 to 1180 nm are more than 0.83; at the wave trough 1020-1030 nm it is 0.96. The optimum regression equation between wave band reflectance and snow density is within the range 800-1100 nm, i.e. Landsat MSS-7 band. Their regression equations and statistical parameters are given in Table 1, where: R_j is the correlation coefficient; S is the residual standard deviation; g^2 is the goodness of fit; $\Delta\rho max(\%)$ is the maximum relative error between the predicted value and the measured value;

TABLE 1 Parameters of linear regression equations between density of snow and spectral reflectance

Wavelength or spectral band (nm)	*Regression equation*	R_j	*S*	g^2	$\Delta\rho_{max}$ *(%)*
1020-1030	$\rho = 0.65-0.672r$	*0.960*	*0.028*	*0.942*	*43.7*
800-1100	$\rho = 0.77-0.727r$	*0.946*	*0.040*	*0.895*	*60.6*

r is the reflectance: and, ρ is the snow density (g cm^{-3}).

The characteristics of spectral reflection curves for ice

According to early research, it has been noted that the mountain glacier ice in the west of China is transformed from snow cover. Through the infiltration and refreezing of melting water (congelation), settling and recrystallization, snow cover becomes firn, infiltration ice, infiltration-congelation ice and recrystallization ice. Their physical features are different from each other in each stage of the long duration of ice formation. Based on the differences of spectral reflectance, the distribution of the accumulation area, ablation area and firn line can be interpreted from remote sensing images. Figure 2 shows the spectral reflection curves of fresh snow (A), firn snow (B), refreezing

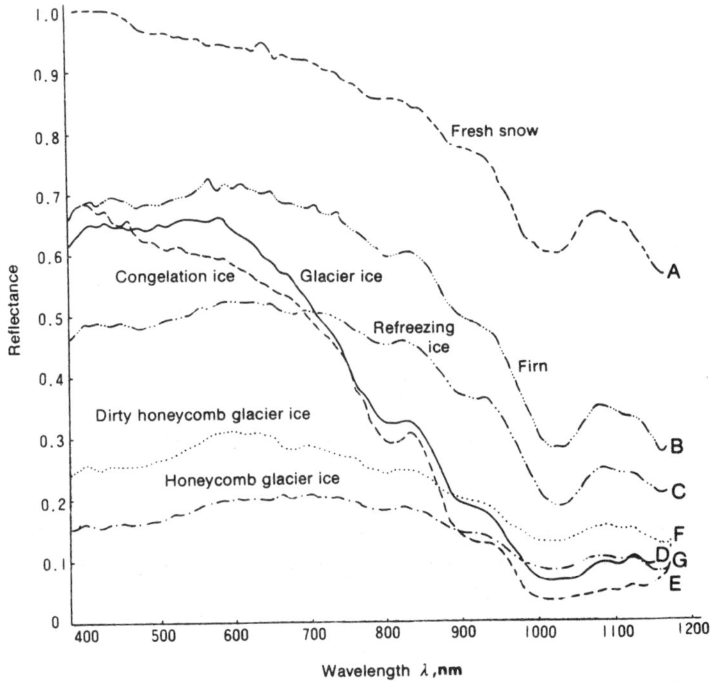

FIG.2 The curves of spectral reflectance for ice in different formation stages.

ice (C), glacier ice (D), and congelation ice (E). Figure 2 shows that the spectral reflectance declines from 0.95 to 0.60 in the visible range as the snow cover metamorphoses to glacier ice. The spectral reflectance curves of glacier ice (blue ice band) is similar to that of congelation ice. The ice surface on the terminal glacier is honeycombed because of the dirty moraine and nonuniform distribution of ablation, and its spectral reflectance rapidly declines (curves F,G) from 0.60 to 0.30 in the visible range, but rises a little in the infrared due to dirty moraine.

The characteristics of spectral reflection for turbid water

In order to reduce the influence of unstable platforms and other environmental conditions on the spectral reflectance measurement, we brought the water samples from the rivers or lakes for measurement on the bank. The volume of the square metal bucket holding the water sample was 50 x 50 x 35 cm^3; its bottom and walls were covered by nonlight black paint and the water depth was more than 25 cm to satisfy the condition of unlimited water depth. Other measurement steps were the same as above. Microscrope examination showed that the main mineral components of the silt were quartz and different kinds of debris, secondary being hornblende etc. The size of silt is a degree of fine, powdery sand and mud. The spectral reflection curve of baked dry silt is shown in Fig.3.

The spectral reflection curves of different silt content in the same river is shown in Fig.3. It appears that the wavelength corresponding to maximum reflectance has drifted towards the

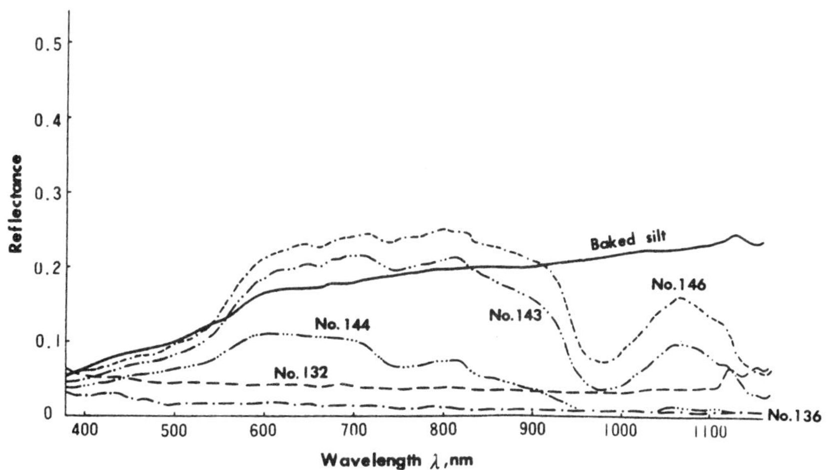

FIG.3 The curves of spectral reflectance for water with different silt contents, distillation water and water from a clean salt lake.

No.146 water in the Yellow River
No.144 water in the Yellow River
No.136 distillation
No.143 water in the Yellow River
No.132 water in clean salt lake

infrared with increasing silt content, i.e. the phenomenon of "Red Drift" (Swain *et al.*, 1978). The relationship between the wavelength point for maximum reflectance and the silt content is nonlinear, and the point is stable near 820 nm if the silt content is more than 5400 mg l^{-1}. Based on 17 spectral reflectance observations for water with different silt content in the same river, the statistics show that the optimum linear logarithmic equations relating silt content and reflectance within the range from 380 to 1200 nm at intervals of 10 nm have been obtained using regression analysis. The average correlation coefficient within the range from 380 to 1200 nm is 0.839. The optimum wave band is 730-1090 nm and its correlation is 0.903.

The data statistics show that the relationship between average band reflectance and silt content of water is nonlinear for Landsat MSS-4,5,6,7 or Landsat-D, TM-1 (450-520 nm), TM-2 (520-600 nm), TM-3 (630-690 nm), TM-4 (760-900 nm).

To represent the silt content of turbid water (mg l^{-1}) Y1, Y2, Y3, Y4 represent MSS-4,5,6,7 band average reflectance and Z1, Z2, Z3, Z4 represent TM-1,2,3,4 band average reflectance. We can assume the regression equations are as follows:

$$X = b_0 + b_1Y_1 + b_2Y_2 + b_3Y_3 + b_4Y_4 + b_5Y_1^2 + b_6Y_2^2 + b_7Y_3^2 + b_8Y_4^2 \quad (1)$$

$$X = b_0 + b_1Z_1 + b_2Z_2 + b_3Z_3 + b_4Z_4 + b_5Z_1^2 + b_6Z_2^2 + b_7Z_3^2 + b_8Z_4^2 \quad (2)$$

where b_0, b_1, ..., b_8 are the regression coefficients of each term. Selecting the significance level of F = 0.1 and using the equations (1) and (2), the regression coefficients and multiple correlation coefficients, r_m, have been estimated using a stepwise correlation and regression procedure on the computer. All these coefficients are listed in Table 2. It shows that the relationship between the silt content in turbid water and the spectral reflectance of MSS-6 or TM-3 is the best.

THE CLASSIFICATION OF ICE, SNOW, AND WATER AND THE SELECTION OF OPTIMUM BANDS FOR REMOTE SENSING

The method and result of classification

There are many methods for classification, but only two methods have been used in this paper, i.e. principal components analysis and type-Q clustering method.

Principal components analysis is a method that synthetically analyses the interrelation within the same object and its reflectance values of each wavelength point to find out the principal component factors; then the measured objects can be classified by virtue of the size of partition value that each object has acquired in the coordinate axes of principal components. This method was used to analyse many reflectance curves; each curve was broken into 41 points at intervals of 20 nm within the range from 380 to 1200 nm; the reflectance for each point was taken as a variable to analyse. These include 14 reflectance curves of

TABLE 2 The statistic parameters of equations (1) and (2)

Band	Parameter: b_0	b_1	b_3	b_5	b_6	b_8	b_2, b_4, b_7	r_m	F
MSS-4,5,6,7	-384.7	-10.3	309.98	0	-16.97	31.98	0	0.989	139.35
TM-1,2,3,4	-2888.7	0	614.63	-2.87	-24.73	0	0	0.820	8.89

NOTES: r_m is the multiple correlation coefficient:

For MSS bands: $X = -384.7 - 10.3Y_1 + 309.98Y_3 - 16.97Y_2^2 + 31.98Y_4^2$

For TM bands: $X = 2888.7 + 614.63Z_3 - 2.87Z_4 - 24.73Z_2^2$

congelation ice, glacier ice, additional ice and firn ice under different states and 38 samples of water from water bodies (distilled water, clean fresh water in a high mountain lake, salt water in an inland lake and turbid water with different salt contents).

Although principal components analysis has some advantages, such as fast, low cost computation (short CPU time) and so on, many subjective factors of the operators will be brought into the analysis during the last process of merging classes. Furthermore a certain quantitative scale of the interclass deviation size of each class cannot be obtained. Especially, if a few measured objects could not be obviously divided, in comparison with practice, a larger error in the classified result will exist.

The Type-Q clustering method can solve such defects as above. Using this method, one can incorporate the objects with similar reflectance curves into a class while the dissimilar ones are incorporated into different classes, until all objects are divided and make up a classification system, the classes being developed from small to large. Finally, a natural families diagram can be obtained in response to the closeness of the relationship among measured objects. The sum of square error in the merged point groups can be found quantitatively; different classification criterion can be selected by virtue of demand of different classification accuracy and the corresponding point groups can be obtained. The defect of this method is more CPU time required.

The classification results from the above-mentioned 14 curves of ice and 38 of water spectral reflectance obtained by the methods of Type-Q and principal components analysis are shown in Figs 4, 5, 6 and 7. It has been noted from Figs 4 and 5 that the spectral reflectance of glacier ice is mainly influenced by roughness and impurities on the ice surface. The spectral reflectance of pure clear glacier ice (blue ice band) is the same as that of congelation ice. Figures 6 and 7 show that the clean water as well as distilled water, clean fresh water from a high mountain lake and salt lake water from the inland lake are of the same type, but turbid water with different silt contents (fresh or salted) is the other type. It is proved that the spectral reflectance for water has

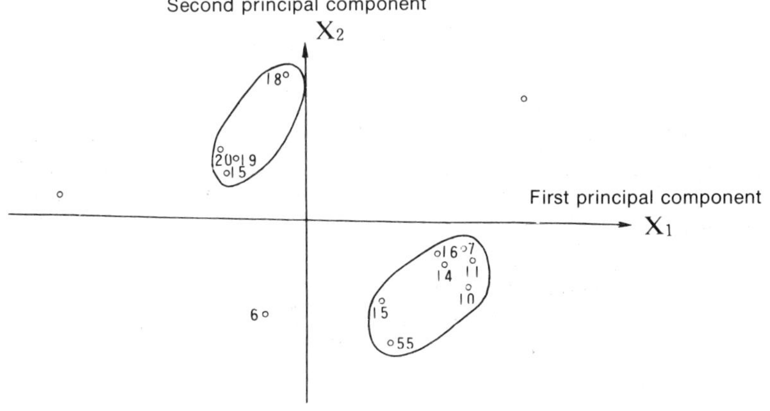

FIG.4 The result of principal component classification for glacier ice at Tian Shan Glaciological Station.

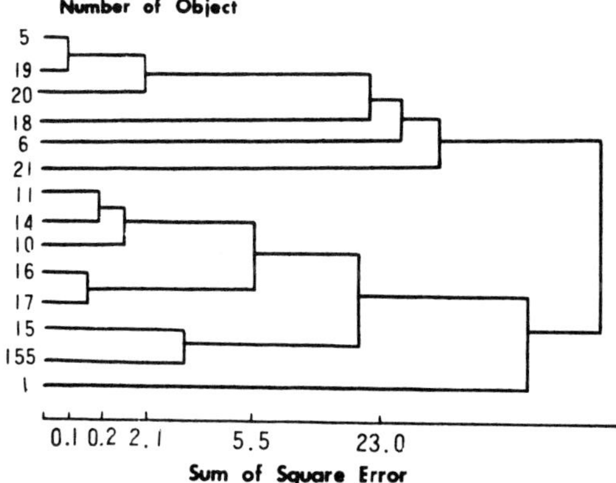

FIG.5 The result of classification for glacier ice at Tian Shan Glaciological Station, using the Type-Q clustering method.

nothing to do with the colourless inorganic salt content in water, but its variation is decided by the silt content suspended in water. There were 38 water samples used in the analysis; according to the spectral reflectance characteristics, the corresponding silt contents are listed in Table 3.

The selection of the optimum remote sensing band for ice, snow, and water

The optimum remote sensing band must satisfy the following criteria:

(a) obtaining the greatest information from the earth objects within a limited spectral band;

(b) overlapping information among different objects is a minimum,

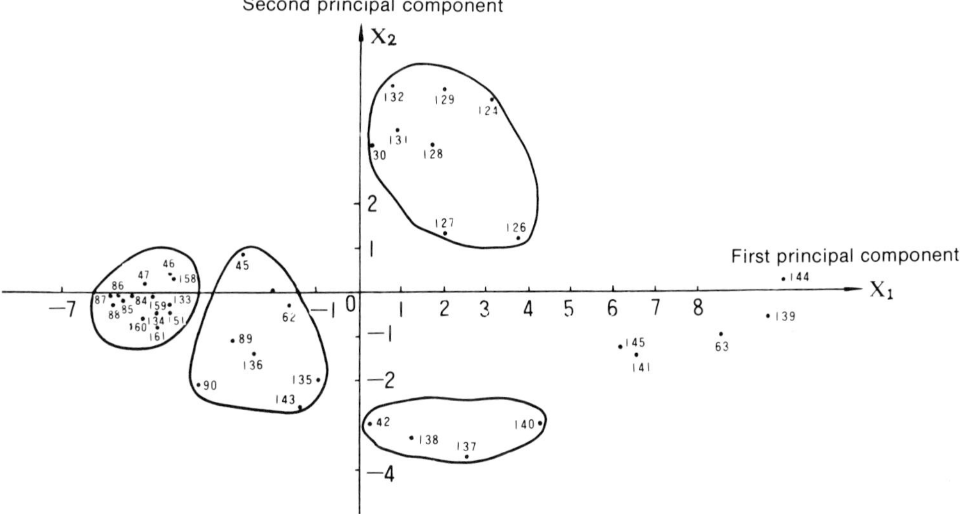

FIG.6 The result of classification for water used by the principal component analysis method.

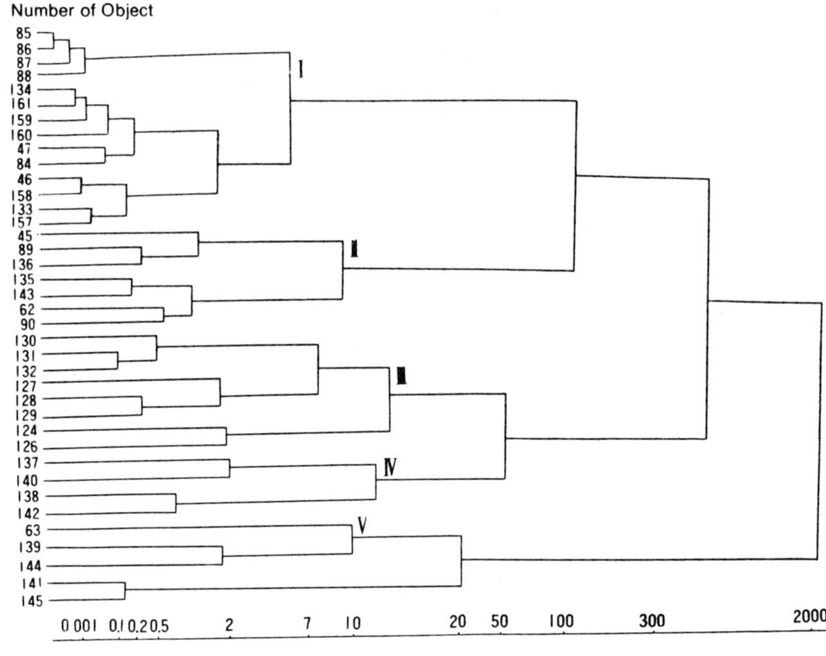

FIG.7 The result of classification for water using the Type-Q clustering method.

such that the difference of spectral reflection among different types of objects is the maximum and that among the same type is a minimum;

(c) there is maximum energy of reflective radiation in the same signal to noise ratio of the sensor.

It has been shown that using a t-test as well as considering the ratio M_j, C_v and energy reflective radiation of the optimum remote sensing band, the ratio M_j reveals the relationship between interclass and intraclass variation, the C_v being a discrete coefficient in interclasses, and is calculated as follows:

$$M_j = \frac{\left(\frac{\Sigma_{i=1}^{n_1}\Sigma_{k=i+1}^{n_1}(x_{ij} - x_{kj})^2}{n_1(n_1-1)}\right)^{\frac{1}{2}} + \left(\frac{\Sigma_{i=1}^{n_2}\Sigma_{k=i+1}^{n_2}(y_{ij} - y_{kj})^2}{n_2(n_2-1)}\right)^{\frac{1}{2}} + \left(\frac{\Sigma_{i=1}^{n_3}\Sigma_{k=i+1}^{n_3}(z_{ij} - z_{kj})^2}{n_3(n_3-1)}\right)^{\frac{1}{2}}}{\left(\frac{\Sigma_{i=1}^{n_1}\Sigma_{k=1}^{n_2}(x_{ij} - y_{kj})^2}{n_1 n_2}\right)^{\frac{1}{2}} + \left(\frac{\Sigma_{i=1}^{n_1}\Sigma_{k=1}^{n_3}(x_{ij} - z_{kj})^2}{n_1 n_3}\right)^{\frac{1}{2}} + \left(\frac{\Sigma_{i=1}^{n_2}\Sigma_{k=1}^{n_3}(y_{ij} - z_{kj})^2}{n_2 n_3}\right)^{\frac{1}{2}}} \quad (3)$$

where x, y, z, are spectral reflectance for the three types of objects, respectively; n_1, n_2, n_3, are the sample size for three types of objects, respectively; and j is the wavelength point at an interval of 10 nm within the range from 380 to 1200 nm, $j = 1, 2, \ldots, 83$. The smaller the M_j value is, the better the measured objects is divided.

Based on the significance level, value M_j (Fig.8) and the energy of reflective radiation etc., we have selected the optimum remote sensing bands for snow, ice and water. They are listed in Table 3.

TABLE 3 Optimum remote sensing bands for snow, ice and water

Parameter	Snow:			Ice:			Water:			
	Snow	Fine-middle firn	Coarse firm	Glacier ice	Honeycomb glacier ice	Congelation ice	Clean	Low silt content	Turbid	High silt content
Density (g cm^{-3})	<0.12	0.16-0.35	>0.35							
Silt content (mg l^{-1})							<100	<250	<350	>2500
Selecting band (μm)		0.42-0.45 0.84-1.18			0.65-0.81			0.62-0.82		
The optimum band (μm)		0.42-0.45 0.84-0.91 0.95-1.11			0.67-0.76			0.73-0.81		

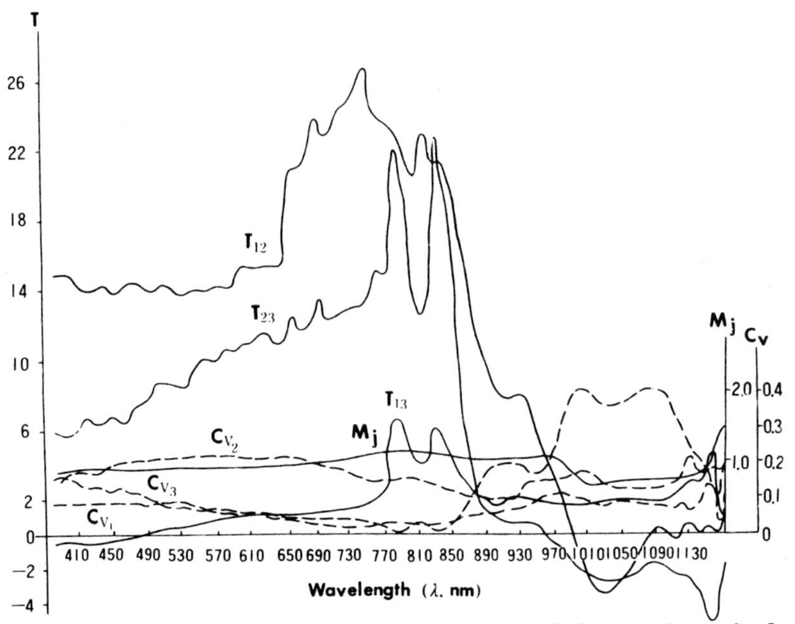

FIG.8 Distribution of T, M_j and C_v with wavelength for three kinds of ice (1 - glacier ice, 2 - honeycomb glacier ice, 3 - congelation ice).

REFERENCES

Swain, P.H. *et al.* (1978) *Remote Sensing: The Quantitative Approach.* McGraw-Hill, New York.

Xie Zichu (1965) The development of the snow-firn layer and ice formation on Glacier No. 1. In: *Tian Shan Glaciological Station Researches on Glaciology and Hydrology in Urumqi River Basin.* S.A.A.G, 1-13.

5 Remote sensing: surface water

Hydrological Applications of Remote Sensing and Remote Data Transmission
(Proceedings of the Hamburg Symposium, August 1983) IAHS Publ. no. 145.

Satellite information for surface water research

V. V. KUPRIANOV
State Hydrological Institute, 2 Linija 23,
199053 Leningrad, USSR

ABSTRACT Satellite information reflects hydrological events and the environment which determines those events with a different rate of spatial generalization. Particular problems correspond to the different spatial scales. As for surface water problems, high resolution imagery from up-to-date satellite systems, such as Landsat, Salut and Soyuz, provide basic information for the parameterization of conditions for different hydrological regimes and for water resources evaluation. Regular information from Meteor, NOAA and partially from GOES satellites is the basis to obtain operational data and to develop runoff model parameters in a real time scale. Satellite information in combination with ground data is an unseparable part in the development and solution of fundamental problems in hydrology and operational practice.

L'information satellite pour les recherches d'eaux de surface
RESUME L'information satellite représente les phénomènes hydrologiques et le milieu qui détermine ces phénomènes avec le différents degrés de généralisation dans l'espace. A chaque degré de généralisation correspondent des problèmes particuliers. En ce qui concerne les eaux de surface la haute résolution de l'imagerie des systèmes satellites modernes du type Landsat, Salut et Soyuz assure l'information de base pour paramètrisation des conditions de formation du régime hydrologique et l'évaluation des ressources en eau. L'information régulière des satellites météorologiques Meteor, NOAA et partiellement GOES présente la base pour obtenir les données opérationnelles des régimes et développer les paramètres des modèles d'écoulement à l'échelle du temps réel.

INTRODUCTION

Information from satellites is becoming more and more important for environmental research; an important part of this information concerns water - an element most essential for man, its phases and peculiarities. If the Earth's surface images are available, the information obtained may be considered as a spatial model of a natural event. The problem is to interpret the model, to measure its basic parameters, to discover interrelations between the events and to determine changes introduced to the environment.

It should be noted, however, that the development of satellite remote sensing of the Earth has been much more rapid than the development of methods for using the satellite information in hydrology. One of the reasons for this is that an approach is needed to use this information compared to the routine presentation based on traditional surface point measurements.

One of the peculiarities of satellite data is that, depending on the equipment, we get an image of a certain event with a different degree of spatial resolution. Moreover, every survey scale, every degree of resolution provides a solution of an absolutely definite scope of problems.

Another reason retarding the introduction of satellite data is an attempt to use satellite data without a properly organized system of ground surveys and aerial observations. In practice, a qualitatively new solution of many urgent hydrological problems may be obtained when there is a reasonable combination of satellite and ground-measurement data.

Nevertheless, the extraordinary results obtained from the use of satellite data have given rise to a number of new branches of science, such as satellite meteorology, satellite geodesy and satellite oceanography. A new term "satellite hydrology" has originated, and it may be subdivided into the following three main sections:

(a) system of ground observation data collection, storage and transmission;

(b) global water circulation research;

(c) obtaining space-time characteristics of the basins of different water bodies and the parameters which determine their regimes.

This paper describes only those problems which are related to surface water research. The problems of ground data collection and retransmission via satellite are not discussed. Attention is focused on the particular results of the use of satellite data in different countries and on some perspectives for possible applications in the near future.

For convenience the use of satellite data for land hydrology is discussed from two aspects:

(a) Research for developing theory for runoff computations and forecasts, for water resources assessment and their changes and for the determination of parameters for the simulation of hydrological processes, i.e. the so-called "Resources Hydrology" as termed in some countries. These problems usually require information of a greater resolution timed to specific phases of the regime of water bodies and the state of basins.

(b) Operational hydrology: obtaining data on the state of water bodies and factors determining those water bodies, and the determination of parameters of regimes of water bodies for the development of operational hydrological forecasts in real time. High frequency and regular receiving of information, as well as a large areal coverage, are usually required for operational hydrology.

Strictly speaking, there is no clear difference between operational hydrology and resources hydrology. Operational data collection made according to a specified programme is the basis for the development of stochastic and deterministic models of hydrological processes and events. Nevertheless, this division is rather convenient relative to satellite data since it is often connected with different types of applications.

RESOURCES HYDROLOGY

Basin characteristics determining the peculiarities of the regimes of water bodies and areas form the basic information for the development of the theory of hydrological computations and runoff modelling. Before satellites appeared, those characteristics were determined from maps for different years and from various surveys. At present, when natural resources and transformation of the environment are intensively developed by man, qualitatively new information is required which would reflect the dynamics of the water cycle peculiarities under varying land use conditions. This information may be practically obtained only from satellites, and in some specific cases, from aerial methods. The cartographic base for the study and development of models of hydrological processes of the required resolution and periodicity is provided at present by information from orbital stations and from the USA Landsat. In particular, Landsat images, with a resolution of 80 m on the ground in four bands of the visible spectrum, make it possible to compile charts on a scale of 1:250 000 with the specified altitudinal and plane cartographic requirements. This scale of survey provides a reliable solution to numerous hydrological problems, main basin characteristics reflecting physiographic characteristics and land use systems.

In this connection it is reasonable to mention the work initiated early in the 1970s at Texas University for the development of a design model for a snowmelt flood; it was based on parameters (except precipitation) including characteristics of the river network and basin obtained from satellites (mainly from Landsat) (NASA, 1979; Baker *et al.*, 1979).

It also should be noted that Landsat images have been used for determining land areas of different permeability, in particular, for the development of a hydrological model of a partially urbanized basin of 342 km^2 in Maryland, USA (Ragan & Jackson, 1975).

In the USSR the TV images from Meteor satellite with average resolution were used to compile maps of natural complexes in the mouth area of rivers discharging into the Caspian Sea, maps of natural complexes of ancient deltas and maps of shallow water areas (up to 2 m deep) in the northern area of the Caspian Sea. These maps show all the changes in the terrain, in the shore line, islands, hydrographic network, different types of vegetation, and in the main shapes of the undersea topography, etc.

Possibilities of using natural mapping from satellite images for hydrological computations were demonstrated in some papers at the COSPAR Symposium in 1979 in Bangalore, India. Scientists from Roorkee University (India) have developed models for the evaluation of annual, seasonal and maximum flows for the Himalaya rivers using images from Landsat. For some basins, with areas from several hundred up to 5000 km^2, the models of the multiple regression were applied, such as

$$Q = a + bx + cy + dz$$

where a, b, c and d are regression coefficients; x, y and z are characteristics of the basin and land use parameters determined from the Landsat data. The basic parameters determined from the satellite data were as follows: orography, density and type of the erosion network, plant characteristics, forest area and land use type, areas of free water surfaces, and snow cover boundaries.

Comparison of satellite data with air photographs taken at the same time showed a very good agreement. The prospects of runoff computations from natural basin characteristics and land use determined from the satellite data are quite evident. The use of periodically repeated satellite data makes it possible to investigate man's effect on the hydrological regime.

Similar investigations using satellite data for the parameterization of physiographic characteristics determining the formation of the hydrological regime of a locality and of water bodies are now widely applied in the USSR, USA, Canada, China, India and in other countries.

The experience of India, a developing country, should be emphasized. In India, a special institute was organized for the interpretation of aerial surveys and photographs; besides the research activity, the objective of that institute is to train specialists engaged in the studies of natural bodies. Aerial survey and satellite data are used in India for surface water mapping (drainage zone, large water bodies), in snow hydrology (snow cover, runoff prediction during snowmelt period), and in flood hydrology (dangerous zones, evaluation of flood damage). These data are also applied to erosion studies (basin erosion, sediment transport in rivers and reservoirs) and for water pollution studies (the distribution of pollutants in rivers and lakes).

In conclusion, it is possible to state that on the basis of satellite data at present there is no problem in mapping physiography and land use peculiarities under which hydrological events are formed and occur.

It should be emphasized again, however, that the satellite image is not a measured value but a reflection of an event - a model which should be calibrated. Therefore, modelling and parameterization of hydrological events require a properly coordinated system of obtaining data, i.e. from satellite, aerial methods and ground measurements.

OPERATIONAL HYDROLOGY

In solving problems of operational hydrology the main requirement for information (besides resolution) is frequency and regularity of its input. Therefore, the studies are usually based on the data of images from Meteor and NOAA type satellites with the resolution of 0.2-1 km. In a cloudless sky these satellite systems make it possible to obtain images of the same terrain once or even twice a day, which, in turn, provides a storage of observation series essential for studying the dynamics of hydrological events. Images of higher resolution, which are not available as frequently, such as from orbital stations or from Landsat, provide additional, extremely useful information for solving problems in operational hydrology.

Evaluation of runoff from effective precipitation determined by remote sensing

Liquid precipitation, rainfall floods One of the main problems of the global hydrology is to obtain a more complete inventory of water resources in the atmosphere, as a source of moisture for recharge of the hydrosphere. Application of remote sensing methods for the study of water circulation in the atmosphere is discussed in other papers. Here we will only mention the determination of precipitation, which is the main design parameter of models reproducing the processes of surface water regime formation.

Satellite assessments of precipitation by different methods (image analysis, multi-spectral and microwave methods) differ both in the methods of application and in the reliability of the results. The determination of precipitation from TV images is based on the correlation between precipitation area and cloud covered area. In the case of frontal cloudiness, correlation coefficients are on the average equal to 0.70 and depend on the type of cloud (varying from 0.77 for frontal to 0.61 for stratus). The relationship of the dimension of cloud elements with the texture characteristic in the images makes it possible to separate cloud types for different rainfall intensities.

The use of infrared images (temperature of the upper cloud boundary) may serve as an additional feature to determine precipitation on the basis of the availability or absence of ice crystals in the upper part of the cloud. It is natural that this does not exhaust all of the opportunities of remote sensing to determine precipitation and its regime, but our main problem at present is to know how this information may be practically applied for hydrological computations. In this regard we may mention a report prepared by researchers from Ruhr University in which the results are given on the application of infrared surveys from NOAA satellites (range 10.5-12.5 μm; resolution - 0.8 km) for computing monthly runoff from four experimental basins (1000 km^2 each) in the southwest of France. The idea of this method is to develop and calibrate a mathematical model which correlates runoff data and cloud cover and the temperature of the cloud surface as determined from NOAA satellite survey.

It is too early to speak about the use of results in operational practice. However, the importance of those results is quite evident for the development of fundamental and applied hydrology.

The importance of the described approaches for determining the incoming part of the hydrological cycle - i.e. precipitation, or factors determining precipitation, by remote sensing methods, goes far beyond the solution of operational problems. Remote sensing data from ever improved satellite surveys in active and passive microwave sensing will undoubtedly be the basis for fundamental research in the modelling of climate and the hydrological cycle.

Solid precipitation, snowmelt runoff Data on the dynamics of snow cover and water equivalent of the snow pack are the initial parameters for the computation of runoff in rivers where snow covers all or a large portion of the basin.

Possibilities for snow cover mapping in the plains and in mountains are discussed in detail in other papers. Here were discuss only the problems on the use of derived snow cover information for the simulation of hydrological processes.

Attempts to use data on snow cover dynamics from satellite images for runoff computation have been attempted since satellite data first became available.

Traditional methods for snowmelt runoff forecasts, as the main factor, include information on the amount of snow cover, which is characterized by the snow line in mountains. It is natural that routine discrete ground observations cannot provide a sufficiently reliable description of the spatial characteristic for snow cover dynamics, particularly in mountain areas. The main requirement for snow pack information is the frequency and regularity of its input so that it can be applied in the operational practice for hydrological purposes. Therefore, information from orbital stations and Landsat is usually applied for the development of methods for snow cover interpretation with periodic correction of the main input of operational data from meteorological satellites. Up-to-date satellite data do not provide quantitative characteristics of the snow pack concerning its depth and water equivalent.

Determination of hydrophysical properties of the snow pack on the basis of registering its reflective capacity in different spectrum bands is far from being ready to be applied for hydrological computations. Therefore, at present one of the main methods applied in operational hydrology is the search for correlation relations between runoff for a definite period and the dynamics of the snow cover in the zone of runoff formation. Quantitative factors of water yield from the snow pack are established on the basis of relationships with ground meteorological observations. The system of using ground information is extremely variable and directly depends on physiographic features and on the nature of the problems to be solved. The greater the proportion of snowmelt runoff for the body and the period to be computed, the more accurate is the computation and the forecast of the event. In this case, the basic predictor is snow cover and the nature of its distribution; its dynamics of formation and melting are well fixed by satellite images. It is natural that the accuracy of computations tends to decrease with the decrease of the proportion of the snowmelt runoff and the increase of the proportion of rainfall during the snowmelt flood period. In this case, predictors are introduced which reflect the role of rainfall.

Such conditions are most "favourable" for the specialists from Norway. In Norway most of the rivers are regulated by reservoirs and are used for power generation. The proportion of runoff produced by snowmelt is 80% or more. In February the first correction of power generation is made in Norway and a decision is made on its distribution among power plants. Snowmelt runoff is predicted on the basis of the area of snow coverage during maximum snow storage (determined by satellite images) and the snowpack depletion curve, which depends on the hypsographic basin curve and predicted air temperatures.

More complicated models are applied in the USSR and USA where rivers are mainly recharged by rain and snow and where runoff, melt runoff included, is the result of numerous factors, among which rainfall dominates. Here the snow coverage is again determined from satellite imagery while other predictors are determined from ground observations. In the mountains, hypsographic curves are widely applied which reflect the development of the specified event.

Unfortunately, all of the problems on basin snow coverage cannot be solved by satellite data alone. Limitations are produced by clouds; in the case of clouds it is impossible to obtain the snow pack characteristic for a sufficient and constant regularity. The problem of snow coverage interpretation in thick coniferous woods is not totally solved for all physiographic regions. Nevertheless, the economic effect produced by a combination of satellite information, ground measurements and aerial surveys is considerable.

One can say that up-to-date imagery from Landsat and Meteor, with average resolution for basins of more than 100-300 km^2, provides data on snow pack distribution which practically do not differ from aerial surveys, while deviation from smaller resolution data from Meteor and NOAA satellites are within the limits of 5-15%.

Estimation of runoff from determining changes in water storages in water bodies and from moistening of the area

A mass of new information from remote sensing surveys enlarged the opportunities of determining relations between the parameters of river networks and runoff. Some of those opportunities have been discussed above. Here we may mention that from the viewpoint of operational hydrology, correlation between "visible river network density" and the amount of water in it determined by remote sensing methods becomes more and more important. In particular, such correlations have been developed for the Don basin and for some other river basins of the USSR.

Some scientists from the USSR and USA, using satellite imagery have shown that with the selection of a representative river reach and a plot in the hydrographic network, water discharge or water level at the design gauging site may be obtained with greater accuracy by $R = f(A)$ curve. Such relations are usually established from high resolution satellite imagery, or on the basis of aerial surveys. In operational practice, a regular survey from Meteor satellite of average resolution is used for approximate computations and then the water surface in the channel network for a specified data is determined.

The practical application of such ideas will be illustrated in some other papers. In particular, it is worth mentioning some very interesting work done by the specialists of the Geological Bureau of Human Province in China. Using Landsat data they have determined relations between visible water surfaces and water levels in a lake in the Yangtze basin. The correlation coefficient in the derived equation is near 1.0.

Regime characteristics of water bodies

Flood plain inundation To fix catastrophic flooding and design conditions rapidly varying in time it is highly desirable to have information as often as possible (daily information is best). Proceeding from this, it is interesting to consider the possibilities of using imagery from Meteor and NOAA satellites. The principle of using this information is in the following: a typical river reach or river system in a basin is selected, then the area of flood plain inundation is determined from satellite imagery. The determined areas of flooding are related to water levels measured at characteristic points.

The experience of this methodology developed in the USSR for the Ob basin has shown that with the use of multispectral data in the range of 0.5-1.0 μm and resolution of about 1 km, combined with control surveys of 0.5-0.7 and 0.7-1.1 μm and resolution of about 250 m, it is possible to obtain the following operational information for rivers with flood plains more than 3 km wide:

(a) the beginning of water overflow into the flood plain, water levels corresponding to definite areas of flooding;

(b) determination of the dynamics of the snowmelt flood wave, velocities of front movement and type of flooding.

Special recommendations have been developed and published in the USSR for the practical application of this methodology. Of course, this methodology is far from perfect and further improvements in apparatus and in interpretation methods are required to eliminate appropriate disadvantages. In particular, it is not always possible in the images to separate water from supermoistened soils and aquatic plants. In the USA and in some other countries all four bands of Landsat data are used for mapping submerged flood plains together with the information obtained from the NOAA satellite. If images from Landsat show the phase of flooding which should be investigated, then such information may be considered as ideal. This coincidence, however, is hardly possible if the frequency of satellite return is 18 days (9 days in the case of two satellites in orbit); moreover, a cloudless sky is necessary. Some very good images were obtained several years ago. For example, in 1973 it was possible to fix flooding in the Mississippi-Missouri Valley over an area exceeding 53 000 km^2 and to compare with the results of interpretation from visible and infrared images from NOAA satellite.

Landsat images are used quite successfully in India for mapping the Ganges flood plain. Here they are used not only for determining the boundaries of flooding during water overflow but also for studying the flood plain morphology and dynamics. They map flood plain bogs, ox-bows and other water bodies, flood plain deposits, river dykes and alluvial cones. The comparison of successive satellite images as well as maps for different periods provides a method to determine the dynamics of channel and flood plain evolution, which, in turn, provides basic material for developing methods of predicting inundations and their effects.

Ice regime and water bodies To study phase water transformations displayed in seasonal ice in lakes, satellites provide a good source of information. To observe the ice situation visible and infrared images are used from meteorological and resource satellites.

Meteorological satellite imagery provides the required observational frequency, but their resolution capacity is not sufficient for a detailed interpretation of the ice situation. The latter is well done by Landsat imagery, but the frequency of those surveys is not sufficient for a systematic control of ice events. Imagery from meteorological satellites is used in the USA for estimating ice situation in the Great Lakes as well as in the USSR for many large and mid-size lakes and reservoirs.

It has been established that this kind of information, despite its small resolution, provides important data on the ice situation in the lakes. For example, in the case of large lakes (more than 5000 km^2) it is possible to make a reliable mapping of ice events, separating open water areas, ice cover, complete and individual ice fields. In mid-size lakes and reservoirs, such as the Chudsko-Pskovskoje Lake and the Rybinsk Reservoir, it is possible to interpret free water areas and ice covered areas. For small lakes it is possible from successive satellite images to determine the date of ice cover disappearance. Besides using imagery in the visible spectrum they have investigated opportunities for mapping ice situations using infrared images from satellites (already applied for sea ice assessment). There are some reasons to suggest that in the future, infrared surveys of a high resolution will make it possible to determine the structure of the ice pack and its compactness over large fresh water bodies and in river mouths.

CONCLUSION

To prepare this review, numerous publications have been used from different countries as well as the abstracts of papers submitted to the present symposium. The limits and the nature of the lecture make it impossible to cite or refer to individual authors. For example, more than 100 publications were issued during the last 10 years on the problem of the use of satellite data on the snow pack dynamics for hydrological computations in the USSR, USA, Canada, India and Scandinavian countries.

It should be emphasized that more than 100 papers from 21 countries representing five continents have been presented at this symposium.

Proceeding from this, only several monographs, reviews and proceedings of the international symposia are given in the references which provide a detailed description of the up-to-date situation on the achievements and prospects of the use of satellite data for solving problems of surface water hydrology.

REFERENCES

Baker, V.R., Molz, R.K. & Mulke, S.D. (1979) A hydromorphic approach to evaluating flood potential in central Texas from orbital and suborbital remote sensing imagery. In: *Proc. Ninth International Symp. on Remote Sensing of the Environment* (Ann Arbor, Michigan),

vol. 1, 629-645.
Izuchenie Hydrologicheskogo Tsikla Aerokosmicheskimi Metodami (Study of the Hydrological Cycle by Aerial-Cosmic Methods). Research results based on international geophysical projects. (1982) Inter-Agency Geophysical Committee under the Bureau of the Academy of Sciences of the USSR, Moscow.
Kuprianov, V.V. & Prokacheva, B.G. (1979) *Obzor. Sputnikovaya Informatsia v Hydrologicheskikh Issledovaniakh* (Review. Satellite information for hydrological investigations). Obninsk.
NASA (1979) *Operational Applications of Satellite Snowcover Observations* (Proc. of final Workshop held at Sparks, Nevada, April 1979). NASA Publication 2116.
Ragan, R.M. & Jackson, T. (1975) Use of satellite data in urban hydrologic models. *J. Hydraul. Div. ASCE* 101, 1469-1475.
Satellite Hydrology (1981) Proc. Fifth William T.Pecora Memorial Symp. on Remote Sensing (ed. by M.Deutsch, D.R.Wiesnet & A.Rango). Amer. Wat. Resour. Ass., Minneapolis.
The contribution of Space Observations to Water Resources Management (1979) (Proc. Symp. on the Twenty-second Plenary Meeting of COSPAR, Bangalore, India).
Weltraumbilder die dritte Entdeckung der Erde (1974) Y.Bodechtel/ H.-G.Gierloff-Emden. Paul List Verlag KG, München.

Hydrological Applications of Remote Sensing and Remote Data Transmission (Proceedings of the Hamburg Symposium, August 1983). IAHS Publ. no. 145.

Evaluation of flood plain inundations by remote sensing methods

V. F. USACHEV
State Hydrological Institute, 2 Linija 23, Leningrad 199053, USSR

ABSTRACT The possibilities of using aerial and satellite information for correcting representative inundation levels, mapping inundation boundaries and assessing the extent of the inundation of different flood plain sub-areas, for observations on the dynamics of a flood wave by the shape of flooding along the channel and, for searching for correlations between the dimensions of flooded areas, water level and discharge are discussed. Using information from repeated passes of the "Meteor" satellite and aerial photography during the inundation period, the inundation of the River Ob flood plain in its middle reaches was studied; correlations between the flooded area at the hydrological observation site and water level were plotted. The analysis of multiband aerial photography helped to adjust interpretation features of inundated areas when water-loving vegetation and shrubs were present.

Estimation de la submersion des plaines d'inondation par les méthodes de télédétection
RESUME On a analysé les possibilités de l'utilisation de l'information aéronautique et spatiale pour la correction des niveaux représentatifs de la submersion, pour l'établissement des cartes des limites d'inondation des grandes crues et l'estimation du degrè de submersion des différentes parties des plaines d'inondation, pour l'observation de la dynamique de l'onde de propagation de grandes crues d'après les dispositions des inondations le long du lit de la rivière, pour l'établissement des corrélations entre les superficies des zones submergées et le niveau de l'eau et le débit. D'après les données des images réitératives obtenues durant la submersion par le satellite "Meteor" et les photographies aériennes on a précisé les caractéristiques du processus de submersion dans le cours moyen du fleuve Ob et on a établi les corrélations entre la surface submergée près de la station hydrologique et le niveau de l'eau. L'analyse des données des photographies aériennes multizonales a permis de préciser les indices d'interprétation des terrains couverts d'herbes et de buissons.

AERIAL SURVEYS OF FLOOD PLAINS

The flood plain is a part of a river valley bottom flooded during periods of high water when streamflow exceeds the carrying capacity of the normal channel. It results from the deposition of sediments transported by the stream during the process of river bed deformation (Chebotarev, 1978). In hydrology, the dynamic processes associated with river flood plains are interesting: the regime of their flooding and receding and the boundaries of floods of different magnitudes. Such information is used for the evaluation of damage of economic structures situated on flood plains. To obtain this information using surface means is practically impossible. In the case when surface means are used for investigating flood plain inundations, it is necessary to delineate the water edge positions for specific moments of time, corresponding to certain water level marks, and then to carry out topograhic surveys to establish a correlation between them. This can be done only for limited river reaches with narrow flood plains. For rivers with mid-sized and broad flood plains aerovisual survey and aerial photography are used. In the course of such work it is necessary to obtain the following information:

(a) places where water outflows onto the flood plain;
(b) succession of flood plain inundation;
(c) the character of inundation of different parts of the flood plain;
(d) flooded areas at different water levels;
(e) time of the start of flooding of various economical structures and the nature of the damage;
(f) boundaries of maximum flooding;
(g) shape and magnitude of deformation of contours of flood plain massives and characteristics of erosion-sedimentation processes on the surface of the flood plain.

Obtaining the above data by aerovisual surveys is only possible when a large number of land reference-points and a good topographic map are available. In most cases during such observations only the flood boundary is fixed and inundated economical structures are marked out. Aerial photography gives much more information compared to aircraft survey, especially when it is possible to obtain a series of successive photographs during the flooding and recession period (Usachev, 1972). The main difficulty in using aerial photographs for the estimation of flood plain inundation is the determination on water boundaries in places covered by bushes and forest. Within wide, poorly forested, flood plain water edges can be identified reliably even from photographs of a scale up to 1:1 000 000. Water of different turbidity can be well distinguished (dark - snowmelt, lighter - rainfall flood, channel). In most cases the colour (tone) of the photograph indicates the direction of water movement over the flood plain.

SATELLITE SURVEY OF FLOOD PLAINS

Airborne surveying of flood plains during flood stage is difficult, since it requires the favourable coincidence of the inundation level needed for flooding and suitable weather for taking photographs. It is critical for photographs of large flood plains from high altitudes. These difficulties considerably limit the use of aerial photography for studying flood plain inundation over long river reaches. The use of satellite survey and observations for studying the inundation and emptying of river flood plains is very encouraging (*Temporal Methodological Recommendations on the Use of Satellite Data*, 1982). Advantages of observations from high altitudes are obvious: continuous tracking of the land surface, broad coverage, and quick receipt of information. This imagery provides observations for all flood plain rivers during periods of high flood. The high degree of generalization of detail in the case of satellite surveys favours regional investigations and allows the monitoring of most characteristic processes of flooding revealed through regularities of variations of flood plain inundation along the whole river from its head to its mouth. Basic problems associated with this are: difficulties in identifying flood boundaries, feebly marked correlations between visual flood plain components and frequency of its flooding, the absence of reliable criteria for evaluating the precision of results.

For the investigation of inundations, images obtained by photographic systems are used. The possibilities of using infrared and microwave imagery for this purpose are mentioned in the literature only rarely (e.g. Allison *et al.*, 1979; Seifert *et al.*, 1975). Most investigations are based on multiband photography in the visible and near infrared spectrum. In the USA, flood mapping most often uses four bands (0.5-1.1 μm) of Landsat data with a resolution of about 80 m (Rango & Solomonson, 1974; Schwertz *et al.*, 1977). In the USSR, flood mapping uses multiband imagery from the "Meteor" satellite (*Temporal Methodological Recommendations on the Use of Satellite Data*, 1982).

Spectral properties of water

Spectral contrasts of the water surface with different environmental objects show that in order to distinguish water from other objects it is important to choose the appropriate spectral band for photography. In the visible spectrum, water can be easily distinguished from contrasting objects (white sand, ice, snow), but it is practically impossible to do so when it is surrounded by wet soils, meadow grass and cultivated land. Under these conditions, photographs should be taken in the near infrared spectrum band (> 800 nm). With the increase of altitude of observation and photography the factors of optical generalization come into play. This most often results in a decrease of observed contrasts. As well, the resulting image of the water surface is influenced by the light conditions at the time the image is taken, by water depth and by masking by vegetation.

At high sun altitude, reflection of it in the water results in glints on the photograph. In the area of glinting, water on the image seems white; this changes the value of its spectral reflection compared with other objects. The influence of glints on the image gradually decreases in the near infrared zone, since here, characteristics of radiation and absorption are more important compared to reflection from the land surface.

The influence of water depth differs for the various spectral bands. Rays of wavelengths corresponding to the green band

(500-600 nm) penetrate clear water to a depth of 20 m. With the increase of wavelength this depth gradually decreases: for 600-700 nm to 12-15 m, for 700-800 nm to 5-7 m and for the near infrared band (800-1100 nm) to several centimetres (Kravtsova & Safianova). For turbulent water penetration depth gradually decreases, and the image is formed mainly due to reflection from the surface.

Masking of water by vegetation rising above it or floating on its surface can considerably change the image of inundated lands. Here everything is determined by the type of vegetation, its phenological state, the degree of tree-crown unity. For example, in the case of inundation of dense coniferous or leaf-bearing forests in summer when the foliage is fully developed, the image is formed by tree-crowns only. In this case water in the inundated forest cannot be extracted from the image.

Thus, the image of the inundated flood plain is formed by many interesting factors. In the process of interpretation, possible variants of this interaction should be taken into account. It is very important, when decoding imagery, to select photographs taken in the appropriate spectral bands. When exposing water surfaces preference should be given to surveys in the near infrared spectrum. However, for comparative purposes, photographs made in the visible spectrum are also useful. In the case of dry flood plain boundaries, soil-vegetation massives and relief details are often better revealed from such photographs.

Interpretation of satellite imagery

River flood plains, depending on the season of the year and water content at the time, have different image patterns in the case of satellite imagery. The structure of the image pattern of the river flood plain reflects the spatial distribution of flood plain elements as well as their interrelations and the correlations between processes in it. In the image, flood plains are represented against the background of the adjacent landscape, but with their own inner relief characteristics. When using photographs made from aircraft and satellites it is very important to develop extraction features for revealing inundated river flood plains and marking out areas inundated at different extents. The river flood plain structure depends on the physiographic conditions of the region and characteristics of the river water regime. On aerial and satellite photographs the image pattern of the river flood plain depends on its origin, flood phase and peculiarities of optical generalization of geographical features.

For various types of flood plains, different surface structures will have image patterns peculiar to them. This will also depend on the degree of generalization, or the scale, of the survey system (Popov, 1969). Let us consider the characteristics of flood plains represented during inundation periods based on small-scale images from a satellite of the "Meteor" system.

Imagery with low resolution can be obtained in four spectral bands (from 0.5 up to 1.1 μm); resolution in the centre is about 1000 m, and the field of view is 200 km. This information can be applied only for the evaluation control of the flood wave movement on large rivers with wide (> 10 km) flood plains by a series of successive images within the band 0.8-1.1 μm. The control includes: the evaluation of flood plain inundation according to three categories - flood plain not inundated, partly inundated, fully inundated; marking out the position of the front of inundations; and, determination of the time of characteristic states of inundation for different river reaches along its length. Synthesis of multiband images of low resolution does not give additional information on river flood plain inundation, and superposition of images made at different times is practically impossible due to considerable spatial distortion.

Images of medium resolution are obtained in two spectral ranges: 0.5-0.7 and 0.7-1.1 μm; their resolution at nadir is about 250 m and the field of view is 1400 km. Using this kind of information the set of problems that can be solved broadens. They may be applied to the following types of estimation:

(a) correction of representative inundation levels for sites with surface observations (the start of water overflow into the flood plain, and the water level corresponding to a definite degree of flood plain inundation; level when the complete flood plain is inundated);

(b) draft mapping of inundation boundaries along the river with the estimation of the degree of inundation at different reaches;

(c) observation of the dynamics of the flood wave by the shape of flooded areas along the channel (velocity of the movement of the front and the rate of inundation):

(d) determination of the moment of arrival of characteristic states of flood plain inundation for individual reaches along the river length.

On the images made in the spectral range 0.7-1.1 μm the inundation boundary is clearly represented and can be mapped on floodplains of middle and large-sized rivers (a flood plain width > 3 km). Synthesizing of images (positives and negatives) allows the more precise interpretation of landscape and the hydrological situation on the photograph. The water surface of the main channel, streams and lowerings is most clearly seen against the general background of overwatered flood plain and bedrock banks. Superposition of images made at different moments of time on the synthesizing apparatus allows an assessment of the dynamics of flood plain inundation and a comparison of the magnitudes of the phenomena.

Images of high resolution are experimentally obtained in four spectral bands (from 0.4 to 1.1 μm) with a resolution of 80 m at nadir and a field of view of 85 km. Images with this resolution are applicable for the solution of the same scope of problems solved using images of medium resolution. Images of high resolution allow more detailed and reliable mapping of inundations; they are also applicable for investigating flood plains more than 1 km wide.

As seen from the above brief description of the available imagery from the "Meteor" satellite, possibilities for using these data for the estimation of inundations are yet quite limited. In some cases, however, especially for wide flood plains situated in regions which are difficult to access, satellite information is the single source for studying processes taking place in the flood plain.

It is most efficient to use all types of surveys from aircraft and satellites in combination and to supplement them with information obtained from overland stations. Such combined usage of areal and spatial information may be exemplified by the search for correlations between magnitude of inundated flood plain areas and water levels and discharges. Correlations between the degree of flood plain inundation and water level over various sections is quite important for the Hydrometeorological Service. Figure 1 shows such a correlation for the River Ob flood plain. The correlation obtained allows:

(a) the determination of the area of the section representative of flood plain inundation for each hydrological site;

(b) the adjustment of levels of water outflow into the flood plain and its complete inundation as well as the estimation of the variability of these characteristics from year to year for different flood magnitudes;

(c) marking out of flood plain sub-areas where most of the water is accumulated and where the process of outflowing of accumulated water into the channel has already started;

(d) after plotting the substantiated dependences, determination of inundated areas from water level data.

Using aerial and space survey we can also obtain corrrelations between the area of inundated flood plain and water discharge which are important for hydrology. Such correlations are developed for hydrological sites situated directly within the inundated area as well as for sites situated upstream from the section under study; it means that they can be used for diagnostic and forecasting purposes (Fig.2). Using the correlation between flooded area and water level

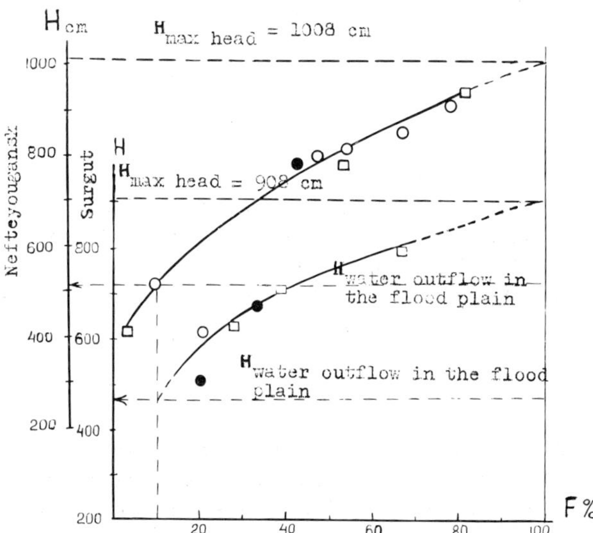

FIG.1 The extent of the River Ob flood plain inundation (F%) in the sub-areas adjacent to hydrological sites Surgut and Nefteyougansk vs. water levels at these sites. The degree of inundation is determined: ○ *, by aerial survey data;* ● *, by satellite imagery;* □ *, by data obtained from "Meteor" satellite.*

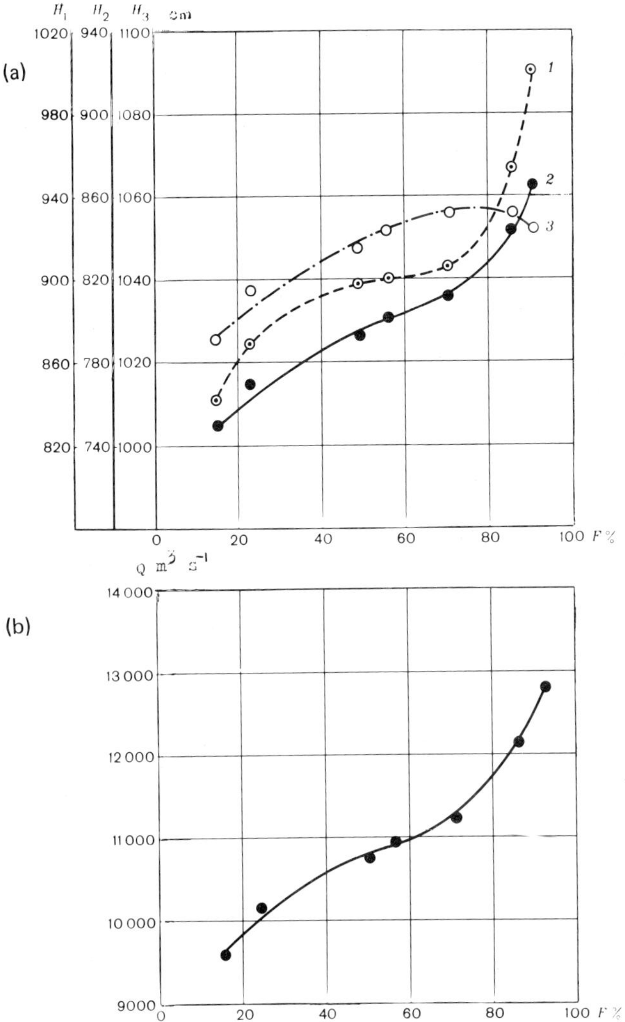

FIG.2 (a) Inundated areas within the reach between the villages of Mogochin and Kargasok (the River Ob) vs. water levels (H) at the hydrological sites: ⊙, Mogochin; ●, Kolpashevo; ○, Kargasok; (b) water discharges (Q) at the town of Kolpashevo.

and discharge it is possible to solve two problems:

(a) using good photographs of floods, to estimate the phase of the hydrological regime and stages of flood passing over the flood plain; and,

(b) using overland observations at hydrological sites, to determine the position of inundation boundaries in case of an absence of good photographs at the given moment of time.

Since inundations are of short duration and occur mostly in cloudy weather, then side-looking radar survey has the most prospects for their study.

REFERENCES

Allison, L.J., Schmugge, T.J. & Byrne, G. (1979) A hydrological analysis of East Australian floods using Nimbus-5 electrically scanning radiometer data. *Bull. Am. Met. Soc.* 60 (12), 1414-1427.

Chebotarev, A.I. (1978) *Gidrologicheskiy Slovar* (Hydrological Glossary). Gidrometeoizdat, Leningrad.

Kravtsova, V.I. & Safianova, G.A. Izutshenie protsessov reliefoobrazovania v pribrezhoi zone po mnogozonalnym snimkam (Investigation of relief formation processes in the coastal zone using multi-zonal imagery). In: *Mnogozonalnaya aerokosmitsheskaya syemka i ee ispolzovanie pri izutshenii prirodnykh resursov* (Multi-zonal Aerial Survey and its Use for Studying Natural Resources). MGU, Moscow.

Popov, I.V. (1969) *Deformatsii Rechnykh Rusel i Gidrotekhnicheskoe Stroitelstvo* (River channel deformations and hydraulic engineering). Leningrad, Gidrometeoizdat.

Rango, A. & Solomonson, V.V. (1974) Regional flood mapping from space. *Wat. Resour. Res.* 10 (3), 473-484.

Schwertz, E.L., Spicer, B.E. & Svehlak, H.T. (1977) Near real-time mapping of the 1975 Mississippi River flood in Louisiana using Landsat imagery. *Wat. Resour. Bull.* 13 (1), 107-116.

Seifert, R.D., Carlson, R.F. & Kane, D.L. (1975) Operational applications of NOAA-VHRR imagery in Alaska. In: *Operational Applications of Satellite Snowcover Observations*, 143-156. NASA-SP-391, Washington, DC.

Usachev, V.F. (1972) Primenenie posledovatelnykh aerofotosyemok dlia issledovania protsessa zatoplenia poim (The use of serial aerial surveys for the investigation of the river flood plain inundation process). *Trans. GGI* 190.

Vremennye Metodicheskie Rekomendatsii po Ispolzovaniu Sputnikovoi Informatsii. Otsenka Zatoplenii Rechnykh Poim (Temporal Methodological Recommendations on the Use of Satellite Data. Estimation of Flood Plain Inundations) (1982) Gidrometeoizdat, Leningrad.

Hydrological Applications of Remote Sensing and Remote Data Transmission (Proceedings of the Hamburg Symposium, August 1983). IAHS Publ. no. 145.

The application of Landsat imagery in the surveying of water resources of Dongting Lake

LIU XIA, ZHANG SHULIN & LI XIANGLIAN
Remote Sensing Geological Station of the Geological Bureau of Hunan Province, Changsha, Hunan, China

ABSTRACT Dongting Lake is the second largest fresh-water lake in China. Connecting with numerous river systems, its area and volume change continuously with the four seasons and the water level fluctuations every year. In order to study the changes, a correlation equation of the level, area and volume of the lake have been worked out based on Landsat images from eight different times and from corresponding on-site water level data. Satisfactory results have been obtained.

Application de l'imagérie Landsat dans la prospection des ressources en eaux du Lac Dongting
RESUME Le Lac Dongting est le deuxième lac d'eau douce de la Chine. En liaison avec de nombreux systèmes d'eau de surface, il voit sa superficie et son volume varier continuellement chaque année avec les variations saisonnières et les montées et descentes périodiques du niveau de l'eau. Pour étudier ses lois de variations, nous avons établi l'équation liant le niveau à la superficie et au volume du lac, en utilisant huit images de Landsat à des époques différentes correspondant à différentes données géométriques de la surface du Lac Dongting. On a ainsi obtenu un bon résultat.

INTRODUCTON

Dongting Lake is at the confluence of the four rivers - Xiang, Zi, Yuan and Li which flow from the south; the Changjiang River flows out to the north (Fig.1). In the flood season, the flood water is regulated by the Cheng-ling-ji exit into the Changjiang River. It is the most important lake for storing and regulating flood water in the Changjiang drainage. Therefore, to research the water resources of Dongting Lake, to study Dongting Lake in a comprehensive way and to evaluate the function of storage and adjustment of the water are very important.

Under the support of the provincial water conservancy department, we applied Landsat imagery and the topographic data of the lake bottom to the study of the water resources of Dongting Lake.

RESEARCHING OF THE AREA OF THE WATER SURFACE

Both the water level and the surface area of Dongting Lake are

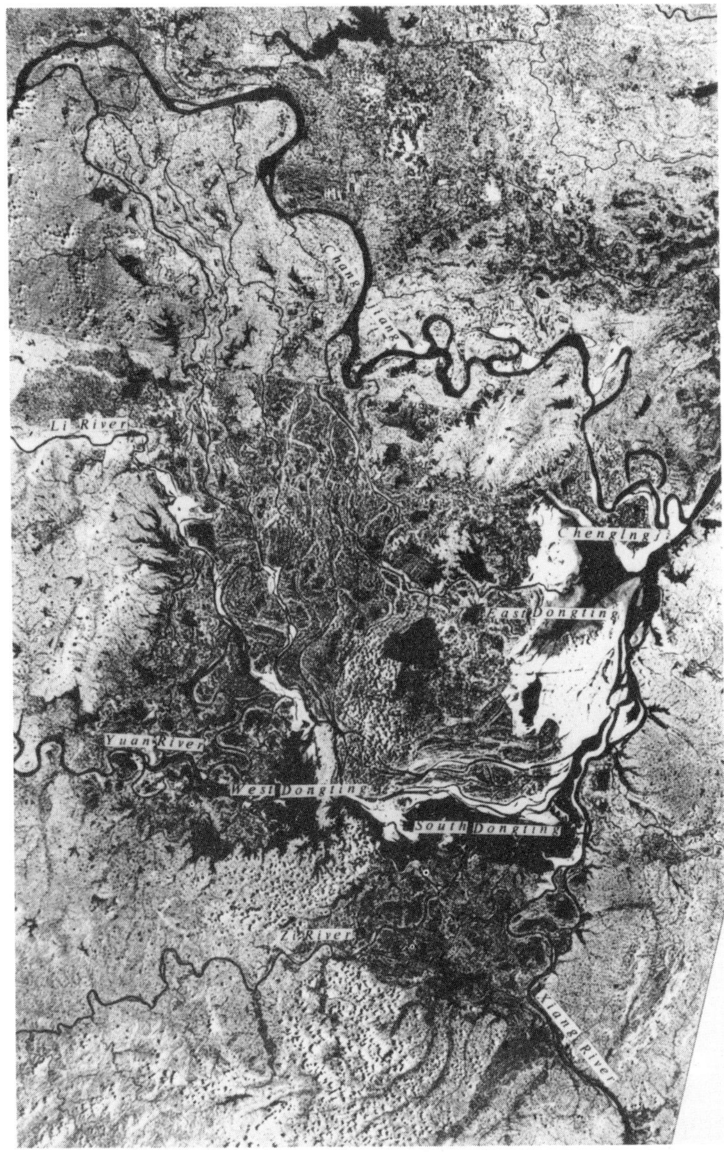

FIG.1 Dongting Lake Landsat MSS-7 image.

controlled by the Changjiang River and the inflow of four rivers from the south. Changes of water level decide the extent of the surface area of the lake.

Determination and calculation of the water surface area

It is well known that the spectrum of reflection of water, approaching the absorbed limit in the near infrared, appears black in a satellite image (MSS-7); while other surface features with a higher reflectance appear grey-white in colour. The boundary between the water and the other surface features is very clear. Therefore, we applied MSS-7 satellite imagery and false colour combination images to delineate the water surface area and calculate its area using the following equation:

$$A = C_1 C_2 N \tag{1}$$

where:
A is the area of the water surface,
C_1 is the contraction coefficient of the photo,
C_2 is the conversion coefficient of the area,
N is the water surface area on the photo.

Through measurement and calculation, in the case of reaching the warning water level (32 m) at Cheng-ling-ji, the water surface area is found to be 2637 km^2. This method of calculation differs by 4% compared with the conventional method. It is demonstrated that the application of Landsat imagery to calculate the water surface area is quite ideal.

The relation between the water level and the water surface area

As the water surface area is continuously expanding and contracting along with the rise and fall of the water level, the water surface area and the water level are correlated. For the sake of studying the degree of their correlation, we calculate the coefficient of the correlation. The coefficients of correlation of Dongting Lake (eastern Dongting Lake, southern Dongting Lake and western Dongting Lake) are 0.913 to 0.986. Another sector, Qilihu, is 0.785.

Figure 2 shows the results of measurement and calculation for the

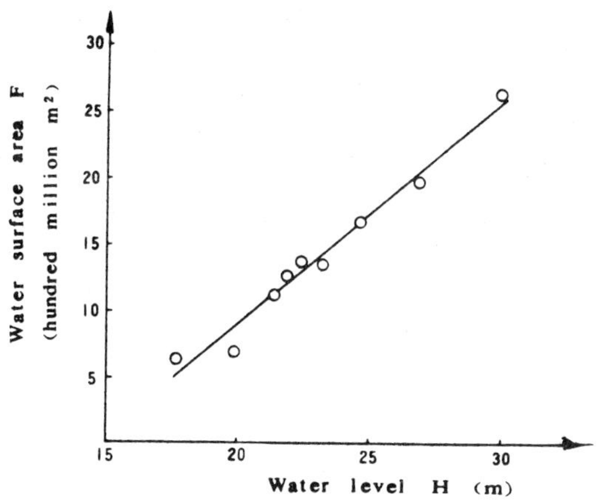

FIG.2 The relationship between the area of the water surface and water level in Dongting Lake.

relation between surface water area and water level. The correlation line obviously conforms to the following linear equation:

$$F = mH + b \tag{2}$$

In this equation, the parameters m and b are calculated from equations (3) and (4), respectively, in accordance with the principle of the least square method:

$$m = \frac{n\Sigma_{i=1}^{n} F_i H_i - \Sigma_{i=1}^{n} H_i \Sigma_{i=1}^{n} F_i}{n\Sigma_{i=1}^{n} H_i^2 - (\Sigma_{i=1}^{n} H_i)^2} \tag{3}$$

$$b = \frac{\Sigma_{i=1}^{n} H_i^2 \Sigma_{i=1}^{n} - \Sigma_{i=1}^{n} H_i F_i \Sigma_{i=1}^{n} H_i}{n\Sigma_{i=1}^{n} H_i^2 - (\Sigma_{i=1}^{n} H_i)^2} \tag{4}$$

According to measurements and calculations of the water surface area, we can get the correlation equation F = f(H) where the water level varies from 17.58 to 30 m.

When the water level of Cheng-ling-ji is higher than 30 m, the water rises along the embankment. With the rising of the water level, the increase of the water surface area is not as large and can be regarded as a constant:

$$F \simeq C \tag{5}$$

Equation (5) holds for the interval from 30 to 32 m.

THE VOLUME OF THE LAKE

Both the water level and the water volume of Dongting Lake are controlled by the Changjiang River and four inflowing rivers. As the water level rises, the water volume increases, when the water level falls, the water volume decreases. The water volume is continuously changing along with the rise and fall of the water level.

The calculation of the water volume

Taking the water level of Cheng-ling-ji as the criterion, when the water level reaches to the warning level, we divide the water volume into three intervals to be calculated according to the water level as follows:

The water volume at the level 17.58 m (V_1) We have collected satellite imagery in the dry season when the level is at 17.58 m. At this level, the volume of the lake basin usually is not adjusted. In order to calculate its volume, we apply the satellite image and the topographic data to sampling, and get the average depth of water as 0.97 m. The water volume is calculated from the equation:

$$V_1 = AH_{cp} \tag{6}$$

where, A is the water area when water level is 17.58 m, and H_{cp} is the average depth of the water. The water volume V_1 of Dongting Lake is calculated to be 6.27×10^8 m^3.

The water volume between levels 17.58 and 30 m (V_2) The water level during a normal season changes within this interval. Its volume is calculated by integrating equation (3):

$$V_2 = \int_c^d (mH + b)dH$$
$$= m \int_c^d HdH + b\int_c^d dH \qquad (7)$$

According to equation (7), the related data, the water volume and the calculation results are listed in Table 1.

TABLE 1 Water volume calculations

Lake	*Water level interval (m)*	*Equation of calculation*	*Water volume $V_2(10^8m^3)$*
Eastern Dongting	*20-30*	$1.6792\int_{20}^{30} HdH - 24.66\int_{20}^{30} dH$	*73.85*
Southern Dongting	*25.19-31*	$0.9688\int_{25.19}^{31} HdH - 21.02\int_{25.19}^{31} dH$	*33.81*
Western Dongting	*26.88-32*	$0.42\int_{26.88}^{32} HdH - 9.93\int_{26.88}^{32} dH$	*12.75*
Qilihu	*28.52-33*	$0.1103\int_{28.52}^{33} HdH - 3.148\int_{28.52}^{33} dH$	*1.1*
TOTAL			*121.51*

From Table 1 we know that the water volume of Dongting Lake between levels 17.58 and 30 m is $12.151 \times 10^9 m^3$.

The water volume between levels 30 and 32 m (V_3) During the flood season, the water level changes mainly in this interval. Its volume is the symbol of the flood adjustment function of Dongting Lake. Its value is calculated by integrating equation (5) as follows:

$$V_3 = \int_E^F cdH \qquad (8)$$

The water volume of Dongting Lake at this interval is calculated as $52.74 \times 10^8 m^3$.

Therefore, the water volume below the warning level of Cheng-ling-ji is:

$$V = V_1 + V_2 + V_3$$
$$= 6.27 + 121.51 + 52.74$$
$$= 18.052 \times 10^8 m^3 \qquad (9)$$

The above result comparing with the result of the conventional calculation differs by only 2%.

The relation between the water volume and the water level

The water volume increases and decreases along with the changes of the water level which rises and falls. To investigate their relationship we plot the curve in Fig.3. It is evident that the equation V = f(H) belongs to the curve of the power function type:

$$V = GH^{t} \tag{10}$$

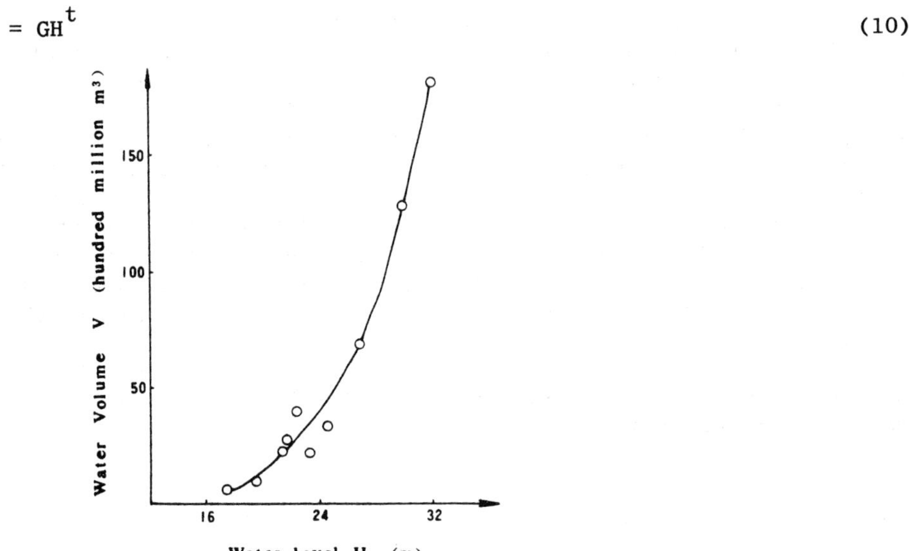

FIG.3 The relation curve of the water volume and water level in Dongting Lake.

In equation (10), the parameters G and t are calculated from equations (11) and (12) using the least square method:

$$t = \frac{\overline{\log H \log V} - \overline{\log H}\ \overline{\log V}}{\overline{\log^2 H} - \overline{\log H}^2} \tag{11}$$

$$\log G = \log V - t \log H \tag{12}$$

Through calculation, equation (10) has the following form:

$$V = 6.0855 \times 10^{-7} H^{5.6316} \tag{13}$$

Equation (13) is an experimental equation which deals with the water volume of Dongting Lake along with the changes of the water level from 17.58 to 32 m in Cheng-ling-ji. The relative error was found to be 1%, which shows the good fit of equation (13).

CONCLUSIONS

(a) Utilizing the Landsat image at different times to investigate the water surface area and the water volume of Dongting Lake, we obtained a good result. It is an effective attempt at researching the water resources of the lake in our province using remote sensing technology.

This method, not confined by the geographic conditions, possessing a number of advantages, such as low cost, high speed and good results, manifests the superiority of the remote sensing technology applied to the surveying of water resources.

(b) As determined by investigation, the water surface area of Dongting Lake is 2637 km^2. This area compared with the calculation in the conventional method differs by 4% and the water volume is $18.052 \times 10^8 m^3$, which differs by 2% from the result calculated by the conventional method. It is demonstrated that the application of satellite imagery to research the water resources is very effective.

(c) We used the Landsat MSS-7 image and the false colour combination image to determine the water surface area, calculate the water volume and establish the correlation between water surface area, water volume and water level. This is reasonable and its result is reliable.

(d) The Landsat image and the topographic data used are not from the same year, and this will exert a certain influence upon the result of investigation.

Hydrological Applications of Remote Sensing and Remote Data Transmission (Proceedings of the Hamburg Symposium, August 1983). IAHS Publ. no. 145.

Estimation of monthly river runoff data on the basis of satellite imagery

G. STRÜBING & G. A. SCHULTZ
Ruhr-Universität Bochum, 4630 Bochum, Federal Republic of Germany

ABSTRACT For the generation of long time series of hydrological design data, e.g. monthly runoff values, a method is presented using information obtained from the NOAA Polar Orbiting Satellite System. This method consists of four consecutive steps, namely: (a) satellite remote sensing data processing, (b) development and calibration of a mathematical model, which correlates measured runoff values (ground truth) with satellite data, (c) generation of long monthly runoff time series on the basis of satellite data alone, and (d) by means of a stochastic model and the time series computed under (c): simulation of synthetic runoff time series, which are long enough to meet the requirements of a potential application. First results of the application of this method in a basin in southwestern France are described.

Estimation des écoulements mensuels à l'aide données de satellite
RESUME Dans ce rapport une méthode est présentée pour le calcul d'une série chronologique d'écoulements mensuels d'un bassin versant à partir de la série de longue durée des données d'un satellite météorologique à orbite polaire. La méthode comporte quatre parties essentielles: (a) le traitement et l'analyse des données de la télédétection, (b) la mise au point d'un modèle mathématique et la détermination des paramètres de ce modèle à partir des séries simultanément observées et de courte durée d'écoulement et d'information par satellite, (c) le calcul d'une série chronologique des écoulements mensuels à l'aide du modèle mis au point en (b) et en utilisant seulement les données de la télédétection du satellite, et (d) la simulation d'une série d'ecoulement d'une durée suffisante en ce qui concerne une application potentielle avec un modèle stochastique se basant sur la série calculée en (c). L'application de la méthode et les premiers résultats pour un bassin versant au sud-ouest de la France sont décrits.

INTRODUCTION

The planning and design of water resources systems is often based on only short or inadequate time series of hydrometric data, particularly in developing countries. In modern hydrology, stochastic methods have been developed in order to generate long term time series of hydrological data with shorter observed time series having a higher uncertainty in the generated data.

In order to overcome this problem a method is presented using remote sensing data obtained from satellites for the generation of long time series of hydrological design data, e.g. monthly runoff values. In recent years extensive research programmes were devoted to the use of remote sensing techniques for the acquisition of hydrological data, particularly for rainfall (Barrett & Martin, 1981), soil moisture and snow cover, but less for the estimation of runoff data (Amorocho, 1975).

The method presented consists of four consecutive steps, namely:

(a) processing of the satellite data;

(b) development of a mathematical model, which correlates measured runoff values with satellite data and calibration of this model with simultaneous data, available at least for a short period of time for both ground truth and satellite data;

(c) generation of long monthly runoff time series on the basis of the observed long term satellite data by means of the mathematical model calibrated under (b). For more than 10 years remote sensing data have existed for large parts of the world and thus runoff time series can be computed for the same space of time;

(d) depending on the objectives of a potential water project, it may become necessary to generate longer time series on the basis of the data obtained in item (c) by means of a stochastic data generation model.

The first three steps of this method are described in this paper. For test purposes the technique was verified in the basin of the River Baise (southern France, tributary to the River Garonne), which covers an area of about 1000 km^2.

ANALYSIS OF THE SATELLITE IMAGE INFORMATION

Choice of the satellite system

Basically the information from both geostationary and polar orbiting weather satellite systems are suitable for the analysis. For the choice of system the following criteria have been used:

(a) *Rate of image production:* the information from geostationary satellites has a repetition rate of once very 30 minutes, whereas the repetition rate of polar orbiting satellites is considerably smaller (two images per day).

(b) *Spatial resolution:* the spatial resolution of the imagery obtained from polar orbiting satellites is usually more favourable (e.g. NOAA 5: ~0.8 km^2) than that of geostationary satellites (e.g. METEOSAT: ~6 km^2).

(c) *Spectral range:* there is no significant difference between the two systems as both transmit images to the earth in the visible and in the thermal infrared range of the "atmospheric window".

Whilst the above-mentioned criteria depend on the satellite system the following one is independent of the system, but regarding the objectives of this study, namely the generation of long term runoff time series, it is of particular importance:

(d) *Availability of the satellite information:* this means the availability of a long uninterrupted time series of satellite imagery and furthermore the easy access to these data.

After evaluation of all these criteria the NOAA Polar Orbiting Satellite System, which has been operated and maintained by NOAA-NESS (USA) since the late 1980's, was chosen. The spatial resolution and the availability of a long series of satellite imagery led to this decision despite the disadvantage of the rather low resolution in time. As the results show, the number of available images is sufficient for the estimation of monthly runoff values.

Image processing

The NOAA satellites follow a sun-synchronous, polar orbit with an altitude of about 1500 km (NOAA 1-5) and now 830-870 km (NOAA 6-7). They are equipped with a very high resolution radiometer, which transmits images to the earth, both in the visible range of the electromagnetic spectrum (0.6-0.7 μm) and in the infrared range (10.5-12.5 μm). These images have a spatial resolution of about 0.8 km^2 at the nadir of the satellite and a repetition rate of 12 h (0900 h and 2100 h local solar time), i.e. at each point of the earth there are two images every day.

Due to the low rate of image production a "life-history approach" to the variability in time of the cloud size and cloud surface temperature cannot be applied in this study. Accordingly a simple indexing technique (Barrett, 1970) has been adopted which identifies the size of cloud coverage over the observed area as well as the cloud surface temperatures by analysis of the relevant infrared imagery. Different from the commonly used indexing technique, the cloud type is not identified in this study. Therefore an interpretation of the information of the visible channel is not necessary. The indexing technique presented in this paper is based on the following physical principles (Mason, 1971):

(a) the lower the surface temperature of a cloud, the higher is the probability of rainfall below;

(b) the lower the cloud surface temperature, the more intense the rainfall (if it rains at all).

The actual analysis of the information obtained from the infrared channel can be divided into three steps:

Pre-processing of the imagery Due to the large number of images, a pre-selection of all images with no clouds visible over the area was carried out. Only those images exposing cloud cover over the area considered were transposed on fine grain positive film such that parts with low density (i.e. cold temperature) would be developed showing high film contrast. In order to facilitate the identification of the basin the images were enlarged approximately four times, thus yielding a scale of about 1:13 000 000 at the nadir of the satellite.

Navigation By means of a mathematical model simulating the motion of the satellite and scanner, the position of the test area on the image was identified. This model uses the geocentric system of longitudes and latitudes as terrestrial reference system. Input data are the coordinates of landmarks visible on the images, the coordinates of the area and of the satellite's ground track, which can be computed by prediction of the satellite's orbit. As a result of the simulation the position of the test area is identified using the chosen landmarks as reference points. In this way, it was possible to specify the border of the test area in the images.

Quantitative approach Since the satellite information is available on film in analogous form and its interpretation is based on simple enhancement with subsequent area determination, the images are evaluated using an integrated false colour TV device. The whole film density (from base density to maximum) is divided into six density ranges. Thus each density value of the six-step calibration scale visible on the image is the mean value of one density range. This calibration technique based on the image grey scale is necessary, because within the photo-technical process small brightness deviations from image to image cannot be excluded and in this way the values of the images become comparable. Within the next step of image processing, partial areas (within the test area) covered by each density range are determined. Since only infrared images are used, each density range can be considered as certain temperature ranges. The analysis revealed that the partial areas of only the three coldest temperature ranges represent cloud surfaces. Thus the sum of these values forms the cloud coverage over the test area at the time the image was taken. The remaining density ranges can be interpreted as the emission of the earth's surface, including vegetation, etc.

THE HYDROLOGICAL MODEL

The purpose of the model is to compute mean monthly runoff values for a river basin as the basis for the design of water resources projects.

A linear black-box model is applied (somewhat analogous to the unit-hydrograph concept) which computes indicators of daily runoff values by convoluting the satellite image information as an input with a specified system function. From these indicators mean monthly runoff values are determined. Although the model itself is time invariant, a time variance over the year is introduced by subdividing the year into seasons.

Input data Given the values of the partial areas of the three low density ranges per image and the two images per day, a "mean daily temperature-weighted cloud cover index" B(T) is calculated as input:

$$B(T)_l = 0.5 \sum_{k=1}^{2} \sum_{i=1}^{3} B(T_i)_{k,l}^{a_i} \qquad (1)$$

where

$B(T_i)_k$: fractional cloud cover index of density range i (i = 1,2,3) on image k (k = 1,2) of day l

l : number of day

a_i : weighting coefficient of the i-th density range (i = 1,2,3).

Since only two images per day are available, no statement about the potential within-day variation of the cloud coverage is possible.

Therefore, the information gap between two images is bridged by a linear approach.

The weighting coefficients, a_i, are determined by a simple direct search method. The objective function used for this optimization technique is the minimization of the sum of squares of differences between estimated and recorded mean monthly runoff values. The constraints are specified by the aforementioned physical principles, i.e. the smaller the density range (≙ colder temperature) the higher the value of the coefficient a_i.

The mathematical model The transformation of the (satellite derived) cloud cover index B(T) into runoff values is based on a linear transfer model of the form:

$$Q_m(m,j) = \frac{1}{n} \sum_{t=tb(m,j)}^{te(m,j)} \sum_{k=1}^{S} h_k \, B(T)_{l-k+1} \qquad (2)$$

where

$Q_m(m,j)$: mean monthly runoff value of month m, year j (m^3s^{-1})
tb(m,j) : number of the first day of month m, year j
te(m,j) : number of the last day of month m, year j
S : memory of the system in days
h_k : discrete value of the response function h(t) of the system (m^3s^{-1}), k = 1,...,S.
$B(T)_{l-k+1}$: mean cloud cover index of day l - k + 1
l : number of day
n : number of days in month m, year j

The time length S of the memory is defined as the duration (in days) during which the response of the system to an input shows a significant difference from zero. It is equal to the length of the response function of the system. This length is determined by the autocovariance function of the recorded runoff values. Since these runoff time series are short (according to the purpose of this study), the estimation of the autocovariance function is rather uncertain. Therefore the influence of the length of the memory should be estimated by means of a sensitivity analysis.

The discrete values h_k (k = 1,...,S) of the response function are estimated by a least square procedure in order to minimize the sum of squares of the differences between recorded daily flows and computed daily indicators of the runoff. These indicators can be computed with the aid of the following expression in equation (2):

$$q_l = \sum_{k=1}^{S} h_k \, B(T)_{l-k+1} \qquad (3)$$

where

q_l : indicator of the runoff of day l (m^3s^{-1})

The reduction of time resolution from daily indicators (input) to monthly values (output) acts as a low-pass filter by which the negative effect of the small rate of image production and thus large (within day) information gaps of the input data is reduced.

APPLICATION OF THE METHOD IN THE BAISE RIVER BASIN

The model was calibrated and tested with data from the Baise River

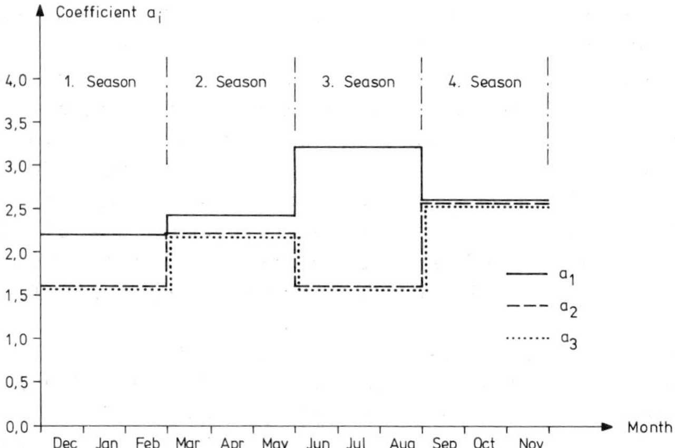

FIG.1 Seasonal variation of the weighting coefficients a_i of the fractional cloud cover index of density range i; i = 1,2,3.

basin, an area of about 1000 km^2. Mean daily discharge has been recorded for 17 years. For calibration and verification purposes the period of October 1975 to October 1977 was chosen, because these two years deviate significantly from average conditions in both

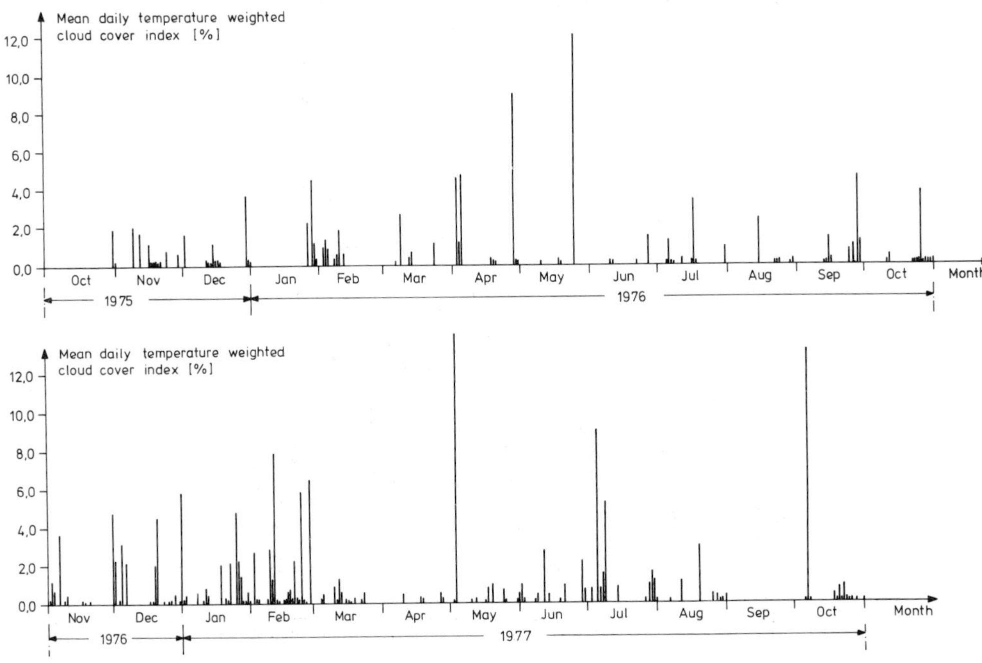

FIG.2 Input data: mean daily temperature weighted cloud cover index in per cent of the maximum possible value (total cloud coverage of the first density range).

directions. In this manner the performance of the method is tested even for extreme events. The time period between November 1975 and October 1976 was chosen for model calibration, the period November 1976 to October 1977 for independent model verification.

The subdivision of the year into seasons (see Fig.1) was based on climate diagrams from surrounding climate stations. The best agreement between computed mean monthly runoff values and measured data was obtained from those coefficients a_i (for the calculation of the mean daily temperature-weighted cloud cover index) presented in Fig.1. The cloud cover indices, B(T), computed with the aid of equation (1) and the coefficients, a_i, are shown in Fig.2.

A comparison between computed and recorded mean monthly runoff values for the River Baise is presented in Fig.3. The computed values are based on a seasonal, varying response function with memory of seven days. The deviation between computed and recorded values

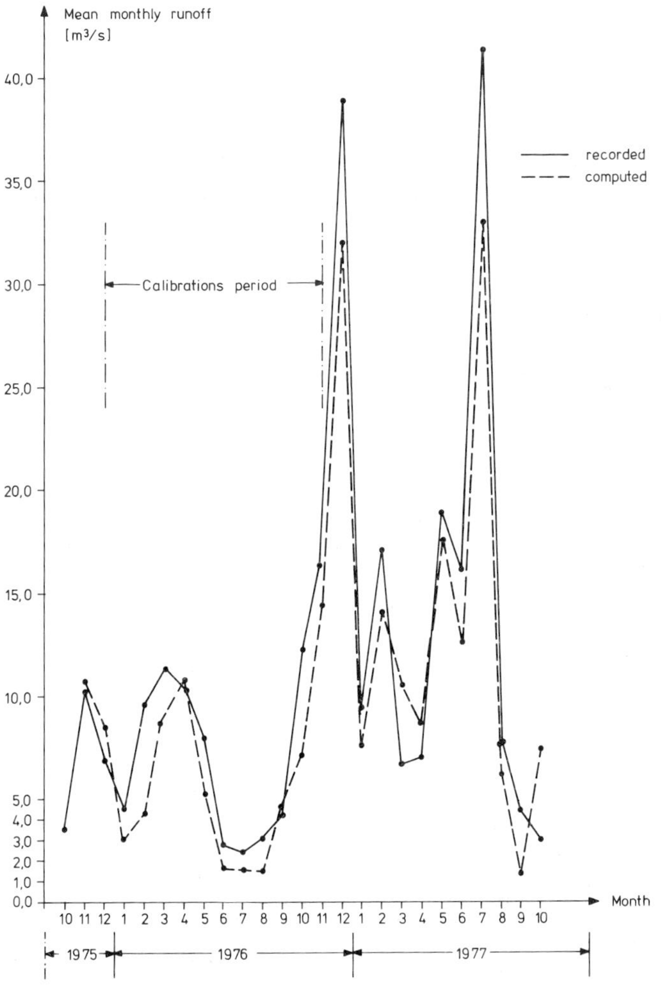

FIG.3 Comparison between computed and recorded mean monthly runoff values for the River Baise.

lies between +65% (9.77) and -148% (10.77); the mean deviation, however, amounts to +9%. For the extreme events in December 1976 and July 1977, the adaption of the computed runoffs to the measured data can be considered as reasonably good.

Definite statements about the quality of the described method for very long time series cannot be given, since results for only two years are available. For greater assurance, it is normally advisable to have more than one year for calibration and verification, respectively. However, given the good results obtained so far, the method seems suitable to reduce the problems occurring in the planning of water resources projects based only on short time series of hydrological data.

REFERENCES

Amorocho, J. (1975) An application of satellite imagery to hydrologic modelling the upper Sinu River Basin, Columbia. *Proc. International Symposium and Workshop on the Application of Mathematical Models in Hydrology and Water Resources Systems*, Bratislava.

Barrett, E.C. (1970) The estimation of monthly rainfall from satellite data. *Mon. Weath. Rev.* 98, 322-327.

Barrett, E.C. & Martin, D.W. (1981) *The Use of Satellite Data in Rainfall Monitoring*. Academic Press, London.

Mason, B.J. (1971) *The Physics of Clouds*. Clarendon Press, Oxford, UK.

Hydrological Applications of Remote Sensing and Remote Data Transmission
(Proceedings of the Hamburg Symposium, August 1983). IAHS Publ. no. 145.

Assessment and monitoring of sedimentation in the Aswan High Dam Reservoir using Landsat imagery

SCOT E. SMITH
Department of Civil Engineering, The Ohio State University, Columbus, Ohio 43210, USA
K. H. MANCY
School of Public Health, The University of Michigan, Ann Arbor, Michigan, USA
A. F. A. LATIF
The Egyptian Academy of Scientific Research and Technology, Cairo, Egypt.
E. A. FOSNIGHT
Technicolor Graphic Services, Inc., EROS Data Center, Sioux Falls, South Dakota USA

ABSTRACT Landsat images have been used to monitor the advance of the Nile's flood in the Aswan Reservoir. Reflectance data in bands 4 (0.4-0.6 μm) and 5 (0.6-0.7 μm), correlated with ground truthed observations during satellite overpass, provided instantaneous mapping of surface turbidity of the southern portion of the reservoir. The accumulation of sediment deposits during the flood period was found to correlate closely with surface turbidity. This was used to determine the temporal distribution of sedimentation in the reservoir over a period of eight year (1972-1980). Processing of Landsat data utilized the Multispectral Data Analysis System (MDAS) and the Landsat Interactive Grey Map and Level Slice System (LIGMALS). These techniques were used to categorize turbidity regimes during the flood period. The images depicted areas of homogeneous surface turbidity and clearly defined the flood front. Three-dimensional calcomp plots of the portion of the reservoir where sedimentation occurs were prepared. These plots provided a clear illustration of the process of delta formation and changes in reservoir morphology. Assuming certain water levels in the reservoir, and for a given sediment load, it will be possible to predict the accumulation of sediment deposits. This information will be most valuable for assessing the storage capacity and life expectancy of the reservoir. Furthermore, future morphological changes in the reservoir have to be taken into consideration in shoreline development programmes.

Détermination et contrôle de la sédimentation dans le Réservoir du Haut-Barrage d'Aswan utilisant les images du satellite Landsat

RESUME Les images de Landsat ont été utilisées pour observer la progression de la crue du Nil dans le reservoir d'Aswan. Les données obtenues par la réflection sur les bandes 4 (0.5-0.6 μm) et 5 (0.6-0.7 μm) lors du passage du satellite après comparaison avec les observations de vérité au sol, ont permis d'établir une cartographie instantanée de la turbidité au sol de la partie sud du réservoir. Ceci a été utilisé pour établir la distribution temporelle de la sédimentation dans le réservoir sur une période de huit ans (1972-1980). L'analyse des données de Landsat a été faite en utilisant le "Multispectral Data Analysis System (MDAS)" et le "Landsat Interactive Grey Map and Level Slice System (LIGMALS)". Ces techniques ont été utilisées pour caractériser les régimes de turbidité durant les périodes de crue. Les images montraient des surfaces de turbidité homogène et définissaient clairement le front de crue. Des graphes tri-dimensionnels "calcomp" de la portion du réservoir où la sédimentation se produisait ont été préparés. Ces graphes ont procuré une illustration précise du processus de formation d'un delta et des changements de la morphologie du réservoir. En supposant certains niveaux d'eau dans le réservoir, et pour une charge connue de sédiments, il est possible de prédéterminer l'accumulation de dépôts de sédiments. Cette information est essentielle pour évaluer la capacite utile et la durée de vie du réservoir. De plus, les futurs changements morphologiques du réservoir devront être pris en considération pour les programmes d'aménagement des rives du réservoir.

INTRODUCTION

Since 1964, as a result of the construction of the Aswan High Dam (AHD), virtually all of the annual 80-110 million tons of sediment load carried by the Nile River has been deposited behind the dam. The main concern has been for the effect of accumulation of these huge sediment deposits on the reservoir's storage capacity and hydropower production capability.

Early prognostications depicted that sedimentation in the reservoir would limit its storage capacity within a few years after the construction of the AHD (Sterling, 1972; George, 1972). Eighteen years after the closure of the river at Aswan, it seems that these predictions were highly exaggerated. Research findings presented in this report provide an up-to-date quantitative assessment of the temporal and geographical distribution of sediments in the reservoir. This information is considered essential for the development of more realistic predictions of the effect of sedimentation and appropriate management of the reservoir. The reported studies are part of the River Nile Project, a joint research project between the University of Michigan and the Egyptian Academy of Scientific Research and Technology and is sponsored by the US Environmental Protection Agency and the Ford Foundation.

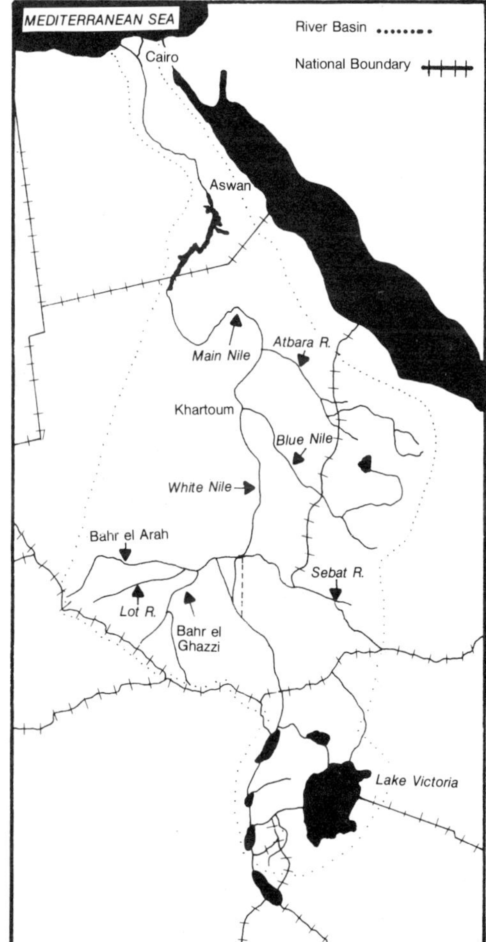

FIG.1 The Nile basin.

Nile sediment load

The Nile has several sources, as seen in Fig.1, but the principle ones include the East Equatorial Lakes, Bahr El Gazal basin and the Ethiopian Mountains. The Blue Nile drains from the Ethiopian Plateau where it descends from a height of 2000 m a.s.l. through Lake Tana and a series of rapids and a deep gorge region. Lake Tana supplies the river with about one fourteenth of its total flow. The river then flows west and northwest through the Sudan and joins the

White Nile at Khartoum. Along the greater part of its course from Lake Tana down to the Sudan plains, the Blue Nile drops more than 1000 m, cutting deep in canyons and ravines. While the White Nile at Khartoum is a river of almost constant year-round flow, the Blue Nile brings a large volume of water and sediments during the flood period (July-September).

The Atbara, the last tributary of the Nile, joins the river nearly 350 km north of Khartoum. Its origin is in Ethiopia at heights of approximately 3000 m. The Atbara rises and falls rapidly, like the Blue Nile. In the flood period, it becomes a large muddy river, and in the dry season it is a string of pools, with no net flow. Below Khartoum, the Nile flows 3050 km to Aswan. The riverbed alternates between gentle stretches and a series of rapids until it approaches the Aswan High Dam Reservoir (AHDR). The river velocity decreases rapidly and at Dal Cataract, the river changes into a lake.

The origin of the Nile sediment load is the Ethiopian Highlands, carried by the Blue Nile and the Atbara. These huge amounts of silt are added to the river during the two to three month flood period. Approximately 80% of the Nile's annual discharge occurs during the flood period. The relative contribution of the main Nile tributaries is shown in Fig.2.

After the construction of the AHD, the Nile sediment load was entirely deposited in the reservoir. The water released from the dam for downstream users is essentially sediment free. This is illustrated in Fig.3.

The deposition of this huge load may seriously limit the utility of the reservoir. It is imperative to monitor the distribution and amount of sedimentation and assess their impacts. Remote sensing measurements accompanied by field surveys were used to monitor these changes.

METHODS

Ground-based surveys were conducted before and after each flood period. Using echo-sounding techniques at 27 cross sections of the reservoir, the thickness of the deposited sediment was determined

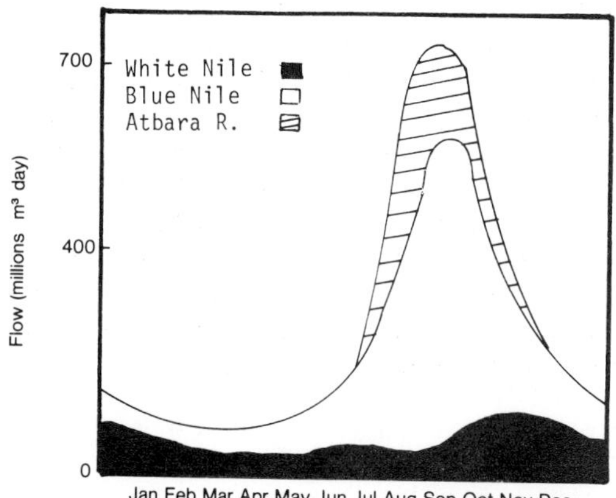

FIG.2 Main inputs to the Nile.

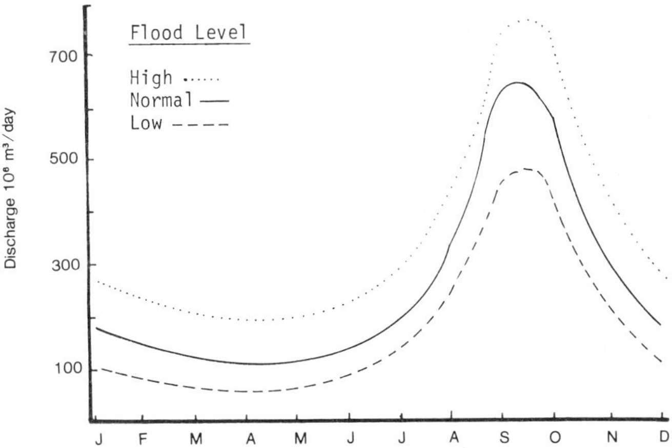

FIG.3 Monthly variation of Nile discharge at Aswan.

from one flood season to the next (Mostafa, 1978). Figure 4 shows cross section locations along the reservoir. Sedimentation measurements by the Aswan High Dam Authority, were primarily done at cross sections numbers 13 to 40.

Secchi disc measurements collected at certain cross sections were used to calibrate satellite surface reflectance data in bands 4 (0.5-0.6 μm) and 5 (0.6-0.7 μm). This provided surface turbidity mapping of the southern portion of the reservoir at different stages of the flood periods during 1977 and 1979.

Landsat imagery was attractive as a means for monitoring the process of sedimentation in the reservoir primarily because of its ability to yield an instantaneous picture of the entire situation, thus eliminating time-lapse interpretation problems and errors.

Landsat data

Landsat I, II, and III imagery were employed in this research. The satellite's highly precise behaviour and fast period coupled with the low amount of atmospheric attentuation exhibited by an arid environment allowed for optimum monitoring conditions. Until recently, cloud cover over the reservoir did not present a problem in securing a clear view. Increasing cloud coverage has been observed in the Landsat scenes. The cloud formation is very specific to the reservoir suggesting a microclimate formation.

Landsat multispectral digital data were acquired from both the Earth Resources Observation System Data Center (EROS) in Sioux Falls, South Dakota and the European Space Agency's station in Frascati, Italy. Two computer processing systems were used in this study: the Multispectral Data Analysis System (MDAS) at the Remote Sensing Centre in Cairo; and, the Landsat Interactive Grey Map and Level Slice System (LIGMALS) at the University of Michigan.

The Multispectral Data Analysis System (MDAS)

The MDAS uses a multivariate categorical processing technique which bases classification decisions on the likelihood of a pixel belonging

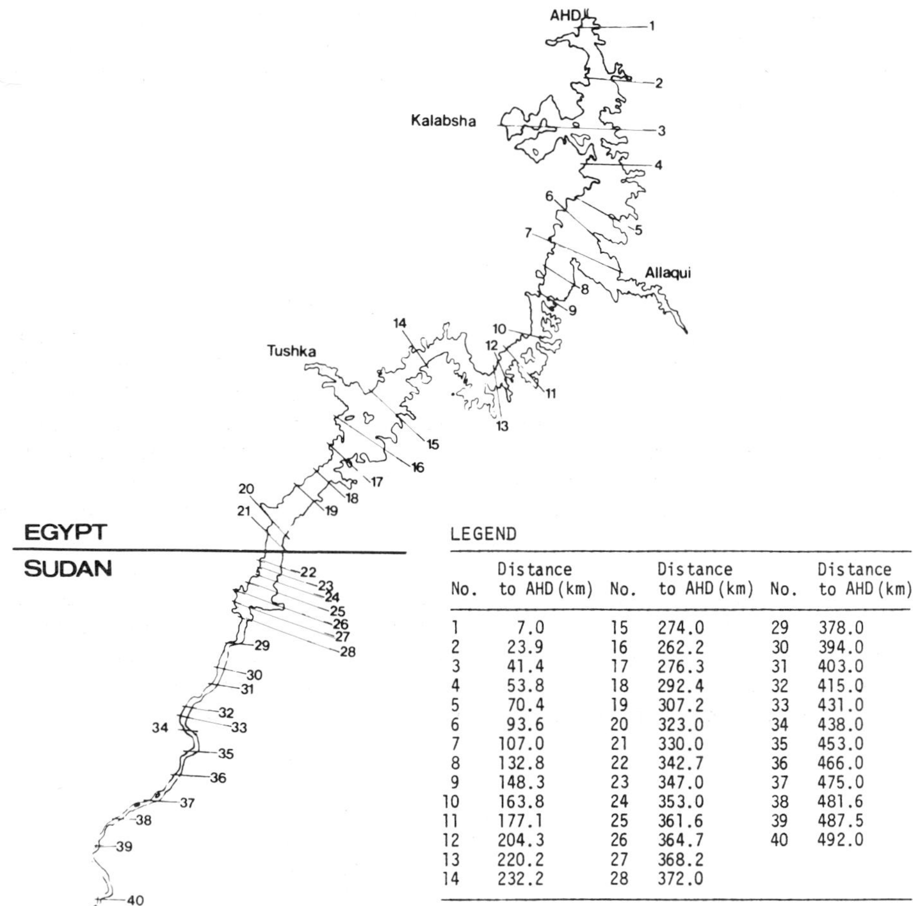

LEGEND

No.	Distance to AHD (km)	No.	Distance to AHD (km)	No.	Distance to AHD (km)
1	7.0	15	274.0	29	378.0
2	23.9	16	262.2	30	394.0
3	41.4	17	276.3	31	403.0
4	53.8	18	292.4	32	415.0
5	70.4	19	307.2	33	431.0
6	93.6	20	323.0	34	438.0
7	107.0	21	330.0	35	453.0
8	132.8	22	342.7	36	466.0
9	148.3	23	347.0	37	475.0
10	163.8	24	353.0	38	481.6
11	177.1	25	361.6	39	487.5
12	204.3	26	364.7	40	492.0
13	220.2	27	368.2		
14	232.2	28	372.0		

FIG.4 Cross section locations on Aswan High Dam Reservoir.

to a certain group in a transformed coordinate system (Bendix Aerospace Systems Division, 1976). A maximum of 49 training sets are chosen from a scene, colours are assigned and classification is performed within a predetermined sigma limit. Final products from the MDAS include a colour photograph of the classified scene and accompanying statistics.

Landsat Interactive Grey Map and Level Slice System (LIGMALS)

The LIGMALS uses the parallelepiped classifier method for pattern recognition. The parallelepiped uses three spectral channels in three dimensional space to describe a training set (Wagner, 1976). In addition to the classifier, individual spectral bands were extracted from the Landsat data by LIGMALS. The use of separate channels vastly reduced processing time and the cost of analysis, while still allowing for accurate classification of sediment transport in the reservoir. A ratio of spectral bands 4 and 5 was found to provide the most detailed picture of silt load. Products from the LIGMALS include symbol maps produced at a scale of 1:300 000 printed directly from a conventional computer printer, four colour maps at a scale of 1:700 000 drawn by a Calcomp Plotter and accompanying statistics from both.

RESULTS

Morphometry of the Aswan High Dam Reservoir

The penetration of the brown sediment-laden Nile flood in the clear waters of the reservoir could be clearly seen in the Landsat imagery. This was due to the sharp contrast in the colour of the water afforded by the high concentration of suspended sediments. The distribution of the turbid flood water in the reservoir for 17 September 1977 is shown in Fig.5. This indicates that, by this date, the flood water had penetrated through the southern third of the reservoir.

Immediately after the broadening of the reservoir at the second cataract near Wadi Halfa in the Sudan a shift in surface turbidity or sediment load is evident. The reservoir at this juncture changes abruptly from riverine to more lacustrine characteristics due to reduced velocity. Higher levels of surface turbidity are evident along the western shore of the extreme southern end of the reservoir. This correlates with greater sediment depths recorded by echo-sounding on the leeward side.

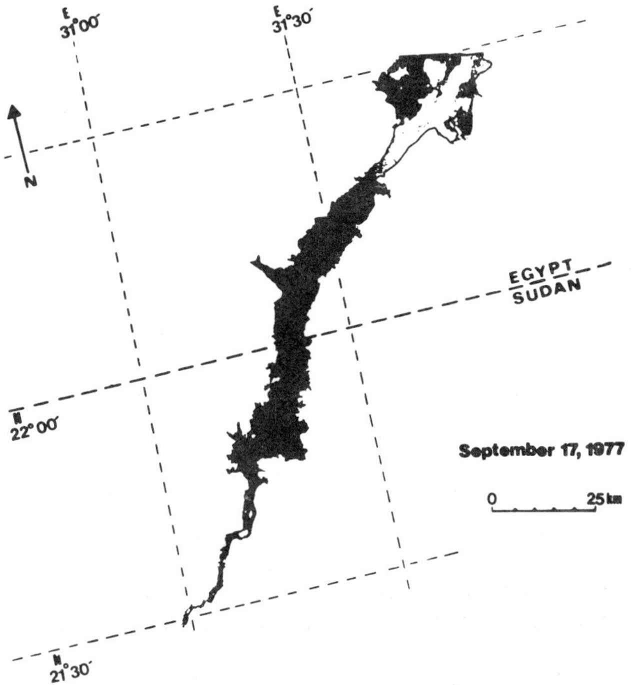

FIG.5 Landsat spectral image of surface turbidity processed by the MDAS of the southern portion of the Aswan High Dam Reservoir.

The pattern of surface turbidity changes about 20 km northward at Khor Sarra and stays constant for 20 km until Khor Orr. After this point, surface turbidity gradually lessens, according to the Landsat image, to Khor Tushka where turbid-free water prevails.

It is interesting to note the irregular distribution of the turbid water at Tushka. The widening of the reservoir at this point is accompanied by further slowing of the velocity of the incoming flood. The moving front of turbid water seems to advance mostly along the original river channel.

It is also interesting to note that the turbid water did not penetrate through the Tushka embayment. The presence of two small islands strategically located at the mouth of the embayment seems to protect it from flood water intrusion.

Landsat surface turbidity data were found to correlate closely with sedimentation. Areas with high surface turbidity showed deeper sediment deposits, as compared to regions with low surface turbidity. The distribution of sedimentation depicted by this method reflects the prevailing hydrodynamic characteristics in the affected areas of the reservoir.

An illustration of this correlation is shown in Fig.6. Sedimentation profiles for 1973, 1975 and 1978 are shown on the

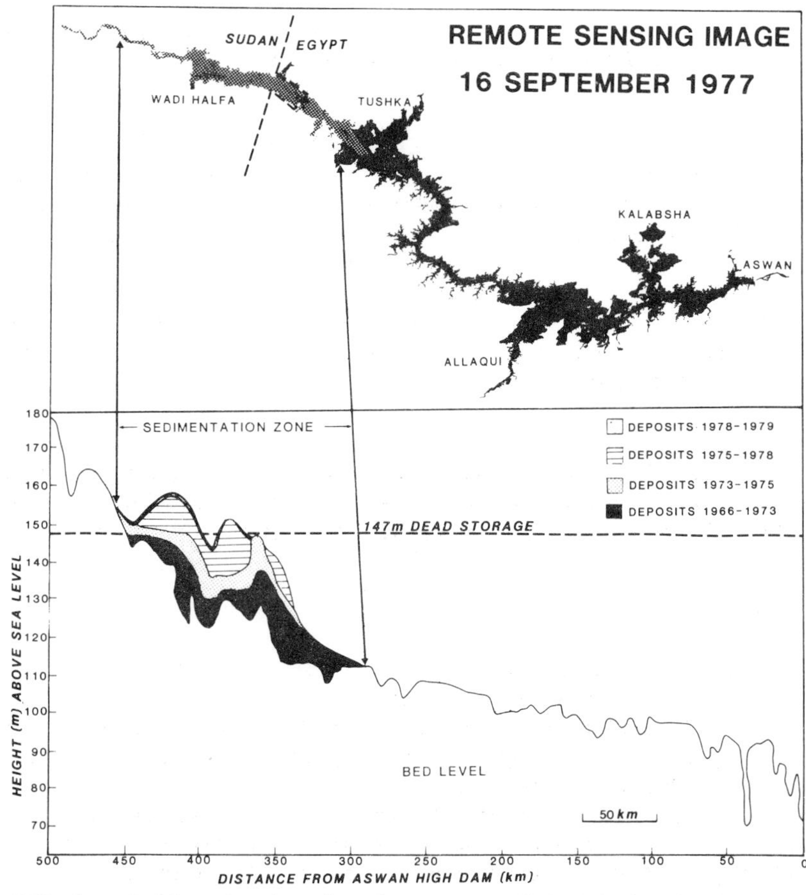

FIG.6 Sedimentation in the Aswan High Dam Reservoir.

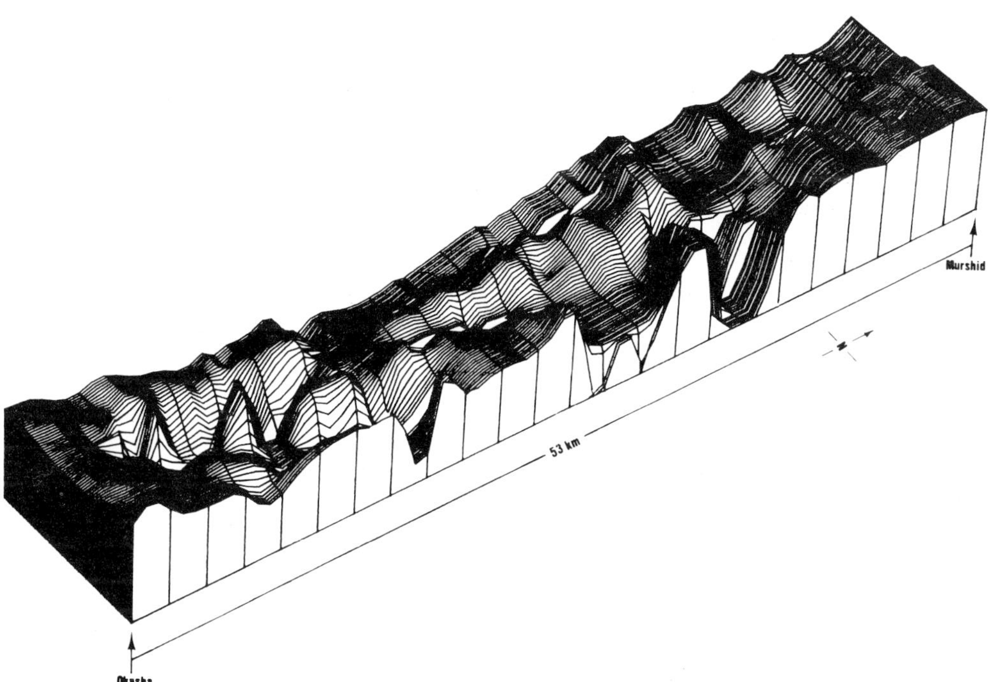

FIG.7 Perspective plot of reach bathymetry between Okasha and Murshid, October 1978.

lower part of the figure. Satellite surface turbidity measurements are shown in the top of the figure. Accordingly, sedimentation for these periods occurred in the region between Kulb and Abu Simbel, over a 185 km range.

A more detailed picture of sedimentation is provided by three-dimensional perspective maps, as shown in Fig.7. This type of mapping over a 10-year period (1969-1979) shows the distribution of sedimentation within the cross sections and sediment transport along the affected region.

ACKNOWLEDGEMENT This study was supported, in part, by grants from the US Environmental Protection Agency, the Ford Foundation and the Egyptian Academy of Scientific Research and Technology.

REFERENCES

Bendix Aerospace Systems Division (1976) *MDAS Technical Description BSR no 4210*. Ann Arbor, Michigan.

George, C.J. (1972) In: *The Careless Technology: Ecology and International Development* (ed. by Farvar & Milton). The National History Press, Garden City.

Mostafa, M.G. (1978) Sediment processes in the Nile River. *United Nations Development Program Report no EGY/73/024, New York.*

Sterling, C. (1972) The Aswan disaster. In: *Our Chemical Environment* (ed. by G.Giddings & J.B.

Wagner, H.L. (1976) The Landsat Interactive Grey Map and Level Slice System. Master of Science Thesis, the University of Michigan, Ann Arbor, Michigan.

6 Remote sensing: soil moisture groundwater wetlands

Hydrological Applications of Remote Sensing and Remote Data Transmission (Proceedings of the Hamburg Symposium, August 1983). IAHS Publ. no. 145.

L'humidité des sols en hydrologie: intérêt et limites de la télédétection

MICHEL VAUCLIN
*Institut de Mécanique de Grenoble, BP 68,
F-38402 Saint Martin d'Hères Cédex, France*

RESUME A l'évidence, l'humidité des sols constitue une variable d'état fondamentale dans plusieurs sciences de l'environnement, telles que l'agronomie, l'hydrologie, la météorologie. De nombreuses études spécifiques le plus souvent, mais non exclusivement, menées en physique du sol, ont montré l'intérêt et les limites des méthodes de détermination soit *in situ*, soit par télédétection. On en présente ici une revue générale mettant en évidence leurs avantages et inconvénients ainsi que leur degré de faisabilité, vis à vis des contraintes expérimentales imposées à l'hydrologue: détermination de l'humidité et de ses variations temporelles dans le premier mètre de sol; observations fréquentes et sur de grandes surfaces avec une résolution la plus fine possible. Les techniques de télédétection ne permettant de déterminer l'humidité que dans une couche superficielle de sol de 5 à 10 cm d'épaisseur, la satisfaction de ces critères et la nécessité de quantifier les transferts hydriques dans le profil et entre le sol et l'atmosphère imposent l'utilisation de modèles. Dans cette optique, on présente également quelques modélisations de type agro-météorologique et hydrologique en mettant l'accent sur leurs possibilités d'utiliser l'humidité de surface obtenue par télédétection.

Soil moisture in hydrology: advantages and limitations of remote sensing

ABSTRACT Soil moisture is of great importance to several disciplines of the environmental sciences such as agronomy, hydrology and meteorology. Many studies, mostly conducted in soil physics, have shown both the advantages and limitations of *in situ* and remotely sensed methods for soil moisture determination. This paper presents a survey of these methods in connection with experimental requirements imposed by practical applications: an estimate of soil moisture and its variation within the top 1 m of soil; frequent observations over large study areas with a resolution as fine as possible. Since remote sensing approaches seem to be suitable for determining the water content of only a surface layer about 5-10 cm thick, satisfying these criteria and quantifying moisture transfers within deeper layers of soil and between soil and atmosphere require the use of models. A brief review of some existing agrometeorological and hydrological models is given. Emphasis is put on their potential capabilities to use remotely sensed observations of soil moisture.

NOTATIONS

a	diffusivité thermique du sol
CV	coefficient de variation
d	diamètre d'antenne
E	flux d'évaporation
FC	capacité au champ
G_o	amplitude du flux thermique à la surface du sol
h	altitude du senseur
k	coefficient d'échange sol-atmosphère
K	conductivité thermique
L	résolution spatiale du senseur
N	nombre d'observations *in situ*
P	effusivité thermique
r	albédo
R_A	rayonnement atmosphérique
R_G	rayonnement solaire incident
R_n	rayonnement net
S	surface
t	temps
$t(\alpha')$	variable de Student
T_a	température de l'air
T_B	température de brillance
T_c	température du couvert végétal
T_S	température de surface du sol
T_z	température du sol à la profondeur z
U	vitesse du vent
W	humidité pondérale
α	coefficient de Priestley et Taylor
β	coefficient de Barton
γ	constante psychrométrique
Δ	pente de la courbe de pression de vapeur saturante
ε	erreur relative sur une valeur moyenne
ε_λ	émissivité
θ	concentration volumique en humidité
λ	longueur d'onde
ρC	capacité calorifique volumique
ρ_d	masse volumique seche du sol
σ	constante de Stefan-Boltzmann
σ_o	coefficient de rétrodiffusion du signal radar
ϕ	angle d'incidence du senseur
ψ	pression effective de l'eau
ω	fréquence angulaire

INTRODUCTION

La connaissance de l'humidité du sol et de son évolution spatio-temporelle est primordiale dans de nombreuses disciplines des Sciences de l'Environnement, telles que l'agronomie, l'hydrologie, l'hydrogéologie ou la météorologie.

Ainsi, la prédiction de la production agricole, l'optimisation des irrigations nécessitent des informations sur l'état hydrique du sol et sur ses variations. En hydrologie, il est bien connu que l'humidité de surface antérieure à une précipitation conditionne très fortement le ruissellement et l'infiltration efficace de la pluie dont tout ou partie peut recharger les aquifères. En météorologie et climatologie, l'humidité de surface contrôle les contributions relatives des flux de chaleur latente (évaporation) et sensible au rayonnement net. Dans toutes ces applications, la zone de sol intéressée est typiquement de l'ordre de 1 à 2 m de profondeur au minimum.

L'objet de cet exposé est une présentation critique des possibilités qu'offrent les différentes techniques de télédétection actuellement disponibles pour inférer l'humidité des sols avec les contraintes suivantes:

(a) détermination du contenu en eau d'une tranche de sol de 1 à 2 m d'épaisseur,

(b) observations fréquentes afin de suivre les évolutions temporelles,

(c) observations sur de grandes surfaces, avec une résolution la plus fine possible, afin de connaître les variations spatiales et les hétérogénéités.

Compte-tenu des préoccupations de l'auteur, cette analyse est essentiellement orientée vers l'utilisation de ces techniques et non vers la technologie proprement dite (traitement des images, transmission des informations, etc.). Cela implique la question importante suivante: comment peut-on utiliser l'information "humidité du sol" pour quantifier les transferts et résoudre les problèmes pratiques qui se posent à l'agronome, l'hydrologue, le météorologue etc.?

DETERMINATION DE L'HUMIDITE DES SOLS

Les différentes approches, à l'heure actuelle disponibles pour mesurer l'humidité des sols peuvent se classer en deux groupes: mesures *in situ* et mesures par télédétection.

METHODES DE MESURES IN SITU

Le Tableau 1 regroupe les différentes techniques ainsi que leurs principaux avantages et inconvénients. On notera que plusieurs d'entre elles sont classiquement utilisées pour la calibration des senseurs et la "verité-terrain" des mesures d'humidité par télédétection. Bien que ces techniques permettent de déterminer les profils hydriques avec une précision en général acceptable (de 0.01 à 0.02 cm^3cm^{-3} environ), l'aspect très local de la mesure les disqualifie pour obtenir l'humidité sur de grandes surfaces. En effet, la variabilité spatiale des propriétés hydrodynamiques et de l'humidité des sols, mise en évidence dans de nombreuses études (Nielsen *et al.*, 1973; Cassel & Bauer, 1975; Bell *et al.*, 1980) impose un grand nombre d'observations dont l'ordre de grandeur, en fonction du coefficient de variation est donné par:

$$N = t^2(\alpha)(CV/\varepsilon)^2 \qquad (1)$$

Tous les symboles sont définis dans la liste des notations. Ainsi, d'après l'équation (1) un coefficient de variation CV = 30% (cas fréquent) impose une trentaine de mesures de l'humidité pour estimer

TABLEAU 1 Avantages et inconvénients des méthodes de mesures in situ de l'humidité des sols

Techniques	*Avantages*	*Inconvénients*
GRAVIMETRIQUE	*Simplicité; faible coût*	*Destructive - représentativité spatiale doute - manuelle; humidité pondérale → humidite volumique: θ $(\rho_d/\rho_w)W$*
NUCLEAIRE:		
Diffusion neutronique	*Non destructive; humidité sous toutes ses formes (liquide, solide, vapeur); profils hydriques θ(z,t) accessibles*	*Etalonnage (propriétés physico-chimiques des sols); volume de mesure (15 cm); peu précise à la surface; utilisation manuelle; risques de pollution radio-active*
Gammamétrie	*Non destructive; θ(z, t); mesures près de la surface (transmission)*	*Etalonnage sensible à des variations de ρ_d; utilisation manuelle; pollution*
ELECTROMAGNETIQUE (Sondes résistives et capacitives)	*Mesure directe de l'humidité; faible volume de mesure θ(z,t); acquisition automatique*	*Implantation délicate (contact sol-senseur); étalonnage délicat (solutés); acquisition coûteuse*
THERMIQUE	*Faible volume de mesure θ(z,t); acquisition automatique peu coûteuse*	*Mesure indirecte de l'humidité (ρC(θ) = K(θ)/a(θ); contact sol-senseur*
TENSIOMETRIQUE	*Peu coûteuse; faible volume de mesure*	*Mesure indirecte: étalonnage via courbe ψ(θ); hystérésis; valable pour ψ > -0.8 bar*
HYGROMETRIQUE	*Pressions ψ << -1 bar; enregistrement automatique*	*Mesure indirecte (humidité relative); étalonnage délicat (variation de température)*

la valeur moyenne à 10% près au seuil de 95%. On notera que l'estimation donnée par l'équation (1) suppose implicitement l'indépendance des observations. En cas d'autocorrélation, ce nombre serait supérieur (Sisson & Wierenga, 1981; Vauclin *et al.*, 1982). On concoit ici les limites pratiques de ces méthodes liées au problème de l'échantillonnage de l'humidité sur de grandes surfaces.

METHODES DE MESURES PAR TELEDETECTION

Rappelons qu'il s'agit d'inférer l'humidité par une mesure du rayonnement émis ou réfléchi par la surface du sol. Le Tableau 2 récapitule les différentes méthodes potentielles, classées en fonction des bandes spectrales considérées. Notre propos ici est essentiellement d'en dégager les avantages et inconvénients en relation avec les objectifs de hydrologue. Pour une revue plus detaillée,

TABLEAU 2 Avantages et inconvénients des méthodes de télédétection de l'humidité

Domaines spectraux	*Avantages*	*Inconvénients*
GAMMA	*Utilisable pour une "vérité terrain" d'autres techniques*	*Faible altitude d'observations (h = 150 m); nombreuses corrections liées à l'environnement*
VISIBLE	*Résolution élevée*	*Couverture nuageuse; corrections atmosphériques; albédo est fonction de la couleur, rugosité, texture du sol; reponse à l'humidité sur quelques mm de sol; sol nu*
INFRA-ROUGE	*Résolution élevée; physique bien comprise*	*Couverture nuageuse; sensible à la météorologie locale; complications avec végétation et topographie; reponse à l'humidité sur quelques cm de sol*
MICRO-ONDE		
Passive	*Indépendance avec l'etat de l'atmosphére; faible effet de la végétation*	*Mauvaise résolution spatiale; influence de la température et de la rugosité; interférence avec les rayonnements artificiels; humidité sur quelques cm de sol*
Active	*Indépendance avec l'état de l'atmosphère; fine résolution spatiale possible; faible effet de la végétation*	*Calibration ($\theta = a\sigma_o + b$); sensible à la rugosité, topographie; humidité sur quelques cm de sol*

on pourra se reporter à l'excellent article de Schmugge (1978).

Domaine gamma

Le principe repose sur la mesure de l'atténuation du rayonnement gamma naturel émis par le sol, due à la présence d'une plus ou moins grande quantité d'eau.

Des résultats récents (Loijens, 1980; Jones & Caroll, 1983) montrent que cette technique permet d'obtenir l'humidité volumique dans les 10 premiers centimètres avec une précision absolue de 0.03 $cm^3 cm^{-3}$. Néanmoins, son utilisation pour une large couverture spatiale de routine semble limitée par la nécessité d'effectuer les mesures à faible altitude (150 m environ).

Domaine visible

Les travaux de Idso *et al.* (1974, 1975a,b) ont mis en évidence des variations d'albédo au cours des trois phases du déssèchement d'un sol, à partir de sa saturation naturelle.

Il est clairement montré que, après avoir éliminé les variations horaires par normalisation, seule l'humidité dans les premiers millimètres de sol est responsable de ces variations. De plus, d'autres facteurs tels que la rugosité de surface, la texture, la présence de matière organique influencent également la réflectance du sol. Cela disqualifie les mesures de réflectance dans les domaines visible et proche infra-rouge pour déterminer l'humidité.

Domaine infra-rouge

Cas des sols nus La résolution de l'équation linéaire de la chaleur dans un sol soumis à une excitation périodique montre que l'amplitude journalière de la température de surface s'exprime par:

$$\Delta T_S = T_{S,max} - T_{S,min} = 2G_o/P(\theta)\omega^{\frac{1}{2}} \tag{2}$$

où $P(\theta)$ est l'effusivité thermique (improprement appelée "inertie thermique") définie par:

$$P(\theta) = \sqrt{\rho C(\theta) K(\theta)} \tag{3}$$

L'équation (2) montre que ΔT_S dépend de facteurs externes (rayonnement solaire, température et humidité de l'air, vitesse du vent) qui déterminent par le bilan énergétique le flux de chaleur G_o et internes (propriétés thermiques) au sol. L'effusivité étant une fonction croissante de l'humidité, ΔT_S est d'autant plus faible que le sol est plus humide, toutes choses étant égales par ailleurs et notamment l' environnement climatique. Une étude très complète de sensibilité de ΔT_S à ces différents facteurs est donnée par Becker (1980).

Des études de faisabilité conduites par Idso *et al.* (1975b) ont montré une relation quasi-linéaire décroissante entre ΔT_S mesurée par thermocouples et l'humidité volumique sur 0-2 et 0-4 cm. Un comportement analogue a été constaté en considérant la différence $\Delta T = T_{S,max} - T_{a,max}$, avec la température de l'air mesurée à 1.5 m au-dessus du sol. La même étude effectuée sur des sols différents a montré que l'effet de la texture peut être réduit en considérant la pression effective de l'eau, au lieu de l'humidité. Cela revient à normaliser cette dernière par la capacité au champ correspondant à 1/3 bar et dont une estimation simple a été proposée par Schmugge (1980).

$$FC(\%) = 25.1 - 0.21(\%\ \text{sable}) + 0.22(\%\ \text{argile}) \quad (4)$$

Des données supplémentaires (Reginato *et al.*, 1976; Schmugge *et al.*, 1978) obtenues à la fois par radiomètres infra-rouge portables et aéroportés ont confirmé ces comportements.

Cas des sols couverts d'une végétation Des études semblables menées sur sol cultivé (Idso *et al.*, 1976) ont montré que cette méthode, dite d' "inertie thermique" est difficilement applicable pour inférer l'humidité de la zone racinaire. En revanche, la différence de température entre le sommet d'un couvert végétal (T_C) et l'air (T_a) peut être considérée comme un bon révélateur de l'état de la culture vis à vis de son alimentation hydrique (Wiegand & Namken, 1966; Ehrler & Van Bavel, 1967; Ehrler, 1973). Suivant cette idée, Jackson *et al.* (1977) ont développé un indice (stress-degree-day) défini par:

$$SDD = \sum_{i=1}^{n} (T_C - T_a)_i \quad (5)$$

où n est le nombre de jours du cycle végétatif.

De nombreuses expérimentations (Idso *et al.*, 1977; Reginato *et al.*, 1978; Walker & Hatfield, 1979; Idso *et al.*, 1980) effectuées sur des sols, des spéculations agricoles et pour des conditions climatiques différentes, ont montré une bonne corrélation, de type linéaire décroissante, entre la production végétale et SDD. Millard *et al.* (1978) confirment l'interêt de cette approche, à partir de mesures aéroportées de T_C. Conscients, néamoins de certaines limitations de ce concept, liées notamment à la variabilité des paramètres climatiques (Idso *et al.*, 1981); Jackson *et al.* (1981) ont proposé l'indice CWSI ("crop water stress index") dérivé à partir de la formulation de Monteith (1973) du bilan énergétique au sommet du couvert végétal.

Cette approche très prometteuse notamment pour la conduite des irrigations ne permet pas d'estimer l'humidité des sols cultivés, mais plutôt de détecter son influence sur le comportement des plantes, à travers principalement l'évapotranspiration.

Domaine des microondes

Le principe général repose sur le fait que, dans une bande spectrale donnée, l'émission (méthode dite passive) ou la réflection (méthode dite active) des ondes électromagnétiques à la surface du sol dépendent des propriétés diélectriques du milieu qui sont elles-mêmes fonction de l'humidité.

Méthode passive Il s'agit ici de mesurer, dans un domaine de longueurs d'onde compris entre 1 cm et 30 cm, l'émission thermique de la surface du sol dont l'intensité est proportionnelle à la température de brillance, qui en première approximation (pour $\lambda > 2$ cm) est égale à:

$$T_B = \varepsilon_\lambda T_S \quad (6)$$

Au cours de la dernière décennie, de nombreuses études effectuées à l'aide de radiomètres montés sur grue (Poe *et al.*, 1971; Newton, 1976), aéroportés (Schmugge *et al.*, 1974; Barton, 1978; Burke *et al.*, 1979; Choudhury *et al.*, 1979) ou embarqués à bord de satellites (Eagleman & Lin, 1976) ont mis en évidence des corrélations linéaires décroissantes entre T_B et l'humidité de surface. Les enseignements pratiques suivants peuvent être dégagés:

(a) Seule l'humidité dans une couche de sol d'épaisseur sensiblement égale à quelques dixièmes de la longueur d'onde est accessible à la mesure.

(b) L'absorption due à la présence d'une végétation est d'autant plus faible que la longueur d'onde utilisée est grande (Basharinov & Shutko, 1978).

(c) L'effet de la texture du sol est notablement réduit en normalisant l'humidité par la valeur de la capacité au champ (Choudhury *et al.*, 1979).

(d) La sensibilité de la méthode de mesure (pente de la régression entre T_B et (θ/FC) dépend de la rugosité de la surface notamment en conditions humides.

(e) Afin d'augmenter sensiblement la profondeur d'investigation de l'humidité et diminuer l'absorption de la végétation, il semble donc nécessaire d'effectuer les observations à des longueurs d'onde supérieures à 10 cm.

Cela se fait évidemment au détriment de la résolution spatiale L, estimée par:

$$L = h\lambda/(d \cos^2\phi) \quad (7)$$

Ainsi, pour d = 1 m, λ = 21 cm et h = 800 km (Skylab) la formule (7) donne un pouvoir de résolution au sol de 200 x 200 km environ. A l'évidence, cela pose le problème de l'intérêt hydrologique d'une mesure de l'humidité sur de telles surfaces.

Méthode active Il s'agit de déterminer l'humidité du sol par une mesure du coefficient de rétrodiffusion σ_o d'un signal émis par un radar. D'un point de vue théorique, σ_o est fonction des propriétés géométriques (rugosité et nature) et diélectriques de la surface du sol, ainsi que des caractéristiques de fonctionnement du radar lui-même. L'importance relative de ces différents facteurs est déterminée par le choix des paramètres de fonctionnement du diffusiomètre (longueur d'onde, angle d'incidence, polarisation). Des expériences intensives réalisées a l'Université du Kansas, Etats Unis (Ulaby, 1974; Ulaby *et al.*, 1974; Ulaby *et al.*, 1978; Ulaby *et al.*, 1979), ont mis en évidence un choix optimum de ces paramètres (λ = 6 cm, angle d'incidence compris entre 7 et 17°; polarisation HH) rendant le signal rétrodiffusé pratiquement insensible à la végétation.

Utilisant un autre radar, mais avec le même jeu de paramètres, Bernard *et al.* (1982) trouvent que la sensibilité de σ_o à l'humidité dans les cinq premiers centimètres est en très bon accord avec celle obtenue par Ulaby *et al.* (1979) à condition d'exprimer l'humidité comme un pourcentage de la capacité au champ.

Une étude récente (Bradley & Ulaby, 1981) montre également que l'influence d'une rugosité structurée résultant des pratiques agricoles (sillons) sur σ_0 peut être minimisée en utilisant une polarisation croisée HV.

Conclusions

Une brève synthèse des avantages et inconvénients des différentes techniques de télédétection de l'humidité des sols, potentiellement utilisables, est reportée Tableau 2.

Certaines limitations peuvent être considérées comme fondamentales parce qu'inhérentes à la méthode elle-même telle que la présence d'une couverture nuageuse pour les mesures dans les domaines du visible et de l'infra-rouge. D'autres peuvent être réduites par une technologie plus avancée (grandes antennes, développement de procédures de calibration des radars à synthèse d'ouverture) afin d'améliorer la résolution au sol des méthodes hyperfréquences passives et actives respectivement. Néanmoins, il apparaît que toutes ces techniques présentent un inconvénient majeur: elles ne permettent de mesurer l'humidité que dans les couches superficielles du sol (5 à 10 cm au maximum). La question qui se pose alors est l'intérêt d'une telle mesure pour la pratique agrométéorologique et hydrologique, notamment si le but est la quantification des transferts d'humidité dans le système sol-plante-atmosphère.

Cela ne peut être réalisé, à notre avis, que par l'utilisation de modèles adaptés ou conçus pour admettre ce type d'information comme conditions aux limites.

MODELISATION DES TRANSFERTS HYDRIQUES

Malgré le caractère plus ou moins arbitraire de toute classification, nous pensons pouvoir distinguer deux groupes de modèles différant essentiellement par les objectifs poursuivis: les modèles agrométéorologiques orientés principalement vers les échanges sol-atmosphère et les modèles hydrologiques orientés plutôt vers les transferts dans le sol et les échanges nappe-rivière. Dans le cadre de cet exposé, il n'est pas possible d'effectuer une analyse critique de tous ces modèles. Seule une brève revue est donnée en relation avec la télédétection de l'humidité.

MODELES AGROMETEOROLOGIQUES

Approche complète

L'analyse physique des transferts simultanés de masse et de chaleur dans le sol (Philips & De Vries, 1957; Bories *et al.*, 1978; Camillo & Schmugge, 1981; Milly, 1982) couplée aux échanges sol-atmosphère par l'intermédiaire du bilan énergétique de surface (Rosema, 1975; Van Bavel & Hillel, 1976; Vauclin *et al.*, 1977; Soer, 1977) conduit à une modélisation complète du système sol-atmosphère.

Cette approche a été utilisée pour effectuer des études de sensibilité du comportement hydrique et thermique de la surface d'un sol nu à des variations climatiques (température et humidité de l'air, vitesse du vent; rayonnement solaire) et hydrologiques (température et position de la nappe).

Pour des conditions initiales et aux limites prescrites, elle permet de prédire les transferts d'eau (sous toutes ses formes physiques) et de chaleur dans le sol et de calculer les différentes composantes du bilan hydrique (évaporation, drainage profond, infiltration et ruissellement). Elle a servi de base à des études locales de faisabilité de certaines techniques de télédétection, notamment dans le domaine infrarouge (Rosema, 1975; Soer, 1977; Vauclin, 1978; Recan, 1982). Pour être opérationnelle à grande échelle d'espace, cette approche se heurte cependant à de sérieuses limitations:

(a) Le caractère très fortement non linéaire de l'équation des transferts de masse impose de très faibles pas de temps de résolution (de quelques minutes à 1 h) difficilement compatibles avec les observations par télédétection.

(b) Cette modélisation nécessite la connaissance de nombreuses variables d'entrée, ainsi que d'un grand nombre de paramètres dont beaucoup ne peuvent pas être obtenus par télédétection.

(c) Son caractère local est également peu compatible avec les mesures de télédétection. En effet, son extension spatiale se heurte à la variabilité des propriétés thermiques et hydrodynamiques des sols. On notera néanmoins la possibilité d'utiliser la théorie de mise en facteurs d'échelle comme le montrent les études récentes de Lascano & Van Bavel (1982) pour la température et Bernard *et al.* (1981) pour l'humidité de surface. De plus, ces derniers auteurs utilisent ce type de modélisation, en condition d'isothermie, pour étudier l'influence de la fréquence des observations du coefficient de rétrodiffusion σ_o sur la détermination de l'humidité de surface pour inférer l'évaporation réelle d'un sol nu.

Malgré ces limitations, Soer (1980), Nieuwenhuis (1981) présentent une application intéressante de ce type de modélisation à l'estimation de l'évapotranspiration réelle régionale à partir de mesures de la température de surface obtenues par le satellite HCMM. Cet exemple met clairement en évidence l'un des rôles important joué par un modèle de transferts: relier, de facon déterministe des valeurs de flux quasi-instantanés, obtenues lors des passages de satellites, à des valeurs journalières, plus représentatives de l'échelle de temps des phénomenes hydrologiques.

Approches simplifiées

A côté de cette modélisation complète et par conséquent complexe, plusieurs approches simplifiées peuvent présenter un intérét potentiel, vis à vis de la télédétection de l'humidité.

Pour la plupart, il s'agit de paramétrisations des échanges sol-atmosphère et plus particulièrement de l'évaporation.

(a) Une idée simple consiste à relier, de facon plus ou moins arbitraire l'évaporation et l'humidité de surface, normalisées respectivement par l'évaporation dite "potentielle" et par la "capacité au champ" (Lowry, 1959; Manabe, 1969; Baier, 1969; Choisnel, 1977; Cordova & Bras, 1981). Ce type de relation ne constitue cependant qu'une approximation grossière du fonctionnement hydrique des sols, puisque l'évaporation n'est liée qu'a l'état de surface.

(b) Pour pallier cet inconvénient Deardorff (1977) propose d'exprimer l'évolution temporelle de l'humidité de surface en fonction de l'humidité moyenne du profil. Si cette méthode semble fournir des résultats intéressants pour des sols nus (Deardorff, 1977; Vauclin & Vachaud, 1981) elle se heurte à la détermination, cas par cas, de deux constantes caractéristiques des sols et elle présuppose que les flux de drainage ou de remontée capillaire sont constamment nuls à une certaine cote.

L'extension de cette paramétrisation au cas des sols couverts de végétation (Deardorff, 1978) semble encore plus délicate, dans la mesure où elle nécessite la connaissance d'un plus grand nombre de paramètres et de variables d'entrée.

(c) La plupart de ces paramétrisations ont été utilisées pour déterminer la condition à la limite inférieure des modèles de circulation atmosphérique. Elles ont été developpées indépendamment des techniques de la télédétection. Il nous apparaît cependant que ces dernières offrent des possibilités de déterminer l'évaporation à l'échelle régionale (10-15^5 km^2) definie par (Seguin, 1980):

$$\overline{E} = \frac{1}{S} \sum E_i \; S_i \tag{8}$$

à l'évaporation E_i relative à chaque surface élémentaire, S_i est donnée par lc bilan énergétique:

$$E_i = (1 - r_i)R_G + R_A - \varepsilon_\lambda \sigma \; T_{S_i}^4 - \frac{K_i}{z} (T_{S_i} - T_z) - k_i(U_i)(T_{S_i} - T_a) \tag{9}$$

où les variables R_G, R_A, T_z, T_a et U_i seraient obtenues à partir des données du réseau météorologique synoptique, r_i et T_{S_i} à partir d'observations satellitaires dans les domaines du visible et de l'infrarouge respectivement; K_i et rugosités aérodynamiques déterminées une fois pour toutes pour chacune des surfaces S_i.

Les résultats présentés par Seguin (1980), bien qu'encourageants permettent de cerner les points critiques, notamment la nécessité d'une précision de 1 à 2°C sur la mesure de T_{S_i}, et d'observations fréquentes (satellites géostationnaires) afin d'éviter la mise en oeuvre de procédures de reconstitution temporelle de l'évaporation, à partir de mesures instantanées.

De plus, la rugosité aérodynamique semble jouer un rôle important, notamment en conditions sèches.

(d) Dans le même ordre d'idée, l'évaporation à l'échelle régionale (pour laquelle les apports advectifs d'énergie perdent leur importance devant les apports radiatifs) peut également être estimée par:

$$E_o = \alpha \frac{\beta\Delta}{\beta\Delta + \gamma} R_n \tag{10}$$

en négligeant le flux de chaleur dans le sol.

Cette expression constitue une généralisation de la formule de Priestley & Taylor (1972) au cas des surfaces non saturées en eau par l'introduction du paramètre β qui dépend de l'humidité de surface (Barton, 1979). Le paramètre α varie de 1 à 1.3 (Perrier, 1981), sauf dans le cas des forêts (Monteith, 1981). Là encore, l'utilisation simultanée de domaines spectraux différents (visible et infra-rouge pour le rayonnement net, microonde pour l'humidité de surface) rend potentiellement utilisable la télédétection pour estimer l'évaporation à grande échelle.

MODELES HYDROLOGIQUES

De nombreux modèles hydrologiques sont à l'heure actuelle disponibles. Ils diffèrent essentiellement par les aspects suivants:

- méthode utilisée pour calculer l'évapotranspiration potentielle, l'évaporation et la transpiration réelles;
- méthode de calcul de l'infiltration et du ruissellement;
- prise en compte ou non du couplage entre zone saturée et non saturée;
- choix du nombre de couches de sol utilisées;
- choix du pas de temps.

Ils ont été historiquement développés avant et/ou indépendamment des techniques de la télédétection, et sont par conséquent peu applicables directement. Néanmoins, plusieurs stratégies sont possibles pour utiliser l'humidité dans ces modèles.

(a) *Utilisation comme variable d'entrée*. Dans ce cas, le modèle ne peut pas être exécuté sans cette information qui doit être aussi précise que possible. L'adéquation entre les pas de temps des observations et d'éxécution doit être totale. Cela implique en général une modélisation très simple, excluant notamment toute possibilité de modéliser la dynamique de l'eau et l'évaporation.

(b) *Utilisation pour réinitialiser l'état hydrique du modèle*. La connaissance de l'humidité n'est plus nécessaire à chaque pas de temps de calcul. Sa mesure peut être utilisée périodiquement pour contrôler et éventuellement modifier l'état hydrique calculé afin d'éviter toute divergence du modèle par rapport à la réalité.

(c) *Utilisation pour calibrer certains paramètres*. Des observations régulières de l'humidité peuvent servir à recalibrer les modèles en réajustant périodiquement certains paramètres qui sont souvent déterminés une fois pour toutes.

Une revue bibliographique (Peck *et al.*, 1981) montre à l'évidence que la plupart des modèles hydrologiques existants n'offre pas le potentiel nécessaire pour utiliser directement l'humidité obtenue par télédétection.

Deux voies semblent possibles pour intégrer cette information:

(a) Adapter les modèles existants en introduisant une couche superficielle de sol contrôlant les relations infiltration-ruissellement et dont l'épaisseur serait compatible avec les mesures d'humidités, particulièrement dans le domaine des microondes. Cela conduit, néanmoins à de nombreuses modifications, notamment pour le calcul des différentes composantes du bilan hydrologique.

(b) Developper une nouvelle génération de modèles (ou de sous-programmes) prenant en compte les caractéristiques inhérentes aux possibilités qu'offre la télédétection de l'humidité. Elle nous semble constituer la voie la plus prometteuse.

On notera que ces remarques sont également valables pour d'autres variables (cartographie de la couverture neigeuse, des zones imperméables,gelées et couvertes de végétation, densité et nature de la végétation, température de surface etc.) recensées comme nécessaires dans les modèles hydrologiques et potentiellement measurables par télédétection. Seules les précipitations semblent utilisables directement dans les modèles existants.

CONCLUSIONS

A l'issue de cette revue non exhaustive, les principales conclusions suivantes peuvent être dégagées:

Au plan de la mesure

De nombreux phénomènes physiques (pour la plupart d'ores et déjà identifiés) interviennent dans toute mesure de l'énergie emise ou réfléchie à la surface du sol. Inférer l'humidité par télédétection nécessite donc l'utilisation conjointe de plusieurs senseurs (domaines visible, infra-rouge et micro-onde) afin de séparer les différentes influences (Jackson *et al.*, 1982).

Au plan de la modélisation

Un effort important doit être fait pour développer de nouveaux modèles soumis aux contraintes (extension spatiale, fréquence des observations, discrétisation verticale) imposées par la télédétection des variables d'intérêt, notamment mais non exclusivement, l'humidité. Cela ne peut,à notre sens, être fait sans une étroite collaboration entre les spécialistes des deux domaines concernés.

REFERENCES

Baier, W. (1969) Concepts of soil moisture availability and their effects on soil moisture estimates from a meteorological budget. *Agric. Met.* 6, 165-178.

Barton, I.J. (1978) A case study comparison of microwave radiometer measurements over bare and vegetated surfaces. *J. Geophys. Res.* 83, 3513-3517.

Barton, I.J. (1979) A parameterization of the evaporation from non saturated surfaces. *J. Appl. Met.* 18, 43-47.

Basharinov, A.Y. & Shutko, H.M. (1978) Determination of the moisture content of the earth's cover by microwave radiometric methods. *Radio Engng Electron. Phys.* 23, 1-12 (Engl. Transl.).

Becker, F. (1980) Thermal infra-red remote sensing principles and applications. In: *Remote Sensing Applications in Agricultural and Hydrology* (ed. par G.Fraysse), 153-213. AA Balkema Press, Rotterdam.

Bell, K.R., Blanchard, B.J., Schmugge, T.J. & Witczak, M.W. (1980) Analysis of surface moisture variations within large field studies. *Wat. Resour. Res.* 16, 796-810.

Bernard, R., Vauclin, M. & Vidal-Madjar, D. (1981) Possible use of active microwave remote sensing data for prediction of regional evaporation by numerical simulation of soil water movement in the unsaturated zone. *Wat. Resour. Res.* 17, 1603-1610.

Bernard, R., Martin, Ph., Thony, J.L., Vauclin, M. & Vidal-Madjar, D. (1982) C-band radar for determining surface soil moisture. *Remote Sens. Environ.* 12, 189-200.

Bories, S., Crausse, P., Bacon, P. & Gaudu, R. (1978) Etude expérimentale et simulation numérique des transferts de chaleur et de masse en milieux poreux. 6° Congrès International des Transferts de Chaleur et de Masse (Toronto, Canada). *Proceedings HM1,* 317-321.

Bradley, G.A. & Ulaby, F.T. (1981) Aircraft radar response to soil moisture. *Remote Sens. Environ.* 11, 419-438.

Burke, W.J., Schmugge, T. & Paris, J.F. (1979) Comparison of 28- and 21- cm microwave radiometer observations over soils with emission model calculations. *J. Geophys. Res.* 84, 287-294.

Camillo, P. & Schmugge, T.J. (1981) A computer program for the simulation of heat and moisture flow in soils. *NASA Tech. Report 82121.*

Cassel, D.K. & Bauer, A. (1975) Spatial variability in soil below depth of tillage, bulk density and fifteen atmosphere percentage. *Soil Sci. Soc. Am. Proc.* 39, 247-250.

Choisnel, E. (1977) Le bilan d'énergie et le bilan hydrique du sol. *La Météorologie* 6, 103-133.

Choudhury, B., Schmugge, T., Newton, R.W. & Chang, A. (1979) Effect of surface roughness on the microwave emission from soils. *J. Geophys. Res.* 84, 5699-5706.

Cordova, J.R. & Bras, R.L. (1981) Physically based probabilistic models of infiltration soil moisture and actual evapotranspiration. *Wat. Resour. Res.* 17, 93-106.

Deardorff, J.W. (1977) A parameterization of ground surface moisture content for use in atmospheric prediction models. *J. Appl. Met.* 16, 1182-1185.

Deardorff, J.W. (1978) Efficient prediction of ground surface temperature and moisture, with inclusion of a layer of vegetation. *J. Geophys. Res.* 83, 1889-1903.

Eagleman, J. & Lin, W. (1976) Remote sensing of soil moisture by a 21-cm passive radiometer. *J. Geophys. Res.* 81, 3660-3666.

Ehrler, W.L. (1973) Cotton leaf temperature as related to soil depletion and meteorological factors. *Agron. J.* 65, 404-409.

Ehrler, W.L. & Van Bavel, C.H.M. (1967) Sorghum foliar responses to changes in soil water content. *Agron. J.* 59, 243-246.

Idso, S.B., Reginato, R.J., Jackson, R.D., Kimball, B.A. & Nakayama, F.S. (1974) The three stages of drying of a field soil. *Soil Sci. Soc. Am. Proc.* 38, 831-837.

Idso, S.B., Jackson, R.D., Reginato, R.J., Kimball, B.A. & Nakayama, F.S. (1975a) The dependence of soil albedo on soil water content. *J. Appl. Met.* 14, 109-113.

Idso, S.B., Schmugge, T.J., Jackson, R.D. & Reginato, R.J. (1975b) The utility of surface temperature measurements for the remote sensing of soil water status. *J. Geophys. Res.* 80, 3044-3049.

Idso, S.B., Jackson, R.D., Reginato, R.J. (1976) Compensating for environmental variability in the thermal inertia approach to remote sensing of soil moisture. *J. Appl. Met.* 15, 811-817.

Idso, S.B., Jackson, R.D. & Reginato, R.J. (1977) Remote sensing of crop yields. *Science* 196, 19-25.

Idso, S.B., Reginato, R.J., Hatfield, J.L., Walker, G.K., Jackson, R.D. & Pinter, P.J., Jr (1980) A generalization of the stress-degree-day concept of yield prediction to accommodate a diversity of crops. *Agric. Met.* 21, 205-211.

Idso, S.B., Jackson, R.D., Pinter, P.J., Jr, Reginato, R.J. & Hatfield, J.L. (1981) Normalizing the stress-degree-day concept for environmental variability. *Agric. Met.* 24, 45-55.

Jackson, R.D., Reginato, R.J. & Idso, S.B. (1977) Wheat canopy temperature: a practical tool for evaluating water requirements. *Wat. Resour. Res.* 13, 561-656.

Jackson, R.D., Idso, S.B., Reginato, R.J. & Pinter, P.J., Jr (1981) Canopy temperature as a crop water stress indicator. *Wat. Resour. Res.* 17, 1133-1138.

Jackson, T.J., O'Neill, P.E., Coleman, G.C. & Schmugge, T.J. (1982) Aircraft remote sensing of soil moisture and hydrologic parameters. Chickaska, Okla 1980 Data Report. *Agric. Res. Report AAR-NE-14, USDA, Beltsville, Maryland, USA.*

Jones, W.K. & Carroll, T.R. (1983) Error analysis of airborne gamma radiation soil moisture measurements. *Agric. Met.* 28, 19-30.

Lascano, R.J. & Van Bavel, C.H.M. (1982) Spatial variability of soil hydraulics and remotely sensed soil parameters. *Soil Sci. Soc. Am. J.* 46, 223-228.

Loijens, H.S. (1980) Determination of soil water content from terrestrial gamma radiation measurements. *Wat. Resour. Res.* 16, 565-573.

Lowry, W.P. (1959) The falling rate phase of evaporative soil moisture loss: a critical evaluation. *Bull. Am. Met. Soc.* 40, 605-608.

Manabe, S. (1969) Climate and the ocean circulation. 1 - The atmospheric circulation and the hydrology of the earth's surface. *Mon. Weath. Rev.* 97, 739-774.

Millard, J.P., Jackson, R.D., Goettelman, R.C., Reginato, R.J. & Idso, S.B. (1978) Crop water-stress assessment using an airborne thermal scanner. *Photogramm. Engng Remote Sensing* 44, 77-85.

Milly, P.C.D. (1982) Moisture and heat transport in hysteretic, inhomogeneous porous media: a matric head based formulation and a numerical model. *Wat. Resour. Res.* 18, 489-498.

Monteith, J.L. (1973) *Principles of Environmental Physics.* Edward Arnold, Londres.

Monteith, J.L. (1981) Evaporation and surface temperature. *Quart. J. Roy. Met. Soc.* 107, 1-27.

Newton, R.W. (1976) Microwave sensing and its application to soil moisture detection. *Tech. Report RSC-81, Remote Sensing Center at Texas A et M University, USA.*

Nielsen, D.R., Biggar, J.W. & Erh, K.T. (1973) Spatial variability of field-measured soil-water properties. *Hilgardia* 42, 215-260.

Nieuwenhuis, G.J.A. (1981) Application of HCMM satellite and airplane reflection and heat maps in agrohydrology. *Adv. Space Res.* 1, 71-86.

Peck, E.L., Keefer, T.N. & Johnson, E.R. (1981) Strategies for using remotely sensed data in hydrologic models. *Rapport NASA-CR 66729.*

Perrier, A. (1981) Land surface processes in atmospheric general circulation models: vegetation. Conférence à Greenbelt, Maryland, USA.

Philips, J.R. & De Vries, D.A. (1957) Moisture movement in porous materials under temperature gradients. *EOS Trans. AGU* 38, 222-232.

Poe, G.A., Stogryn, A.A. & Edgerton, A.T. (1971) Determinations of soil moisture content using microwave radiometry. *Final Report 1684 FR 1, Aerojet. General Corp., El Monte, Californie, USA.*

Priestley, C.H.B. & Taylor, R.J. (1972) On the assessment of surface heat flux and evaporation using large scale parameters. *Mon. Weath. Rev.* 100, 81-92.

Recan, M. (1982) Simulation numérique du comportement thermique et hydrique d'un sol nu. Application à l'étude de l'évaporation par télédétection. Thèse à l'Institut National Polytechnique de Toulouse, France.

Reginato, R.J., Idso, S.B., Vedder, J.F., Jackson, R.D., Blanchard, M.B. & Goettelman, R. (1976) Soil water content and evaporation determined by thermal parameters obtained from ground based and remote measurements. *J. Geophys. Res.* 81, 1617-1620.

Reginato, R.J., Idso, S.B. & Jackson, R.D. (1978) Estimating forage crop production. A technique adaptable to remote sensing. *Remote Sensing Environ.* 7, 77-80.

Rosema, A. (1975) A mathematical model for simulation of the thermal behaviour of bare soils, based on heat and moisture transfers. *NIWARS publ. n° 11,* Delft, Netherlands.

Schmugge, T.J. (1978) Remote sensing of surface soil moisture. *J. Appl. Met.* 17, 1549-1557.

Schmugge, T.J. (1980) Effect of texture on microwave emissions from soils. *Inst. Elect. Electron. Engrs Trans. Geosci. Remote Sensing* GE18, 353-361.

Schmugge, T.J., Gloersen, P., Wilheit, T., Geiger, F. (1974) Remote Sensing of soil moisture with microwave radiometers. *J. Geophys. Res.* 79, 317-323.

Schmugge, T.J., Blanchard, B., Anderson, A., Wang, J. (1978) Soil Moisture sensing with aircraft observations of the diurnal range of surface temperature. *Water Resour. Bull.* 14, 169-178.

Seguin, B. (1980) Determination de l'évaporation réelle dans les bilans hydrologiques par la télédétection en thermographie infra-rouge. *Hydrol. Sci. Bull.* 25 (2), 143-153.

Sisson, J.B. & Wierenga, P.J. (1981) Spatial variability of steady-state infiltration rates as a stochastic process. *Soil Sci. Soc. Am. J.* 45, 699-704.

Soer, G.J.R. (1977) The TERGRA-model - a mathematical model for the simulation of the daily behaviour of crop surface temperature and actual evapotranspiration. *Nota ICW 1014, Wageningen, Netherlands.*

Soer, G.J.R. (1980) Estimation of regional evapotranspiration and soil moisture conditions using remotely sensed crop surface temperatures. *Remote Sensing Environ.* 9, 27-45.

Ulaby, F.T. (1974) Radar measurement of soil moisture content. *Inst. Elect. Electron. Engrs Trans. Antennas Progagat.* AP22, 257-265.

Ulaby, F.T., Cilhar, J. & Moore, R.K. (1974) Active microwave measurements of soil water content. *Remote Sensing Environ.* 3,

185-203.

Ulaby, F.T., Batlivala, P.P. & Dobson, M.C. (1978) Microwave backscatter dependence on surface roughness, soil moisture and soil texture. Part I. Bare soil. *Inst. Elect. Electron. Engrs. Trans. Geosci. Electron.* GE16, 286-295.

Ulaby, F.T., Bradley, G.A. & Dobson, M.C. (1979) Microwave backscatter dependence on surface roughness, soil moisture and soil texture. Part II. Vegetation-covered soil. *Inst. Elect. Electron. Engrs Trans. Geosci. Electron.* GE17, 33-40.

Vauclin, M., Hamon, G. & Vachaud, G. (1977) Simulation of coupled heat and water flows in a partially saturated soil. Determination of the surface temperature and evaporation rate from a bare soil. Dans: *Influence des Gradients Thermiques sur les Transferts d'Humidité dans la Zone Non Saturée.* Action thématique Hydrogéol. 1652, CNRS Paris, France.

Vauclin, M. (1978) Modèle local des transferts de masse et de chaleur entre le sol et l'atmosphère. Problèmes posés par son extension spatiale. In: *Compte-rendus du Colloque National sur les mécanismes de transfert d'énergie et de masse entre sol et atmosphère* (Ed. F. Becker et C. Pastre), 76-105.

Vauclin, M. & Vachaud, G. (1981) Bilan hydrique dans le Sud-Tunisien. II - Modélisation numérique et prévision des transferts hydriques en sol stratifié. *J. Hydrol.* 49, 53-73.

Vauclin, M., Vieira, S.R., Bernard, R. & Hatfield, J.L. (1982) Spatial variability of surface temperature along two transects of a bare soil. *Wat. Resour. Res.* 18, 1677-1686.

Van Bavel, C.H.M. & Hillel, D.H. (1976) Calculating potential and actual evaporation from a bare soil surface by simulation of concurrent flow of water and heat. *Agric. Met.* 17, 453-476.

Walker, G.K. & Hatfield, J.L. (1979) Test of the stress degree day concept using multiple planting dates of red kidney beans. *Agron. J.* 71, 967-971.

Wiegand, C.L. & Namken, L.N. (1966) Inflence of plant moisture stress, solar radiation and air temperature on cotton leaf temperatures. *Agron. J.* 58, 582-586.

Hydrological Applications of Remote Sensing and Remote Data Transmission (Proceedings of the Hamburg Symposium, August 1983). IAHS Publ. no. 145.

Remote sensing of soil moisture from an aircraft platform using passive microwave sensors

T. J. JACKSON
Hydrology Laboratory, Agricultural Research Service, Beltsville, Maryland 20705, USA
T. J. SCHMUGGE & P. O'NEILL
Nasa Goddard Space Flight Center, Greenbelt, Maryland 20771, USA

ABSTRACT A series of experiments were conducted over several years using an aircraft platform to study the relationships between passive microwave data and surface soil moisture. Sensor systems included thermal infrared and multifrequency passive microwave instruments. Aircraft measurements were obtained concurrently with ground observations of soil moisture and land cover. Test sites included areas in both humid and semiarid regions of the USA. Data analyses indicated that the basic cause and effect relationships between the sensor measurements and soil moisture can be extrapolated from theory and small scale tests to larger resolution elements observed by the aircraft. Pastures in different climatic regions showed similar responses. Vegetation canopy attenuation was verified. Based on these studies the optimal surface soil moisture sensor using passive techniques was a 21 cm wavelength radiometer.

Mesure par télédétection de l'humidité des sols à partir d'une plateforme sur avion avec micro-ondes passives
RESUME Une série d'expériences a été effectuée pendant plusieurs années avec emploi d'une plateforme sur avion pour étudier le rapport entre les données micro-ondes passive et l'humidité des sols. Les systèmes de détection comportent l'infra-rouge thermique et les micro-ondes passives de diverses fréquences. Les mesures à partir de l'avion sont effectuées concurremment avec l'observation au sol de l'humidité et du couvert végétal. Les campagnes de mesures couvrent des régions de la zone humide et de la zone semi-aride aux Etats-Unis. L'analyse des données a indiqué que les relations entre les mesures par télédétection et l'humidité du sol peuvent être extrapolées depuis la théorie et les observations sur petites surfaces jusqu' aux éléments de grande surface tels qu'on peut les observer par avion. Les pâturages de diverses régions climatiques ont donné des réponses similaires. L'atténuation du couvert vegétal a également été vérifiée. Suivant ces recherches, le meilleur senseur pour mesurer l'humidité des sols avec techniques passives a été un radiomètre avec longueur

d'onde de 21 cm.

INTRODUCTION

Hydrological forecasts and agricultural water management decisions can be improved by timely and accurate observations of soil moisture. However, conventional measurements are impractical when frequent observations over large regions are required. For this reason, remote sensing techniques are being evaluated for soil moisture determination.

Previous research has shown that several sensor systems can be used to estimate surface soil moisture (Schmugge *et al.*, 1980). Microwave systems appear to be the best suited to potential remote sensing applications because they provide a direct estimate of soil moisture, are extendable to satellite platforms, and are weather independent.

In this study, a series of experiments was conducted over a three-year period to determine the optimum passive microwave system for measuring surface soil moisture from an aircraft platform in several geographic areas. Multifrequency sensor system measurements from an aircraft were obtained concurrently with ground observations of soil moisture and land cover. Data analyses were conducted to determine the sensitivity of the relationship between soil moisture and passive microwave measurements considering the effects of canopy cover and geographic location and sensor system configuration.

TEST SITES AND GROUND SAMPLING

Data presented in this study were collected over the period 1976-1980 over sites in Florida, Oklahoma, and South Dakota. The majority of these data were collected between 1978 and 1980 in Florida and Oklahoma. Additional sites were evaluated in these studies; however, the data were unsuitable for analysis due to either inadequate ground sampling or sensor coverage.

Oklahoma test sites

Oklahoma test sites were small rangeland basins monitored by the USDA-ARS Southern Plains Watershed and Water Quality Laboratory near Chickasha, Oklahoma. Two flightlines covered a total of four rangeland (R5, R6, R7, and R8) or pasture basins which ranged in size from 8 to 18 ha. The rangeland basins were nearly adjacent and had similar silt loam soils.

Soil moisture samples were collected using a gravimetric technique for depth intervals of 0-2.5, 2.5-5, and 5-15 cm. Soil temperature measurements were obtained at depths of 2.5 and 15 cm. Gravimetric soil moisture data for each depth interval were converted to volumetric when combined with bulk density.

Flights were conducted on three dates in 1978: 1, 12 and 30 May. All these dates had relatively wet soil moisture conditions. To extend the analysis to a greater range of conditions, three additional flights were conducted in 1980 on 24 June, 14 August, and

9 September. Two of these dates were very dry and one was in the moderate range observed in 1978. Additional details of the sites and the data collected are presented in Jackson *et al.* (1980) and (1982a).

Florida test sites

The sampling locations in Florida were all in or west of the Taylor Creek Experimental Watershed, which is monitored by the USDA-ARS. They are in Okeechobee County just north of Lake Okeechobee.

Two flightlines were flown over the area on 30 November 1978, and 2 May, 22 May, and 13 June 1979. One flightline covered six orange grove sites each of which was about 40 ha (100 acres). Soils on this flightline were mostly fine sandy loams. A second flightline covered five pastures and two wooded sites with standing water. Soils were generally fine sands except for the two wooded sites.

Soil moisture samples were collected at eight points for each site. Data were obtained at four depth intervals: 0-2.5, 2.5-5, 5-10, and 10-15 cm. Gravimetric samples were gathered using an undisturbed core sampling device which yielded estimates of the bulk densities. Bulk density values in the 0-2.5 cm soil layer at these sites were low. Values in the orange grove sites average 1.02 g cm^{-2} for the 0-2.5 cm layer and 1.38 g cm^{-2} in the 2.5-5 cm layer. The pasture sites had an average bulk density of 0.87 gm cm^{-3} in the 0-2.5 cm soil layer. Additional information on these test sites is presented in Jackson *et al.* (1981).

South Dakota test sites

Aircraft experiments were conducted on sites in Hand County, South Dakota, on nine dates covering the period of 1976-1978. Several pasture sites covered in these experiments were used in the current investigation. A total of five 400 by 400 m fields were studied; however, all fields were not sampled on each date.

Soil moisture samples for depth intervals of 0-2.5, 0-5, and 0-10 cm were collected. Soils were generally loams and silt loams. Four to six samples were obtained on each 16 ha field. Since several of the pastures were longer than 400 m, the number of samples ranged up to 18 for a 1200 m long field.

REMOTE SENSING SYSTEMS

The NASA 929 (C-130B) aircraft was the sensor platform used in these experiments. A nominal altitude of 305 m (1000 ft) and a ground speed of 278 km h^{-1} (150 knots) were chosen. The systems assessed in this study included cameras, a thermal infrared radiometer and multifrequency microwave radiometers.

Colour infrared photography was obtained by using a Zeiss 23 cm (9 in.) camera with Kodak 2443 film. A 15 cm (6 in.) focal length at the specified altitude resulted in a nominal scale of approximately 1:2000 on the photo products. Forward overlap of 10% was used.

Thermal infrared radiometer data were also obtained by using a Barnes precision radiation thermometer (PRT5) with a spectral range from 8 to 14 microns. This is a fixed beam sensor with a field view of 2°. The ground swath width at the flight altitude was 24 m (79 ft).

The multifrequency microwave radiometer (MFMR) is a collection of five separate radiometers operating over the frequency range 1.414-37 GHz. The characteristics of these radiometers are described in Table 1. The instruments are basically Dicke radiometers in which the incoming radiation is compared with internal reference sources

TABLE 1 Passive microwave sensor systems

System designation	*Centre frequency (GHz)*	*Wave-length (cm)*	*Receiver band-width (MHz)*	*Antenna beam-width (°)*	*Swath width (m) for 305 m altitude: 0° look angle*	*40° look angle*
L band	*1.41*	*21.00*	*27*	*15*	*75*	*120*
C band	*5.00*	*6.00*	*50*	*6*	*30*	*50*
Ku band	*18.00*	*1.67*	*200*	*6*	*30*	*50*
K band	*22.00*	*1.35*	*200*	*6*	*30*	*50*
Ka band	*37.00*	*0.81*	*200*	*6*	*30*	*50*

at known temperatures to obtain the quantitative values of the brightness temperature (T_B) of the incoming radiation.

Look angles of 0° and 40° were used for the C, L, and K band radiometers. Horizontal and vertical polarization data were collected for the C and K bands and only horizontal polarization data for the L band.

RESULTS AND DISCUSSION

All microwave data used in these analyses are expressed as emissivity or normalized brightness temperatures. These values are computed by dividing observed brightness temperature by a weighted soil/canopy temperature (Choudhury *et al.*, 1982). All soil moisture values are expressed in per cent by volume.

Oklahoma pasture sites analyses

A significant problem in remote sensing experiments is trying to control the site variables so that a particular factor can be studied. This is especially true in aircraft studies. One set of data which were collected in this series came as close as possible to maintaining homogeneous conditions over an extended period so that the effects of soil moisture could be evaluated.

Data were collected on four rangeland basins located near Chickasha, Oklahoma, on three dates in 1978 and three dates in 1980. Qualitative observations revealed some changes and differences in the pasture density; however, these differences were small. Surface roughness and topography were similar at all sites with R7 and R8 being slightly rougher due to erosion.

Figure 1 shows a plot of the 0-5 cm soil moisture *vs.* normalized brightness temperature for all observations in 1978 and 1980. It is obvious from this plot that a single line could be fitted to the scatter of points to describe the relationship for both years.

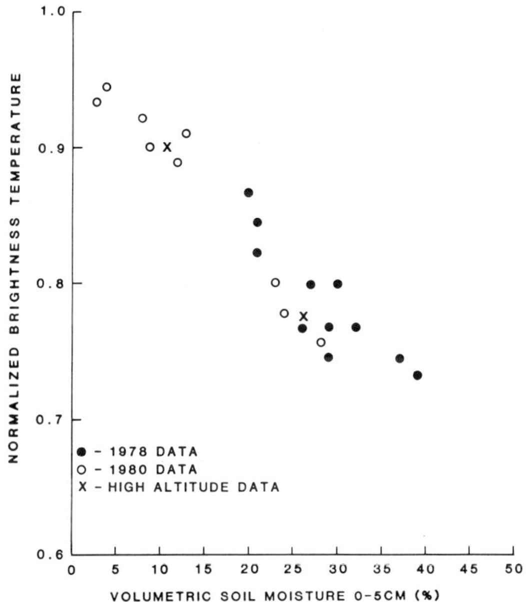

FIG.1 L band soil moisture data.

Based on this and water calibration data, we concluded that the microwave radiometers operated consistently between the two years.

To determine the optimal sensor configuration and the accuracy of these sensor systems on this group of watersheds, a linear regression function was applied to each system data set. The results, parameters and coefficients of determination are summarized in Table 2. The analysis was repeated for three soil moisture depths.

A review of these results shows that L band systems have a stronger linear relationship and are more sensitive to near-surface soil moisture than the C band systems (where sensitivity is based on the regression slope parameter). This is in agreement with the results of Wang *et al.* (1982) who observed a substantial decrease in sensitivity for grass covered fields at C band.

Theoretical models of the relationship between the L band T_B and surface soil moisture (determined by the Fresnel equation for smooth surfaces) indicate that the sensitivity of the instrument should be greater at 40° look angle than it is at 0°. On the other hand, studies by Jackson *et al.* (1982b), Wang *et al.* (1982), Ulaby *et al.* (1983) and Kirdiashev *et al.* (1979) have shown that the presence of vegetation generally reduces microwave sensitivity to soil moisture. Therefore, one might expect that as look angle increases and consequently the thickness of the viewed vegetation layer increases, that sensitivity would decrease going from 0° to 40°. The results

TABLE 2 Estimating normalized brightness temperature from soil moisture for rangeland basins, Oklahoma, 1978 and 1980

Soil moisture (cm)	*Regression parameter*	*System*					
		L		*C*			
		H		*H*		*V*	
		0°	*40°*	*0°*	*40°*	*0°*	*40°*
0-2.5	*Intercept*	*0.95*	*0.91*	*0.95*	*0.90*	*1.00*	*0.91*
	Slope	*0.0059*	*0.0073*	*0.0031*	*0.0030*	*0.0039*	*0.0015*
	R^2	*0.93*	*0.91*	*0.77*	*0.64*	*0.82*	*0.60*
0-5	*Intercept*	*0.96*	*0.92*	*0.96*	*0.90*	*1.00*	*0.91*
	Slope	*0.0067*	*0.0082*	*0.0036*	*0.0034*	*0.0044*	*0.0017*
	R^2	*0.95*	*0.92*	*0.78*	*0.67*	*0.82*	*0.63*
0-15	*Intercept*	*0.97*	*0.94*	*0.97*	*0.91*	*1.01*	*0.92*
	Slope	*0.0079*	*0.0095*	*0.0042*	*0.0040*	*0.0050*	*0.0020*
	R^2	*0.88*	*0.83*	*0.72*	*0.63*	*0.70*	*0.58*

shown in Table 2 for L band indicate that the vegetation density of these pastures does not significantly affect the typical bare soil responses.

The effects of polarization can only be examined for C band, since there were no vertical polarization L band data. In general, the vertical polarization data have a stronger relationship at 0° and a weaker relationship at 40°; however, the accuracy of all the C band relationships is relatively low and precludes a conclusion.

Based upon these results it appears that the L band sensor operating at either 0° and 40° is the best system configuration for the remote sensing of surface soil moisture under low biomass or short vegetation conditions. The data cover a very wide range of soil moisture conditions and a linear function describes the relationship very well, based upon the coefficient of determination.

The coefficient of determination for the C band systems based on a linear regression is not a completely fair measure of these systems. Figure 2 is a plot of the C band data collected at 0° and horizontal polarization. Early investigators (Schmugge *et al.*, 1974) have observed that the relationship between soil moisture and normalized brightness temperature at this and shorter wavelengths is not linear. A better descriptor is a flat line to some soil moisture with a linear function beyond that point. Our data show this trend.

The use of a nonlinear function to describe the relationship might result in an improved coefficient of determination; however, it would not mean that the C band sensor is very good for this application. A zero slope relationship from zero to about 20% soil moisture, as in this case, indicates that the sensor is not responsive to variations in this range. In contrast, the L band sensor is sensitive, as shown in Fig.1.

A possible problem with linear analysis of this type is the

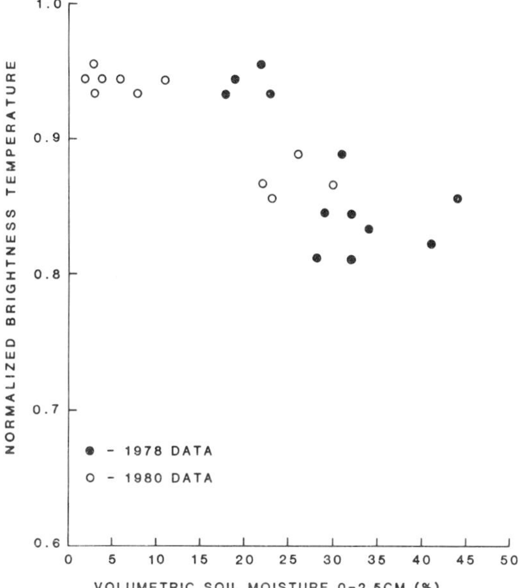

FIG.2 C band soil moisture data.

selection of an appropriate soil moisture sampling depth with which to compare the microwave measurements. It is quite likely that a shallower soil layer, such as 0-1 cm or 0-0.5 cm, is more directly related to the microwave response at C band (Wang *et al.*, 1982). If the average soil moisture in this shallower depth were plotted against the microwave data in Fig.2, a more linear fit might result. However, since our intent is to find the sensor most sensitive to soil moisture in the deepest depth possible, L band still appears to be a better choice than C band.

Along the same line of thought, we considered the relationship between the soil moisture in several soil layers and the microwave response, emphasizing the L band system at a 0° look angle. The coefficient of determination values in Table 2 suggest that the strongest relationship exists between the microwave data and the 0-5 cm soil layer. However, the other two thicknesses also show a fairly strong relationship.

One reason why we do not see marked differences in these statistics is that in a pasture there is generally a good surface cover with a well-developed root system. Under these conditions, evaporation of soil moisture is controlled by transpiration, and, if the root system is not extremely different over the near surface depths, the soil moisture will tend to be fairly uniform with depth. This situation will change after smaller rainfall events, when near-surface soil moisture gradients may form.

We are seeking the most sensitive relationship and it appears that sensitivity increases with depth. However, we must also consider the accuracy. Based upon these two factors, it appears that the L band response is determined primarily by the 0-5 cm soil layer moisture.

Another factor that we considered in these experiments was the effect of the sensor footprint on the soil moisture-microwave relationship. On two flight dates in 1980, data were collected at higher altitudes, 1500 and 3000 m, over the rangeland basin group. At these altitudes the ground resolutions for L band were 375 and 750 m, respectively, at a 0° look angle. Soil moisture values from the four basins were averaged and plotted *vs.* the normalized brightness temperatures among the low-altitude data in Fig.1. Fortunately, two very different soil moisture conditions were observed. These results fall right in the range of the low altitude data and suggest that the relationships can be extended to higher altitudes and larger footprints.

Canopy cover effects

Experiments conducted in Florida included mostly pasture, forest, and orange grove sites on basically the same soil types. It has been observed in previous research by Jackson *et al.* (1982b) that the effect of increasing canopy cover on soil emission is a decrease of microwave sensitivity to soil moisture changes. Larger soil moisture changes are needed in the presence of vegetation canopy to produce the emissivity change observed over bare soils.

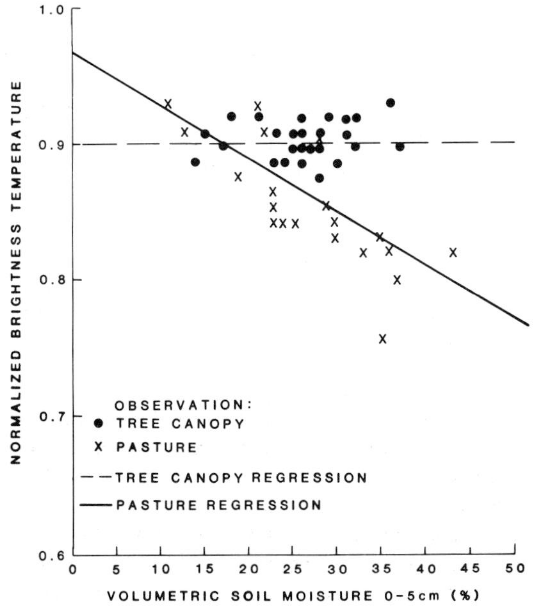

FIG.3 Florida pasture and tree cover data for L band.

Data from the Florida experiment were grouped into two categories, pasture and trees, and were statistically analyzed. Figure 3 is a plot of the L band data at a look angle of 0° *vs.* the 0-5 cm volumetric soil moisture. Although there is a great deal of scatter, the discrimination of the trends for the two groups is apparent. Microwave data obtained over pasture sites show sensitivity to soil moisture, while the tree sites all produce the same microwave response regardless of the underlying soil moisture, which included a considerable range of values.

Linear regression results are summarized in Table 3, using only the 0-5 cm volumetric soil moisture. Pasture site results indicate that a linear function explains a significant portion of the variance of the data for L band systems. C band results indicate that vegetation of this density attenuates the sensitivity to the point where the trend is not significant. This lack of sensitivity at C band implies that the difference between the Florida and Oklahoma pastures is due to the increased biomass observed for the Florida pastures, which was qualitatively verified at both locations.

TABLE 3 Estimating normalized brightness temperature from 0-5 cm soil moisture for Florida pasture and tree sites

Regression parameter	*System*				
	L		*C*		
	H		*H*		*V*
	0°	*40°*	*0°*	*40°*	*0°*
PASTURE					
Intercept	*0.97*	*0.96*	*0.96*	*0.95*	*0.98*
Slope	*0.0041*	*0.0052*	*0.0006*	*0.0009*	*0.0010*
R^2	*0.62*	*0.64*	*0.14*	*0.21*	*0.21*
TREES					
Intercept	*0.90*	*0.90*	*0.94*	*0.94*	*0.95*
Slope	*0.004*	*0.0006*	*0.0005*	*0.0001*	*0.0044*
R^2	*0.03*	*0.07*	*0.02*	*0.00*	*0.04*

Results of the tree canopy cover regression indicate no sensitivity to soil moisture variations. These results may seem strange for the citrus orchards where the aerial photographs indicate that there is a considerable amount of space between the rows of trees. However, we must recall that the photograph is made in the visible portion of the spectrum, i.e. at wavelengths almost a million times shorter than the microwave observations. As a result, the orchard canopy behaves almost as uniform vegetation rather than a mixture of low and high emissivity targets.

Data for other canopy types on similar soils were too sparse to allow comparison. Pasture site data from Oklahoma and South Dakota sites were primarily from areas with silt loam soils. Florida pastures were in areas with sandy soils and high organic levels. Pastures in Florida had a greater biomass than those in South Dakota and Oklahoma based on visual observations.

Vegetation effect theory states that increasing the biomass should result in a decreased microwave sensitivity to soil moisture (Jackson *et al.*, 1982b). Comparing the L band data at a 0° look angle for the pasture sites shows that, in general, the microwave data are less responsive to moisture variations in the denser Florida sites than in the South Dakota and Oklahoma sites. Figure 4 illustrates this point. Regression parameters for each state are summarized in Table 4.

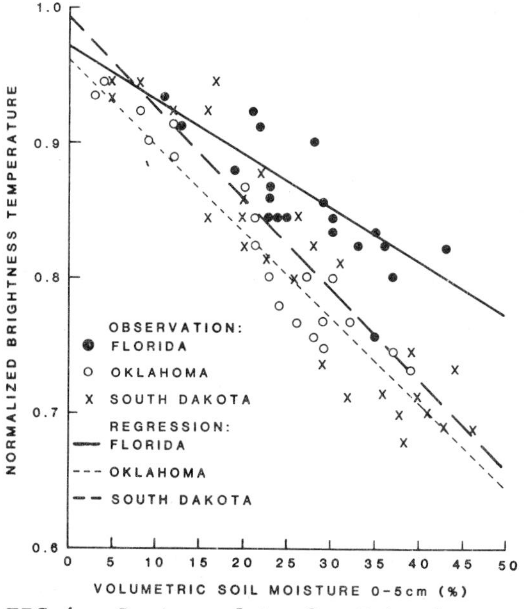

FIG.4 Pasture data for L band.

Some caution must be exercised in direct comparisons between the three test sites because differences in soil type and organic matter content may be influencing the results. Schmugge (1980) showed that a silt loam soil would have a smaller slope to its linear regression than a sandy soil. Thus, the sandy Florida sites, if bare, should have a steeper regression slope than the silt loam soils in Oklahoma and South Dakota. If soil type differences were the only factor to consider, then the effect of the denser Florida pastures in decreasing microwave sensitivity to soil moisture would probably be greater than a comparison of the regression lines in Fig.4 now indicates. However, the Florida sites were also characterized by soils with high organics and very low bulk densities, which tend to increase the water-holding capacity of the soil. Since a

TABLE 4 Pasture site regression results L band H polarization 0° look angle, 0-5 cm soil moisture

Parameters	*Sites:* South Dakota	*Oklahoma*	*Florida*
Intercept	*0.99*	*0.96*	*0.97*
Slope	*0.0068*	*0.0067*	*0.0041*
R^2	*0.90*	*0.95*	*0.62*

sandy loam with high organics could "act" like a loamy soil with low organics, soil type information alone is not sufficient to normalize data from different test sites in order to analyse the microwave response to soil moisture. Additional work by a truck mounted system on the effects of soil organics and bulk density is needed before such a comparison can truly be accurate.

REFERENCES

Choudhury, B.J., Schmugge, T.J. & Mo, T. (1982) A parameterization of effective soil temperature for microwave emission. *J. Geophys. Res.* 87, 1301-1304.

Jackson, T.J., Schmugge, T.J., Coleman, G.C., Richardson, C., Chang, A., Wang, J. & Engman, E.T. (1980) Aircraft remote sensing of soil moisture and hydrologic parameters, Chickasha, Oklahoma and Riesel, Texas, 1978 data report. *US Dept Agric. ARR-NE-8*

Jackson, T.J., Schmugge, T.J., Allen, L.H. Jr, O'Neill, P., Slack, R., Wang, J. & Engman, E.T. (1981) Aircraft remote sensing of soil moisture and hydrologic parameters, Taylor Creek, Florida, and Little River, Georgia, 1979 data report. *US Dept Agric. ARR-NE-13.*

Jackson, T.J., O'Neill, P.E., Coleman, G.C. & Schmugge, T.J. (1982a) Aircraft remote sensing of soil moisture and hydrologic parameters, Chickasha, Oklahoma 1980 data report. *US Dept Agric. ARR-NE-14.*

Jackson, T.J., Schmugge, T.J. & Wang, J.R. (1982b) Passive microwave sensing of soil moisture under vegetation canopies. *Wat. Resour. Res.* 18 (4), 1137-1142.

Kirdiashev, K.P., Chukhlantsev, A.A. & Shutko, A.M. (1979) Microwave radiation of the earth's surface in the presence of vegetation cover. *Radiotecknika i Elecktronika* 24, 256-264, NASA translation.

Schmugge, T.J. (1980) Effect of texture on microwave emission from soils. *Inst. Elect. Electron. Engrs Trans. Geoscie. Remote Sens.* GE-18 (4), 353-361.

Schmugge, T., Gloersen, P., Wilheit, T. & Geiger, F. (1974) Remote sensing of soil moisture with microwave radiometers. *J. Geophys. Res.* 79, 317-323.

Schmugge, T.J., Jackson, T.J. & McKim, H.L. (1980) Survey of methods for soil moisture determination. *Wat. Resour. Res.* 16 (6), 961-979.

Ulaby, F.T., Razani, M. & Dobson, M.C. (1983) Effects of vegetation cover on the microwave radiometric sensitivity to soil moisture. *Inst. Elect. Electron. Engrs Trans. on Geosci. Remote Sens.* GE-21 (1), 51-61.

Wang, J.R., Schmugge, T.J., Gould, W.I., Glazar, W.S., Fuchs, J.E. & McMurtrey, J.E. (1982) A multi-frequency radiometric measurement of soil moisture content over bare and vegetated fields. *Geophys. Res. Lett.* 19 (4), 416-419.

Hydrological Applications of Remote Sensing and Remote Data Transmission (Proceedings of the Hamburg Symposium, August 1983). IAHS Publ. no. 145.

Détermination de la teneur en eau des sols par radiométrie passive en hyperfréquences

R. CALOZ, J. P. ANTILLE & P. MEYLAN
Institut de Génie Rural - Ecole Polytechnique Fédérale de Lausanne, 33 Avenue de Cour, CH-1007 Lausanne, Suisse

RESUME L'émission thermique de quatre sols nus, placés en lysimètres de 3 x 3 m, a été mesurée en 1981 et 1982 avec un radiomètre hyperfréquences à 2.2 et 3.8 GHz. Les résultats sont présentés et discutés à la lumière des récentes publications de Newton et Schmugge. Nous mettons en évidence les difficultés d'interprétation dues à la variabilité de la structure du sol et à l'incertitude sur la profondeur d'auscultation. La relation émissivité-humidité est analysée sous trois aspects: (a) forme non linéaire de la relation, (b) sensibilité de la réponse radiométrique à l'humidité, et (c) influence de la texture du sol. La profondeur d'auscultation, déterminée expérimentalement, de l'ordre de 1-2 pour un sol saturé, peut atteindre environ 10 cm en sol non saturé.

Soil moisture determination with passive microwave radiometry
ABSTRACT Thermal emission of four bare soils, placed in 3 x 3 m lysimeters, was measured in 1981 and 1982 with a microwave radiometer at both frequencies 2.2 and 3.8 GHz. Results are presented and discussed with reference to the recent publications from Newton and Schmugge. We point out the difficulties of the interpretation, due to the soil structure variability and to the uncertainty about the auscultation depth. Three aspects of the emissivity-humidity relation are analysed: (a) nonlinear shape of the relation, (b) sensitivity of the radiometrical response to moisture, and (c) soil texture influence. The experimentally determined auscultation depth is in the range of 1-2 cm in a saturated soil and can reach about 10 cm in unsaturated conditions.

NOTATIONS

w	humidité pondérale du sol (%g g^{-1})
w_{max}	capacité de rétention ou capacité au champ (%g g^{-1})
w_{pf}	point de flétrissement (%g g^{-1})
T	température (K) ou ($^{\circ}$C)
TR	température de radiance (K)
TS	température d'antenne, mesurée par le radiomètre (K)
TA	température de radiance recue par l'antenne (K)
e	émissivité (-)
η_r	rendement radiométrique de l'antenne (-)

η_d rendement directionnel de l'antenne (-)
$\varkappa$ coefficient d'atténuation linéïque (cm^{-1})

INTRODUCTION

La mesure de l'humidité du sol par radiométrie hyperfréquences passive, malgré les remarquables progrès accomplis ces dernières années se heurte encore, à notre avis, à de nombreuses difficultés. Elles sont de nature pratique et fondamentale selon que prédomine le point de vue de l'utilisateur ou celui du chercheur. Les modèles proposés jusqu'à ce jour souffrent de la même lacune: ils sont incapables de donner une bonne approximation de la profondeur de sol que le radiomètre est capable d'ausculter. En effet, la théorie de l'électromagnétisme prévoit qu'une couche de sol d'épaisseur variable, selon son état d'humidité, est la source principale de rayonnement hyperfréquences mesuré au-dessus de ce sol. Or, dans les sols naturels, la teneur en eau et la température varient en fonction de la profondeur, de sorte que l'émission thermique percue par le radiomètre est une résultante des émissions propres de chaque couche de sol et des effets produits par l'interface sol-air. Newton *et al.* (1982) mettent en évidence la nature dynamique des paramètres d'humidité mesurés en vue de l'interprétation des données radiométriques, rendant difficile la comparaison des résultats obtenus en début et en fin d'expérience, le sol passant d'un état saturé à celui de faible humidité. La profondeur d'auscultation (au terme pénétration nous préférons celui d'auscultation, plus proche de la réalité physique en radiométrie passive) est ainsi différente dans les deux cas. Il en résulte qu'il est pratiquement impossible de calculer une température de radiance ou l'émissivité, qui aurait la même signification pour les différents états hydriques ou thermiques du sol.

Newton *et al.* (1982) passent en revue divers modèles théoriques, les comparent à des résultats expérimentaux et présentent une remarquable analyse du problème soulevé dans cette introduction. Ils concluent, en ce qui concerne la profondeur d'auscultation, que seule la couche superficielle du sol d'environ 2 cm détermine la température de radiance vue par le radiomètre. Certains résultats expérimentaux que nous publions laissent supposer que cette conclusion n'est valable que pour les sols très humides. Notre contribution se propose d'apporter des éléments de réponse aux deux questions suivantes: (a) sensibilité de la radiométrie à la teneur en eau et au type de sol, et (b) profondeur d'auscultation.

RADIOMETRIE DE L'HUMIDITE DU SOL

Dispositif expérimental et procédures de mesure

Description générale La station d'essai a été concue de manière à permettre la mesure de la température de radiance sur quatre types de sols placés en lysimètres de 3 x 3 m. L'humidité de ces sols peut être partiellement contrôlée par couverture des cases. Le radiomètre hyperfréquences est monté sous le bras d'une grue à environ 15 m d'altitude, et peut être amené à la verticale de chaque échantillon de sol. L'orientation de l'antenne est commandée depuis de sol et contrôlée par une caméra TV dont l'axe optique est parallèle à celui de l'antenne. Lors de chaque mesure radiométrique le profil de température du sol ainsi que les paramètres météorologiques sont mesurés par un ordinateur et des prélèvements de sol sont effectués pour la détermination du profil d'humidité. Les mesures ont été acquises durant les étés 1981 et 1982, par périodes de deux à trois semaines, temps nécessaire pour que le sol passe, par assèchement naturel, de l'humidité à saturation à une teneur en eau n'excédant pas le pourcent pour le sable le plus grossier.

Caractéristiques des sols mesurés Afin de limiter le nombre de paramètres, l'étude a porté sur des sols peu structurés (sables fin et grossier) et, pour comparaison, sur une terre végétale prélevée sur le site expérimental (sol 1). La variation temporelle de la structure est négligeable pour les sols 3 et 4. Les sols 1 et 2 ont par contre montré une importante variation de structure (tassement, croûtage) attestée par la forte dispersion des valeurs de densité (cf. Tableau 1). La même hétérogénéité est d'ailleurs constatée sur

TABLEAU 1 Caractéristiques des sols mesurés

Sol numéro	*1*	*2*	*3*	*4*
Désignation	*limon sableux*	*sable*	*sable*	*sable*
Gravier (% du total)	*16*	*5*	*0*	*0*
Argile (% frac. < 2 mm)	*12*	*2*	*0*	*0*
Silt fin (% < 2 mm)	*17*	*2*	*0*	*1*
Silt grossier (% < 2 mm)	*13*	*12*	*2*	*1*
Sable fin (% < 2 mm)	*28*	*63*	*33*	*12*
Sable grossier (% < 2 mm)	*30*	*21*	*65*	*86*
Porosité (%)	*50-53*	*44-53*	*47-50*	*44-45*
Densité app. sèche	*1.33-1.55*	*1.35-1.59*	*1.38-1.49*	*1.51-1.57*
w_{max} *(%g g^{-1})*	*20*	*20*	*10*	*5*

la verticale d'un profil, rendant problématique l'analyse fine des humidités en termes volumiques. Sur une parcelle agricole ce problème de structure sera encore plus aigü, du fait des traitements culturaux, de la pluie et de l'assèchement superficiel.

Mesure de l'humidité La nécessité de pouvoir étudier en détail les profils d'humidité des sols avec une résolution spatiale de l'ordre de 2 cm a conduit à l'abandon de la méthode neutronique et de la méthode tensiométrique. La détermination de l'humidité a donc été effectuée par la méthode pondérale, pour des profondeurs de 0-2, 4-6 et 8-10 cm.

Mesure de la température La mesure du profil de température des sols est effectuée par sondes du type AD 590, reliées à l'ordinateur, pour les profondeurs de 0.5, 2.5, 6, 12, 24 et 48 cm et par radiométrie infrarouge.

Radiométrie hyperfréquences Le radiomètre utilisé est du type Dicke à boucle de rétroaction, construit par le Laboratoire d'Electromagnétisme et Accoustique (LEMA) de l'Ecole Polytechnique Fédérale de Lausanne (cf. Tableau 2).

TABLEAU 2 Caractéristiques du radiomètre LEMA - EPF-L

TYPE : Dicke avec boucle de rétroaction
FREQUENCES CENTRALES : 2.2 et 3.8 GHz commutables
BANDE PASSANTE : 400 MHz
PLAGE DE MESURE RADIOMETRIQUE : 110-300 K
RESOLUTION : 0.8 K
CALIBRATION INTERNE : par référence de température à 77.3 K (azote liquide) et 320 K (enceinte thermostatée)
TEMPS D'INTEGRATION : 15.5 ms

Antenne	*3.8 GHz*	*2.2 GHz*
Parabolique diam. (cm)	*92*	*92*
Bande de fréquence (GHz)	*3.7-4.2*	*2.0-2.4*
Angle d'ouverture (degrés)	*5.5*	*10.7*
Gain (dB)	*28.6*	*23.6*
Temp. de bruit (K)	*75*	*89*
Polarisation	*H et V*	*H et V*

Le radiomètre proprement-dit a été calibré en laboratoire par mesure d'une charge adaptée (corps noir) à température connue.

A partir de la température d'antenne TS, la température de radiance TA recue par l'antenne est donnée par la relation:

$$TA = TS/\eta_r - (1 - \eta_r)\ T_{ant}/\eta_r$$

où T_{ant} est la température physique de l'antenne. La détermination du rendement radiométrique η_r de l'antenne a été effectué par visée d'un corps de radiance connue: une piscine, de dimension suffisante pour que l'on puisse négliger l'effet des lobes latéraux. Si l'on néglige l'effet de la radiation du ciel on obtient la relation:

$$\eta_r = (TS - T_{ant})/(TR_{eau} - T_{ant})$$

Les valeurs obtenues sont $\eta_r = 0.75$ pour l'antenne 3.8 GHz et 0.63 pour l'antenne 2.2 GHz.

La température de radiance TA arrivant à l'antenne peut s'écrire (selon Ulaby *et al.* 1981):

$$TA = \eta_d\ TR_{cible} + (1 - \eta_d)\ TR_{par}$$

où l'indice "par" désigne l'environnement (parasite) de la cible visée. La détermination du rendement directionnel η_d des antennes a été effectuée par visée d'une cible connue (l'eau), de même dimension que les cases de sols étudiées. TR_{par} est mesurée par observation indépendante de l'environnement de la cible test. Dès lors:

$$\eta_d = (TA - TR_{par})/(TR_{eau} - TR_{par})$$

Les valeurs obtenues sont η_d= 0.92 pour l'antenne 3.8 GHz et 0.79 pour 2.2 GHz.

Les résultats des mesures sur les sols ont été corrigés uniquement pour le rendement radiométrique η_r de l'antenne (par hypothèse: TR_{sol} = TA). La contribution céleste au signal est donc négligée, de même que l'effet des lobes latéraux: dans la disposition de notre expérience, l'environnement de chaque case de sol est en effet trop complexe pour être pris en compte. L'erreur introduite par cette dernière simplification peut être estimée, en terme d'émissivité, dans les cas les plus défavorables à 0.02 pour la fréquence 3.8 GHz et 0.06 pour 2.2 GHz.

Résultats bruts

A titre d'exemple, la Fig.1 présente, sur un graphique à abcisse temporelle logarithmique, l'évolution des trois principaux paramètres lors d'une séquence typique d'assèchement du sol après irrigation par aspersion.

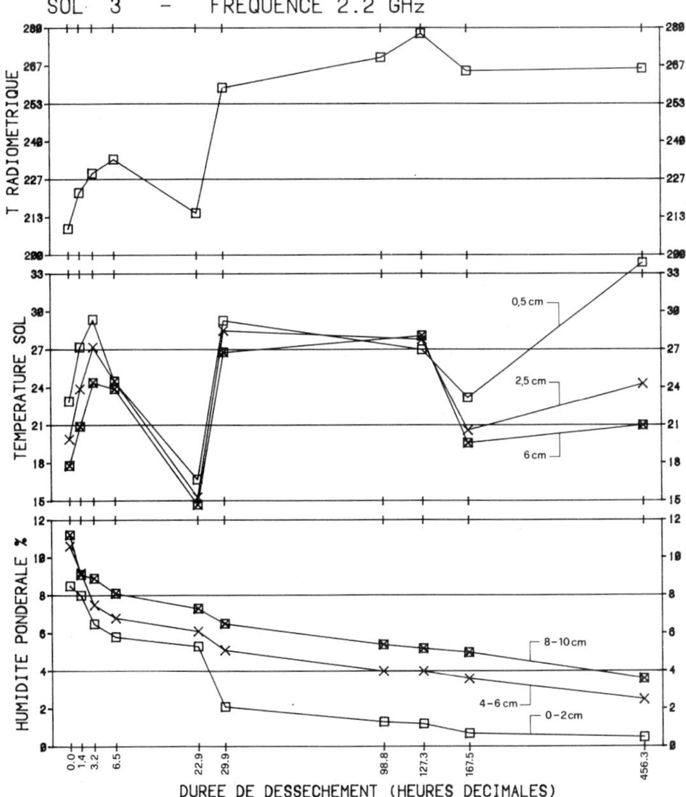

FIG.1 Evolution des paramètres au cours d'une séquence typique d'assèchement.

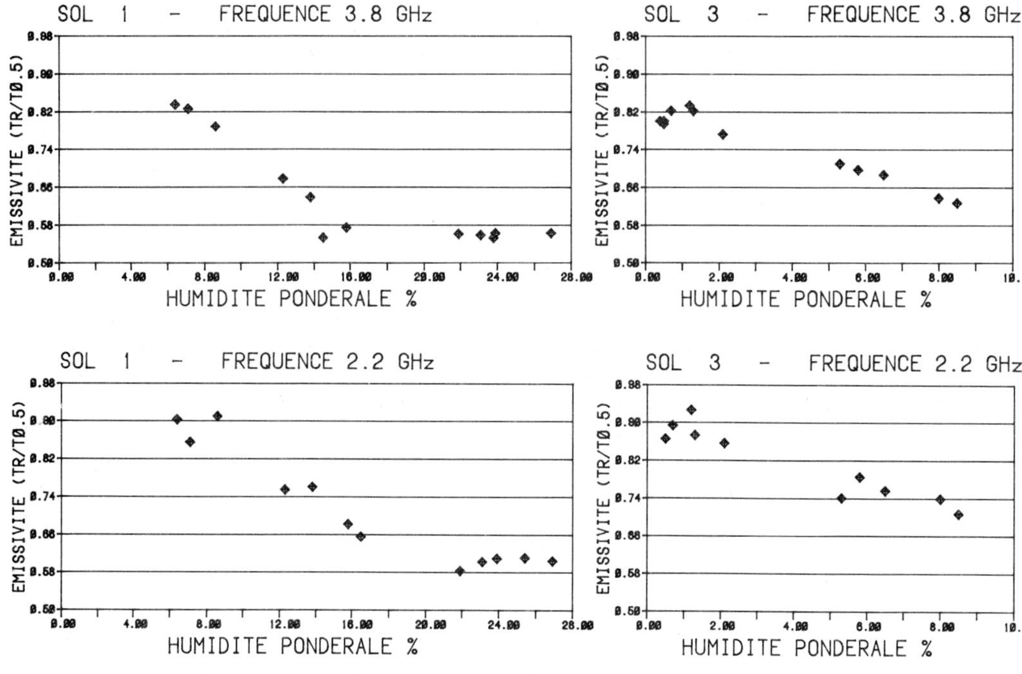

FIG.2 Exemples de relation e_a-w.

Dans le domaine des hyperfréquences, où l'approximation de Rayleigh-Jeans est applicable, l'émissivité d'un corps homogène semi-infini est défini par e = TR/T. Pour mettre en évidence une dépendance de e à l'humidité du sol nous normalisons la température de radiance par la température du sol à 0.5 cm et définissons ainsi une "émissivité apparente" $e_a = TR/T_{0.5\ cm}$. Cette normalisation est arbitraire dès que le profil est hétérogène en température ou en humidité, mais tient compte de la nature "volumique" de l'émission thermique par la couche superficielle du sol et permet en outre de comparer nos résultats à ceux d'autres chercheurs, par exemple Newton & Rouse (1980). La Fig.2. présente quatre graphiques typiques des résultats obtenus.

Interprétation

Les interactions électromagnétiques sont complètement déterminées par la constante diélectrique du milieu concerné. Dans le sol, celle-ci dépend principalement de l'humidité, de la teneur en sels minéraux et en matière organique. Les effets produits par les deux derniers paramètres n'ont pas été abordés dans notre étude. Si nous ne considérons que l'humidité, il faut encore tenir compte du degré de mobilité de l'eau du sol. On doit en effet s'attendre à ce que la diélectricité de l'eau adsorbée soit assez proche de celle des éléments solides du sol. Seule la "teneur volumique en eau libre" est responsable des modifications de constante diéléctrique, et donc de l'émissivité du milieu sol-eau. Il en résulte que ce paramètre devient primordial pour l'interprétation des températures de radiance. Or, pour l'expérimentateur, la seule technique assurant une résolution spatiale assez fine est la détermination pondérale de l'humidité. Deux problèmes difficiles restent dès lors en suspens pour passer à la teneur volumique en eau libre: (a) la détermination fine de la densité apparente sèche, dont on a vu par ailleurs la variabilité, tant spatiale dans le profil, que temporelle sous l'effet des influences extérieures modifiant la structure du sol, et (b) la détermination de la mobilité de l'eau en fonction de l'humidité (relation potentiel-teneur en eau), sur laquelle la structure du sol a une importance prépondérante.

Forme de la relation émissivité-humidité Dans la plupart des interprétations de l'émissivité des sols en fonction de l'humidité, une relation linéaire est mise en évidance par les auteurs. Becker (communication personnelle), analysant plusieurs résultats publiés, a proposé une relation non linéaire que nous avons déjà utilisée dans de précédents travaux (Meylan *et al.*, 1980; Schanda *et al.*, 1980). Dans le domaine des faibles humidités, l'inflexion de la relation obtenue pourrait être due au fait que l'eau n'est pas libre. Elle est plus ou moins fortement liée aux grains du sol, ce dont témoigne la relation bien connue liant le potentiel de l'eau du sol à son humidité. Pour ce qui est de l'autre extrémité de la courbe, la non-linéarité de la relation est moins systématiquement observée par les divers chercheurs. Son explication n'est d'ailleurs pas encore satisfaisante. Vu la très faible profondeur de pénétration du rayonnement dans l'eau (de l'ordre du 2o-ème de la longueur d'onde) on peut émettre l'hypothèse d'un effet d'écran de l'eau, masquant le reste du volume de sol, saturé ou non.

Sensibilité A l'exclusion des deux extrêmités de la courbe, il est possible d'évaluer la sensibilité de l'émission thermique hyperfréquences à l'humidité du sol en étudiant la pente de la droite de régression. Cependant les valeurs ainsi calculées n'ont pas une signification rigoureuse, car la nature de nos mesures ne satisfait pas aux hypothèses d'échantillonnage aléatoire, nécessaires a la construction d'intervalles de confiance sur les résultats obtenus. Elles permettent cependant d'apprécier les ordres de grandeur de la sensibilité (cf. Tableau 3).

TABLEAU 3 Sensibilité de la réponse radiométrique, normalisée à 300 K, à l'humidité pondérale 0-2 cm, intervalle de confiance à 95%

Sol	*Fréquence 2.2 GHz sensibilité (K $\%^{-1}$)*	*Fréquence 3.8 GHz sensibilité (K $\%^{-1}$)*
1	*4.9-6.6-8.2*	*7.1-9.1-11.2*
3	*5.0-7.0-9.1*	*5.7-6.8-7.9*
4	*5.4-7.2-9.1*	*4.1-5.6-7.1*

Les sensibilités que nous avons mesurées et calculées sont supérieures à celles observées par différents chercheurs, en particulier Newton & Rouse (1980) qui donnent environ 5.4 K $\%^{-1}$. La différence de sensibilité entre les deux fréquences n'est pas statistiquement significative. On note cependant une sensibilité légèrement supérieure pour la fréquence la plus basse, ce qui va dans le sens des observations de Newton & Rouse (1980) et Meylan *et al.* (1980), basées sur un spectre de fréquences beaucoup plus large, montrant une sensibilité plus forte lorsque la fréquence diminue.

Influence du type de sol Pour se soustraire autant que possible de la texture du sol, Schmugge (1980) propose d'exprimer l'humidité en pourcent de la capacité de rétention du sol. Cette normalisation a été utilisée depuis par plusieurs auteurs. Appliquée à nos résultats de mesure, cette normalisation ne donne pas satisfaction (cf. Fig.3(a)). Il convient de relever que les mesures utilisées par Schmugge proviennent d'une campagne aéroportée et que son interprétation a un caractère plutôt statistique qu'expérimental. De plus les types de sols que nous analysons ne correspondent pas forcément à ceux étudiés par Schmugge.

Considérant les remarques formulées à propos du rôle de l'eau libre dans la diélectricité du sol, nous avons tenté une normalisation en utilisant la quantite $w - w_{pf}$ comme indicateur d'humidité (correspondant intuitivement à la quantité d'eau libre). La Fig.3(b) présente les résultats de cette tentative. Notons qu'il serait préférable d'exprimer cette eau libre en termes volumiques. Cette facon de procéder doit être considérée comme une hypothèse de travail, qu'il conviendra de mettre à l'épreuve avec une gamme plus large de types de sols.

ETUDE EXPERIMENTALE DE LA PROFONDEUR D'AUSCULTATION

Introduction

Une estimation satisfaisante de la profondeur de sol que le radiomètre actif ou passif est capable d'explorer reste, à notre avis, la question centrale des recherches poursuivies dans ce domaine. Les différents modèles proposés par divers auteurs, cités par Newton *et al.* (1982), conduisent à des prévisions contradictoires. De l'un à l'autre la profondeur auscultée varie de 0-2 cm à 15-20 cm pour des fréquences de quelques GHz. Selon l'approche classique, présentée par exemple par Ulaby *et al.* (1981), on peut s'attendre à ce que cette profondeur augmente lorsque l'humidité du sol diminue, ou que la longueur d'onde augmente. Newton *et al.* (1982), invoquant la prédominance des effets de l'interface sol-air, concluent que la température de radiance dépend uniquement de la couche superficielle du sol, de 0-2 cm, et que l'humidité des couches plus profondes peut tout de même être estimée, simplement parce qu'elle est fortement corrélée à celle de la surface. A ce jour peu d'expériences ont été réalisées pour mesurer cette profondeur d'auscultation.

Dispositif expérimental et interprétation

La méthode utilisée a été proposée par Mätzler *et al.* (1979). Elle consiste à enterrer une grille métallique (réflecteur parfait en

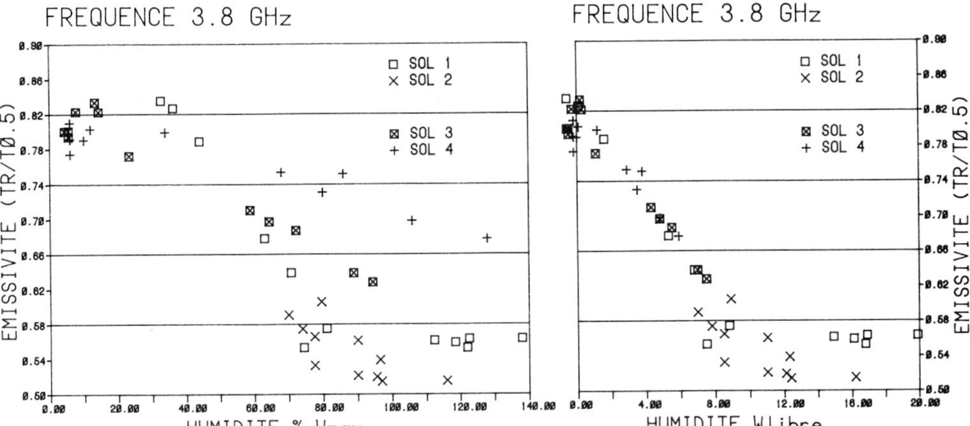

FIG.3 Normalisation de l'humidité (a) par la capacité de rétention w_{max}, et (b) par la teneur en eau libre $w - w_{pf}$.

hyperfréquences) dans le sol, et à observer la température de radiance pour différentes profondeurs z de la grille. Le radiomètre voit alors le ciel, réfléchi par la grille, à travers une épaisseur 2 z de sol, ainsi que la radiance thermique émise par cette même épaisseur 2 z de sol. Le modèle simple d'interprétation de Schanda *et al.* (1980) conduit à:

$$(TR - e\,T_{sol})/(TR_{ciel} - e\,T_{sol}) = \exp(-\varkappa 2z)$$

Si l'on dispose d'une série de mesures à profondeurs z différentes, le coefficient $\varkappa$ peut se lire comme la pente de la droite de régression (par l'origine) sur un diagramme d'abcisse z et d'ordonnée $y = -\frac{1}{2}\ln[TR - e\,T_{sol})/(TR_{ciel} - e\,T_{sol})]$. L'expérience réalisée sur le sol 4, à la fréquence 3.8 GHz et pour une humidité inférieure à 1% conduit à une profondeur de pénétration $d = 1/\varkappa$ de 12-15 cm (intervalle de confiance à 95%). On constate un bon accord du modèle classique avec nos résultats.

TABLEAU 4 Diminution de e_a due à la présence d'une grille à la profondeur z

Sol	*1*	*1*	*2*	*2*	*2*	*3*	*3*	*3*	*3*
Fréquence (GHz)	*2.2*	*3.8*	*2.2*	*2.2*	*3.8*	*2.2*	*2.2*	*3.8*	*3.8*
w ($\%g\ g^{-1}$)	*19*	*19*	*16*	*16*	*16*	*2*	*9*	*2*	*9*
z (cm)	*5*	*5*	*5*	*10*	*10*	*10*	*10*	*10*	*10*
$\Delta\ e_a$ (%)	*≈0*	*≈0*	*16*	*14*	*3*	*35*	*8*	*27*	*11*

Dans une deuxième phase, nous avons répété l'expérience de manière simplifiée pour les autres sols et pour d'autres niveaux d'humidité (cf. Tableau 4). Au vu de ces résultats, qui méritent d'être affinés, les conclusions de Newton paraissent trop restrictives. S'il se confirme (sol 1) qu'en situation de forte humidité la profondeur d'auscultation se réduit aux 2 premiers cm environ, il apparaît qu'elle augmente sensiblement avec la diminution de la teneur en eau. Nous observons, pour les sols 2 et 3 une diminution de 9% environ de l'émissivité apparente lorsque la grille est placée à 10 cm et que le sol est à saturation. On en conlut que dans cette situation, la grille est encore "perçue" par le radiomètre.

En introduisant ces données dans le modèle de Schanda, nous obtenons les résultats du Tableau 5, qui sont compatibles avec les valeurs de diminution de e_a observées.

TABLEAU 5 Interprétation par le modèle de Schanda

Sol	*2*	*3*	*3*	*3*	*3*
Fréquence (GHz)	*3.8*	*3.8*	*3.8*	*2.2*	*2.2*
Humidité (%g g^{-1})	*16*	*2*	*9*	*2*	*9*
Prof. ausc. (cm)	*6.5*	*16.7*	*9.8*	*20.*	*9.0*

REMERCIEMENTS Cette recherche a été financée par le Fonds National Suisse de la Recherche Scientifique. Le site d'essais a été mis à notre disposition par l'Ecole Cantonale d'Agriculture de Granges-Vernay près Moudon.

REFERENCES

Mätzler, Ch., Hofer, R., Wyssen, D. & Schanda, E. (1979) On the penetration of microwaves in snow and soil. *Proc. 13th Int. Symp. on Remote Sensing of the Environment.* Ann Arbor, Michigan, USA.

Meylan, P., Morzier, C., Caloz, R., Schanda, E. & Mätzler, Ch. (1980) Soil moisture determination: experiments with passive radiometers. In: *Proc. 10th European Microwave Conf.*, 256-260.

Newton, R.W. & Rouse, J.W. (1980) Microwave radiometer measurements of soil moisture content. *Inst. Elect. Electron. Engrs Trans. Automat. Control* 28 (5), 680-686.

Newton, R.W., Black, Q.R., Makanvand, S., Blanchard, A.J. & Jean, B.R. (1982) Soil moisture information and thermal microwave emission. *Inst. Elect. Electron. Engrs Trans. GE* 20 (3), 275-281.

Schanda, E., Wyssen, D., Meylan, P. & Morzier C. (1980) Soil moisture estimation by correlated ground-based and Seasat microwave observation. In: *The Contribution of Space Observation to Water Resources Management* (ed. by V.V.Salomonson & P.D.Bhavsar), 89-97. Pergamon Press, Oxford.

Schmugge, T.J. (1980) Effect of texture on microwave emission from soils. *Inst. Elect. Electron. Engrs Trans. GE* 18 (4), 353-361.

Ulaby, F.T., Moore, R.K. & Fung, A.K. (1981) *Microwave Remote Sensing, Active and Passive.* Addison-Wesley, Reading, Massachusetts, USA.

Hydrological Applications of Remote Sensing and Remote Data Transmission
(Proceedings of the Hamburg Symposium, August 1983). IAHS Publ. no. 145.

Validation of a soil-plant-atmosphere model for soybeans and an approach to inferring root-zone soil water potential from the canopy temperature

BHASKAR J. CHOUDHURY
Hydrological Sciences Branch, Goddard Space Flight Center, Greenbelt, Maryland 20771, USA

ABSTRACT A soil-plant-atmosphere model for soybeans is used to simulate leaf water potential, stomatal resistance and canopy temperature at various soil water potentials. For soil water potentials near field capacity the simulation gives a "base line" relationship between the canopy-air temperature difference (δT) and air vapour pressure deficit (VPD) which agrees well with a linear regression equation developed from observations. The δT values at lower soil water potentials are found to be uniquely related to the base line δT values, which suggests that the root zone soil water potential may be inferred from observed δT and the base line δT calculated from air and dew point temperatures. Simulated stomatal resistances and leaf water potentials are in fairly good agreement with observations.

Validation d'un modèle atmosphère-plante-sol pour le soja et approche pour déduire le potentiel en eau du sol dans la zone des racines de la température de surface de la couverture végétale

RESUME Un modèle sol-végétation-atmosphère utilise les données météorologiques (considérées à l'échelle horaire) pour simuler le potentiel en eau des feuilles, la résistance stomatale et la température superficielle de la couverture végétale pour toute une gamme de potentiels en eau du sol dans le cas d'une culture de soja (*Glycine max.* L.). Quand le potentiel en eau du sol approche de la capacité au champ, la simulation donne une relation de base entre la différence de température de l'air à la surface de la couverture végétale (δT) et le déficit de tension de vapeur de l'air (VPD) qui est bien en accord avec une régression linéaire déduite des observations. Les valeurs de δT pour les valeurs les plus basses du potentiel en eau du sol sont ainsi qu'on le constate, seulement en relation avec les valeurs de δT telles qu'elles sont calculées par l'équation de base ce qui indique que l'on peut calculer le potentiel en eau du sol dans la zone des racines à partir des valeurs observées de δT et des valeurs de bases de δT calculées à partir de la température de l'air et de la température du point de rosée. Les valeurs simulées des résistances stomatales et des potentiels en eau des feuilles sont en assez bon accord avec les observations.

INTRODUCTION

Effective use of irrigation water is rapidly becoming a subject of considerable interest, and a method for irrigation scheduling based upon crop temperature measurements has been suggested (Aston & van Baval, 1972). This technique for irrigation scheduling is well suited for infrared radiometric remote sensing. It has long been recognized (Tanner, 1963) that crop temperature can be used as an indicator for soil water stress; as plant-available soil water decreases the canopy temperature increases. To identify crop water stress more-or-less unambiguously by crop temperature measurements, it is necessary to quantify the effects of weather variables on the canopy temperature.

Carlson *et al.* (1972) observed that air temperature and vapour pressure deficit (VPD) are the significant weather variables affecting soybean canopy temperature. Using data from different geographic locations, Idso *et al.* (1981) showed that during a significant portion of daylight periods unique linear relationships exist between the canopy-air temperature difference (δT) and VPD for non-stressed alfalfa, soybean and squash. The linear relationships are, however, different for different crops, that is, the unstresses canopy temperatures of different crops are not identical. A model to understand canopy temperatures must recognize the crop specific nature of these temperatures.

The present modelling approach parallels Soer (1980) for grasses, Choudhury (1983) for corn, and Choudhury & Idso (1984) for sunflower, and recognizes the crop specific nature of transpiration and canopy temperature through the radiation absorption coefficient of the canopy (Kanemasu *et al.*, 1976) and resistances for water flow through plant, and heat and vapour exchange with the atmosphere (Zur *et al.*, 1983; Carlson *et al.*, 1979; Jones *et al.*, 1982). The soybean model is validated against the observations of Idso *et al.* (1981) for canopy temperatures, Brady *et al.* (1974) for leaf water potential, and Brady *et al.* (1975) and Sivakumar & Shaw (1978) for stomatal resistances. The present model does not consider soil evaporation, non-uniform root distribution and soil drying, and plant dehydration.

INPUT DATA

Significant linear relationships between δT and VPD observed by Idso *et al.* (1981) for soybeans included data from different geographical locations and covered a wide range of atmospheric variables. Since weather variables are not totally uncorrelated, the present simulation is done using observed (US Department of Commerce) hourly weather data for clear skies during summer at Phoenix (Arizona) and at Baltimore (Maryland). A total of 16 days data consisting of four days for Baltimore during June and July and 12 days for Phoenix during May and June were used. The weather variables during 1000 to 1400 h LST (local standard time) covered a wide range; VPD from 1.6 to 8.3 kPa, wind speed from 1.5 to 6.5 m s^{-1} and air temperature from 23 to 43°C. Phoenix weather data are used in the simulation for examining the behaviour of the model predictions at high VPD, although Phoenix is actually not a commercial soybean growing area.

A crop height of 0.9 m and a leaf area index of 4 is assumed to be representative of a mature soybean crop. Based on the observations of Arya *et al.* (1975) the root length per unit area was assumed to be $1.4 \times 10^4 m^{-1}$.

SIMULATION RESULTS

At the soil water potential of -1 m the simulated dependence of δT on VPD is shown in Fig.1 together with the regression line calculated by Idso *et al.* (1981) using observations on non-stressed soybeans at Kansas, Nebraska and North Dakota. In the observations VPD did not exceed 6kPa, and for this range of VPD the simulation generally agrees with the prediction based on the regression line to within 0.5K. The data plotted in Idso *et al.* (1981) indicates a standard

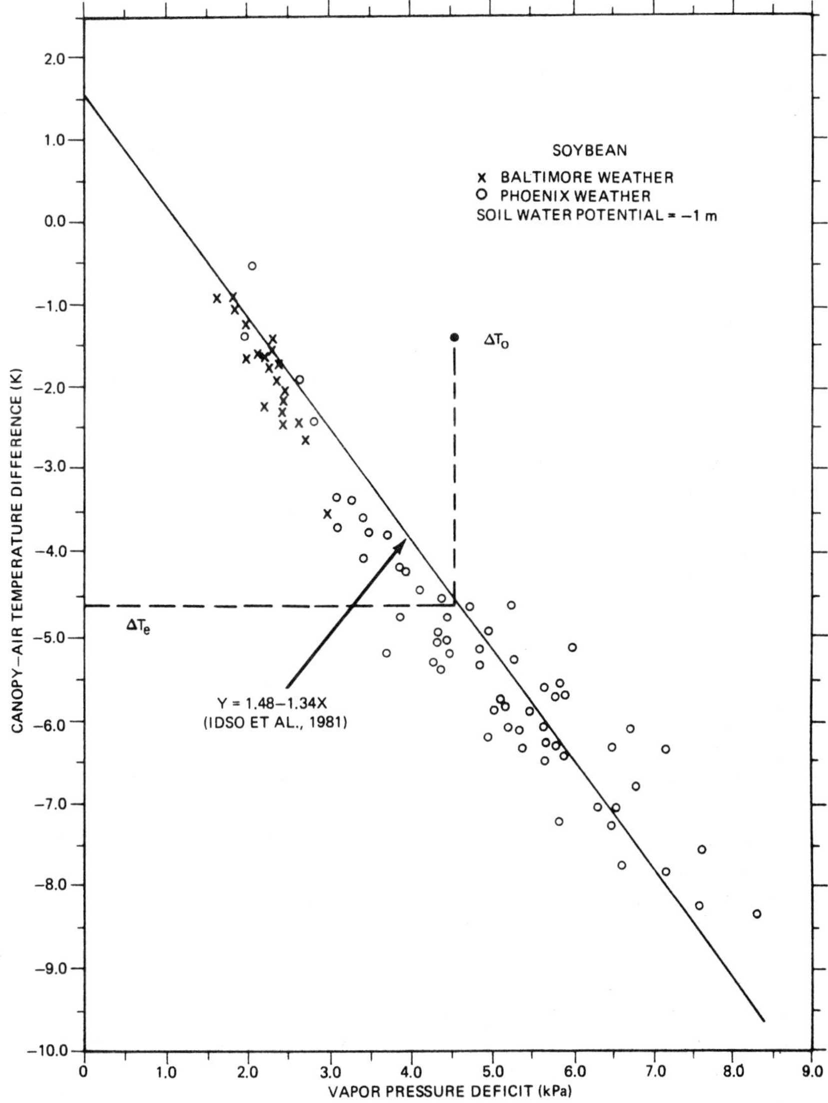

FIG.1 Simulated variation of soybean canopy-air temperature difference with air vapour pressure deficit. The regression equation calculated by Idso et al. (1981) from observations on unstressed canopies is plotted. The soil water potential is -1 m.

error of about 1°K with respect to the regression line. Whereas the observed data are scattered evenly with respect to the regression line, the simulated results are seen to be somewhat biased (lower δT values), particularly in the VPD range of 2.5 to 4.5 kPa. Considering the range of weather variables used in this simulation, the scatter in Fig.1 supports Idso *et al.* (1981) in showing that air and dew point temperatures are the significant weather variables affecting the canopy temperature during most of clear sky day period.

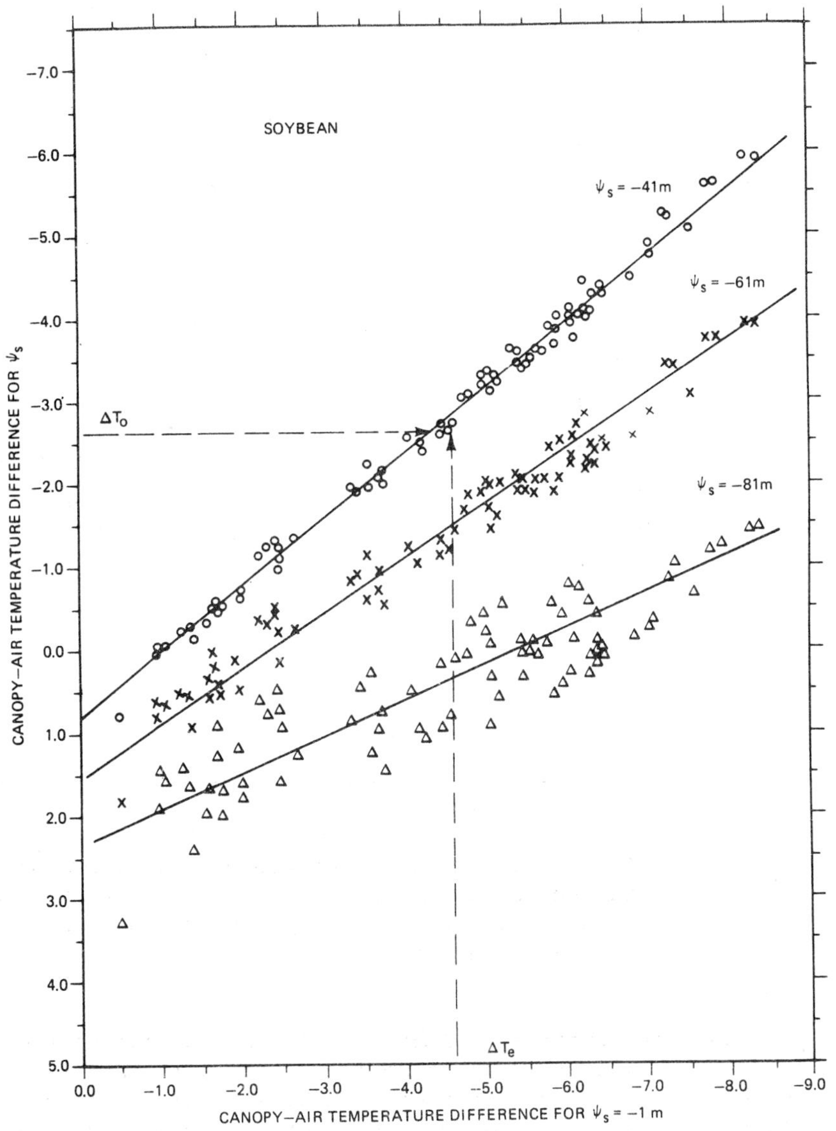

FIG.2 Relationship of the canopy-air temperature differences at the soil water potentials of -41, -61, and -81 m with respect to the soil water potential of -1 m. With decreasing soil water potential the scatter increases due to differing wind speeds.

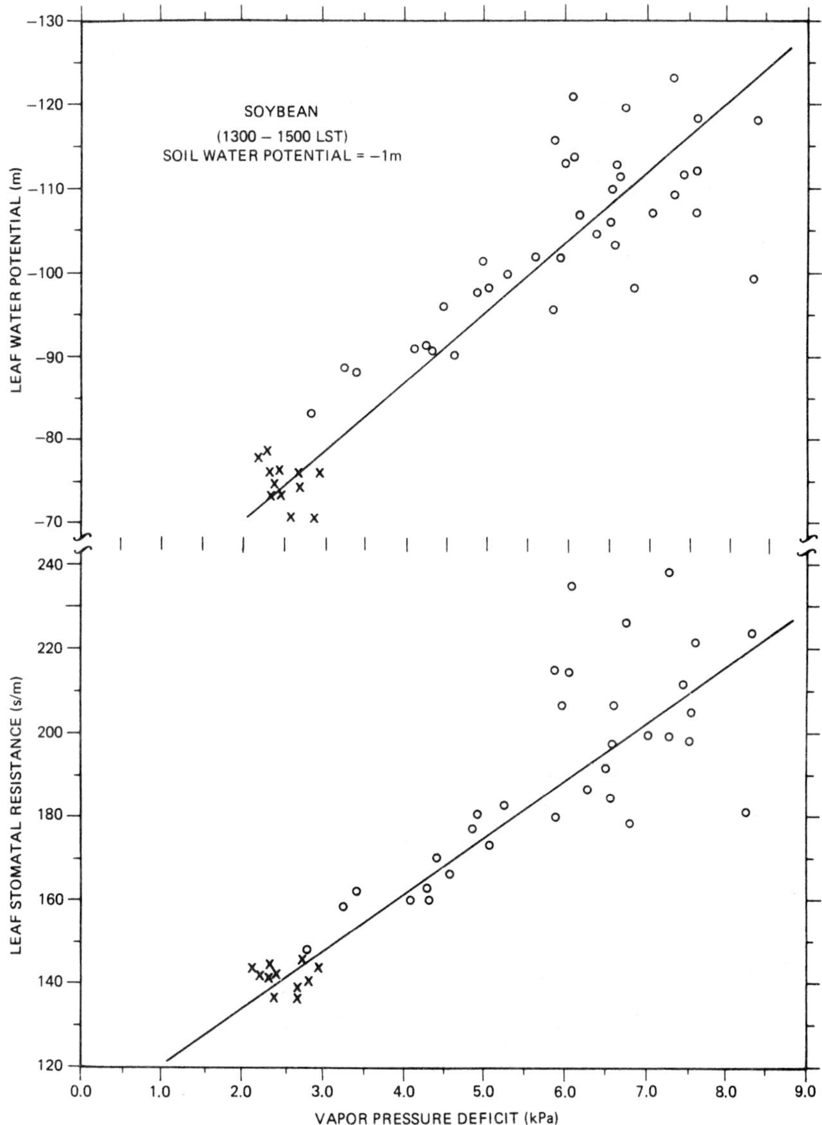

FIG.3 Simulated dependence of leaf stomatal resistance and leaf water potential on the air vapour pressure deficit. The soil water potential is -1 m. Straight lines are drawn to show the trend.

Canopy temperature reflects the integrated response of the plant to the existing weather and soil water conditions. If the effect of weather variables can be accounted for in terms of air and dew point temperatures, e.g. by Fig.1, it may be possible to infer the soil water conditions from the canopy temperature measurements. Figure 2 shows the relationship between the δT values at the soil water potential of -1 m (as shown in Fig.1) and the δT values at the potentials of -41, -61 and -81 m. Significant linear relationships between these sets of δTs seen in this figure are consistent with the observations of Walker & Hatfield (1983), and appear potentially useful in the remote sensing of root-zone soil water conditions. Referring to Fig.1, let us assume that the observed value of δT is δT_o. If the soil water potential were -1m (which is close to the field capacity) the observed value would have been δT_e (one may calculate this knowing air and dew point temperatures using the regression equations of Idso *et al.*, 1981). This δT_e value can now be used as the X-coordinate and δT_o value as the Y-coordinate in Fig.2 to bracket the soil water potential. In the example shown the observed δT corresponds to the soil water potential of about -40 m. It should be noted that δT_o *vs.* VPD and δT *vs.* δT_o relationships are crop specific, and therefore Figs 1 and 2 may not be used for crops other than soybean. The highly correlative nature of δTs at two different soil water potentials (as seen in Fig.2) is an expected result from energy balance (Choudhury, 1983).

Apart from canopy temperatures, the leaf stomatal resistances and the leaf water potentials were also simulated for comparison with observations.

The simulated leaf stomatal resistances at the soil water potential of -1 m are shown in Fig.3 as a function of VPD. The data in Idso *et al.* (1981) show that VPD in Kansas generally does not exceed 6 kPa, and Fig.3 shows that for VPD up to 6 kPa the range of stomatal resistance is 136 to 215 s m^{-1}. This range for simulated resistances is in good agreement with the observed range, from 140 to 190 s m^{-1}, by Brady *et al.* (1975).

The range of stomatal resistances for VPD from 2.2 to 6 kPa at various soil water potentials is shown in Fig.4. The increase in stomatal resistance with decreasing soil water potential is consistent with observations of Sionit & Kramer (1976). The empirically derived regression equations by Brady *et al.* (1975) and Sivakumar & Shaw (1978) for soybean crops are also plotted to show agreement with the simulation.

The dependence of leaf water potential of VPD during 1300 to 1500 LST is shown in Fig.3 at the soil water potential of -1 m, and the range of the potential corresponding to stomatal resistances in Fig.4 is shown in Fig.5. The regression equation for soybean calculated by Brady *et al.* (1974) is plotted in Fig.5 to show that the observed data as expressed through the regression equation and their standard error of estimate (8.7 m) are fairly well represented in the simulation.

In appraising the above comparison results it is pertinent to consider the measurement uncertainties and errors. The leaf and soil water potentials measured by Brady *et al.* (1974) before sunrise did not follow a 1:1 relationship which, as such, disagrees with the assumption of plant- and soil-water equilibrium. The pressure chamber method used for leaf water potential measurements did not include xylem osmotic potential, which Brady *et al.* estimate could be as much as -10 m when the pressure potential is -80 m. If the leaf water potentials calculated from the regression equation of Brady *et al.* (1974) are to be uniformly decreased by 10 m, the prediction based on the regression equation would still pass through the simulated range; however, the standard error of estimate for the regression equation would go beyond the lower bound of the range for most soil water potentials. Thus, if the apparent contradiction of data with soil- and plant-water equilibriums is to be reconciled by decreasing the measured leaf water potentials by 10 m or more, then the simulation will be less satisfactory with respect to these potentials. There also appears to be some ambiguity in interpreting a neutron probe measurement of soil water potential (Brady *et al.*, 1974) as the root-zone water potential (see Federer, 1979). The seasonal average predawn and midday values of irrigated soybean leaf water potential (planted in silt loam soil) observed by Jung & Scott (1980) were, respectively, -42 and -116 m. If under the assumption of soil- and plant-water equilibrium, the predawn value of leaf

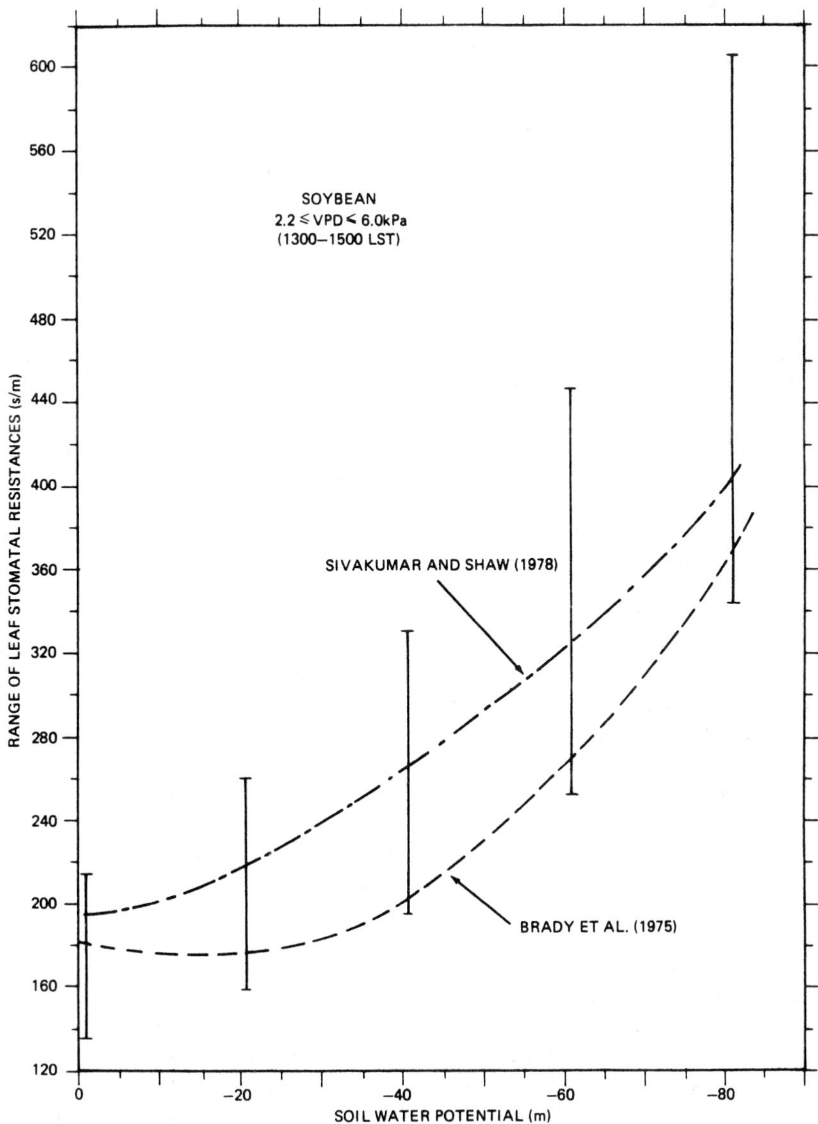

FIG.4 The simulated range of leaf stomatal resistances at various soil water potentials. The dependencies inferred from observations by Brady et al. (1975) and Sivakumar & Shaw (1978) are also plotted.

water potential is assumed to represent the soil water potential then the observed midday value of the leaf water potential (-116 m) would not be inconsistent with the present simulation. However, the corresponding observed seasonal average midday leaf stomatal resistance of 60 s m^{-1} is about a factor of three smaller than that predicted by the simulation. Thus, although the present simulation

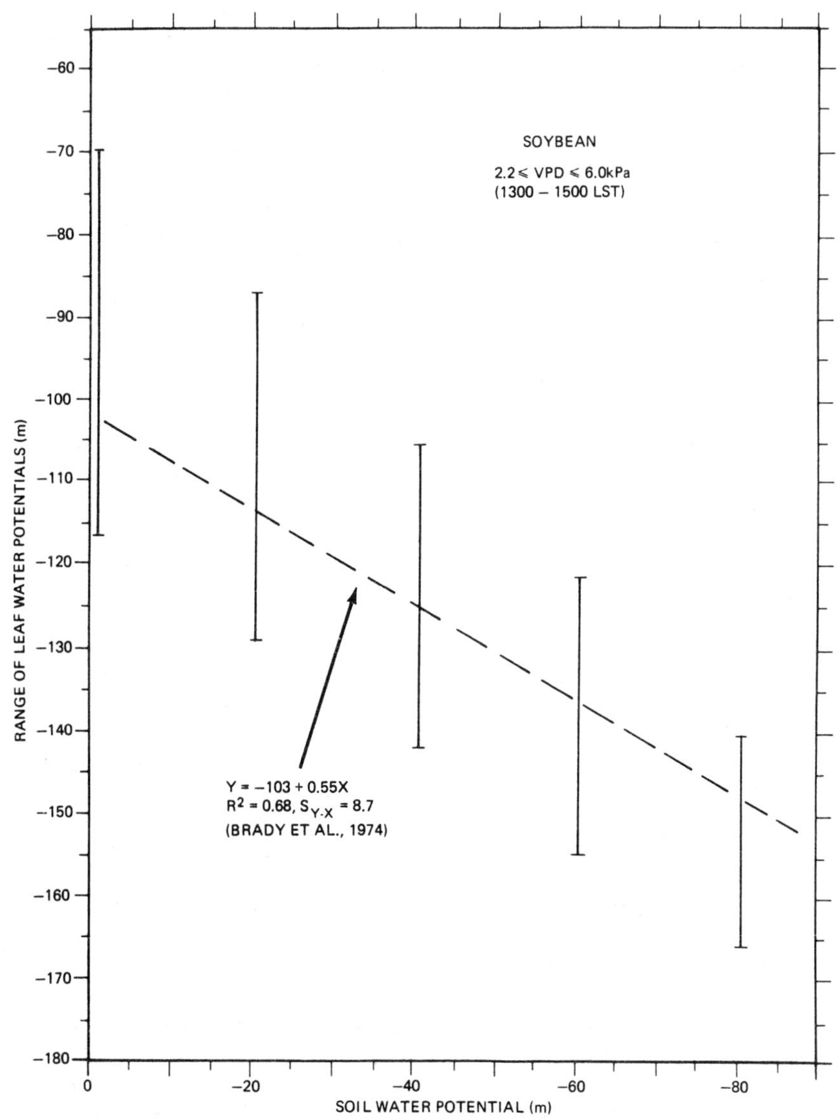

FIG.5 The range of leaf water potentials at various soil water potentials. The regression equation calculated by Brady et al. (1974) is shown.

provides some qualitative understanding of a few independent sets of observations, it also shows the need for a better quantification of the stomatal resistance-leaf water potential relationship (Carlson *et al.*, 1979; Zur *et al.*, 1983) for different soybean cultivars and changes resulting from environmental adaptation. It is also pertinent to quantify the mechanics of osmotic regulation and the role of leaf turgor in the stomatal control (cf., Turner *et al.*, 1978; Zur & Jones, 1981).

SUMMARY

A soil-plant-atmosphere model for soybean has been developed, and simulation results using observed hourly weather data were compared with observed canopy temperatures, stomatal resistances, and leaf water potentials. The possibility of inferring root-zone moisture from infrared radiometric observations of the canopy temperature appears from the analysis of results in Figs 1 and 2. For well-watered soybeans Fig.1 illustrates that the canopy-air temperature difference is largely determined by the air vapour pressure deficit, i.e. for unstressed canopies the ambient air and dew point temperatures determine the canopy temperature. From Fig.2 we see that the canopy temperature of stressed canopies would be related to that of an unstressed canopy by a linear regression equation, whose coefficients are functions of root-zone water potential. Thus, infrared radiometric observation in addition to ambient air and dew point temperatures could provide information about the root-zone water potential.

REFERENCES

Arya, L.M., Blake, G.R. & Farrell, D.A. (1975) A field study of soil water depletion in presence of growing soybean roots: III. Rooting characteristics and root extraction of soil water. *Soil Sci. Soc. Am. Proc.* 39, 437-444.

Aston, A.R. & van Bavel, C.H.M. (1972) Soil moisture depletion and leaf temperature. *Agron. J.* 64, 368-373.

Brady, R.A., Powers, W.L., Stone, L.R. & Goltz, S.M. (1974) Relation of soybean leaf water potential to soil water potential. *Agron. J.* 66, 795-798.

Brady, R.A., Goltz, S.M., Powers, W.L. & Kanemasu, E.T. (1975) Relation of soil water potential to stomatal resistance of soybean. *Agron. J.* 67, 97-99.

Carlson, R.E., Yarger, D.Y. & Shaw, R.H. (1972) Environmental influences on the leaf temperatures of two soybean varieties grown under controlled irrigation. *Agron. J.* 64, 224-229.

Carlson, R.E., Momen, N.M., Arjmand, O. & Shaw, R.H. (1979) Leaf conductance and leaf-water potential relationships of two soybean cultivars grown under controlled irrigation. *Agron. J.* 71, 321-325.

Choudhury, B. (1983) Simulating the effects of weather variables and soil water potential on a corn canopy temperature. *Agric. Meteorol.* 29, 169-182.

Choudhury, B.J. & Idso, S.B. (1984) Simulating sunflower canopy temperatures to infer root-zone water potential. *Agric. For. Meteorol.* 31, 69-78.

Federer, C.A. (1979) A soil-plant-atmosphere model for transpiration and availability of soil water. *Wat. Resour. Res.* 15, 555-562.

Idso, S.B., Jackson, R.D., Pinter, P.J., Jr, Reginato, R.J. & Hatfield, J.L. (1981) Normalizing the stress-degree-day parameter for environmental variability. *Agric. Meteorol.* 24, 45-55.

Jones, J.W., Zur, B., Boote, K.J. & Hammond, L.C. (1982) Plant resistance to water flow in field soybeans: I. Non-limiting soil moisture. *Agron. J.* 74, 92-98.

Jung, P.K. & Scott, H.D. (1980) Leaf water potential, stomatal resistance, and temperature relations in field grown soybeans. *Agron. J.* 72, 986-990.

Kanemasu, E.T., Stone, L.R. & Powers, W.L. (1976) Evapotranspiration model tested for soybean and sorghum. *Agron. J.* 68, 569-572.

Sionit, N. & Kramer, P.J. (1976) Water potential and stomatal resistance of sunflower and soybean subjected to water stress during various growth stages. *Plant Physiol.* 58, 537-540.

Sivakumar, M.V.K. & Shaw, R.H. (1978) Relative evaluation of water stress indicators for soybean. *Agron. J.* 70, 619-623.

Soer, G.J.R. (1980) Estimating regional evapotranspiration and soil water conditions using remotely sensed crop surface temperatures. *Remote Sens. Environ.* 5, 137-145.

Tanner, C.B. (1963) Plant temperatures. *Agron. J.* 55, 210-211.

Turner, N.C., Begg, J.E., Rawson, H.M., English, S.D. & Hearn, A.B. (1978) Agronomic and physiological response of soybean and sorghum crops to water deficit. III. Components of leaf water potential, leaf conductance, $^{14}CO_2$ photosynthesis, adaptation to water deficits. *Austral. J. Plant Physiol.* 5, 179-194.

Walker, G.K. & Hatfield, J.L. (1983) Stress measurement using foliage temperatures. *Agron. J.* 75, 623-629.

Zur, B. & Jones, J.W. (1981) A model for water relations, photosynthesis, and expansive growth of crops. *Wat. Resour. Res.* 17, 311-320.

Zur, B., Jones, J.W. & Boote, K.J. (1983) Field evaluation of a water relations model for soybean. I. Validity of some basic assumptions. *Agron. J.* 75, 272-280.

Hydrological Applications of Remote Sensing and Remote Data Transmission (Proceedings of the Hamburg Symposium, August 1983). IAHS Publ. no. 145.

Photographic detection of groundwater pollution

J. ŠVOMA & A. PYŠEK
Stavební Geologie n.p., Záhřebská 33, 120 00 Praha 2, Czechoslovakia

ABSTRACT Efforts to protect surface and groundwater quality are urgently required. Groundwater pollution by industrial fertilizers, oil leaks and natural gas leaks were studied in actual emergencies and on experimental sites. Remote sensing, particularly aerial photography, can be used to detect vegetation changes caused by groundwater pollution. Mechanisms involved in the spreading of contaminants are summarized and the response of vegetation cover to this contamination is tabulated. The results of using colour and colour infrared photography to identify the responses on the experimental plots are outlined.

Détection photographique de la pollution des eaux souterraines
RESUME Il est urgent de faire un effort pour protéger la qualité des eaux de surface et des eaux souterraines. La pollution des eaux souterraines par les engrais chimiques, les fuites de pétrole et de gaz naturel a été étudié dans des cas d'urgence et à des sites expérimentaux. La télédétection et en particulier la photographie aérienne peut être utilisée pour déceler les changements de végétation provoqués par la pollution des eaux souterraines. On résume les mécanismes mis en jeu par la propagation des produits polluants et on a mis en tableau la réponse du couvert végétal à cette pollution. On décrit rapidement les résultats de l'utilisation de photographies en couleur et à partir de l'infra rouge pour identifier les réponses sur les parcelles expérimentales.

INTRODUCTION

Like other countries situated on continental watershed divides, Czechoslovakia has very limited water resources. The intensification of agricultural and industrial production is responsible for the pollution of surface water and groundwater, so that efforts to protect their quality are becoming more and more urgent.

For several years there has been an effort to make hydrogeological surveys more effective by means of remote sensing methods.

This paper deals with the following subjects:

(a) Groundwater pollution by industrial fertilizers because of the huge areas affected.

(b) Oil pollution, which is the most frequent cause of groundwater pollution.

(c) Natural gas leaks.

The former two types of pollution have been studied during actual emergencies and all three on experimental sites where the contaminant was intentionally introduced into the ground.

The presence of harmful substances in a ground formation causes changes in vegetation, which can be detected by remote sensing methods. Influences on the state of health of a plant are manifested by changes in the colour of leaf pigments and of the state of the cellular turgor. Remote sensing in the near-infrared region (700-1000 nm) is based on the higher reflectivity of healthy plants compared with that of damaged vegetation. The entire near-infrared region is not suitable for these purposes. The 700-750 nm interval is regarded by Collins (1978) as a transient zone where the use of wide-band filters (≥50 nm) does not provide information for the remote sensing of plant life. The use of plant indicators is rendered difficult by other unfavourable effects on vegetation such as drought, industrial emissions, etc. That is why aerial photography should be combined with a detailed botanical survey. (However, sometimes it is possible to utilize this phenomenon for the purposes of detection, for instance, of the white fungal coatings covering plants affected by natural gas leaks without any other changes detectable by photography.)

The following films have been employed in aerial photographic surveys: panchromatic black-and-white (BW) Fuji, Orwo; infrared BW (BWIR) Kodak High Speed Infrared, Orwo NI 750; colour inversion film (C) Orwochrome UT 18; and colour IR inversion film (CIR) Kodak Ektachrome IR. The camera lenses were equipped with blue, green and red filters for BW films, with Wratten W 70, W 87 and W 87 C filters for BWIR films, and with W 12 filter for CIR films.

MECHANISM INVOLVED IN THE SPREADING OF CONTAMINANTS

Industrial fertilizers

As a result of the increasing application of fertilizers, pollution of groundwater with nitrates has been rising since the 1950s to a degree which presents a worldwide problem.

When the nutrients are applied in amounts higher than the capacity of the plants to absorb them and the retention capacity of the soil, they would unavoidably be leached into the groundwater. Rocks of low permeability will permit only a very slow transfer of nitrates by the pore water [80-100 cm per annum (Young *et al.*, 1976)]. As soon as the gravity water is affected, the nitrates will spread at a rate given by the equation

$$v = k\ J\ n_o^{-1} \qquad (1)$$

where k is the coefficient of hydraulic conductivity ($m\ s^{-1}$), J is the hydraulic slope, and n_o is effective open porosity.

It can take decades for the vertical advance of the nitrate front in unconfined aquifers with deep groundwater tables (30-50 m) to cause serious groundwater pollution. The only way to control groundwater pollution is to regulate the amount of fertilizers used and the methods of their application. It is therefore important to map and monitor the potentially dangerous (over-fertilized) agricultural areas.

Oil and oil products

Oil products penetrate the ground mostly as a result of leaks from tanks or pipelines, or following traffic accidents. From the point where a surface spill occurs the oil spreads vertically through the aerated zone like a piston as soon as the so-called residual saturation of the soil is exceeded. Having passed to the groundwater table or to its capillary fringe, the oil starts to spread laterally, forming a so-called oil pancake. Its area varies from tens or hundreds of square metres in the case of small spills, up to hundreds or even thousands of square metres in the case of large spills or leaks (Arbeitskreis, 1970).

The oil film on the groundwater table will rarely spread farther than 100 m in porous ground. However, in fissured, permeable sandstone in the vicinity of Prague airport, aviation kerosene penetrated springs at a distance of 700 m from the source of the leak in only five months (Svoma & Houzim, 1983).

At the contact of the oil body hydrocarbons are subject to washing out, dissolution and subsequent transportation by convection. According to the type of product, concentrations of hydrocarbons in groundwater attain values of up to tens of mg l^{-1} in the proximity of the oil film, and values of tenths to units of mg l^{-1} in a wide surrounding, which may be of the order of square kilometres.

Natural gas

Natural gas passes into ground formations through leaks in pipelines. From the point of leakage it spreads under high pressure forming equipressure spherical areas also reaching below the pipe: under low pressure, there occur combinations of spherical and planar equipressure areas.

RESPONSE OF VEGETATION COVER TO CONTAMINATION

Nitrogen is an essential biogenic element for all vegetation. By their luxuriant growth and shadowing effect nitrophilous species (nettle) in areas rich in nitrogens tend to eliminate plants demanding less nitrogen.

Vegetation covers show diverse reactions to contamination from oil hydrocarbons. First of all there occurs a differentiation of its components: petroleophobic species lose their vitality, receding from the affected areas e.g. meadow grass. Petroleophilous species thrive in contaminated soil and their density generally increases, e.g. wood small-reed.

Most species react negatively to natural gas, for instance by a change in the characteristic colour shade of leaf green (e.g. lucerne), by reduced covering power, by a change in the leaf colour from green to red-violet (e.g. fodder cabbage).

RESEARCH RESULTS AND DISCUSSION

Pollution by industrial fertilizers

The Šāmsín locality at altitude 500 m has an acidic, brown soil and geology of paragneiss, with a clay-sand eluvium; the groundwater table is 1-7 m below ground level.

The experiment of washing out of nitrogen into groundwater was carried out on seven plots with a total area of 30 ha which were provided with boreholes. The plots were sown with barley or wheat; the fertilizers were applied in the respective doses of 0, 70 and 140 kg of nitrogen per hectare, taken as net nutrient.

Higher fertilizer doses give rise to lush corn growth and a change in colour: unfertilized barley 85 days after sowing was yellow-green, that fertilized with 70 kg and 140 kg N was green and dark green, respectively.

On the C and CIR films there are highly distinguishable areas showing the various degrees of fertilization. Pictures on a 1:5000 scale provide information on the uniformity of fertilizer distribution over the area.

The sharpness of the contours on aerial photographs makes it possible to determine the areas where liquid fertilizers have been applied (diffuse boundaries). In this way it is also possible to assess the degree of the endangering of the groundwater.

Pollution with oil hydrocarbons

The Točník locality near Klatovy has an altitude of 400 m, compost soil and a geology of granite with a 10 m thick sand-clay eluvium

The plants were contaminated with a 2:3 mixture of petrol and diesel oil as shown in Table 1. During the vegetation season the

TABLE 1

Row	*Dose 1978*	*Σ 1978*	*Dose 1979*	*Σ 1979*
0	*0*	*0*	*0*	*0*
I	*1 mg l^{-1}*	*0.032 g*	*3 mg l^{-1}*	*0.14 g*
II	*10 mg l^{-1}*	*0.32 g*	*30 mg l^{-1}*	*1.14 g*
III	*10 mg l^{-1} + 40 ml (once a week)*	*499.20 g*	*30 mg l^{-1} + 90 ml (once a fortnight)*	*652.14 g*

mixture was applied twice a week so as not to contaminate the leaves. In row III the mixture was injected with a syringe. Experimental plants were petunia, Scots pine, spruce, Oregon grape, wood small-reed, elder, mugwort, and stinging nettle.

According to botanical evaluation, the most resistant plant was spruce which showed no reaction at all. Pine needles started to turn yellow only after application of doses II or III. The botanical manifestations are summarized in Table 2.

TABLE 2 Response of some plants to critical amounts of contaminants

STIMULATION			PLANT	DAMAGE		DESTRUCTION		SUBSTANCE
OIL	NO_3	conc.		conc.		conc.	decay	
140 A dark green	70 A green	10 A	barley[xx]	-				N - NO_3
	lush growth	0.11 a	elder[x]	1.14 a	vitality loss	652 a	100 %	petrol + Diesel oil
dark green	lush growth	0.11 a	oregon grape[x]	1.14 a	light green	652 a	50 %	ditto
	lush growth	0.11 a	petunia[x]	1.14 a	sickly plants	652 a	80 %	ditto
	lush	0.11 a	mugwort[x]	0.32 a	yellowing	?		ditto
0.16 v.lush	lush	0.02 a	nettle	532 a	lower growth	?		aviation kerosene
		-	wheat (green)[xx]	0.04 E	yellowing	0,778 E	100 %	petrol + Diesel oil
			maize[xx]	?	small cover	26 E	100 %	oil
			corn (Mitchell 1979)	?		10 - 20 l m^2	?	oil
			spruce (Hutchinson 1975)	?		9 l m^2	total	oil

a - amount applied in g m^{-2} per annum (gradually during the vegetatión season)
A - amount applied in kg ha^{-1} p.a.
E - concentration in soil in g kg^{-1}
x - changes detectable by photography
xx -changes well discernible by photography
N - not tested

manifestations are summarized in Table 2.

Using photographic detection, the most distinct effect was observed on petunias in row III by decreased infrared reflectance. The presence of the contaminant was further indicated by a decrease in canopy density. The stimulating effect of small doses of the contaminant (Table 2) was revealed on the CIR film by deep rich red and magenta colours.

Natural gas

The Běleč Tabák locality near Beroun was at an altitude of 360 m, and had Palaeozoic shales and quartzites covered with gravel-clay eluvium. Natural gas was carried by pipelines under a young mixed forest comprising Scots pine and European larch.

The changes were most distinct on the larches. A leak was detected in the infrared region a fortnight before any visual changes had become discernible. On CIR Kodak Ektachrome film the damage to larch was revealed by the whitish, faintly violet colour of the needles. The leak manifested itself in this way 21 days after the start of the experiment, i.e. at a dose of 15 m^3 of methane (Pyšek & Švoma, 1978).

CONCLUSION

The mechanism of spreading of pollution indicates the significance of time in groundwater protection; a contaminant may migrate underground at the rate of up to several metres per day.

The limiting factor in the photographic detection of the potential pollution of the ground with nitrates is the spectral resolution. The possibility of discriminating between different kinds of pollution is additionally affected by spatial resolution.

The presence of a contaminant on bare ground can be detected photographically only at the site of its actual infiltration or only at the discharge of the aquifers.

Underground migration of contaminants can only be detected through their effects on the vegetation cover. Critical concentrations of diverse harmful substances that lead to a reaction in the plants show considerable variations. For example, with oil hydrocarbons this may be the application dose of min.0.5 kg m^{-2} or the presence of hydrocarbons as a separate phase, or tens of mg l^{-1} of hydrocarbons dissolved in groundwater. A necessary precondition is that the roots come into contact with the contaminated groundwater table or its capillary fringe. Volatile oil substances and methane, or CO_2 produced by the biodegradation of hydrocarbons contaminate the ground air, thus facilitating detection.

Various species of plants react with different sensitivity shown particularly by their *germination*, density growth, general habitat, *a shift in phenophases*, by their *vitality*, by *decline* and by a change in the composition of species communities. Only the changes in italic are detectable by photography, the best results being provided by C and CIR films.

There are several reasons which restrict the applicability of remote sensing methods based on the response of vegetation, including:

(a) Owing to their "low" concentrations and physiological effects on vegetation, nitrates dissolved in an aquifer cannot be detected at all.

(b) The hydrocarbons dissolved in an aquifer can only be determined close to the actual oil body.

(c) Detection of oil substances "in phase" is limited by the groundwater table depth (4-6 m) or by the presence of plants with extremely deep roots.

(d) Natural gas leaks under highly permeable soil (sand) will manifest themselves over only a small area (diameter 1 m).

(e) For reasons so far unexplained it is sometimes impossible to decode the symptoms of pollution which are otherwise botanically evident and theoretically discriminated by photography.

At present, photographic methods find the following applications in groundwater protection:

(a) Stock-taking of point sources of potential industrial and agricultural pollution.

(b) Surveys of soil utilization (intensity of fertilization) in vulnerable and significant hydrogeological structures.

(c) Optimizing the points of sampling representative vegetation and soil and water on the basis of the area distribution of the contaminant.

(d) Planning and control of decontamination activities in cases of large-scale ground pollution.

In the surveying of oil spills, very good results have been obtained with small-camera photography from a radiocontrolled delta-wing model airplane. Under complex conditions, such as in the surveying of mixed forests, it was necessary to use multispectral photography and more demanding evaluation techniques: multispectral projection, densitometry and digitization.

In future it may be possible to introduce remote sensing methods into the monitoring of groundwater quality and into the surveillance of gas and oil pipelines in regions critical from the standpoint of technical vulnerability and the strong ecological effects of large spills.

REFERENCES

Arbeitskreis (1970) Waser und Mineralöl. Beurteilung und Behandlung von Mineralölunfällen auf dem Lande im Hinblick auf den Gewässerschutz. Bundesministerium des Innern, Bonn.

Collins, W. (1978) Remote sensing of crop type and maturity. *Photogramm. Engng and Remote Sens.* 44 (1), 43-55.

Pyšek, A. & Švoma, J. (1978) Geobotanical and photographical indication of oil spills. Proc. IAH International Symp. *Groundwater Pollution by Oil Hydrocarbons,* 363-378. Stavebni Geologie Praha, Czechoslovakia, 5-9 June 1978.

Švoma, J. & Houzim, V. (1984) Protection of groundwater from oil pollution in the vicinity of airports. *Environ. Geol. Wat. Sci.* 6 (1), 21-30.

Young, C.P., Oakes, D.B. & Wilkinson, W.B. (1976) Prediction of future nitrate concentration in ground water. *Ground Water* 14 (6), 426-438.

Hydrological Applications of Remote Sensing and Remote Data Transmission (Proceedings of the Hamburg Symposium, August 1983). IAHS Publ. no. 145.

Water volume estimates by Landsat data

AARON L. HIGER & DANIEL G. ANDERSON
US Geological Survey, PO Box 026052, Miami, Florida 33102, USA

ABSTRACT Digital data from the Landsat multispectral scanner were processed by an interactive system to determine depths and water volumes in Water Conservation Area 3A of the Florida Everglades. Key parts of the analysis are: (a) water-level and depth information obtained at 23 gauging stations; (b) general relation of a water-vegetation distribution as a function of depth and duration of inundation; and (c) capability of the computer system to classify Landsat digital data into water-depth classes. The total volume was the sum of all of the products of the depth times the area of all the water-vegetation categories for Water Conservation Area 3A for 19 October 1974 (high water), and 3 March 1975 (low water). Water volumes computed for 19 October, using Landsat data, compared favourably with computations by the South Florida Water Management District and the US Army Corps of Engineers.

Estimation des volumes d'eau par les données de Landsat
RESUME Les données sous forme digitale provenant du scanner multispectral de Landsat ont été traitées par un système interactif pour déterminer les profondeurs et les volumes d'eau dans la zone de conservation de l'eau 3A des Everglades de la Florida. Les parties essentielle de l'analyse sont: (a) l'information obtenue sur le niveau de l'eau et les profondeurs obtenues à 23 stations de jaugeage; (b) une relation générale de la répartition de la végétation aquatique qui est fonction de la profondeur et de la durée de l'inondation; et (c) la possibilité pour le système d'ordinateur de clarifier les données digitales de Landsat en classes de profondeurs d'eau. Le volume total est la somme de tous les produits de la profondeur multiplié par la surface de toutes les catégories de végétation aquatique pour la zone de conservation de l'eau 3A à la date du 19 octobre 1974 (hautes eaux) et à la date du 3 mars 1975 (basses eaux). Les volumes d'eau calculés pour la date du 19 octobre avec les données de Landsat sont comparées et montrent une bonne concordance avec les résultats des calculs du district du Water Management du Sud de la Florida et du US Army Corps of Engineers.

INTRODUCTION

The Everglades is a wetland extending southward from Lake Okeechobee for about 160 km to the tidal estuaries of Florida Bay and the Gulf of Mexico. The Everglades is about 65 to 110 km wide, usually less than 0.9 m deep, and is underlain by peat and limestone. The elevation of Lake Okeechobee is about 5 m a.m.s.l. Outflow from the lake slowly filters through the low-gradient (0.03 m km^{-1}) sawgrass praire and around numerous small tree-covered islands called hammocks.

The quantity of water moving through and stored in the Everglades has an annual cyclical pattern. Because of the low gradient and heavy rainfall during the wet season (May-October), about 90% of the Everglades may be inundated by the end of October. The declining phase of the annual wet-dry cycle usually extends from November to April.

The US Army Corps of Engineers (COE), in cooperation with the South Florida Water Management District (SFWMD), maintains and operates the present system of levees, canals, control structures, pumping stations, and water storage areas for flood control and water management. The system provides for storage and movement of water between Lake Okeechobee and three water conservation areas, and for the seasonal transfer of water to agricultural and urban areas. Basic water-level information used in this study was obtained from 23 water-level and rainfall recording gauges. A land based microwave-relay transmission system operated by COE and SFWMD which provides rainfall and water-stage data in near-real time is a basis for water-management decisions.

An alternative near real-time data collection system (DCS), installed on Landsat-1, was demonstrated to be a feasible means of transmitting hydrological data to the SFWMD (Paulson, 1973: Higer *et al.*, 1973, 1975). Studies in the Everglades demonstrated that the areal extent and stage of surface water stored in various components of the SFWMD could be obtained via Landsat (Higer *et al.*, 1973, 1975). The inundated areas were determined by use of the Landsat multispectral scanner (MSS) data and water stages from suitably placed DCS-equipped hydrological stations.

The purpose of this study was to determine the feasibility of utilizing Landsat data for surface-water mapping. The objectives of this study were to: (a) map surface-water distribution; (b) analyse the changes in surface-water distribution with time; (c) determine the water depth and calculate the water volume; and (d) input volumetric water data into water-management models.

LANDSAT-MSS DATA

Landsat-MSS data of Florida were generally acquired on an 18-day or 9-day repeat cycle during the 1974-1975 period. The orbiting and operation parameters of Landsat have been defined by the National Aeronautics and Space Administration (NASA) (1971, revised in 1976) and by the US Geological Survey (USGS) (1979). The Landsat-MSS data for Florida were received at NASA Goddard Space Flight Center (GSFC), Greenbelt, Maryland.

To prepare for the data processing, MSS band-5 and band-7 (shortened to MSS-5 and MSS-7 hereafter) images covering September 1974 through March 1975 were acquired and examined to select the scene with least cloud cover, best contrast, and best coverage of the study area. For this demonstration study, Landsat images of 19 October 1974 and 3 March 1975 were selected to depict wet and dry seasons, respectively.

DATA-PROCESSING SYSTEM USED

Landsat-MSS computer-compatible tapes (CCT) were processed on the electronic computer facilities at the Bendix Aerospace Systems Division. The equipment included: a Bendix Datagrid Digitizer System 100* for digitizing geographical map data, a Bendix Multispectral Data Analysis System (MDAS) for the analysis of Landsat CCT, and an Optronics P-1500 model 30-D film recorder to produce land-water cover overlays and images from the categorized Landsat tapes.

The equipment and techniques have been used in other environmental studies (Rogers *et al.*, 1975a-c). The data-processing steps used to transform the Landsat CCT into the desired water-vegetation area categories and the methods used to determine the water volumes are described below.

EARTH TO LANDSAT COORDINATE TRANSFORMATION

The Landsat scene was geometrically corrected to locate accurately the Data Collection Platforms (DCP), determine area boundaries, and adjust the scale to the final categorized image. First, 11 ground control points (GCP) were selected (mainly corner points of levees) that could be clearly identified on Landsat data as shown on the cathode ray tube (CRT) and the appropriate USGS topographic map. The 11 points were successively digitized and transformed to adjust for spacecraft heading, altitude, earth rotation, and scan rate so that the GCP could be positioned with respect to their correct Landsat picture elements or pixels (57 x 79 m) on the CRT. The transformation thus made was approximate, but was improved by using the cursor to designate the GCP position to the MDAS computer to derive an improved geometric transformation believed accurate to within 1.0 pixel. After the geometric corrections were made, the locations (coordinate positions) of 23 water-level gauging stations were input to the computer and positioned with respect to the Landsat scene.

ESTABLISHMENT OF SURFACE-WATER DEPTH CLASSIFICATION SYSTEM

The general relation between seasonal water levels (depth and duration of flooding) and vegetation distribution recognized by many authors is the basis for the following classification analysis. In this paper, the terms "water-vegetation categories" and "water-depth classes" will be used to discriminate between the computerized

**The use of company or brand names in this report is for descriptive purposes only and does not constitute endorsement by the US Geological Survey.*

categorization and the subsequent assignment into depth classes.

For each of the two sets of Landsat data, the entire Landsat scene was processed to classify surface-water depths based upon a water-vegetation categorization in the area of investigation. Landsat records an average reflectance from water and vegetation over each picture element (about 0.45 ha), an area large enough to minimize effects of small vegetation anomalies but small enough to usually represent a single-depth class. The preprocessing was based upon Landsat digital tapes and imagery and ground-truth data. Ground-truth data are the depths measured and water data recorded at 23 gauging stations applicable to the time of Landsat overpasses.

To simultaneously detect water-vegetation categories, which are indicative of water depth, a false-colour display was developed on the MDAS system based upon the radiometric levels (counts) recorded in MSS-5 and MSS-7. The percentage solar radiation reflected for each category of clear water, typical of the Everglades, and of growing vegetation, approximates those listed in Table 1.

TABLE 1 Approximate per cent reflectance for water and vegetation in the Everglades

	Approximate per cent reflectance	
	MSS band-5 (0.6-0.7 μm)	*MSS band-7 (0.8-1.1 μm)*
Water	*6*	*0*
Vegetation	*8*	*40*

Areas of deeper water (about 0.9 m) generally have a large proportion of water surface containing sparse, wet-prairie vegetative species, areas of moderately deep water (about 0.5 m) tend to contain moderately dense sawgrass; shallow areas (about 0.1 m) support mixed communities of dense willows and sawgrass; and the islands are areas which are generally above water and contain dense vegetation including trees.

Using the MDAS, red was assigned to MSS-5 and yellow to MSS-7 with varying intensities determined by a linear relation expressed by the following equation:

$$P = ax + b + cy + d$$

where:

P = colour displayed for pixel;
x and y = MSS-5 and MSS-7 radiometric levels, respectively;
a and c = integer gain units on the MDAS;
b and d = offsets.

Maximum discrimination for the water-vegetation combination was determined to approximate the relationship:

$$P = 2x + 2y + 5$$

This two-band, false-colour technique was used in combination with field observations and water-level data to identify areas of relatively different water depths. Computer analysis was able to discriminate between several signatures based upon the water-vegetation mix representing depths and to portray the decision on the CRT display. Training sets were then established to associate the various depths to signatures identified by the computer. The computer was used to develop a set of coefficients to represent the spectral characteristics of each water-vegetation category, as defined by the mean and standard deviation for each of the four Landsat bands and covariance matrix about the mean of the pixels within the training area boundaries. Each separate category was assigned to a depth class and colour identification. The computer could then assign pixels to one of the depth classes, or if outside of all threshold levels, as "uncategorized".

Gauging stations and their respective pixels were displayed on the CRT to compare the colour they were assigned in the computer to the known water depths at the gauging stations.

VOLUME OF WATER ESTIMATION

The Landsat data of 19 October 1974 for Water Conservation Area 3A was differentiated into 10 water-depth classes using the Bendix MDAS connected to an Optronics P-155 model 30-D film recorder. Of these classes, eight represent water depth, and two represent "uncategorized" and "vegetation above high water".

The Landsat data of 3 March 1975 (Water Conservation Area 3A nearly dry), was differentiated into four water-depth classes. Two of these classes represent water depths of 0.1 and 0.25 m, and the other two represent "uncategorized" and "vegetation above high water". New computer coefficients were developed for use in classifying the 3 March data.

When comparing the two classifications, the delineation seems reasonably consistent for the deeper water areas. The large increase in unclassified areas for 3 March was expected because of changes in the reflectance characteristics for areas where the water receded below ground level.

The volumes of water in Water Conservation Area 3A on 19 October 1974, and 3 March 1975, were determined by multiplying the area of each class by its respective depth, and for each date, adding the respective products.

DISCUSSION OF WATER-MANAGEMENT APPLICATIONS

Knowledge of water volumes in the component parts of the southern Florida water system (Lake Okeechobee, the water conservation areas, Shark River Slough, and Everglades National Park) is fundamental to the water-management responsibility shared by the COE and SFWMD. Through the elaborate system of controls, those agencies strive to manage the available water resources of the area for the benefit of all (reduce floods and conserve water for the people, fauna, and flora of the area).

The methods of determining water volume, as described in this study (hereafter called USGS-Landsat) and those of the COE and SFWMD, are all based upon multiplying depth times an area to establish a stage-volume relation although each method is slightly different. The discharge volumes for Water Conservation Area 3A obtained by the COE (Brannen, written communication, 1975) and SFWMD (Marban, written communication, 1978) are compared with results obtained by the US Geological Survey from methods using USGS-Landsat in Table 2.

TABLE 2 Comparison of water volumes for water conservation area 3A (dam^3)

Date	*SFWMD*	*COE*	*USGS-Landsat*
19 October 1974	*677 844*	*931 293*	*708 609*
3 March 1975	*37 845*	*181 324*	*36 669*

Table 2 represents three volumetric solutions based upon somewhat different methods although some of the water-level data at gauging stations are involved in all three methods. There is no reasonable means to verify the correct volumes or to say which method is the most accurate. The 19 October difference between USGS-Landsat and SFWMD is about -5%. Considering the opportunity for variation, the percentage differences are within reason.

ACKNOWLEDGEMENTS The authors express their appreciation to Dr Larry E.Reed of the Bendix Aerospace Systems Division for his assistance in processing the Landsat computer compatible tapes, to Dr Jorge A.Marban of the South Florida Water Management District for providing computations from the Network Simulation Model, to Mr T.E.Brannen of the US Army Corps of Engineers for providing information on methods used to determine water volumes for Water Conservation Area 3A, and to NASA officials for providing funding support, under NASA Contract no. 21580, and the Landsat data used in this study.

REFERENCES

Higer, A.L., Coker, A.E. & Cordes, E.H. (1973) Water management models in Florida from ERTS-1 data. *3rd Earth Res. Technol. Satellite-1 Symp.*, (Washington, DC, USA, 10-14 December), vol. 1, sec. B. NASA SP-351.

Higer, A.L., Cordes, E.H., Coker, A.E. & Rogers, R.H. (1975) Water management model in Florida from Landsat-1 data. *Proc. NASA Earth Res. Sur. Symp.* (JSC, Houston, Texas, USA, June), vol. 1-D. NASA TM X-58168.

National Aeronautics and Space Administration (1971) *Earth Resources*

Technology Satellite, Data Users Handbook. NASA, Goddard Space Flight Center, Greenbelt, Maryland, USA, September, Document no. 71SD4249.

National Aeronautics and Space Administration (1976) *Landsat Data Users Handbook*. NASA, Goddard Space Flight Center, Greenbelt, Maryland, USA, September, Document no. 76SDS4258.

Paulson, R.W. (1973) An evaluation of the ERTS data collection system as a potential operational tool. *3rd Earth Res. Technol. Satellite-1 Symp.*, (Washington, DC, USA, 10-14 December), vol. 1, sec. B. NASA SP-351.

Rogers, R.H., McKeon, J.B., Reed, L.E., Schmidt, N.F. & Schecter, R.N. (1975a) Computer mapping of Landsat data for environmental applications. *Workshop for Environmental Applications of Multispectral Imager*, (11-13 November, US Army Engineer Topographic Labs, Ft Belvoir, Virginia, USA).

Rogers, R.H., Reed, L.E., Schmidt, N.F. & Mara, T.G. (1975b) Landsat-1: Automated land-use mapping in lake and river watersheds. *Proc. Am. Soc. Photogramm.* (28-31 October, Phoenix, Arizona, USA). Am. Soc. Photogramm., Falls Church, Virginia, USA.

Rogers, R.H., Wilson, C.L., Reed, L.E., Shah, N.J., Akeley, R., Mara, T.G. & Smight, V.E. (1975c) Environmental monitoring from spacecraft data. *Proc. Symp. on Machine Processing of Remotely Sensed Data*. (June, Purdue Univ., West Lafayette, Indiana, USA). IEEE Cat. no. 75 CH 1009-0-C.

US Geological Survey (1979) *Landsat Data Users Handbook*. USGS revised edn.

7 Remote sensing: hydrological modelling water planning and management

Hydrological Applications of Remote Sensing and Remote Data Transmission
(Proceedings of the Hamburg Symposium, August 1983). IAHS Publ. no. 145.

Hydrological research in the AgRISTARS programme

A. RANGO, E. T. ENGMAN, T. J. JACKSON,
J. C. RITCHIE & R. F. PAETZOLD
Hydrology Laboratory, Agricultural Research Service, Beltsville, Maryland 20705, USA

ABSTRACT The Agriculture and Resources Inventory Surveys Through Aerospace Remote Sensing (AgRISTARS) programme is a cooperative research effort between the US Department of Agriculture (USDA), the National Aeronautics and Space Administration (NASA), and several other USA government agencies. Hydrological research results thus far indicate that microwave techniques can be used to measure soil moisture in the upper layer (0-10 cm) of the soil through vegetation cover. Several modelling techniques are being tested to obtain a soil moisture profile from this surface layer measurement. A portable nuclear magnetic resonance instrument for making rapid surface soil moisture measurements over large areas has been developed for ground-truth purposes and is being field tested. The microwave approach is also being employed to extract characteristic properties of the snow-pack under all-weather conditions. Few hydrological models currently accept direct input of remotely-sensed data. Most models will accept only point data, however, some are being modified to interface with the remote data. Alternatively, a new family of hydrological models is being designed to enhance compatibility with remote sensing characteristics and capabilities.

Les recherches hydrologiques dans le programme AgRISTARS

RESUME Le programme "AgRISTARS", c'est-à-dire un inventaire des ressources agricoles et naturelles par la télédétection spatiale, est un projet de recherche coopératif avec participation du département de l'agriculture des Etats Unis (USDA), de l'administration nationale aéronautique et spatiale (NASA), ainsi que de quelques autres agences gouvernementales. Les recherches hydrologiques executées jusqu'à présent indiquent que les méthodes utilisant des micro-ondes permettent de mesurer l'humidité du sol dans la couche superficielle (0-10 cm) en traversant la couverture de végétale. Des modèles différents sont testés pour obtenir un profil d'humidité du sol à partir de ces mesures concernant la couche superficielle. Un appareil portatif a été construit sur la base de la résonance nucléaire magnétique pour les rapides mesures comparatives (vérité au sol) de l'humidité du sol à grande échelle. On est en train de tester cet instrument sur le terrain. Les méthodes des micro-ondes sont également utilisées pour évaluer les caractéristiques de la couche de neige indépendamment des conditions météorologiques. A présent, peu de modèles hydrologiques acceptent directement comme entrées les données obtenues par la télédétéction. Les autres modèles n'acceptent, dans la majorité, que les données ponctuelles. Quelques autres modèles sont en cours de modification en vue d'admettre les télé-données. En même temps, une famille nouvelle des modèles hydrologiques est mise au point pour améliorer la compatibilité avec les caractéristiques et possibilités de la télédétéction.

INTRODUCTION

The Agriculture and Resources Inventory Surveys through Aerospace Remote Sensing (AgRISTARS) research programme began in 1979 in response to an initiative by the US Department of Agriculture (USDA) for increased research on the application of remote sensing technology to agricultural problems. AgRISTARS is a cooperative research effort among USDA, the National Aeronautics and Space Administration (NASA), the National Oceanic and Atmospheric Administration (NOAA), the US Department of Interior, and the US Agency for International Development.

The objective of the AgRISTARS research programme is to develop the information necessary to effectively integrate remote sensing data into USDA operational programmes and to improve timeliness, cost effectiveness, and accuracy of information used for the management of agricultural resources.

AgRISTARS research programmes are coordinated by USDA in three project areas.

(a) *Domestic Commodity Assessment Research:* Investigations aimed at providing crop area, yield, and condition assessment data to meet the USA information needs of the Statistical Reporting Service (SRS) of USDA.

(b) *Foreign Commodity Assessment Research:* Investigations similar to (a) but directed toward providing international information needed by the Foreign Agricultural Service of USDA.

(c) *Land Resources Monitoring Research:* Development of techniques to use remotely-sensed data to meet the requirements of the Soil Conservation Service and other USDA agencies, for measuring and monitoring soil, water, and related resources and to provide domestic land cover data for use by the SRS in monitoring and updating sample frames and evaluating crop acreage estimates.

Summaries of research accomplished are available in AgRISTARS Annual Reports (AgRISTARS Program Support Staff, 1981, 1982; AgRISTARS Program Management Group, 1983).

Water resources research is an integral part of the AgRISTARS programme. The application of remote sensing technology for soil moisture monitoring, snow properties monitoring, and hydrological modelling has great potential for providing new data and systems for operational hydrology programmes. This paper reviews current AgRISTARS research efforts on the application of remote sensing to hydrology and provides some ideas on future applications.

SOIL MOISTURE RESEARCH

Microwave soil moisture measurements

The AgRISTARS project includes a major effort to develop and evaluate remote sensing techniques for estimating soil moisture over large areas.

A large body of research indicates that surface soil moisture can be sensed by the microwave portion of the spectrum. In this region there is a unique relationship between soil water and the electrical properties that affect the microwave measurements. These sensors have several desirable features including the capability for observations through clouds, most precipitation, and herbaceous vegetation.

Both active and passive microwave systems are under investigation. Research emphasizing passive techniques has utilized three levels of study. The truck-based programme in cooperation with NASA has been used to study sensor-variable relationships under relatively well controlled conditions. Figure 1 shows the truck system.

FIG.1 Passive microwave truck system for measuring soil moisture.

An aircraft system is used to study similar phenomena on a larger scale typical of high altitude platforms and to extend low-level (truck-based) results.

Finally, the modelling approach is used iteratively with the experimental systems to design experiments, extrapolate limited data sets, and understand the basic physics. Some of the significant results of the research programme are described in the following sections.

Soil and surface properties A rough soil surface reduces the sensitivity of microwave instruments to soil moisture changes (Schmugge *et al.*, 1980). Recent research has focussed on parameterizing and modelling these effects (Choudhury *et al.*, 1979; Tsang & Newton, 1982). These experiments have shown that the effects of surface roughness could be accounted for by a root mean square surface variation estimate and a spatial correlation parameter.

The effect of texture on the microwave measurement of soil moisture has also been evaluated. Results presented by Schmugge (1980) show that the microwave instrument is more sensitive to moisture variations in coarse texture soils (sand) than in clays. The effect of texture is accounted for using the one-third bar tension moisture content (estimated using textural properties) to normalize the relationships. While this does help to normalize the data, research is still needed to explain the basic physical effects.

Vegetation effects Vegetation dampens the sensitivity of microwave instruments to soil moisture variations as shown in Fig.2. Truck experiment results have shown that this effect is predictable (Wang *et al.*, 1980) and can be modelled deterministically (Jackson *et al.*, 1982; Mo *et al.*, 1982). The principal controlling vegetation parameter appears to be the green biomass. Because biomass can be estimated using visible and near infrared data, an algorithm to extract vegetation effects based solely on remotely sensed data is possible. Jackson *et al.* (1985) and Theis *et al.* (1982) have shown the extension of the basic vegetation effect to results from low altitude aircraft.

Coupling surface layer measurements to the soil moisture profile Microwave remote sensing techniques can only estimate the moisture in the upper layer of the soil from 0 to 10 cm (or 15 cm

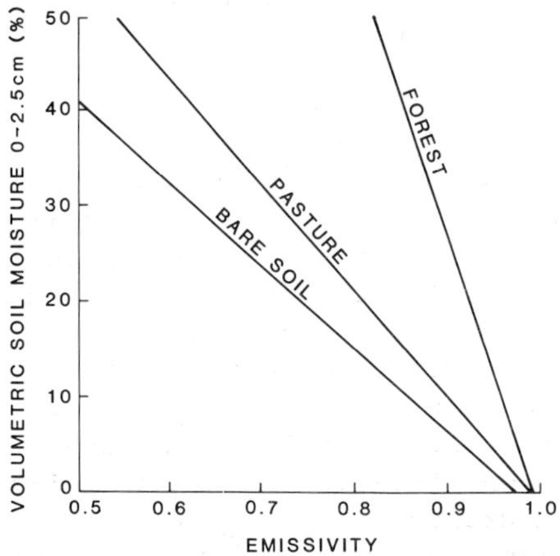

FIG.2 Vegetation effect on passive microwave sensitivity to soil moisture variations.

at the most). An approximation for predicting the volumetric soil moisture in the lower soil profile as a function of measured surface-layer soil moisture, soil properties throughout the profile, and assumption of hydraulic equilibrium was tested (Jackson, 1980). Under bare soil conditions the model could simulate lower profile conditions within acceptable error bounds. The testing indicated that the surface layer measurements should be obtained just prior to dawn and that the thickness of the surface layer should be about 10 cm. More definitive information about the soil moisture profile under a vegetation canopy may be obtained from thermal infrared monitoring of plant canopy temperatures.

In situ measurements

In situ measurements of soil moisture are necessary for calibration and evaluation of remotely-sensed data. Volumetric water content of the upper few centimetres of the soil and its areal distribution need to be measured over large areas within relatively short time periods. Currently, the most commonly used methods of *in situ* soil moisture measurement in truck and aircraft experiments are the gravimetric and neutron meter techniques. Both of these techniques are time consuming, and it is difficult to characterize soil moisture over large areas with them.

In order to meet the requirements imposed by remote sensing methods and to overcome the limitations of current methods, a prototype soil moisture instrument based on nuclear magnetic resonance (NMR) principles was developed. It measures volumetric soil water content in three 13 mm increments from 32 to 71 mm depth. The NMR unit is mounted on a tractor, and the non-intrusive instrument floats on the soil surface, continuously measuring soil moisture as the vehicle travels across the landscape.

Laboratory tests indicate that, as expected, the NMR signal correlates better with soil moisture content on a volumetric rather than gravimetric basis. Preliminary field tests were conducted on two soils, a gravelly sandy loam and a clay loam, with the unit stationary and moving with a ground speed of 0.97 km h^{-1}. The NMR signal had a correlation coefficient of 0.92 with soil water content. More extensive field data will be acquired in 1983.

Remaining fundamental research problems

The most important research questions that remain to be answered in the remote measurement of soil moisture involve a quantification of the effects of various soil and vegetation properties on the microwave emission. Deterministic studies should be conducted using the truck-based approach to identify the specific effects of bulk density, organic matter content, moisture tension, and texture. It has been shown that vegetation water content has a significant effect and there is reason to suspect that the vegetation canopy structure is just as important. Isolating these two vegetation effects is a difficult task that must be addressed.

After these basic scientific issues have been addressed, several important research problems remain:

(a) Extrapolation of truck-observed relationships to large

footprints through aircraft experiments.

(b) Acquisition of time series soil moisture data from airborne sensors and analysis in the time frame of the potential application, e.g. for irrigation scheduling it should be 24 h.

(c) Examination of how these new kinds of soil moisture data can be used in models and for management decisions. Testing for the following application areas should be considered: irrigation scheduling and efficiency; streamflow simulation and flood prediction; drought evaluation; partial area hydrology; pre-planting soil moisture assessment and pre-emergence crop evaluation; crop yield prediction; and range production and management.

SNOW RESEARCH

Microwave investigations of snowpack properties have proceeded in a fashion similar to the soil moisture work with the passive microwave approach being tested more extensively because of its relative simplicity when compared to the active approach.

A passive microwave radiative transfer model was developed to estimate snow water equivalent based on input of microwave frequency, polarization, incidence angle, brightness temperature, mean grain size, snowpack temperature, and underlying surface condition (Chang *et al.*, 1982). The model was successfully tested using data from several aircraft and truck experiments as shown in Fig.3. From this

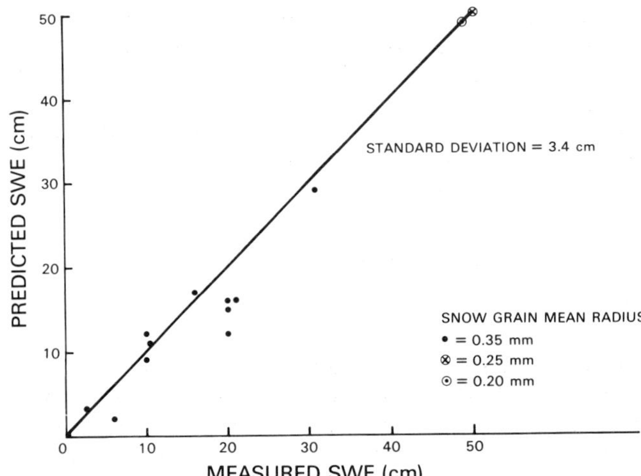

FIG.3 Comparison between model predictions at 37 GHz and field measurements of snow water equivalent (SWE).

testing, it was evident that the effects of grain size and snow wetness must be accounted for in order to make estimates of snow water equivalent.

Subsequent tests using satellite data were conducted over the high plains of the USSR where both an empirical relationship and the model generated result compared closely as shown in Fig.4 (Chang *et al.*, 1982). A definite potential exists for estimating the snow

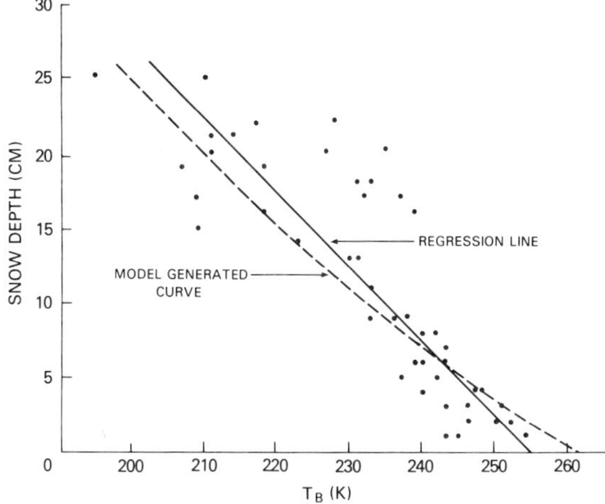

FIG.4 Nimbus-7 SMMR 37 GHz vertically polarized microwave brightness temperature (T_B) vs. snow depth in the USSR.

depth which has direct application to snowmelt runoff prediction, winterkill estimates, and crop yield estimation.

Certain research must be completed before any operational applications, other than mapping of the area covered by snow, are possible. These tasks include development of methods for obtaining the mean snow grain size, accounting for the effects of snowpack structure (layering), wetness and vegetation (see Hall *et al.*, 1982), and better understanding active microwave snow interactions. These research efforts will most likely involve the development of more definitive models to explain the microwave-snow interaction. Well coordinated truck, aircraft, and satellite data collection will be required for testing and validation purposes.

HYDROLOGICAL ANALYSIS AND MODELLING

Flooding assessment

Assessment of damages to agriculture by flooding is important for world food planning and distribution. Rango & Salomonson (1974) demonstrated the use of Landsat data for mapping the areal extent of flooding. Potential cloud cover and the 16-day repeat cycle limit the applicability of Landsat data for timely or operational evaluation. Because of this a flood evaluation system based on 1 km resolution data from the more frequently available NOAA satellite has been developed. A basic relationship for discriminating between water, soil, and vegetation using the spectral returns in Advanced Very High Resolution Radiometer Channels 1 and 2 has been developed using a large number of NOAA-6 scenes from different seasons and geographical locations. A look-up table classifier was developed based on these relationships which automatically separates vegetation and soil from water and produces classification maps registered to a global coordinate system.

This global grid system, which is based on i and j coordinates, was adapted for the damage assessment procedure to enable registration of the flood area and to develop a technique for assessing the area of inundation with reasonable accuracy. This technique was tested successfully for measuring agricultural land inundation during a flood along a major river system in Argentina (Tappan *et al.*, 1983).

Conservation assessment

AgRISTARS has research efforts on the application of remote sensing technology for the assessment of soil and natural resources conservation. These activities include inventorying conservation practices, assessing potential and actual soil erosion, and monitoring resulting off-site effects of soil erosion. Remote monitoring to ascertain the current status of these activities is vital because of the significant potential of erosion to damage and reduce prime agricultural land areas.

Research with different sensors on aircraft and satellites has been used to develop recommendations for sensors and resolution necessary to detect the 132 conservation practices recommended by the Soil Conservation Service (1977). Most of the recommended conservation practices can be inventoried using sensors on aircraft, whereas Landsat Thematic Mapper data could be used to detect 30-50% of the practices.

Research has shown that satellite data on land cover and vegetation type can be efficiently and effectively integrated into a geographical information system for estimating potential soil erosion from watersheds using the Universal Soil Loss Equation. Potential soil erosion maps can then be derived and used to determine location of excessive erosion or to estimate sediment loads in the runoff from a basin.

Suspended sediments are the major cause of pollution in inland waters. Suspended sediment loads greater than 150 mg l^{-1} can be monitored in inland lakes using Landsat data (LeCroy, 1982). Recent studies using Thematic Mapper data have shown a strong correlation between suspended sediment loads between 180 and 500 mg l^{-1} and TM bands 2 or 3 (Schiebe *et al.*, 1983). While cloud cover will probably present a problem for monitoring suspended sediment with satellite data, this research has shown the potential for using such data for providing useful information to reservoir managers for decision making.

Hydrological models

In order to have a major impact on water resources and agricultural management, a mutual compatibility between remote sensing data and hydrological models is needed. Presently, a few existing models can accept remote sensing input for application to specific hydrological problems. For example, land-cover and snow-cover information from satellites can be supplied to the Corps of Engineers Hydrologic Engineering Center-1 (HEC-1) model for effective estimation of peak flows (for design purposes) and the Snowmelt-Runoff Model (SRM) for estimation of snowmelt-runoff from mountain basins (for forecasting), respectively (Rango *et al.*, 1983; Rango, 1983). In AgRISTARS, SRM has been developed to use satellite snow-cover input. Testing on a variety of basin sizes and elevation ranges using various quality input data has proven successful. The major remaining task is to develop a forecasting algorithm so that the model can be used by operational agencies.

Most models do not have a mechanism for accepting remotely sensed data. To use remote sensing with conventional hydrological models, modifications to the models have to be made. Several modifications are currently being made to the US National Weather Service River Forecast System model to allow it to accept remote sensing-derived data on soil moisture, snow extent, and snow water equivalent (Peck *et al.*, 1983). Two important phases of this research deal with development of (a) methods to areally average data collected by both conventional and remote sensing means over a basin, and (b) procedures for using these data to update the model. When the method for integrating the conventional and remote sensing data is completed, it should be transferrable to most other conventional models.

A more long-range approach to utilizing this new technology is to design a family of hydrological models to be compatible with remote sensing capabilities. Remote sensing inputs, such as surface layer soil moisture, would drive peak flow and continuous simulation models. The algorithms and interfaces to these models are being designed to resemble conventional hydrological models so that their eventual use by hydrological personnel in the future is easily facilitated. The parameters of the final model would be physically based and optimized to interface with current and anticipated remote sensing capabilities. All input data, both satellite and ground based, will be incorporated into the model through a grid-cell geographical information system. The data base, designed to be developed from digital imagery from polar orbiting and geostationary satellite systems, is to include land cover, solar radiation, snow cover, vegetative stress, cloud cover, temperature estimates, and other physical quantities relative to the synthesis of streamflow from precipitation (Groves & Ragan, 1985).

Future applications

Current applications of remote sensing to hydrology were developed as direct extensions of photogrammetry. The future will provide a unique opportunity for hydrologists to apply remote sensing in entirely new ways. Current research is now focussing on the benefits to be derived from spatial data and the less common wavelengths. Thermal infrared measurements allow us to infer a heat budget and hence estimate crop condition, soil moisture, and evapotranspiration. With microwave data we have all-weather capability plus the ability to penetrate vegetation and to measure soil moisture and snow water content directly. This research, although still experimental, is beginning to treat remote sensing as a unique source of data.

The potential for remote sensing and its application to hydrology is considerably greater than research has addressed thus far. Measuring the characteristics of an area rather than a point, integrating several characteristics with one composite measurement, and improving prediction models with continuous or frequent feedback from satellite measurements are just a few of the aspects that must be explored further. Research is needed if we are to fully realize the potential benefits of remote sensing in hydrology. Treating remotely sensed data as a unique measurement of hydrological characteristics offers the best opportunity for major advances in the field of hydrological modelling.

REFERENCES

AgRISTARS Program Management Group (1983) AgRISTARS research report - fiscal year 1982. *Report AP-J2-0393, NASA Johnson Space Center, Houston, Texas, USA.*

AgRISTARS Program Support Staff (1981) AgRISTARS annual report - fiscal year 1980. *Report AP-JO-04111, NASA Johnson Space Center, Houston, Texas, USA.*

AgRISTARS Program Support Staff (1982) AgRISTARS annual report - fiscal year 1981. *Report AP-J2-04225, NASA Johnson Space Center, Houston, Texas, USA.*

Chang, A.T.C., Foster, J.L., Hall, D.K., Rango, A. & Hartline, B.K. (1982) Snow water equivalent estimation by microwave radiometry. *Cold Regions Science and Technol.* 5, 259-267.

Choudhury, B.J., Schmugge, T.J., Chang, A. & Newton, R.W. (1979) Effects of surface roughness on the microwave emission from soils. *J. Geophys. Res.* 84 (C9), 5699-5706.

Groves, J.R., Ragan, R.M. & Clapp, R.B. (1985) Development and testing of a remote sensing based hydrological model. In: *Hydrological Applications of Remote Sensing and Remote Data Transmission* (Proc. Hamburg Symp., August 1983), 601-612. IAHS Publ. no. 145.

Hall, D.K., Foster, J.L. & Chang, A.T.C. (1982) Measurement and modelling of microwave emission from forested snowfields in Michigan. *Nordic Hydrol.* 13, 129-138.

Jackson, T.J. (1980) Profile soil moisture from surface measurements. *J. Irrig. Drain. Div. ASCE* 106 (IR2), 81-92.

Jackson, T.J., Schmugge, T.J. & Wang, J.R. (1982) Passive microwave sensing of soil moisture under vegetation canopies. *Wat. Resour. Res.* 18 (4), 1137-1142.

Jackson, T.J., Schmugge, T.J. & O'Neill, P. (1985) Remote sensing of soil moisture from an aircraft platform using passive microwave sensors. In: *Hydrological Applications of Remote Sensing and Remote Data Transmission* (Proc. Hamburg Symp., August 1983), 529-539. IAHS Publ. no. 145.

LeCroy, S.R. (1982) Determination of turbidity patterns in Lake Chicot from Landsat MSS imagery. *NASA Contractor Report 165870, Langley Research Center, Hampton, Virginia, USA.*

Mo, T., Choudhury, B.J., Schmugge, T.J., Wang, J.R. & Jackson, T.J. (1982) A model for microwave emission from vegetation-covered fields. *J. Geophys. Res.* 87 (C13), 11229-11237.

Peck E.L., Johnson, E.R. & Keefer, T.N. (1983) Creating a bridge between remote sensing and hydrologic models. *NASA Contractor Report CR-170517, Goddard Space Flight Center, Greenbelt, Maryland, USA.*

Rango, A. (1983) Application of a simple snowmelt-runoff model to large river basins. In: *Proc. of the 51st Annual Western Snow Conference* (Vancouver, Washington, USA), 89-99.

Rango, A., Feldman, A., George, T.S. & Ragan, R.M. (1983) Effective use of Landsat data in hydrologic models. *Wat. Resour. Bull.* 19 (2), 165-174.

Rango, A. & Salomonson, V.V. (1974) Regional flood mapping from space. *Wat. Resour. Res.* 10 (3), 473-484.

Schiebe, F.R., Ritchie, J.C. & Boatwright, G.O. (1983) A first evaluation of Landsat TM data to monitor suspended sediment in lakes. In: *Proc. of the Landsat 4 Early Results Symposium,* (Goddard Space Flight Center, Greenbelt, Maryland, USA).

Schmugge, T.J. (1980) Effect of texture on microwave emission from soils. *IEEE Trans. on Geosci. and Remote Sens.* GE-18 (4), 353-361.

Schmugge, T.J., Jackson, T.J. & McKim, H.L. (1980) Survey of methods for soil moisture determination. *Wat. Resour. Res.* 16 (6), 961-979.

Soil Conservation Service (1977) *National Handbook of Conservation Practices.* Soil Conservation Service, US Department of Agriculture, Washington, DC, USA.

Tappan, G., Horvath, N.C., Doraiswamy, P.C., Engman, T. & Goss, D.W. (1983) Use of NOAA-N satellites for land/water discrimination and flood monitoring. *Report EW-L3-04394, Johnson Space Center, Houston, Texas, USA.*

Theis, S.W., McFarland, M.J., Rosenthal, W.D. & Jones, C.J. (1982) Microwave remote sensing of soil moisture. *NASA Contractor Report CR-166822, Goddard Space Flight Center, Greenbelt, Maryland, USA.*

Tsang, L. & Newton, R.W. (1982) Microwave emission from soils with rough surfaces. *J. Geophys. Res.* 87 (11), 9017-9024.

Wang, J.R., Shiue, J.C. & McMurtrey, J.E. (1980) Microwave remote sensing of soil moisture content over bare and vegetated fields. *Geophys. Res. Lett.* 7 (10), 801-804.

Hydrological Applications of Remote Sensing and Remote Data Transmission (Proceedings of the Hamburg Symposium, August 1983). IAHS Publ. no. 145.

Combining measurement of hydrological variables of various sampling geometries and measurement accuracies

E. L. PECK
Hydex Corporation, Suite 502, 11150 Main Street, Fairfax, Virginia 22030, USA
E. R. JOHNSON
Georgia Institute of Technology, Atlanta, Georgia, USA
T. N. KEEFER
Sutron Corporation, Fairfax, Virginia, USA
A. RANGO
Goddard Space Flight Center, Greenbelt, Maryland, USA

ABSTRACT A method is described for combining measurements of hydrological variables having various sampling geometries and measurement accuracies to estimate the mean areal value over a basin and the accuracy of the value. The technique assigns a weight to each sample proportional to how correlated that sample is with the variable of interest inside the basin area. The method can be used with all types of measurements. Statistical characteristics and accuracies of the various measurement technologies and of the hydrological variables used in the study are discussed. The method provides a means to integrate measurements from conventional hydrological networks and remote sensing. The resulting area averages can be used to enhance a wide variety of hydrological applications including basin modelling.

Combinaison des mesures de variables hydrologiques de plusieurs géométries d'échantillonnage et exactitude de mesure

RESUME Une méthode est décrite pour combiner les mesures de variables hydrologiques ayant plusieurs géométries d'échantillonnage et diverses précisions de mesure afin d'estimer la moyenne spatiale des valeurs sur un bassin et l'exactitude de cette valeur. La technique assigne un poids à chaque échantillon en proportion de la mesure suivant laquelle chaque échantillon est corrélé avec la variable intéressée, à l'intérieur du bassin. La méthode peut être employée avec tous les types de mesure. On étudie les caractéristiques statistiques et l'exactitude des diverses technologies de mesure et les variables hydrologiques qui sont employées dans l'étude. La méthode fournit un moyen d'intégrer les télémesures avec les mesures des réseaux hydrologiques conventionnels. Les moyennes spatiales qui en résultent peuvent être employées afin de faciliter un grand nombre d'applications hydrologiques y compris l'établissement de modèles de bassins.

INTRODUCTION

Measurements of land characteristics and of vegetative cover obtained by remote sensing have proven to be of value for hydrological modelling. However, remotely sensed measurements of hydrological variables (e.g. soil moisture and water equivalent of the snow cover) have had very limited use.

One factor for the limited use of remotely sensed measurements of hydrological variables is that there is not a one-to-one correspondence between the hydrological states (variables) as measured in the real world and states as represented in the models.

Hydrological models presently in use for operational hydrology were developed prior to the availability (at present only experimental) of remotely sensed measurements. Many models (i.e. rainfall-runoff, drought index and crop yield models) have states that represent soil moisture conditions in the upper layer of the soil. The models were not designed to correlate with the measured states as interpreted by remote sensing. In addition, remote sensors may respond to more than the hydrological variable of interest. For example, microwave sensors may infer both soil moisture and vegetative roughness. Even though these measurements do have additional information on the state of the hydrological variable, their use can add to the problem of correspondence between modelled and observed states.

Hydrological models now in operational use generally represent the average conditions for a specific area such as a river drainage basin. Most models are lumped parameter (lumped input) models and require areal average values for input data or for updating (using observations of hydrological variables to keep the modelled states in line with the real world). At the present time areal averages of hydrological variables are determined from standard point (*in situ*) measurements using various statistical methods.

There is considerable information on the state of hydrological variables beyond that available using only standard measurements. One difficulty has been to make effective use of all available information. The inability to take advantage of all available measurements by combining them to provide improved areal averages is a factor that limits the usefulness of remotely sensed measurements in operational hydrology.

The findings in this paper are part of the result of a long-term study to develop and test procedures for incorporating remotely sensed measurements in hydrological modelling. Those portions of the study dealing with the problems posed by the lack of one-to-one correspondence between modelled and observed hydrological states have been reported by Peck *et al.* (1981a, 1981b, 1983).

This paper describes the correlation area method designed to help overcome the limitations resulting from the inability to effectively use remotely sensed measurements with standard measurements. The method is a technique for combining measurements of hydrological variables of various sampling geometries and measurement accuracies to produce estimates of mean areal averages for use in hydrological modelling.

The correlation area method has not been tested. The lack of adequate "ground truth" information precludes a direct approach. As part of the long-term research study an indirect evaluation is being conducted. This test is evaluating the degree of improvement for predicting streamflow obtained by incorporating remotely sensed measurements (using the correlation area method) in hydrological models as compared with predictions using only standard measurements. Only a brief discussion of the procedure and of the required information on the accuracy and statistical characteristics of the measurement technologies is presented in this paper. Complete information on the method has been published by Johnson *et al*. (1982).

CRITERIA FOR THE METHOD

For a technique to be of maximum value for estimating areal averages of hydrological variables from all available measurements the following criteria should be satisfied:

(a) it should not be dependent on particular measurement technologies;

(b) it should be an objective technique;

(c) it should work regardless of the mix of data available in any one time step;

(d) it should explicitly recognize the sampling geometry of the data;

(c) it should explicitly recognize differences in measurement accuracy of different technologies; and

(f) it must produce some estimate of the accuracy of the areal estimate.

CORRELATION AREA METHOD

The correlation area method meets the criteria listed above for estimating areal averages from data of various sampling characteristics. This algorithm performs in a desirable fashion giving greater weight to measurements that are more accurate and that cover a large portion of the basin.

The algorithm is a heuristic procedure (an engineering approach) that takes liberties at certain points with a more theoretically correct approach in the interest of simplicity and operational capability.

The weight assigned to each sample in computing an areal average value of the hydrological variable is determined by:

(a) the normal correlation between that type of measurement and the hydrological variable; and

(b) the area of the basin that is best represented by that measurement.

Illustration of method

To illustrate the basic principles, a simple case is discussed. There are three measurements for the hydrological variable for the basin as shown in Fig.1. There are a point, a transect (line) and an areal sample. The areal sample covers more than the basin of interest.

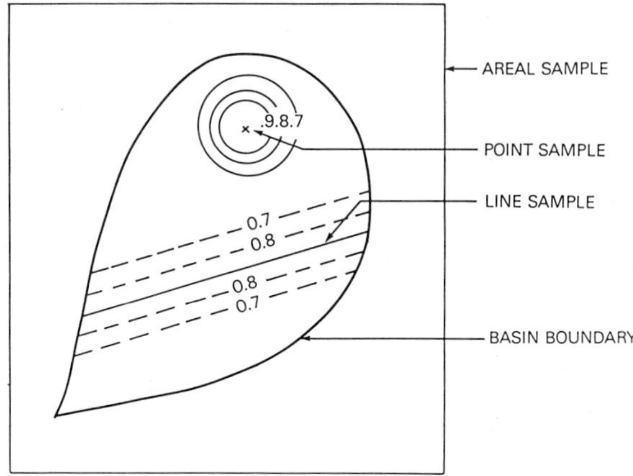

FIG.1 Example of correlation area method for assigning conventional (point), aircraft (line) and space (areal) measurements to representative basin areas.

For the purpose of this illustration, the following assumptions are made regarding the correlation of each measurement with the random field of a hydrological variable:

(a) the areal measurement has a correlation of 0.7 with the true areal average over the sample domain;

(b) the line measurement has a correlation of 0.85 with a random point along the flight line; that correlation decreases on either side of the line as shown by the values of the parallel dashed lines on Fig.1;

(c) the point measurement has a correlation of 0.94 with the variable at the point, decreasing around the point as shown by the values of the circles on Fig.1.

The area of the basin not encompassed within the 0.7 correlation lines for the line measurement and the 0.7 circle for the point measurement indicates that the areal sample provides the best estimate for this area. The areal sample measurements have a 0.7 correlation with the random field of the variable for this area. For the rest of the basin, the point measurement (within the 0.7 correlation circle) and the line measurement (between the 0.7 dashed lines) provide a better estimate than does the areal sample measurement. The areas assigned to each of the three measurements are shown by the shaded areas in Fig.2.

The informational value of each measurement is dependent upon how much area is assigned to that measurement and on how well that information correlates with the random variable in that area. Since the correlation of the point and line measurements varies for different portions of these areas, the informational values are not consistent over these areas.

The approach to determining the best average values for the basin includes a weighting for each area. The correlation area is equal

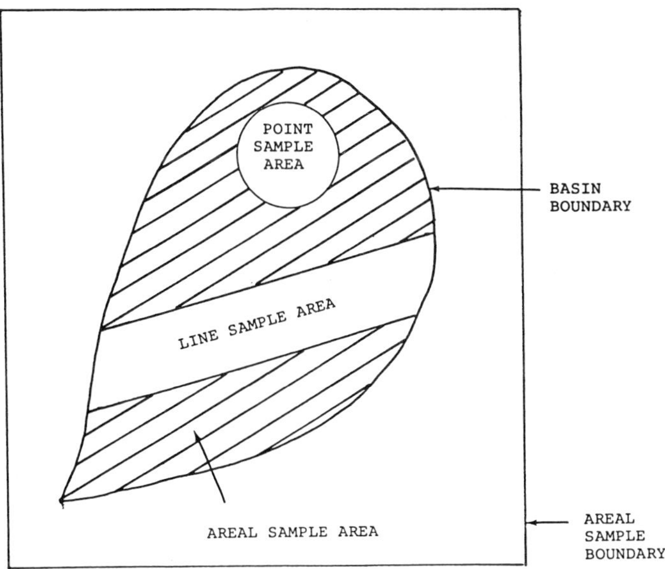

FIG.2 Areas assigned to point, line and areal measurements (example).

to the sums of the products of the correlation multiplied by the portion of the area assigned to that measurement covered by that correlation.

For example, the correlation area for the point sample, A_p, in the case illustrated in Figs 1 and 2 is approximately:

$$A = 0.92 \times (\text{area inside the 0.9 circle}) + 0.85 \times (\text{area between the 0.9 and 0.8 circles}) + 0.75 \times (\text{area between the 0.8 and 0.7 circles})$$

The correlation area for the line measurement, A_ℓ, is determined by the sum of the products of the average correlation multiplied by the area between each correlation line on either side of the flight line as shown in Fig.1.

In this example, the correlation area for the areal sample, A_a, is 0.7 times the area of the basin assigned to the areal measurement as shown on Fig.2.

The final estimated areal average value, $\hat{P}$, of the variable for the basin is simply a weighted average of the measurements. The weight (λ_i) for a measurement is equal to its correlation area (A_i) divided by the sum of all the correlation areas for the basin.

$$\lambda_i = A_i/\Sigma A_i \tag{1}$$

A measure, ω_m, of the overall accuracy of the final estimate ($\hat{P}$) is obtained by dividing the sum of the correlation areas (A_i) by actual area of the basin (B).

$$\omega_m = \Sigma A_i/B \tag{2}$$

By its definition ω_m must be between 0 and 1 and can be loosely referred to as the correlation of the estimated value ($\hat{P}$) with the actual average (P) of the parameter over the basin.

The algorithm has an intuitively reasonable behaviour; more accurate measurements get a larger sample area, a larger correlation area, and, thus, a larger weight than less accurate samples. The locations of the samples also affect the shape of the sample area.

When multiple line, point, and areal samples are considered, the shape of the sample areas becomes considerably more complex than for the simple case shown in Fig.1, but the basic concept is unchanged. Details on the algorithms to handle complex cases are described by Johnson *et al.* (1982)

DATA REQUIREMENTS

The application of the correlation area method requires knowledge of the statistical characteristics of each measurement type to properly weight it. The statistics required are:

(a) the correlation of a point measurement with the true value (C_p);

(b) the correlation of a point measurement in a line with the true line average (C_ℓ);

(c) the correlation of an areal average with the true areal average (C_a);

(d) the rate at which the point or line correlation decays with distance (α); and

(e) the measure of randomness in an areal distributed random field (σ).

The sampling correlation functions listed above require that several covariance parameters be estimated to implement the correlation area technique. These covariance parameters are related to both the accuracy of particular measurement technologies and to the correlation decay in space of the random field under study.

A brief discussion pertaining to each of the data requirements listed above is given below.

Point, sample correlation, C_p

The value of C_p is the correlation of a point measurement with the true value at that point. Based on investigations of the accuracy of ground sampling technologies, it should be relatively easy to estimate C_p. Furthermore, it is expected that C_p will be generally "large", say, approximately 0.9 or better, for most technologies.

Line sample correlation, C_ℓ

The value of C_ℓ is the correlation of a flight-line sample with the value at a point randomly located along the flight line. Presumably, historical ground truth experiments will be sufficient to estimate C_ℓ. It should be understood that C_ℓ actually mixes two effects. The first is the accuracy of the technology as it measures the true flight-line average, and the second is the correlation of a point along the flight line with the flight-line average. A more accurate technology will increase C_ℓ, but even a perfect measurement technology would not guarantee a C_ℓ of 1.0 because of the variability of point values along the flight line. Thus, C_ℓ should be expected to be less than C_p.

Areal sample correlation, C_a

The value of C_a is the correlation of an areal sample with the true areal average over the sampling domain. Presumably ground truth experiments will provide information to estimate C_a, but some degree of subjectivity may be needed as well.

Decay parameter, α

A large set of measurements of a variable under study can be modelled as a random field. This random field, whether soil moisture, snow water equivalent, or whatever, is assumed to have a homogeneous mean value and variance and isotropic covariance in space described by a simple exponential covariance function. The decay parameter, α, describes the value of information at one location in estimating the random field at another site.

Three possible approaches for estimating the value of α are the use of historical data, real time data, and a conceptual model. Of these three approaches, the historical approach and the conceptual model approach offer the most promise for operational estimates of α.

Historical data Historical data on soil moisture or snow water equivalent can be analysed to estimate α. Then the value of α can be assumed to apply to current conditions. The difficulties with this approach are: (a) procuring an historical data base, and (b) developing a procedure to "stratify" the data for different values of α related to some easy-to-identify property of current conditions.

Real time data If enough point data are available in real time, a value of α can be estimated for the current condition of the random field. Using remotely sensed data for this approach is rather difficult because of the sample averaging properties of this type of data.

Conceptual model The conceptual model approach can be illustrated by considering soil moisture as the product of two random fields: the field capacity and the fraction of field capacity that is filled. The variability of the field capacity can be related to a soil map. If a conceptual model is developed to relate the statistics of the "fraction of field capacity" to some easy to estimate parameters (e.g. the antecedent precipitation index), it may be possible to estimate α for the soil moisture without actual measurements of soil moisture.

Measure of randomness, σ

The same three approaches for estimating the decay parameters, α, can be employed to estimate the randomness measure, σ.

Data base availability

The data base to compute the statistical parameters for the correlation area method is often unavailable. However, for the agricultural areas of the north central plains area of the United States and for the central area of Russia there are sufficient historical data for deriving initial estimates for using the correlation area method for soil moisture and water equivalent of the snow cover. As the data base from remotely sensed measurements of hydrological variables increases, more information to estimate the required statistical parameters will be available.

APPLICATION OF METHOD

The primary application for which the correlation area method was developed was to provide a means for integrating measurements from conventional hydrological networks and remote sensing for use in operational hydrology. However, the resulting improved estimates of the areal averages of hydrological variables potentially have many other uses. For example, such improved estimates of areal averages of soil moisture should be of value for use with large scale climatic models or agricultural models for predicting droughts and crop yields.

The method can be used in a reverse sense for network design to determine what combined data networks would be required to enhance a model's performance. For example, the accuracy of areal estimates of the water equivalent of the snow cover based on point (*in situ*) measurements are often very poor. Having a knowledge of the accuracy of remote sensing techniques (i.e. aerial gamma radiation surveys (Carroll *et al.*, 1983) or microwave, (Schmugge, 1980)) and an analysis of the data accuracy required for a specific improvement in model performance, the correlation area method could be applied (in reverse) to define the mix of measurement technologies networks required to produce the desired improvement.

ACKNOWLEDGEMENTS This Research was supported by the National Aeronautics and Space Administration (NAS5-27554), Goddard Space Flight Center, Greenbelt, Maryland.

REFERENCES

Carroll, T.R., Glynn, J.E. & Goodison, B.E. (1983) A comparison of US and Canadian airborne gamma radiation snow water equivalent measurements. In: *Proc. 51st Annual Western Snow Conference* (Vancouver, Washington, USA).

Johnson, E.R., Peck, E.L. & Keefer, T.N. (1982) *Combining Remotely Sensed and Other Measurements for Hydrologic Areal Averages*. NASA CR 170457, Goddard Space Flight Center, Greenbelt, M<ryland, USA.

Peck, E.L., McQuivey, R.S., Keefer, T.N., Johnson, E.R. & Erekson, J.L. (1981a) *Review of Hydrologic Models for Evaluating Use of*

Remote Sensing Capabilities. NASA CR166674, Goddard Space Flight Center, Greenbelt, Maryland, USA.
Peck, E.L., Johnson, E.R. & Keefer, T.N. (1983) *Creating a Bridge between Remote Sensing and Hydrologic Models*. NASA CR170517, Goddard Space Flight Center, Greenbelt, Maryland, USA.
Schmugge, T.J. (1980) Microwave approaches in hydrology. *Photogram. Engng and Remote Sensing* 46 (4), 495-507.

Hydrological Applications of Remote Sensing and Remote Data Transmission
(Proceedings of the Hamburg Symposium, August 1983). IAHS Publ. no. 145.

Development and testing of a remote sensing based hydrological model

J. R. GROVES, R. M. RAGAN & R. B. CLAPP
Remote Sensing Systems Laboratory, University of Maryland, College Park, Maryland 20742, USA

ABSTRACT The potential of space platform remote sensing to provide data for the simulation of continuous hydrological processes is rapidly advancing, but applications have been limited by the absence of models structured to accept remotely sensed data. This paper describes the development and testing of a physically based streamflow model specifically structured to incorporate information obtained from current and anticipated sensing systems. The linkage and concepts are similar to those of the Stanford Watershed Model family, but with individual components restructured to interface better with remotely sensed quantities. Both satellite and ground based input data are incorporated into the model through a grid cell geographical information system. Component models are based upon extensive numerical simulations with results reduced to computationally efficient algorithms. A preliminary version of the new model is under evaluation using a midwestern USA agricultural basin and data obtained from Landsat satellites.

Mise au point et essais d'un modèle d'écoulement continu basé sur la télédétection

RESUME La possibilité d'obtenir par télédétection à partir de plateforme spatiale, des données complémentaires pour la simulation des processus hydrologiques continus, est en progrès rapides, mais les applications ont été limitées par l'absence de modèles concus pour accepter des données obtenues par télédétection. Ce travail décrit la mise au point et les essais éffectués sur un modèle d'écoulement continu structuré spécifiquement pour intégrer des informations obtenues par les systèmes de télédétection actuellement existants et à venir. Les liaisons et les concepts opératoires sont semblables à ceux du groupe des modèles des bassins Stanford, mais avec des composants individuels restructurés de facon à mieux s'adapter à des valeurs obtenues par télédétection. Toutes les entrées de données obtenues par satellite ou au sol, sont introduites dans le modèle par un système de grille géographique. Les composants sont basés sur des simulations numériques extensives avec des résultats faciles à obtenir par des algorithmes efficaces. Une version préliminaire du modèle est mise a l'épreuve en utilisant un bassin versant agricole du centre des Etats-Unis et les entrées de données obtenues par le système de satellite Landsat.

INTRODUCTION

Although hydrologists are beginning to recognize the power inherent in digital satellite data, existing hydrological models are not structured to take full advantage of the potential value of such data. In fact, current models were deliberately simplified in their original development because of the absence of the type of spatial and temporal information that modern remote sensing technology is capable of providing.

This report presents results of an ongoing research effort at the Remote Sensing Systems Laboratory, University of Maryland, to develop a new physically-based streamflow model having components that reflect our current understanding of the individual processes of the hydrological cycle and formulated specifically to use remotely sensed inputs and geographic information systems. The complete development and testing of a final operational model is seen as a major effort of several years duration and is contingent upon the successful deployment of advanced sensors such as those that will monitor surface soil moisture.

The first generation model described herein contains new components simulating the infiltration and soil moisture redistribution processes. While validation and testing are limited to runoff volumes from single storms, the framework for continuous simulation is provided and an operational strategy for use on large agricultural watersheds is presented. Subsequent versions of the model will be increasingly sophisticated as new sensor systems are deployed and individual components are completed. The structure of the model is modular to allow for this continued improvement.

BACKGROUND

Hydrological simulation models

Physical modelling of the hydrological cycle is complicated by an incomplete understanding of the physical process, the lack of suitable quantities of the right types of input data, the extreme spatial variation of both meteorological and geographical phenomena, and the complexity of the computations required.

The difficulty of true physical modelling has resulted in the development and use of a series of pseudo-physical models such as the Stanford Watershed Model IV developed by Crawford & Linsley (1966), from which virtually all of the models in popular use today have descended. The Stanford series of models depict and link together individual processes using state-of-the-art understanding, data, and computing capability. Still, most of the resulting algorithms are accurately described as "black-box" routines which generate acceptable results only after laborious and painstaking calibration of up to 30 required input parameters. Ideally, a completely physically based model would require no calibration or fitting of parameters. All parameters would have a physical interpretation or be directly calculated from easily measured physical properties of the drainage basin.

Satellite remote sensing

The present study emphasizes the use of data from sensors currently or potentially aboard satellite or manned space platforms. Other remote sensing data sources include photographic and multi-spectral aircraft sensors, satellite or aircraft platforms used to relay data obtained by ground sensing, and data collection via satellite.

Table 1 is a summary of hydrological parameters currently or potentially available from remote sensing. The summary is based upon a review of current literature and forms the basis for the remote sensing inputs to the physically based modelling concepts presented below.

TABLE 1 Hydrological parameters currently or potentially available from remote sensing

Satellite	*Sensor*	*Physical or hydrological data*
Landsat	*TM or MSS*	*Land use, impervious data, water extent, drainage networks, ice and snow cover, albedo, vegetation species, extent, characteristics groundwater recharge and discharge areas*
Polar Orbitor	*AVHRR*	*Vegetation species, biomass, canopy temperatures, albedo, snow cover*
GOES	*VISSR*	*Cloud cover and movement, solar radiation, surface and canopy temperature, albedo, high altitude winds*
Future	*Microwave or infrared*	*Soil moisture, snow water equivalent, precipitation, soil hydraulic properties*
Future	*LIDAR*	*Elevations and channel cross sections*
Future	*MLA*	*Detailed natural and urban drainage structure, spatial variability with drainage units*

Geographical information systems

While the practicality of using satellite data has been clearly established, the integration of such use into modelling has been relatively slow. One difficulty has been the absence of flexible techniques to merge the satellite data with other forms of information. Coupled with the merging problem has been the need for a management system to handle efficiently the large volumes of data required to take full advantage of the spatial definition available from satellite platforms. The solution to these problems is found in the geographical information system (GIS), a geo-referenced system for the specification, acquisition, storage, retrieval and manipulation of data.

The power inherent to a GIS is realized when the array of stored variables is interfaced directly through a computer to a simulation model. The computer rapidly aggregates combinations of variables to develop or compute input parameters for the model. The data base is easily updated in mid-simulation, such as would occur upon the receipt of periodic soil moisture sensings. The modeller can readily change selected variables to simulate proposed land use or topographical changes, and can simulate predicted meteorological conditions to provide timely flood flow forecasts.

THE STRUCTURE OF THE CONTINUOUS SIMULATION MODEL

It was concluded that the greatest flexibility in producing spatial and temporal variations in hydrological behaviour could be achieved through a deterministic model representing the current understanding of the interrelationships among individual components of the runoff cycle. Models of each individual component must be computationally efficient in computer storage and running time requirements, but, at the same time, must be based on state-of-the-art understanding of that individual process and must have parameters that are physically based and definable through either remote sensing or other available means.

Figure 1 has been adopted as the basic structure of the new model. As in the Stanford model, the individual process elements are relatively simple functional relationships or table look-up subroutines. Efficient computational strategies are mandatory because of the massive storage and running times involved in the computer simulation of a hydrological time series.

A key departure from earlier models is the reliance on extensive numerical experiments to develop the computationally efficient process models. The experiments use numerical solutions of the partial differential equations defining the scientific community's current understanding of the particular process. Numerical simulations are conducted for the range of conditions anticipated in the field. The results are then analysed to develop simple functional relationships that approximate the performance of the more complex numerical approach. The continuous simulation model is being developed by phases as shown in Table 2.

THE RAINFALL EXCESS MODEL

The rainfall excess or direct runoff model developed and tested in the current report uses relatively simple components for interception and depression storage linked with completely new soil moisture redistribution and infiltration components to predict

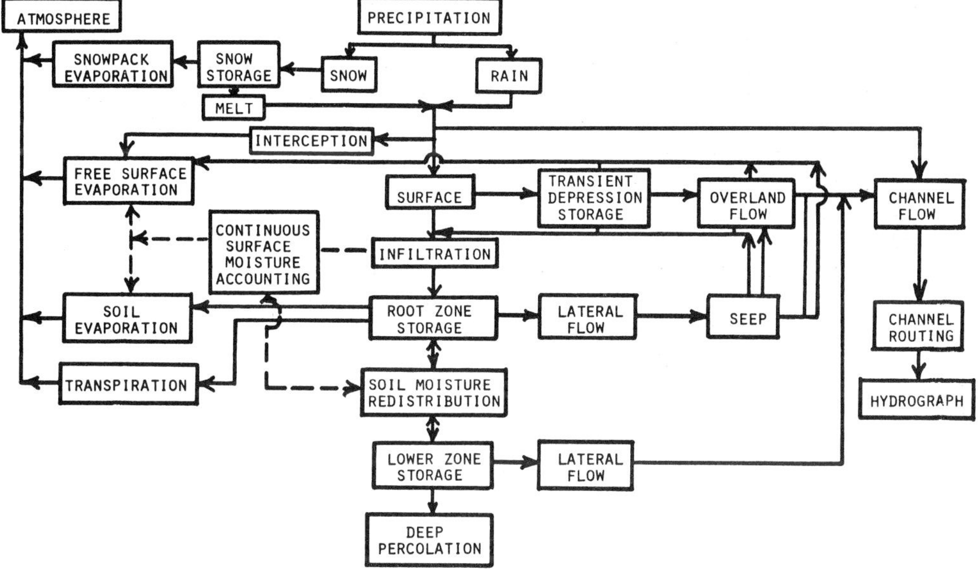

FIG.1 Structure of the model.

volumes of runoff from major storms. This section contains a description of this rainfall excess volume model, the general structure of which is shown in Fig.2.

Simulation is accomplished by watershed segments, which are hydrologically similar response units of the drainage basin identified by the GIS. The number of such segments will vary with the character of the watershed, the level of input data available, and the nature of simulation desired. The definition of the segments is accomplished externally, prior to the execution of the model using

TABLE 2 Sequential model development plan

Phase	*Components*	*Mode*	*Comparison*
I	*RAINFALL EXCESS* *Interception* *Infiltration* *Depression storage* *Soil moisture redistribution*	*Single event*	*Runoff volumes*
II	*HYDROGRAPH GENERATION* *Overland flow* *Channel routing* *Channel-aquifer short-term relations*	*Single event*	*Shape of runoff hydrograph*
III	*CONTINUOUS STREAMFLOW* *Snowmelt* *Evapotranspiration* *Groundwater*	*Continuous simulation*	*Long-term runoff hydrograph*

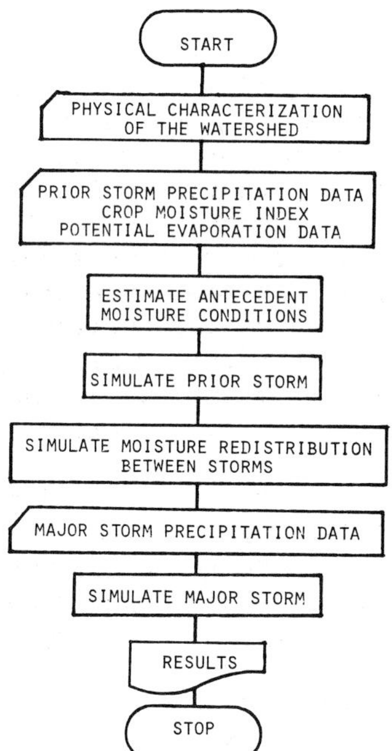

FIG.2 Flow chart of rainfall excess model.

the GIS.

The data requirements for each segment are the soil texture group, the land cover, the slope/elevation class, the area, the depth of soil and the root zone depth. Optional parameters are the type of tillage used, time since last tillage, and six hydraulic properties of the soil (saturated hydraulic conductivity, saturation and residual soil moisture contents, wetting front and air entry suction head, and the pore size distribution index).

Good estimates of the hydraulic parameters of the soils of the watershed are essential to physically based modelling, and the model is structured to accept or provide such estimates in several ways, depending on the information available to the modeller. The optimum inputs are numerical values for the five parameters listed above.

If numerical values are not available, the modeller can choose to describe the soils of the basin by soil texture group or by the Soil Conservation Service Hydrologic Soil Group (HSG), with the choice determined by the level of information available for the specific application. If the information is available, soil texture group provides more discrimination than HSG and is probably the better choice. It is also anticipated that future microwave satellite sensors will be capable of identifying soil texture groups and of providing information on hydraulic parameters.

The model is structured to receive and then assign default values for the required hydraulic parameters for any selected soil discrimination scheme. Parameter values for soil texture groups are available from such sources as Clapp & Hornberger (1978). The model also contains provisions for modifying soil hydraulic parameters to reflect tillage history and crusting, using procedures of Brakensiek *et al*. (1982).

Operations sequence

Actual simulation begins with the routing of a prior storm through the interception and infiltration models. At this point simulation for the prior storm ends since the information required, the infiltration volume within each segment, has been calculated. The Soil Moisture Redistribution (SMR) component next simulates the increase and subsequent decay of the surface soil moisture content during the prior storm and the dry period between the storms as depicted in Fig.3, yielding the important initial moisture content for the major storm of interest. The evolutionary SMR component simulates moisture redistribution, evapotranspiration, and vertical drainage in the soil column, and is essentially the model reported by Clapp *et al.* (1983).

The model next accesses the rainfall data for the major storm. Simulation continues with sequential linking of interception, infiltration, and depression storage components to generate the required volumes of runoff. The sequential linking of the hydrological cycle processes varies somewhat between segments in order to describe accurately the processes as they occur in nature. The sequencing is determined by land cover classes, as shown in Fig.4, from which it can be seen that interception applies only where canopy exists, natural grass and forest soils do not form a crust, etc.

The innovative infiltration component is a modification of an infiltration-storage model developed by Wilkening & Ragan (1982), which was, in turn, based on extensive numerical simulation with the Richards equation for unsaturated flow. The modifications included use of a simple, analytical algorithm that added flexibility while decreasing computational costs.

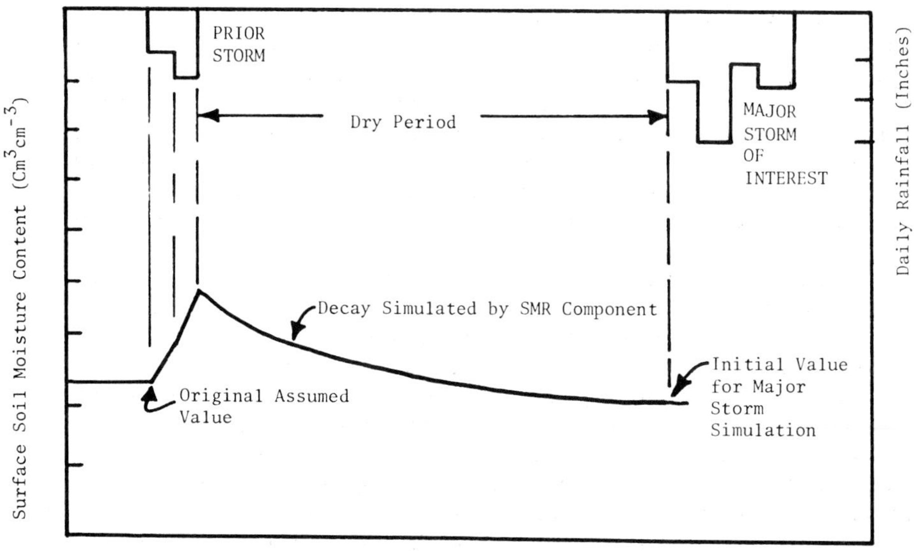

FIG.3 Conceptual operation of soil moisture redistribution component.

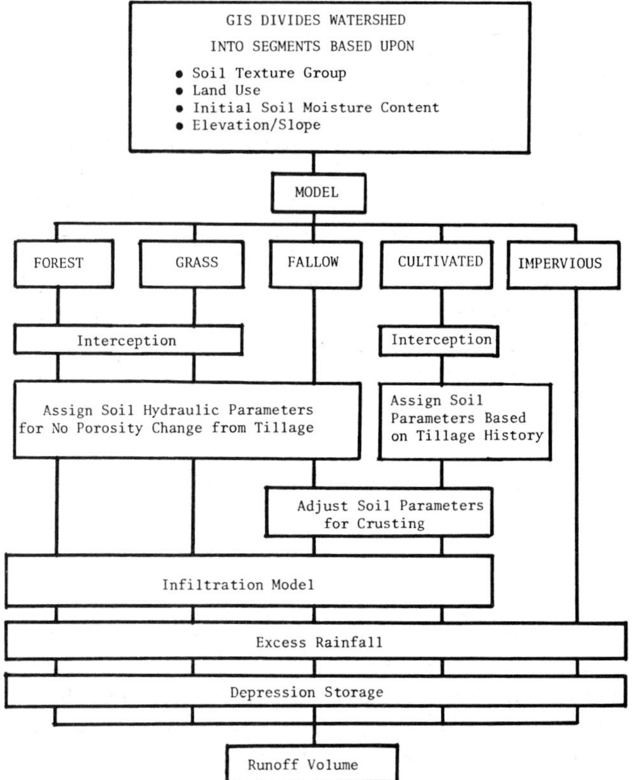

FIG.4 Linkage by land use classes.

TESTING THE RAINFALL EXCESS MODEL

One of the principal objectives of the research was the testing of the runoff volume components of the planned remote sensing based hydrological model as they are currently configured in a single event excess rainfall model. This phase of the research was intended both to test the model in a real world environment and to provide experience with the procedures that will be necessary to use the model as a practical tool prior to the availability of all the anticipated remote sensing systems.

The criteria for selection of a test or demonstration drainage basin included the availability of conventional and satellite data, a moderate rainfall regimen, a mixture of natural and crop vegetation, sufficient size to insure meaningful spatial variation of hydrological variables while remaining manageable, and the availability of soil and topographic maps. These criteria were satisfied in the selection of the Timber Creek basin above the Marshalltown streamgauge, a 305 km^2, predominantly agricultural area in Marshall County, Iowa.

Preparation of the GIS

The GIS prepared for the Timber Creek testing included three data planes: land use, soil texture group, and elevation/slope. In the absence of spatially distributed soil moisture values from remote sensors, initial values were subjectively assigned to hydrologically distinct segments identified by the GIS.

Land use was obtained from a Landsat-3 MSS scene collected on 27 April 1977, supplemented by a Skylab photograph and extensive published descriptions of the area (US Department of Agriculture, 1981). Both supervised and unsupervised classification strategies were used to determine land use from the Landsat data. An unsupervised cluster analysis procedure using the International Imaging System (I^2S - Model 70) was found to produce the best results. Rainfall and streamflow records indicated that the Landsat data had been collected during an extended dry period, which aided the digital data analysis by minimizing signature variations that would have resulted from variations in soil moisture within the watershed.

Information on soils was obtained from the USDA soil survey. Most of the watershed soils belong to three soil associations that are all described as silty clay loam. Two other soil associations are described as silty clays. Both the soil survey and the US Geological Survey topographic maps were used to define hydrologically similar zones. The watershed was divided into flood plains or lowlands along perennial streams with less than 2% slope, hillslopes with greater than 7% slope, uplands areas with less than 2% slope, and all other areas. There were, therefore, four groups in the elevation/slope plane of the GIS (Fig.5).

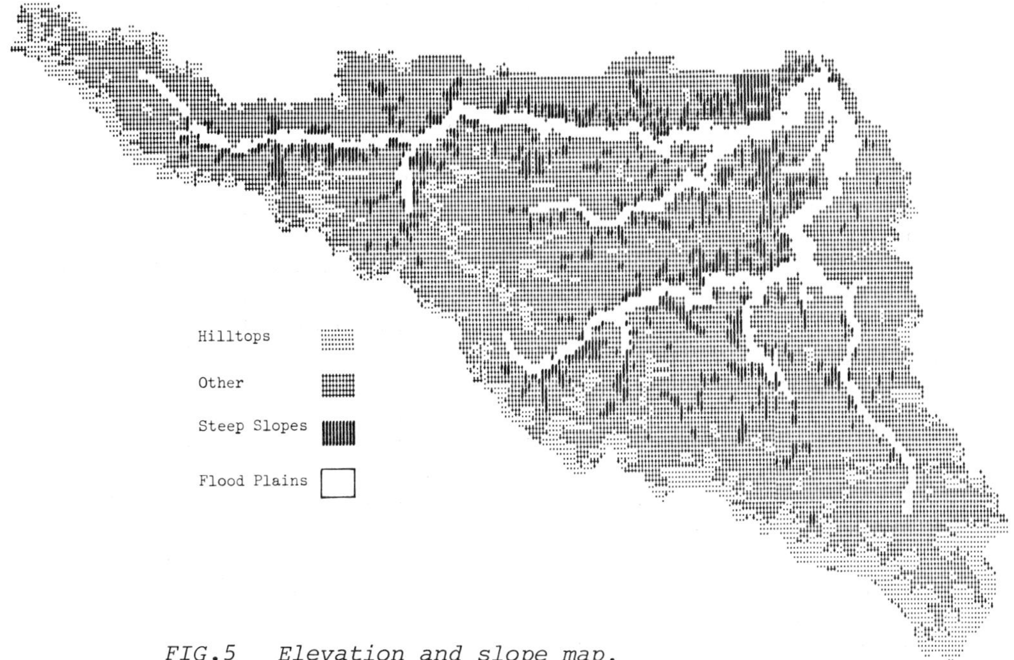

FIG.5 Elevation and slope map.

Selection of segments

The information for each data plane was digitized by polygons using an Altek free cursor digitizer interfaced with a Tektronix 4051 graphic system and software developed in previous research efforts. Results were stored initially in the Tektronix minicomputer and then transferred to the University of Maryland mainframe UNIVAC computer. All data were processed in 90 by 86 grid cell matrices referenced to the 7.5 minute USGS topographic map. Each grid cell was approximately 160 by 120 m. A short algorithm was written to identify and count all the discrete combinations of data elements in the three planes, and a total of 34 possible segments were identified. Small segments were lumped together to reduce this number to a manageable level, resulting in 22 segments for use in the simulations.

The segments do not represent 22 parcels of land; each segment is made up of hydrologically similar grid cells that are not necessarily contiguous. The elevation/slope data plane (Fig.5) proved to be the major discriminator in defining segments by dividing the basin into bottom lands, steep slopes, hilltops and other areas. The soil group and land use data planes permitted further stratification within slope/elevation categories.

Results of simulations

The rainfall excess model was run in a completely uncalibrated mode with the rainfall data of five major storms. The runoff predictions were consistently higher than the measured runoff, with a root mean square per cent difference of 49.5%.

Preliminary sensitivity tests had indicated that the soil texture group assignment, with accompanying default soil hydraulic characteristics, is the most important subjective decision in preparing the model for use. The information available for the Timber Creek watershed was limited to narrative descriptions in the soil survey (US Department of Agriculture, 1981), which do not include numerical values for soil hydraulic properties. It was concluded that the bias in the model was most likely spatial, due to variability in the hydraulic properties of the soils of the basin; a calibration procedure was developed and tested to overcome the bias.

The soil texture group of the largest segment of the watershed, 59.702 miles^2 of silty clay loam, was changed to a mixture of silty clay loam and loam, with the mixture varied to change the model runoff predictions to equal the measured runoff for the first two storms. The average of these two mixtures was used to test the now "calibrated" model on the remaining three storms. While these calibration procedures are subjective in nature, they are not unlike the procedures used to calibrate current watershed models, with the important exception that the parameter selected for calibration adjustment has physical significance and is not an ill-defined fitting parameter of an assumed functional relationship. Figure 6 compares the results of the uncalibrated and calibrated models.

CONCLUSIONS

The hydrological model developed in the present study offers a base for significant improvements in operational streamflow prediction

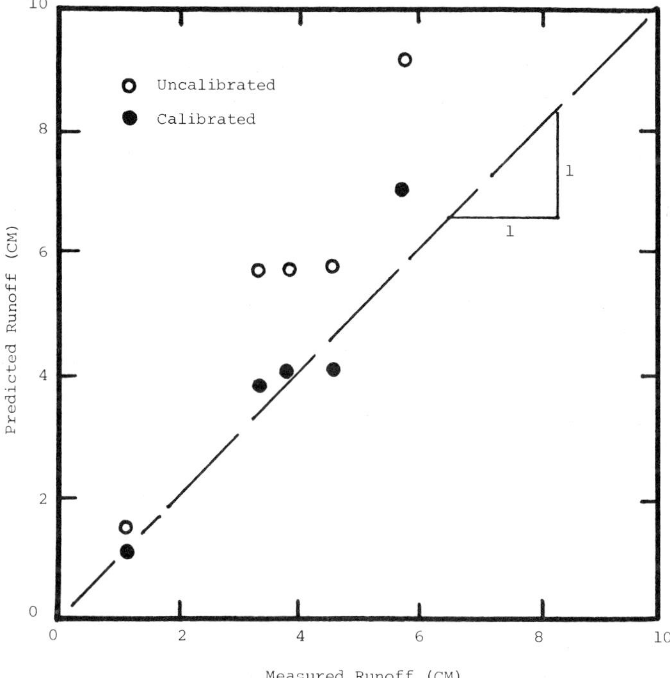

FIG.6 Results of simulations.

with mathematical simulation techniques. The use of remotely sensed data to characterize basin conditions, the emphasis upon physically based individual components with parameters defined from measurable quantities, and the employment of improved computer-based information management capabilities are the key innovative features of a proposed new family of hydrological models.

Several of the component models of the proposed new model were linked and tested as a runoff volume predictor. The infiltration and soil moisture redistribution component models have been shown to perform acceptably in this first generation model. The testing provided essential insights into the sensitivity of the new soil moisture redistribution component that will lead to improvement in subsequent model versions as the application is extended to continuous simulation. The rainfall excess model was tested on an agricultural basin, exhibiting a strong positive bias. However, the new model has a logical base for adjustment or calibration and a shift of a portion of one simulation segment to a coarser soil texture group, a change with logical physical significance, resulted in predicted runoff approximating the measured values.

The rainfall excess model was shown to be a robust model as applied to the demonstration basin for major storms, exhibiting only the anticipated sensitivity to soil characteristics and antecedent moisture conditions. The relatively high degree of segmentation, 22 distinct simulation segments for 305 km^2, appears to provide stability and insulate against abrupt or unexplained changes.

The results of the model testing also demonstrated the expected sensitivity to two major data requirements, the hydraulic properties and the initial moisture content of the soils. Ongoing efforts to obtain these data with remote sensing technology should be continued.

ACKNOWLEDGEMENTS The research was funded by the US Department of Agriculture and the National Aeronautics and Space Administration. Computer support was provided by the University of Maryland Computer Science Center.

REFERENCES

Brakensiek, D.L., Rawls, W.J. & Soni, B. (1982) Infiltration parameter values for transient soil conditions. Paper No. 82-2589, *1982 Winter Meeting of the Am. Soc. Agric. Engrs* (Chicago, Illinois, USA).

Clapp, R.B. & Hornberger, G.M. (1978) Empirical equations for some soil hydraulic properties. *Wat. Resour. Res.* 14 (4), 601-604.

Clapp, R.B., Hornberger, G.M. & Cosby, B.J. (1983) Estimating spatial variability in soil moisture with a simplified dynamic model. *Wat. Resour. Res.* 19 (3), 739-745.

Crawford, N.H. & Linsley, R.K. (1966) Digital simulation in hydrology: Stanford Watershed Model IV. *Tech. Report no. 39, Department of Civil Engineering, Stanford University, Stanford, California, USA.*

US Department of Agriculture (1981) *Soil Survey of Marshall County, Iowa.* Soil Conservation Service, Government Printing Office, Washington, DC, USA.

Wilkening, H.A., III & Ragan, R.M. (1982) Estimating rainfall infiltration in terms of initial soil moisture. *AgRISTARS CP-52-04372, US Dept of Agriculture, Beltsville, Maryland, USA.*

Hydrological Applications of Remote Sensing and Remote Data Transmission (Proceedings of the Hamburg Symposium, August 1983). IAHS Publ. no. 145.

Utilisation de la télédétection pour améliorer la précision des crues de fonte de neige simulées par le modèle CEQUEAU

J. P. FORTIN, G. MORIN, W. SOCHANSKA & L. POTVIN
INRS-Eau, CP 7500, Sainte-Foy, Québec, Canada G1V 4C7

RESUME Des simulations des crues de fonte de neige en 1974 et 1975 avec le modèle CEQUEAU, sur un bassin québécois de 629 km^2, montrent que les erreurs de simulation ne sont pas seulement imputables aux modèles, mais aussi aux données climatologiques et nivométriques disponibles. Une première simulation, réalisée uniquement à partir de données climatologiques met en évidence une fonte légèrement trop hâtive au cours des deux années et un stock de neige trop important en 1975. La correction de la vitesse de fonte journalière est d'abord réalisée, en comparant des cartes d'équivalents en eau de la neige au sol imprimées par le modèle à des images Landsat ou NOAA-4 interprétées visuellement. Une réduction de l'équivalent en eau de la neige au sol, à l'aide des relevés nivométriques, a dû être effectuée uniquement en 1975, juste avant le début de la fonte, pour améliorer le bilan hydrologique. Les résultats obtenus confirment le potentiel de la télédétection en modélisation hydrologique.

Use of remotely sensed data to produce more accurate simulations of snowmelt floods with the CEQUEAU model
ABSTRACT Simulations of the 1974 and 1975 snowmelt floods with the CEQUEAU model, on a 629 km^2 basin in Quebec, show that simulation errors are not only due to models, but also to available climatological and snow course data. A first simulation, based on climatological data alone, is characterized by a daily snowmelt slightly too early for both years, together with an overestimated snowpack in 1975. The daily snowmelt is first corrected, by comparing maps of the water equivalents of the snowpack printed by the model, to visually interpreted Landsat or NOAA-4 imagery, for specific dates. A reduction of the water equivalent of the snowpack, using snow course data, had to be done only in 1975, just before the beginning of the snowmelt period, so as to obtain a better hydrological budget. The potential of using remotely sensed data in hydrological modelling is confirmed.

INTRODUCTION

Au Canada, l'équivalent en eau de chaque chute de neige est généralement obtenu en attribuant une densité constante (100 kg m^{-3} au Québec)

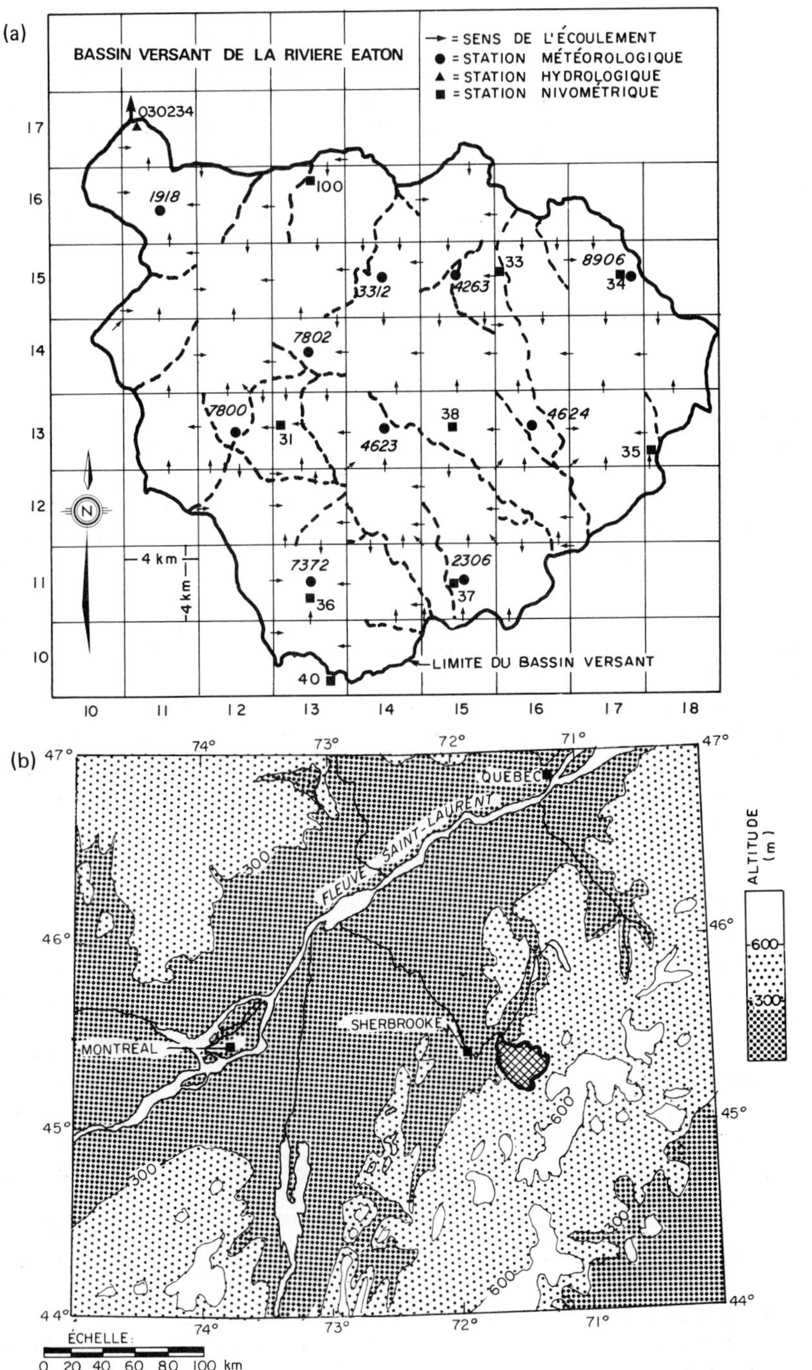

FIG.1 Le bassin de la Rivière Eaton; (a) grille CEQUEAU; (b) localisation du bassin et relief du sud du Québec.

à la hauteur correspondante mesurée à la table à neige. Des estimations significativement plus élevées ou plus faibles que les valeurs effectives du stock de neige peuvent s'en suivre, affectant les résultats obtenus avec un modèle hydrologique. Dans le premier cas, le volume d'écoulement simulé est supérieur au volume observé et les crues ont tendance à être trop faibles au début de la fonte et trop élevées à la fin, alors que c'est l'inverse avec un stock trop faible. Pour contrôler ces estimations, l'avènement de la télédétection par satellite a permis d'avoir accès à un nouveau type de données qui peuvent s'avérer autant, sinon plus utiles, que les données classiques.

METHODOLOGIE DE L'ETUDE

Conçu pour tenir compte de la distribution spatiale des précipitations et du bilan hydrologique sur un bassin a l'aide d'une grille carrée, le modèle hydrologique CEQUEAU (Charbonneau *et al.*, 1977; Morin *et al.*, 1981) offre la possibilité de présenter des cartes de l'équivalent en eau du stock de neige, sur chacun des carreaux du bassin étudié (Fig.1(a)). Les comparaisons avec des informations spatiales indépendantes (télédétection, relevés nivométriques) en sont ainsi facilitées.

L'idée de base de l'étude a consisté à appliquer le modèle au bassin de la Rivière Eaton, qui s'étend sur 629 km^2 dans le sud du Québec (Fig.1(b)), pour en simuler les débits en utilisant, dans un premier temps, uniquement les données recueillies aux stations climatologiques. Par la suite, des modifications ont été apportées tant aux valeurs de certains paramètres du modèle qu'aux stocks de neige, à l'aide de la télédétection et des relevés nivométriques, pour améliorer la simulation des débits.

SIMULATION A PARTIR DES STATIONS CLIMATOLOGIQUES SEULEMENT

Nous avons choisi de simuler les débits des années 1974 et 1975, pour lesquelles nous avions les divers types de données désirées, en utilisant tout d'abord les valeurs des paramètres déterminées précédemment à partir de données climatologiques et hydrométriques uniquement (Morin *et al.*, 1981). Ces années sont différentes l'une de l'autre. On observe quatre crues provenant de la pluie et de la fonte combinées en 1974, et une seule en 1975, due surtout à la fonte de neige. Il en résulte un écoulement saisonnier deux fois plus élevé en 1974 qu'en 1975 (Tableau 1).

En 1974, la simulation des débits est relativement bonne, la crue de mars étant surestimée et la dernière crue d'avril sous-estimée (Fig.2). La lame calculée ne s'écarte que de 3.8% de la lame observée (Table 1); la lame observée est surestimée en février et mars alors qu'elle est sous-estimée en avril et mai. En 1975, la lame totale simulée est de 18.1% supérieure à la lame observée (Tableau 1), toutes les crues étant surestimées, surtout en avril (Fig.3).

COMPARAISON DES DONNEES CLIMATOLOGIQUES ET DES DONNEES NIVOMETRIQUES

Ce qui ressort le plus de la première simulation, c'est l'excédent

TABLEAU 1 Comparaison des lames mensuelles observées, Lo, et calculées, Lc (mm)

Essai		*Fév*	*Mars*	*Avril*	*Mai*	*Total saison*	*Ecart (%)*
1974							
Obs.	*Lo*	*34.70*	*68.30*	*276.23*	*132.15*	*511.38*	
No.1	*Lc*	*42.95*	*93.88*	*243.70*	*111.68*	*492.21*	
	Lc - Lo	*8.25*	*25.58*	*-32.53*	*-20.47*	*-19.17*	*3.8*
No.2	*Lc*	*34.82*	*74.14*	*277.65*	*115.47*	*502.08*	
	Lc - Lo	*0.12*	*5.84*	*1.42*	*-16.68*	*-9.30*	*1.8*
1975							
Obs.	*Lo*	*10.48*	*71.97*	*126.59*	*60.90*	*269.94*	
No.1	*Lc*	*28.13*	*71.03*	*170.62*	*48.96*	*318.74*	
	Lc - Lo	*17.65*	*-0.94*	*44.03*	*-11.94*	*48.80*	*18.1*
No.2	*Lc*	*18.45*	*48.64*	*160.26*	*97.37*	*324.72*	
	Lc - Lo	*7.97*	*-23.32*	*33.67*	*36.47*	*54.78*	*20.3*
No.3	*Lc*	*18.45*	*57.18*	*153.84*	*45.52*	*274.99*	
	Lc - Lo	*7.97*	*-15.69*	*28.26*	*-14.48*	*6.06*	*2.3*

d'écoulement qui provient d'un stock de neige trop important au moment de la fonte, en 1975. Effectivement, le 15 janvier 1975, les équivalents en eau calculés en forêt par le modèle sur chaque carreau où existe une station nivométrique sont déjà nettement supérieurs aux valeurs observées, dont la moyenne est légèrement inférieure à 40 mm (Tableau 2 et Fig.4(a)).

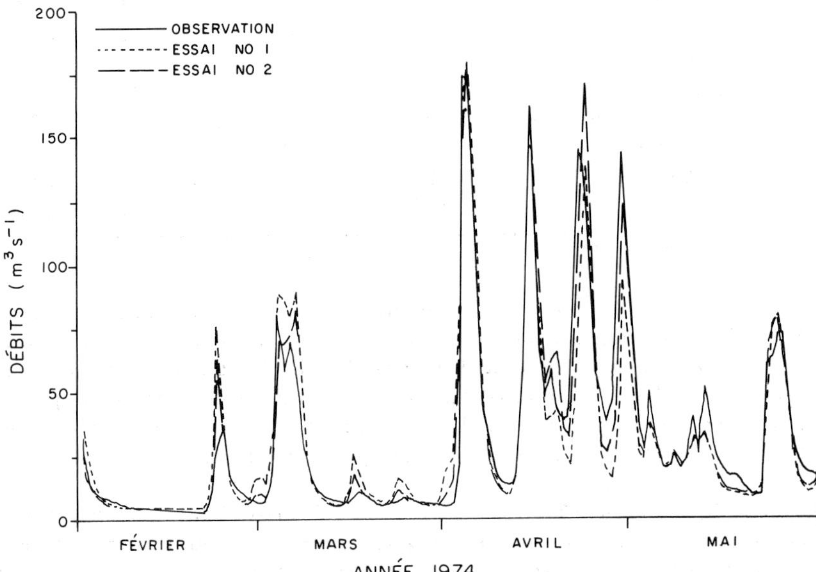

FIG.2 Débits observés et simulés sur la Rivière Eaton à la station 030234 au printemps 1974.

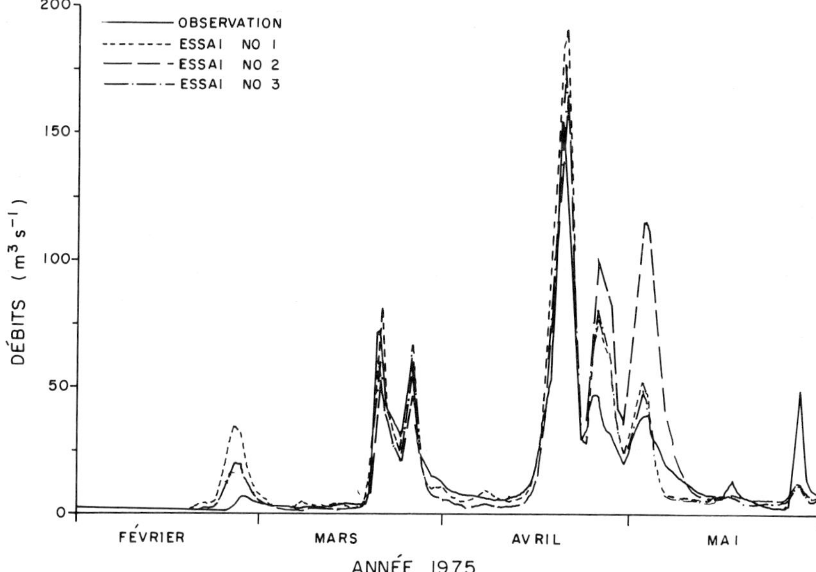

FIG.3 Débits observés et simulés sur la Rivière Eaton à la station 030234 au printemps 1975.

TABLEAU 2 Equivalents en eau (mm) aux stations nivométriques en 1975, sur le bassin de la Rivière Eaton

No.	Nom	Altitude (m)	Dates: 15/1	19/2	19/3	2/4	16/4	30/4
31	Sawyerville North	220	36	114	155	117	112	0
33	Pine Brook North	465	43	127	196	157	175	43
34	West Ditton	488	48	152	226	178	229	79
35	Bellefeuille	571	46	145	211	173	229	102
36	East Clifton North	450	38	132	132	137	157	0
37	Eaton Second Branch	495	30	127	163	130	175	0
38	Maple Leaf	389	30	102	142	99	114	0
40	Saint-Malo	564	25	107	119	124	140	0
100	Bury	335	30	112	185	170	170	0

Parmi les causes possibles de cet écart, on peut mentionner la surestimation de la hauteur réelle des chutes de neige aux stations climatologiques, une densité réelle de la neige fraîche inférieure à 100 kg m^{-3} et la possibilité que la fonte simulée depuis le début de l'hiver soit trop faible, laissant un stock de neige trop élevé au sol. Il faut aussi s'interroger sur la précision et la représentativité des relevés nivométriques.

La période du 15 janvier au 19 février 1975, entre deux relevés nivométriques consécutifs, étant caractérisée par des températures froides, la fonte est nulle. On peut ainsi éliminer les causes d'erreur attribuables au modèle, et s'attacher uniquement à celles qui sont dues aux données. Au cours de cette période, les estimations de l'augmentation de l'équivalent en eau de la neige au sol fournies par les données climatologiques diffèrent de plus de 20% dans certains cas (Fig.4(b)) de celles des relevés nivométriques. Si l'on considère les relevés nivométriques comme représentatifs des conditions d'enneigement, les résultats des Fig.4(a) et (b) démontrent que les données climatologiques peuvent être responsables d'une partie importante des erreurs de simulation et qu'il faut par conséquent pouvoir les corriger judicieusement.

La représentativité des relevés de neige n'est toutefois pas toujours assurée. Ainsi, du 19 février au 19 mars 1975, les stations nivométriques 36 et 40 ont un comportement très différent des autres (Fig.4(b)). Les relevés à ces stations ayant effectivement été recueillis le 20 mars, la fonte de 10 mm produite du 19 au 20 peut être responsable d'une partie de l'écart, mais cela ne suffit pas à expliquer les différences. Par ailleurs, les valeurs correspondantes provenant du modèle sont elles aussi beaucoup plus élevées que celles des stations 36 et 40, alors qu'elles ne s'écartent pas de plus de 20 mm des relevés à cinq des neuf stations. Il importe donc d'utiliser les relevés nivométriques avec précaution en portant une attention particulière à leur représentativité spatiale. L'utilisation de données complémentaires s'avère par conséquent souhaitable.

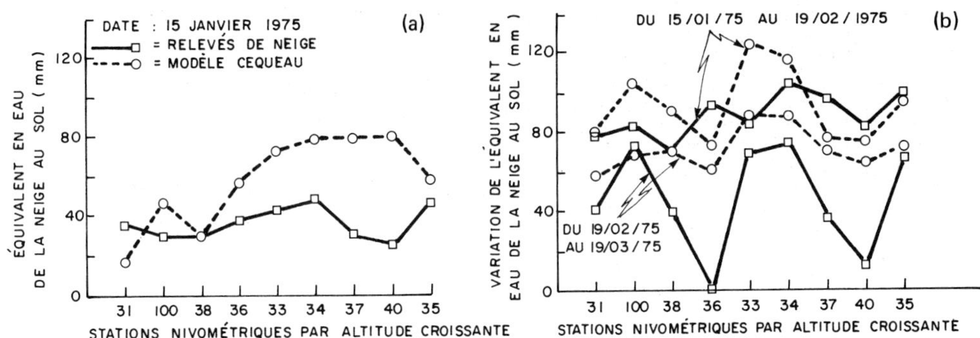

FIG.4 Comparaison des équivalents en eau calculés par le modèle CEQUEAU et des relevés recueillis aux stations nivométriques.

COMPARAISON ENTRE LES CARTES D'EQUIVALENT EN EAU DU STOCK DE NEIGE AU SOL PRODUITES PAR LE MODELE ET LES IMAGES LANDSAT ET NOAA-4 CORRESPONDANTES

Compte tenu des images disponibles, nous avons utilisé des images des satellites Landsat et NOAA-4 dont les caractéristiques sont abondamment citées dans la littérature (Rango, 1977; Bowley *et al.*, 1981).

Comme il est encore (en 1983) plus facile d'avoir accès à des produits photographiques en temps presque réel qu'à des données digitales, la cartographie du couvert nival a été réalisée avec des moyens très simples, à partir de photographies. Par ailleurs, l'interprétation visuelle de l'imagerie satellite, dans le cas de la neige, est préférée par plusieurs au traitement de données numériques par ordinateur (Rango, 1977; Bowley *et al.*, 1981). Toutefois, un nombre croissant d'auteurs utilisent des données numériques (Lillesand *et al.*, 1982; Rochon *et al.*, 1983).

En 1974, une image Landsat était disponible le 20 avril, au cours de la période de fonte intensive. A l'aide d'un rétroprojecteur, nous avons projeté sur une carte du bassin une diapositive couleur (bandes 4, 5 et 7), à l'échelle du 1:1 000 000. Nous avons ainsi identifié une zone complètement dégagée de neige (en gris foncé sur la bande MSS-5 à la Fig.5(a), une zone de transition recouverte de neige en forêt seulement (en gris plus clair, avec des contrastes internes très atténués) et enfin une zone avec un couvert de neige en forêt et en terrain déboisé (en blanc). Les limites de ces zones sont reproduites sur les cartes d'équivalents en eau imprimées par le modèle CEQUEAU, dont la présentation a été améliorée pour faciliter les comparaisons (Fig.5(b) et (c)).

La carte CEQUEAU de la Fig.5(b) ne contient que deux zones, la zone complètement dégagée et la zone partiellement dégagée de neige. La superficie couverte de neige est plus faible que sur l'image Landsat. Cette différence peut être due à une fonte trop rapide dans

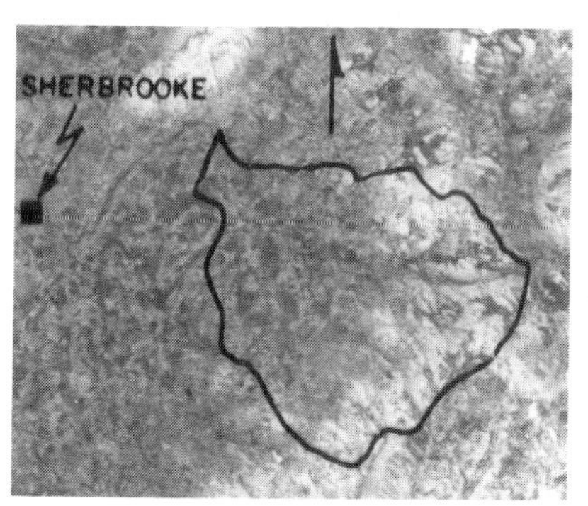

(a)

Pas de neige

55 *Neige en forêt seulement*

116 *Neige en forêt et en terrain déboisé*

55-116 *Equivalent en eau pondéré de la neige au sol (mm)*

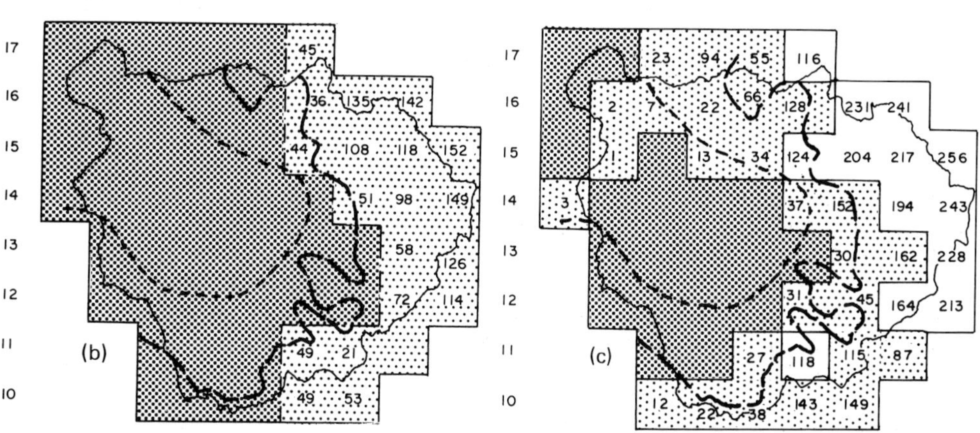

FIG.5 Distribution de la neige au sol sur le bassin de Rivière Eaton, le 20 avril 1974, selon l'image Landsat (MSS-5) et le modèle CEQUEAU; (a) Image Landsat CCRS E-1636-15002-5; (b) essai 1; (c) essai 2.

(a)

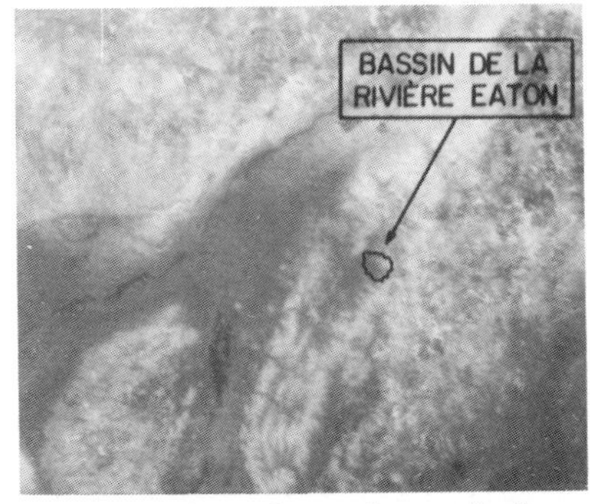

(b)

FIG.6 Progression de la fonte de neige dans le sud du Québec, selon les images NOAA-4 des 17 et 22 avril 1975. (a) orbite 1914, le 17 avril 1975 (distorsion géométrique importante); (b) orbite 1977, le 22 avril 1975.

le modèle ou à un manque de neige. Comme le bilan hydrologique est relativement bon (Tableau 1), les renseignements fournis par télédétection confirment que l'on devrait considérer une réduction de la vitesse de la fonte.

Bien que la résolution spatiale des images NOAA-4 dans le visible soit beaucoup plus faible que celle des images Landsat, une interprétation visuelle de ces images a pu être réalisée en avril 1975, à l'aide du relief de la région (Fig.1(a)). Le 17, le bassin est encore complètement couvert de neige (Fig.6(a)). Par ailleurs, les Fig. 6(b) et 7(a) nous incitent à croire que le 22, la partie inférieure du bassin est partiellement ou complètement dégagée de neige et que le 30, seules les parties les plus élevées en sont encore recouvertes.

La carte produite par le modèle CEQUEAU pour le 30 avril 1975 (Fig.7(b)), indique pour sa part que la neige a complètement disparu en terrain déboisé, mais qu'il reste de la neige en forêt, sur près de la moitié du bassin. Comme l'analyse des données de 1974 indique qu'il serait souhaitable de retarder la fonte, cette constatation suggère une surestimation du stock de neige en 1975.

MODIFICATION DES VALEURS DES PARAMETRES DE FONTE DU MODELE CEQUEAU

Des essais ont d'abord été réalisés afin d'observer l'effet d'un ralentissement de la fonte, estimée par la méthode des degrés-jours, sur les lames mensuelles, les débits journaliers et la distribution de la neige au sol aux dates désirées. Les meilleurs résultats ont été obtenus en diminuant les taux de fonte en forêt et en terrain déboisé, respectivement de 3.5 à 3.0 et de 4.0 à 3.5 mm $^{\circ}C^{-1}$ j^{-1}, et en remontant légèrement le seuil de fonte en terrain déboisé de -3°C à -2°C.

La carte CEQUEAU produite le 20 avril 1974 (Fig.5(c)) compte maintenant trois zones. La distribution spatiale de ces zones correspond beaucoup mieux à celles qui sont identifiées sur l'image Landsat (Fig.5(a)).

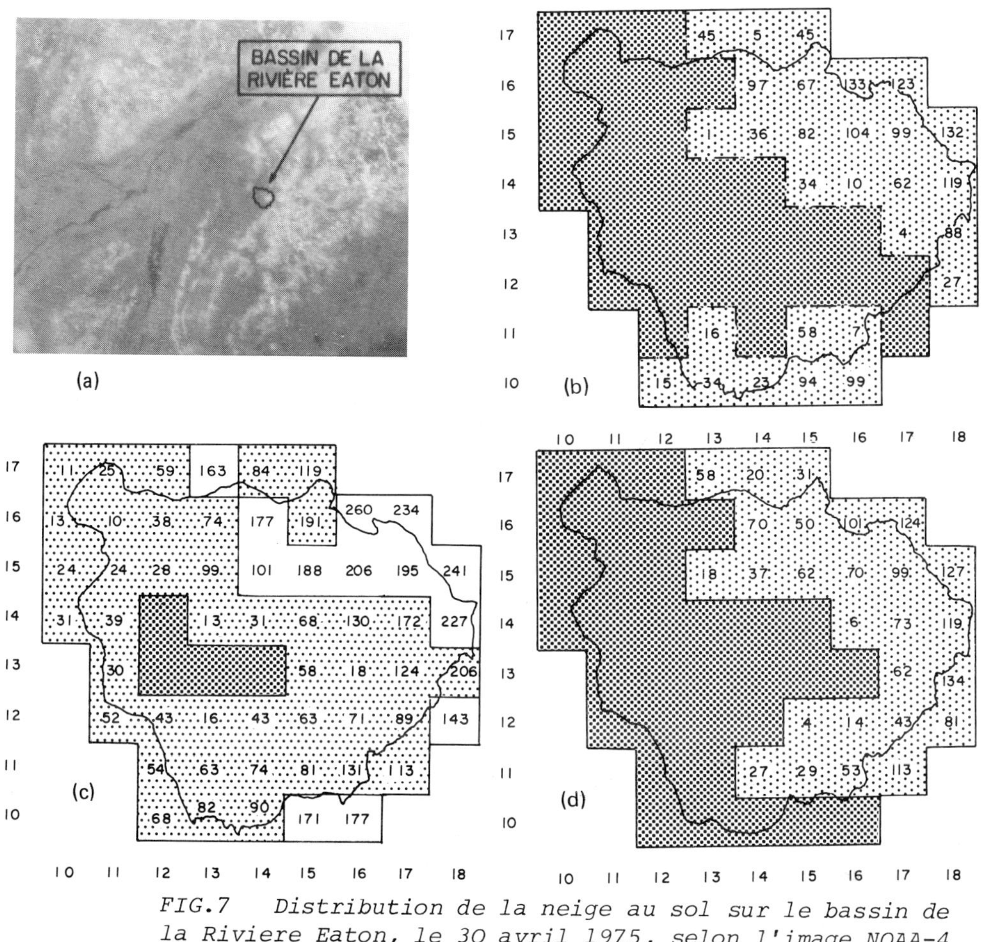

FIG.7 Distribution de la neige au sol sur le bassin de la Riviere Eaton, le 30 avril 1975, selon l'image NOAA-4 et le modele CEQUEAU. (a) orbite 2077, le 30 avril 1975; (b) equivalent en eau (mm) de la neige au sol (essai 1); (c) equivalent en eau (mm) de la neige au sol (essai 2); (d) equivalent en eau (mm) de la neige au sol (essai 3).

On note également une meilleure simulation de l'écoulement saisonnier, de la distribution des lames mensuelles, particulièrement en mars et avril (Tableau 1), ainsi que de trois des quatre crues d'avril (Fig.2).

En 1975, la carte CEQUEAU du 30 avril (Fig.7(c)) confirme qu'il reste manifestement trop de neige sur le bassin, par rapport à l'image NOAA-4. Cette observation est corroborée par la lame saisonnière (+20.3%) et sa distribution mensuelle (Tableau 1), ainsi que par les débits journaliers (Fig.3), les dernières crues de fonte étant beaucoup trop élevées.

MODIFICATION DE L'EQUIVALENT EN EAU DU STOCK DE NEIGE AU PRINTEMPS 1975

Compte tenu des résultats obtenus en ralentissant la fonte de la neige nous avons procédé à une simulation supplémentaire visant à illustrer l'effet d'une diminution du stock de neige sur les débits simulés et la distribution de la neige au sol le 30 avril. Pour ce faire, nous avons utilisé les données nivométriques recueillies les 19 et 20 mars 1975 (Tableau 2), juste avant la première crue de printemps. Rappelons que les valeurs mesurées aux stations 36 et 40 sous-estiment probablement le stock de neige présent dans le sud du bassin.

Suite à cette réduction du stock de neige, la distribution spatiale de la neige au sol le 30 avril 1975 s'accorde mieux que la précédente avec l'image NOAA-4 (Fig.7(d)). De même, l'écart entre la lame saisonnière calculée et la lame observée est réduit de 18.1 à 2.2%, les écarts mensuels demeurant toutefois importants. Quant aux débits journaliers calculés, leur amélioration se fait surtout sentir à la fin d'avril et au début de mai (Fig.3). Compte tenu des dimensions du bassin (Fig.7(d)) et de l'échelle des images NOAA-4 utilisée, nous considérons avoir atteint la limite de ce que peut apporter l'interprétation visuelle de ces images. Selon nous, le contrôle de la distribution spatiale de la neige au sol résultant d'une nouvelle réduction du couvert nival n'aurait été vraiment possible qu'en utilisant des données numériques (Rochon *et al.*, 1983).

CONCLUSION

Les cartes produites par le modèle CEQUEAU se sont avérées d'une grande utilité pour faciliter la comparaison avec l'imagerie satellite, permettant ainsi d'améliorer le calage du modèle et de contrôler l'effet de la correction du stock de neige, sur les débits.

Des recherches devront cependant être poursuivies tant au niveau de l'interprétation visuelle que du traitement numérique de l'imagerie satellite, non seulement dans le visible, mais aussi dans l'infra-rouge thermique et les micro-ondes. D'autres caractéristiques du couvert nival, la température de surface de la neige et l'équivalent en eau du stock pourront ainsi être détectées et utilisées pour obtenir de meilleures simulations. Il est aussi souhaitable que le développement de modèles aptes à utiliser tout le potentiel de la télédétection soit encouragé.

REMERCIEMENTS Ces travaux ont été réalisés grâce à une subvention du CRSNG (Canada) portant le numéro A-1806.

REFERENCES

Bowley, C.J., Barnes, J.C. & Rango, A. (1981) Application systems verification and transfert project, vol. VIII: Satellite snow mapping and runoff prediction handbook. *NASA Tech. Pap. 1829*.

Charbonneau, R., Fortin, J.P. & Morin, G. (1977) The CEQUEAU model: description and examples of its use in problems related to water resources management. *Hydrol. Sci. Bull.* 22 (1), 193-202.

Lillesand, T.M., Meisner, D.E., LaMois Downs, A. & Dewell, R.L. (1982) Use of GOES and TIROS/NOAA satellite data for snowcover mapping. *Photogramm. Engng & Rem. Sensing* 48 (2), 251-259.

Morin, G., Fortin, J.P., Lardeau, J.P., Sochanska, W. & Paquette, S. (1981) Modèle CEQUEAU: manuel d'utilisation. *INRS-Eau, Rapp. Sci.* no. 93.

Rango, A. (1977) Remote sensing: snow monitoring tool for today and tomorrow. In: *Western Snow Conf.* (April 1977), 75-81.

Rango, A. (editor) (1980) Microwave remote sensing of snowpack properties. *NASA Conference Publ. 2153.*

Rochon, G., Bénié, G.B., Fortin, J.P. & Dupont, J. (1983) Cartographie du couvert nival à l'aide de données numériques NOAA-6 et application dans le modèle hydrologique CEQUEAU. Présenté au 8e Symposium Canadien de télédétection, Montréal, Québec, 3-6 mai, 1983.

Hydrological Applications of Remote Sensing and Remote Data Transmission
(Proceedings of the Hamburg Symposium, August 1983). IAHS Publ. no. 145.

Télédétection et modélisation hydrologique

MARC LOINTIER & SERGE PIEYNS
Service Hydrologique de l'Office de la Recherche Scientifique et Technique Outre-Mer (ORSTOM), 70-74 Route d'Aulnay, F-93140 Bondy, France

RESUME La simulation des débits, dans un bassin versant donné, nécessite généralement la connaissance de ses principales caractéristiques physiographiques. Parmi ces caractéristiques, *l'occupation du sol* peut être déterminée à l'aide des techniques de télédétection. Partant des données Landsat et utilisant, d'une part, des traitements photochimiques, d'autre part, des traitements numériques mis au point par le Bureau de Télédétection de l'ORSTOM - procédure Loterie notamment - nous avons constitué un fichier d'occupation du sol du bassin de la Moselle française (11 477 km^2), sur la base d'un carroyage de 25 km^2 par carreau élémentaire. Les résultats ont été comparés à ceux primitivement obtenus à l'aide de méthodes classiques, discutés et jugés acceptables; l'erreur relative est comprise entre ±2 à ±10%, selon le thème étudié. Puis, le fichier a été connecté au modèle à discrétisation spatiale de l'ORSTOM.

Remote sensing and hydrological modelling
ABSTRACT Simulation of streamflows in a given basin generally requires a knowledge of its main physiographical characteristics. Among these characteristics, *land use* can be determined using remote sensing techniques. Starting from Landsat data and using, on the one hand photochemical treatments, and, on the other hand, processes developed by the Remote Sensing Branch of ORSTOM, especially the so-called Lottery process, we set up a file on the land use of the French Moselle basin (11 477 km^2), on a square grid basis, each square of the grid having a 25 km^2 area. Results have been compared to those formerly obtained by conventionnal methods and their accuracy discussed and judged acceptable, with relative error ranging from ±2 to ±10%, depending on the theme one is looking after. The file has then been connected to the ORSTOM spatially distributed model.

INTRODUCTION

Le Service Hydrologique de l'ORSTOM a réalisé, pour le compte de l'Agence de Bassin Rhin-Meuse, un modèle hydropluviométrique déterministe à discrétisation spatiale, permettant de reconstituer les débits moyens journaliers en chaque point du bassin de la Moselle française, soit sur une superficie de 11 477 km^2. Ce modèle, dont la structure est directement inspirée des travaux de Girard *et al.* (1972), utilise, outre les données hydropluviométriques intervenant dans le cycle de l'eau, les caractéristiques physiographiques du bassin.

Dans une première phase, le bassin de la Moselle a été décomposé en 460 carreaux élémentaires de 25 km², calés sur le système de projection Lambert. Pour chacun de ces carreaux, on a recherché les caractéristiques physiographiques et notamment, l'occupation du sol, afin de constituer un fichier de cette caractéristique, essentielle au plan des phénomènes d'infiltration, d'évapotranspiration, de ruissellement et de transfert de l'écoulement qui sont schématisés dans le modèle sous la forme de fonctions de ruissellement et de transfert (Pieyns, 1977).

Ce fichier donne donc, pour chaque carreau du modèle, le pourcentage d'occupation du sol des 10 thèmes suivants: feuillus, résineux, friches et landes, vignes et vergers, zones imperméabilisées, lacs et canaux, marécages, prairies, cultures, rochers et carrières. Ces pourcentages ont été établis avec la collaboration du Centre d'Etudes Géographiques de l'Université de Metz, de manière tout à fait classique: planimétrage sur les cartes au 1:25 000, enquêtes auprès du Ministère de l'Agriculture et de l'Office National des Forêts, utilisation des relevés cadastraux. A cette occasion, on s'est rapidement aperçu des difficultés de l'entreprise et de ses limites, dès lors que l'on s'intéresse à des bassins versants de grande dimension. En effet, cela a représenté un travail long et fastidieux: environ 90 cartes à planimétrer, d'où risques d'erreur. De plus, les résultats ne sont pas homogènes, les dates de remise à jour des différentes cartes pouvant s'étaler sur plus de 20 ans. Ajoutons à cela les difficultés de recalage, dans le système de découpage du modèle, des informations attachées aux limites administratives - thèmes prairies et cultures principalement.

C'est pourquoi et compte tenu de l'état d'avancement des recherches dans ce domaine et des possibilités que nous offrait le Bureau de Télédétection de l'ORSTOM, nous avons entrepris la mise au point d'une méthodologie d'utilisation des données satellitaires pour la constitution d'un fichier d'occupation du sol, utilisable par notre modèle (Pieyns, 1979).

Cette opération impliquait une évaluation de l'incertitude sur les résultats et la résolution de certains problèmes:

(a) mise au point d'une méthodologie de recherche des thèmes, efficace et reproductible dans le temps;

(b) calage géographique des données satellitaires;

(c) introduction du carroyage Lambert;

(d) recherche de "terrain" de bonne qualité afin de définir la précision des traitements réalisés (Lointier & Pieyns, 1979).

METHODOLOGIE

Les données satellitaires utilisées pour cette étude sont celles fournies par Landsat I et Landsat II sur les scènes 211-026 et 212-026 aux dates suivantes: 25 août 1975, 4 mars, 18 avril, 15 mai, 13 et 14 août 1976 (Webb, 1979). Il convient de noter ici que l'année 1976 a été particulièrement peu pluvieuse, ce qui explique que nous n'ayons pas eu trop de problèmes de nébulosité et nous a permis de disposer d'une bonne séquence de données. Nous avons travaillé, pour chaque date, à partir des quatre négatifs au 1:1 000 000e - un par canal - et de la bande magnétique correspondante. Ces deux types de données induisent deux types de traitement qui se sont avérés tout à fait complémentaires, le traitement photochimique et le traitement numérique (Montricher *et al.*, 1979).

Examen des informations photochimiques

C'est une façon de classer les valeurs radiométriques et de sélectionner les meilleures dates utilisables. Il doit être considéré comme une étape avant le traitement numérique. D'autre part, il ne nécessite pas d'équipements trop importants et se révèle peu onéreux (Girard, 1974).

Nous nous sommes donc livrés à une série de manipulations sur les restitutions photographiques parmi lesquelles nous citerons:

L'observation des documents au millionième de chaque canal qui permet en premier lieu de cerner les zones de légère brume susceptible d'altérer les traitements ultérieurs. Ces zones sont mises en évidence par un tirage du canal 4 avec un facteur de contraste (γ) élevé. On a pu vérifier - canal 5 par exemple - que la radiométrie d'un même thème est décalée de 5 ou 6 unités radiométriques, sans que la brume soit observée sur le tirage standard - facteur de contraste égal à l'unité.

L'agrandissement des documents au millionième, en particulier pour les "zones test". Cette étape est à considérer comme un premier traitement, car l'on peut modifier les paramètres photochimiques pour obtenir un étalement des valeurs de gris approprié à un thème recherché. Les échelles classiques d'agrandissement sont comprises entre le 1:500 000e et le 1:100 000e.

La composition colorée qui résulte d'une synthèse soustractive de trois des quatre canaux Landsat. Afin d'obtenir un document "codé" selon les couleurs d'un film infrarouge couleur, on attribue en général le jaune au canal 4, le magenta au canal 5 et le cyan au canal 7.

Les courbes de réponse des films employés couramment - films diazoïques - sont différentes suivant le pigment. Chaque composante colorée est donc une nouvelle dégradation de l'information. Néanmoins, ce procédé permet une première interprétation sur les thèmes recherchés. L'examen d'un tel document peut déjà conduire à préciser la position relative des thèmes, de façon globale et sur de vastes zones. L'observation au rétroprojecteur permet une approche plus fine des zones test retenues et, éventuellement à l'observateur, de faire un zonage des "classes couleurs".

La recherche densitométrique sur des agrandissements au 1:150 000e des zones test. En effet, il nous est apparu intéressant de préciser la position radiométrique relative des différents thèmes étudies, ceci préparant le traitement numérique en l'orientant vers les dates appropriées (Fig.1). C'est en fait une étape que l'on peut qualifier de "dégrossissage" de l'information temporelle et radiométrique. Les mesures ont été effectuées à l'aide d'un densitomètre numérique - cercle de mesure de 1 mm de diamètre - sur les agrandissements des quatre canaux aux six dates disponibles, agrandissements obtenus bien évidemment avec le même type de film et dans des conditions d'exposition et de développement identiques. L'échelle utilisée - le 1:100 000e - permettait de mesurer la densité photographique des parcelles retenues pour la "vérité terrain" et des étangs dont la surface, à cette échelle, s'est avérée comprise entre 10 et 30 mm².

Les résultats obtenus ont été homogénéisés, canal par canal et à toutes les dates permettant ainsi, en peu de temps et à peu de frais, de déterminer les dates les plus adaptées à la sélection d'un thème particulier. C'est ainsi que l'on peut voir, sur la Fig.2, qu'il sera plus aisé de séparer radiométriquement les résineux des feuillus de type 1 en utilisant la vue du 28 août 1975 ou encore celles des 4 mars, 18 avril ou 15 mai 1976 que celle du 13 août 1976, cela dans le canal 4.

L'équidensité et l'équidensité colorée qui utilisent les données densitométriques obtenues à l'étape précédente. On peut choisir la plage de valeurs densitométriques correspondant à un thème donné et à l'aide de films spéciaux à réponse binaire - film trait - il sera possible d'effectuer un classement de ces valeurs radiométriques, de

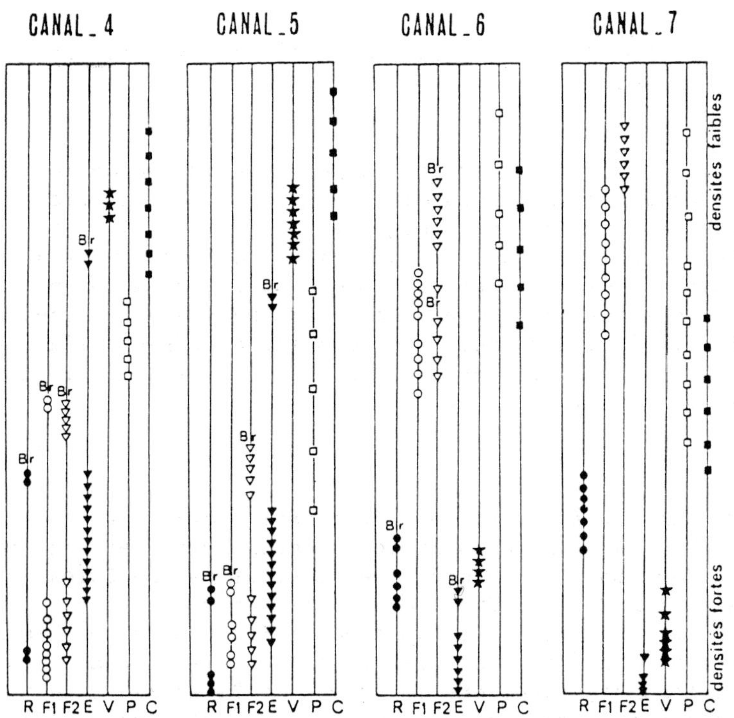

FIG.1 Position relative des thèmes le 13 août 1976 d'après les données densitométriques.

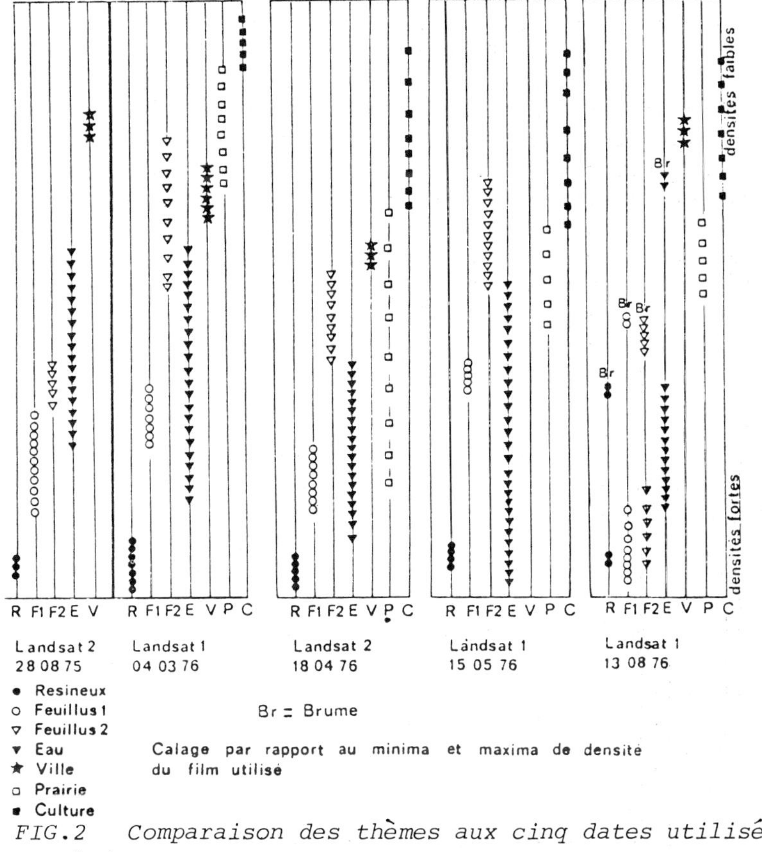

FIG.2 Comparaison des thèmes aux cinq dates utilisées canal 4.

ne faire apparaître que cette plage et donc d'isoler le thème correspondant sur un document photographique. En combinant plusieurs plages et quatre pigments colorés - noir, magenta, cyan et jaune - on a obtenu une équidensité colorée. Ce travail peut être fait en combinant plusieurs canaux et, dans ce cas, l'on a une analogie totale avec un traitement numérique de type Loterie, mais limité à cinq themes. Cette méthode présente l'avantage de tester rapidement, sur une vue complète, la valeur globale du futur traitement numérique.

Le traitement numérique

Les travaux ont été réalisés sur console Pericolor et Mini 6 H.B. 643. La principale procédure utilisée pour cette étude, la procédure Loterie, a été mise au point par le Bureau de Télédétection de l'ORSTOM. Cette méthode d'analyses multivariables a été développée pour s'adapter à la classification d'images numérisées, composées d'un très grande nombre de points. Une vue Landsat, rappelons-le, comporte 31 millions de valeurs radiométriques parmi lesquelles il s'agit d'effectuer des choix informatiques performants. Cette procédure repose sur deux notions principales, celle de serpent et celle de lot.

Notion de serpent Rappelons qu'un pixel est caractérisé par quatre valeurs radiométriques, une par canal. Soit a, b, c, d ces valeurs. On appellera polynombre du niveau 4 la suite des quatre valeurs entières notées:

B_1 = (a, b, c, d) Fig.3(a)

Soit un second pixel représenté par le polynombre B_2 = (e, f, g, h). On appellera serpent, l'ensemble des polynombres dont les valeurs sont comprises entre les polynombres B_1 et B_2.

$$S = \begin{pmatrix} e & f & g & h \\ a & b & c & d \end{pmatrix}$$ Fig.3(b)

Notion de lot On appelle lot "L" l'ensemble des points d'une vue "V" dont les polynombres appartiennent au serpent S. Tous les polynombres associés aux points d'un lot sont, par définition, dans le serpent S_D appelé serpent de définition (Fig.3(d)).

La procédure Loterie permet de construire un ensemble de lots, définis par une ou plusieurs bornes sur chaque canal Landsat. A l'inverse de nombreux algorithmes de traitement d'images, l'initialisation peut s'effectuer sur de vastes zones,

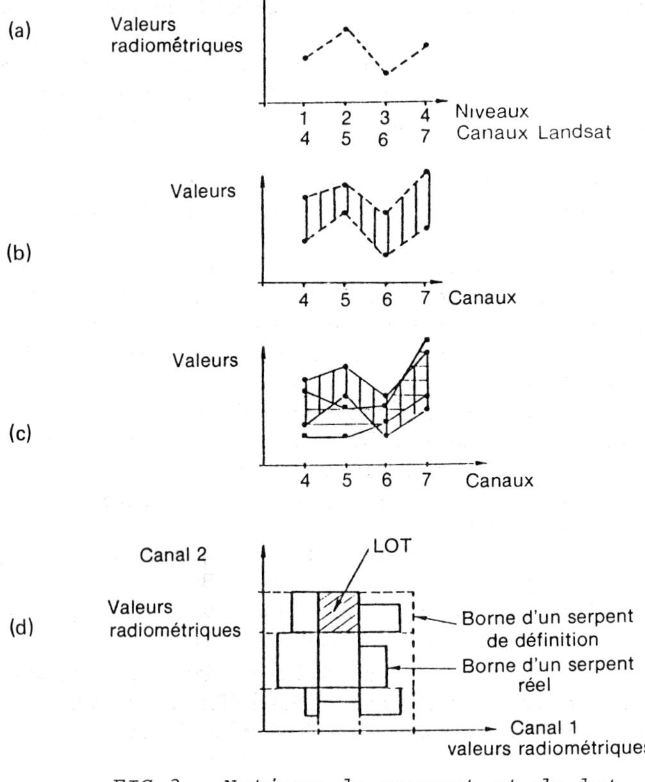

FIG.3 Notions de serpent et de lot.

s'affranchissant ainsi de "parcelles test" pouvant présenter un phénomène radiométrique particulier. On élimine ainsi les hypothèses statistiques de répartition de l'information. Pratiquement, cette initialisation peut s'effectuer sur l'écran du Pericolor - 65 000 pixels. L'opérateur remet en cause les valeurs des bornes à chaque fois que le résultat recherché n'est pas atteint. La méthodologie mise au point comporte sept étapes:

(a) *Dégradation d'un canal Landsat.* On admet, pour cette étape, que les zones test ont été définies et que leur vérité terrain comporte un maximum d'informations. Après un repérage en lignes-colonnes Landsat de la zone à étudier, on procède à la visualisation d'un canal. Ceci permet d'obtenir les premiers éléments de repérage géographique, améliorés au cours des étapes par la découverte d'amers précis.

L'opérateur effectue plusieurs essais sur chaque canal afin de déterminer les bornes cernant au mieux le thème étudié. Dans ce cas, on procède à un premier classement des points par référence avec les données de terrain: on obtient un *ensemble* de points, pour chaque canal, contenant *tous les points* du thème et les points "hors thème".

Chacune des bornes peut être considérée comme la valeur radiométrique maximale ou minimale définissant un thème: on peut les regrouper pour former le "serpent de définition" comportant au maximum huit valeurs - deux par canal (Fig.3(c)).

(b) *Intersection des quatre ensembles.* Application du serpent de définition. La machine trie les points appartenant à l'intersection des quatre ensembles: on obtient *l'image* du serpent de définition précédent ainsi que son serpent réel. L'opérateur revient à la vérité terrain et compare le résultat obtenu. Il peut classer une nouvelle fois les points en deux catégories: les points appartenant au thème et les points hors thème (en général moins nombreux que sur l'essai canal par canal).

(c) *Le compromis.* Recherche des meilleures bornes. L'objectif est de réaliser le meilleur compromis possible entre le thème et les points hors thème.

L'opérateur va utiliser le programme Loterie en testant les combinaisons de nombreux "découpages" sur les canaux. On utilise en général les canaux deux à deux, dans un premier temps, afin d'obtenir une représentation des combinaisons dans un plan (Fig.3(d)).

L'originalité de cette démarche est d'avoir focalisé la recherche vers un thème précis, sans analyser tous les phénomènes radiométriques liés aux points hors thème pour les éliminer ou chercher à leur attribuer une classe particulière.

L'analyse de chaque lot amène à faire les trois catégories suivantes:

lots inclus	tous les points du lot appartiennent au thème,
lots séquents	mélange de points du thème et hors thème,
lots exclus	points hors thème.

Les lots séquents de l'essai le plus satisfaisant sont finalement conservés ou éliminés. Afin de conforter l'opérateur sur son choix, on a imaginé de faire un test de stabilité du serpent de définition obtenu.

(d) *Stabilité d'un lot.* Lorsque l'on définit un serpent, à l'aide de huit bornes (deux par canal), on peut calculer le nombre théorique de polynombres pouvant exister dans ce serpent. Exemple:

$$S = \begin{pmatrix} 20 & 18 & 37 & 22 \\ 10 & 15 & 21 & 04 \end{pmatrix}$$

On a 11 valeurs radiométriques utilisables sur le canal 4, quatre sur le 5, 17 sur le 6, 19 sur le 7. On appellera *importance du serpent*, le nombre théorique de polynombres, égal au produit 11 x 4 x 17 x 19 = 14 212 et noté T_D. De même, sur un serpent réel, on peut calculer l'importance du serpent S_R, notée T_R.

Afin de mieux cerner les valeurs radiométriques d'un serpent, correspondant à un thème particulier, on construit un graphique de Stabilité: soit le serpent réel S_R obtenu par la Loterie et correspondant à un lot recherché. On peut se demander s'il n'en existe pas une meilleur?

L'habillage et le déshabillage du serpent S_R ci-dessus (Fig.4) permet d'étudier la relation entre *l'importance* de chaque serpent ainsi créé et le *nombre de points* qui le composent.

En portant ces deux paramètres sur un graphe (Fig.5) on retiendra pour meilleur serpent celui pour lequel un élargissement des bornes radiométriques n'entraîne pas une augmentation importante du nombre de points. Ceci se traduit par le palier A-B sur le graphe. Un habillage supplémentaire conduit à l'introduction de nouveaux points, d'un autre lot. L'opérateur retiendra le serpent n° 3 comme la meilleure définition du lot recherché. Lorsque l'on applique le serpent d'un thème sur une autre zone que celle où il a été défini, on constate que le résultat n'est pas toujours satisfaisant. On est alors conduit à rechercher la parenté d'un serpent.

(e) *Parenté*. La recherche de la parenté d'un serpent s'effectue lorsque le serpent du thème est défini au mieux, avec l'aide de plusieurs Loteries, complétées ou non par un test de stabilité.

"Initialisé" sur des zones de moins de 100 000 pixels, le serpent d'un lot comportant huit valeurs radiométriques peut présenter des bornes (ou contraintes) inutiles entraînant sur d'autres parties de l'image une "sélectivité" trop importante. Sans étudier tous les

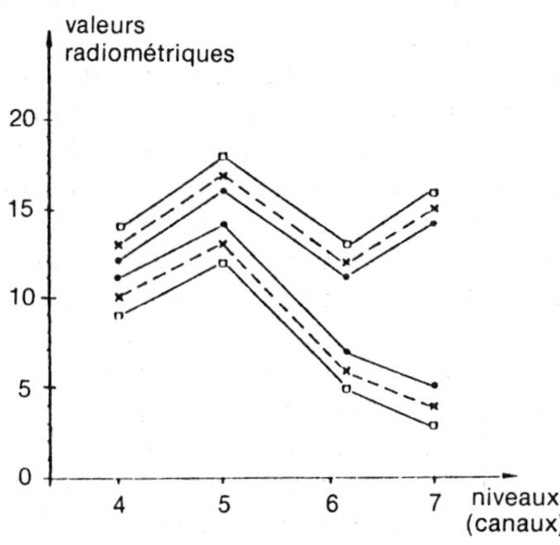

FIG.4 Exemple d'habillage et de déshabillage de serpent.

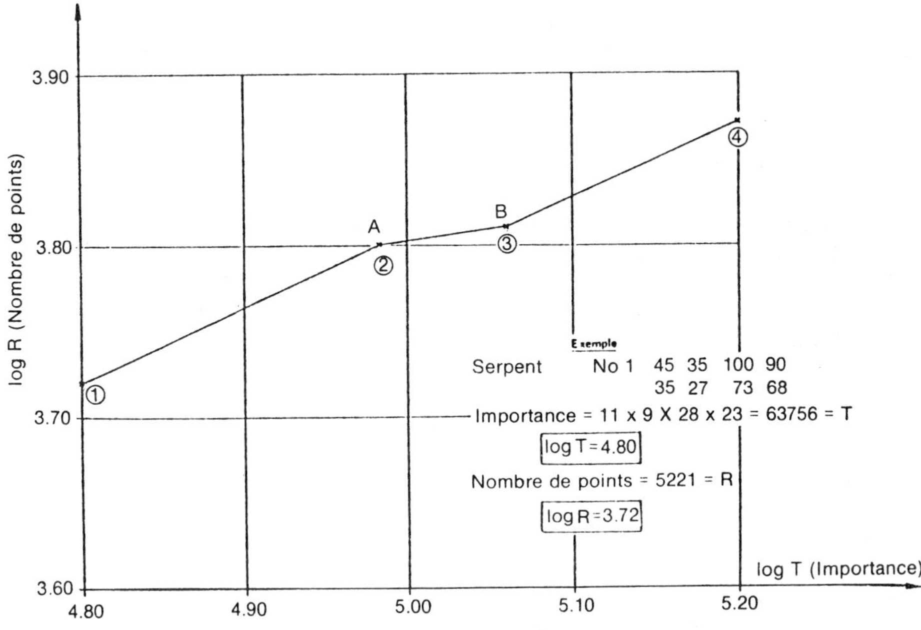

FIG.5 Forêt de fenetrange. Stabilité du lot Forêt.

phénomènes radiométriques liés à un thème recherché, la "Parenté d'un lot" vise à répondre à deux objectifs:

(i) Etre la plus performante sur un thème à visualiser.

(ii) Etre la moins contraignante, afin d'inclure des phénomènes radiométriques non étudiés, mais appartenant au thème recherché.

Cette parenté est notée $P\left|\begin{smallmatrix}-a-c\\--b-\end{smallmatrix}\right|$. Elle est un "opérateur" à appliquer sur la vue, en recherchant les bornes réellement utiles dans la définition du lot du thème recherché.

Deux niveaux de parenté sont définis:

(i) La "Parenté du lot" qui est obtenue sur une zone par essais successifs et systématiques en supprimant une, puis plusieurs bornes dans le serpent de définition.

(ii) La "Parenté du thème" lorsqu'on a pu vérifier le bon résultat sur la vue complète.

(f) *Effacement sélectif des lots.* Le fil conducteur de la démarche précédente était la recherche d'un thème et l'évaluation des performances du traitement. On avait insisté sur la nécessité de "focaliser" le travail sur un thème précis. Le traitement de toute l'information Landsat, pour visualiser tous les thèmes *en même temps*, conduirait à interpréter de nombreux lots: et effet, chaque borne utilisée pour définir un thème introduirait un "découpage" des autres thèmes en plusieurs lots rendant leur visualisation plus délicate. On perdrait, de surcroît, la possibilité de définir une parenté unique pour chaque thème.

Il est donc apparu plus simple d'effacer du fichier de données le ou les thèmes déjà cernés, avant de commencer l'étude d'un nouveau thème. Cet effacement est obtenu en appliquant l'opérateur "Parenté du thème" à l'ensemble des données. On simplifie donc l'information par effacements successifs, évitant ainsi la multiplication des lots à interpréter, tout en conservant la possibilité de définir une "Parenté du thème" pour les points restants.

Un telle démarche pose un nouveau problème: dans quel ordre allons-nous *effacer* les thèmes, c'est-à-dire quel thème *étudier* en premier, en second, etc.

(g) *Hiérarchisation de la recherche des thèmes.* Nous avons vu que l'analyse densitométrique permettait de trouver la position relative des thèmes au sein d'une même vue. On détermine ainsi les thèmes placés dans les premières valeurs radiométriques de chaque canal.

Dans l'exemple étudié, à la date du 13 août 1976 (Fig.1) on remarque que les premières valeurs radiométriques du canal 4 concernent les thèmes feuillus et résineux. Celles du canal 5 regroupent les résineux; celles du 6 et du 7, l'eau libre.

La recherche des bornes définissant ces thèmes va être plus simple, puisqu'il n'ya pas de choix à faire sur les bornes inférieures du serpent les définissant. Ces bornes seront automatiquement celles de la vue si l'on traite toutes les données.

D'autre part, ces remarques mettent déjà l'opérateur sur la voie qui permettra de trouver la Parenté d'un lot.

Le 13 août 1976, on choisira donc d'étudier, en premier lieu, les résineux sur les canaux 4 et 5 et l'eau libre sur les canaux 6 et 7. Après une détermination de la "Parenté du thème" résineux et eau libre on efface ces deux thèmes (dans un ordre quelconque) des données; on est donc ramené au cas initial en ayant à chercher uniquement des bornes supérieures dans le canal 5 pour étudier le thème feuillus (Titus & Wensel, 1977).

On aboutit à la hiérarchie suivante:

1 : eau libre et résineux,
2 : feuillus,
3 : prairies et zones urbaines,
4 : cultures.

Cette démarche présente, en plus, deux avantages: le résidu de points obtenus après tous les effacements ne pose pas de problème thématique, comme dans le cas d'un traitement unique de toutes les données, où l'on serait amené à considérer la valeur des lots composés par ces points, lors de l'interprétation. Si le résidu possède une valeur thématique, on le remarquera facilement en le visualisant et en observant l'homogéneité de sa répartition spatiale.

CALAGE GEOGRAPHIQUE

Le calage géographique est réalisé en deux temps:

(a) Visualisation des informations Landsat à une échelle identique à celle du document de référence. Les principaux thèmes (eau, feuillus, villes), même définis sommairement, fournissent de nombreux amers permettant la superposition avec le document de référence.

(b) La superposition permet de pointer avec une précision de ±1 pixel les intersections du carroyage Lambert et d'en définir les coordonnées Landsat.

INTERSECTION DES DONNEES LANDSAT AVEC LE CARROYAGE LAMBERT

Compte tenu de la précision recherchée, trois intersections Lambert repérées en lignes-colonnes Landsat suffisent à définir toutes les coordonnées d'une centaine de carreaux élémentaires du modèle: un programme effectue alors le comptage des pixels de chaque thème isolé par la méthodologie exposée en première partie, pour chaque carreau. On reconstitue ainsi le fichier "occupation du sol", tel qu'il est utilisé par le modèle. L'erreur maximale dans le positionnement d'un carreau entraîne un décalage de deux lignes et huit colonnes.

PRECISION DES TRAITEMENTS ET VERITES TERRAIN

Le calage géographique précis et la "statistique" par carreau sont deux éléments qui ont permis de mettre au point des procédés d'évaluation de la précision des traitements adaptés à chaque thème.

(a) Le thème "eau libre" a été obtenu avec une erreur ±2.5%. La vérité terrain reposait sur les cartes au 1:25 000 mises à jour avec le concours de l'Agence Financière de Bassin Rhin-Meuse, pour l'été 1976, date des enregistrements Landsat.

(b) Les thèmes "feuillus" et "résineux" sont obtenus avec une erreur de ±2%. Les vérités terrain utilisées concernant plus de 200 parcelles forestières de 10 ha en moyenne, décrites grâce au concours de l'Office National des Forêts (Dejace *et al.*, 1977).

(c) Les résultats sur les thèmes "prairies" (±2.5%) et "cultures" (±5.5%) ont été comparés aux enquêtes réalisées par le Ministère de l'Agriculture, durant le printemps 1976.

(d) Le thème "zones imperméabilisées" est obtenu avec une précision de +10% en moyenne. La vérité terrain reposait sur la carte IGN au 1:25 000 ainsi que sur les enquêtes de terrain pour la mise à jour en 1976.

(e) La séparation des autres thèmes du fichier "occupation du sol" n'a pas reçu de solution satisfaisante. La résolution du Landsat n'a pas permis d'isoler les vignes et les vergers compte tenu de la nature du parcellaire francais. En ce qui concerne les autres thèmes, leur faible extension sur le bassin ne justifie pas un traitement numérique.

REFERENCES

Dejace, J. *et al.* (1977) Computer aided classification for remote sensing in agriculture and forestry in northern Italy. In: *Proceedings of the Eleventh International Symposium on Remote Sensing of the Environment* (Ann Arbor, Michigan, avril), 1269-1278.

Girard, M.C. (1974) De la photographie aérienne à l'image satellite. Méthodologies. In: *Proceedings of the Symposium on Remote Sensing and Photo-interpretation* (Banff, Alberta), 271-731.

Girard, G., Morin, G. & Charbonneau, R. (1972) Modèle précipitations-débits à discrétisation spatiale. *Cah. ORSTOM, Sér. Hydrol.* IX (4).

Lointier, M. & Pieyns, S. (1979) Méthodologie de constitution d'une base de données d'occupation du sol par télédétection. *Rapport Final, ORSTOM, Paris.*

Montricher, G., Duvernoy, J. & Gaignerot, B. (1979) Les traitements en télédétection. *Etat de l'Art, OPIT, Paris.*

Pieyns, S. (1977) Le fichier physiographique de la Moselle française et son programme d'appel. *ORSTOM, Paris.*

Pieyns, S. (1979) Modèle général de reconstitution des débits de la Moselle francaise. Mise au point du modèle sur le bassin de la Meurthe à Malzeville. *ORSTOM, Paris.*

Titus, S.J. & Wensel, L.C. (1977) Use of multispectral data in design of forest sample surveys. In: *Proceedings of the Eleventh International Symposium on Remote Sensing of the Environment* (Ann Arbor, Michigan, avril), 505-514.

Webb, R.P. (1979) Determination of land use from LANDSAT imagery: applications to hydrologic modeling. *The Hydrologic Engineering Center, US Army Corps of Engineers, Research Note no. 7.*

Hydrological Applications of Remote Sensing and Remote Data Transmission (Proceedings of the Hamburg Symposium, August 1983). IAHS Publ. no. 145.

Application of remote sensing for seasonal runoff prediction in the Indus basin, Pakistan

B. DEY & D.C. GOSWAMI
Department of Geology and Geography, Howard University, Washington, DC 20059, USA

ABSTRACT This study indicates that a multiple regression model, with basin snow-covered area and concurrent runoff in the adjoining Kabul River as forecast parameters, explains the variability in the Indus flow better, as compared to the simple bivariate, snow-covered area-runoff, model. NOAA-VHRR satellite images have been used to delineate the areal extent of snow cover for April over the Indus River basin in Pakistan. Simple photo-interpretation techniques, using a Bausch and Lomb Zoom Stereo Transfer Scope, were employed in transferring satellite snow cover boundaries onto base map overlays. A multiple regression model with 1 April through 31 July, 1969-1979, seasonal runoff as a function of April snow cover and concurrent runoff, 1 April through 31 July, in the Kabul River estimated from the snow-covered area-runoff relationship, explains 79% of the variability of the measured flow in the Indus River. Seasonal flows predicted by the multiple regression model lie within 8% of the measured flow. The error in the estimation of 1979 snowmelt runoff by the multiple regression model is 4% as against 10% by the simple bivariate model. Satellite-derived snow-cover area together with parameters related to cross-correlation of flows in adjacent basins provide valuable inputs for snowmelt runoff prediction models in such remote, data-sparse basin as the Indus.

Application de la télédétection pour la prévision de l'écoulement saisonnier dans le bassin de l'Indus, Pakistan
RESUME Cette étude montre qu'un modèle à régressions multiples mettant en jeu la superficie couverte par la neige et l'écoulement à la même époque dans la rivière Kaboul voisine, comme paramètres de prévision, explique la variabilité de l'écoulement de l'Indus mieux que le modèle simple bivariate: superficie couverte par la neige-écoulement. Les images du satellite NOAA-VHRR ont été utilisées pour délimiter l'étendue de la couverture neigeuse en avril sur le bassin de l'Indus au Pakistan. Des techniques simples de photo-interprétation utilisant un "Bausch and Lomb Zoom Stereo Transfer Scope" ont été employées pour transférer les limites de la couverture neigeuse vues par le satellite sur une carte de base. Un modèle à régressions multiples avec l'écoulement saisonnier du 1er avril au 31 juillet de 1969 à 1979

considéré comme fonction de la couverture neigeuse d'avril et l'écoulement à la même époque dans la rivière Kaboul du 1er avril au 31 juillet estimé par des relations superficie couverte par la neige-écoulement, explique 79% de la variabilité de l'écoulement mesuré dans l'Indus. Les écoulements prévus par le modèle à régressions multiples sont situés dans une marge de 8% de l'écoulement mesuré. L'erreur dans l'estimations de l'écoulement de fonte des neiges de 1979 par le modèle de régressions multiples est de 4% chiffre à comparer à l'erreur de 10% par le simple modèle bivariate. La superficie de la couverture neigeuse déduite des satellites utilisée conjointement avec des paramètres relatifs aux corrélations entre écoulement dans des bassins voisins fournit des entrées valables pour les modèles de prévision de l'écoulement dû à la fonte des neiges pour des bassins peu accessibles et où l'on ne peut disposer que de rares données comme dans le cas de l'Indus.

INTRODUCTION

Satellite-observed snow-covered area has proven to be a useful parameter in seasonal streamflow prediction models developed by various researchers in widely diverse environments (Rango *et al.*, 1977; Dey *et al.*, 1979; Rango & Martinec, 1979; Hannaford & Hall, 1979; Rango & Peterson, 1980; Howley *et al.*, 1980). Satellite mapping of snow cover over the Himalayas for estimation of snowmelt runoff was first conducted by Salomonson & MacLeod (1972), followed by Rango *et al.*, (1975, 1977), Ramamoorthi & Subba Rao (1981) and Gupta *et al.*,(1982). In each of these studies a statistically significant relationship was derived between early spring snow-covered area and subsequent snowmelt runoff. The authors of the present study completed research on the snow cover-runoff relationship in the Indus and Kabul basins (Dey *et al.*, 1983) in which the earlier work on the same area by Rango *et al.*,(1977) was extended and the snow cover-runoff relationships over different time periods were compared. The simple linear regression model used, relating basin snow covered area to seasonal snowmelt runoff, explained about 60% of the variability in the Indus snowmelt runoff, although a similar model used in the case of the Kabul River explained about 90% of the variability in flow. The inadequacy observed in the simple regression model for the Indus River led to further research and resulted in the development of a multiple regression model with improved prediction capability, which is presented in this study.

STUDY AREA

The Indus basin rivers rise in the Hindukush, Karakoram and Himalayan mountains at elevations ranging between 4500 and 7500 m. The gauging station at Besham, located at an elevation of 1200 m, commands a drainage area of 162 100 km^2 in northern Pakistan, India and extreme western China (Fig.1). The Indus at Besham, carrying a mean annual flow of 2385 m^3/sec, provides the main artery for inflows to the Tarbela reservoir which is located in the immediate downstream

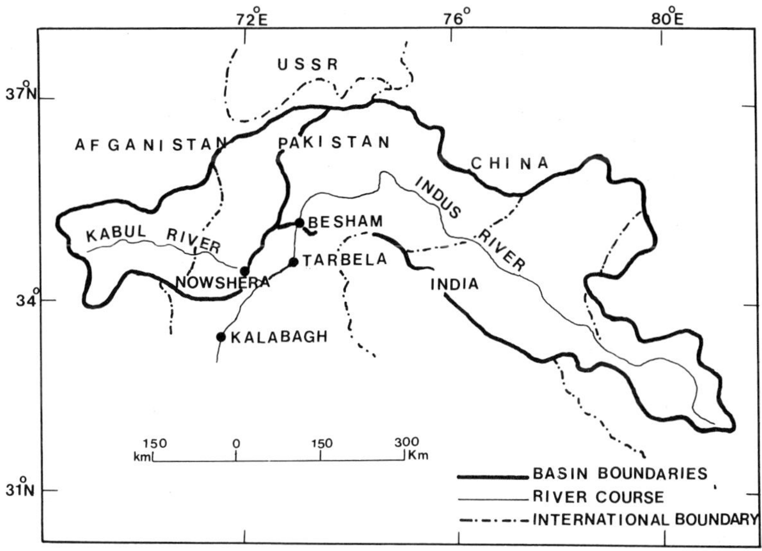

FIG.1 Location map of the Indus and Kabul basins.

section. Snowmelt, starting in March/April and continuing through summer, contributes about 70% of the annual river flow (Tarar, 1982). Since snowmelt runoff is the main source of water for the Tarbela reservoir that provides water and electricity for numerous homes, farms and industries, prediction of snowmelt runoff in the Indus using satellite remote sensing techniques has great potential for operational use in reservoir management and water resources allocation.

METHODOLOGY

NOAA/TIROS satellite images that provide daily coverage of the Indus basin were used to obtain the basin snow-covered area data for the period 1974-1979. For the earlier period, 1969-1973, the data from the study by Rango *et al.*, (1977) were used. NOAA satellites, carrying on board the Very High Resolution Radiometer (VHRR) and Visible and Infrared Spin Scan Radiometer (VISSR) with one visible (0.6-0.7 μm) and one thermal infrared (10.5-12.5 μm) spectral band, have a ground resolution of 0.9 km. Compared to the Landsat images, the NOAA images have lower resolution and suffer greatly from geometric distortion. But, as against the 9 or 18-day repetition cycle of the Landsat satellites, the NOAA images provide daily coverage of the Himalayan snow-covered area. Besides, the distortion suffered by the NOAA images can be optically removed by using a simple device like the Bausch and Lomb Zoom Stereo Transfer Scope. Polar orbital NOAA satellites are, therefore, selected as the main source of snow cover data for this study.

A Bausch and Lomb Zoom Stereo Transfer Scope was employed to transfer April snow-covered areas for the period 1974-1979 onto base map overlays which were then measured with a digital planimeter. The average percent snow cover for April was obtained by comparing average basin snowcovered area for April with the area of the basin. Streamflow data used in this study were obtained from the Pakistan Water and Power Development Authority (WAPDA). The estimated snow cover and measured runoff data are presented in Table 1.

TABLE 1 Snow cover (1-30 April) and runoff (1 April-31 July) data for the Indus River above Besham and the Kabul River above Nowshera in Pakistan for the period 1969-1979 (Dey et al., 1983)

	Indus River above Besham		*Kabul River above Nowshera*		
Year	*Snow cover (%)*	*Runoff ($10^9 m^3$)*	*Snow cover (%)*	*Runoff ($10^9 m^3$)*	*Remark*
1969	*79.5*	*40.71*	*41.5*	*18.96*	*1969-1973 data from Rango et al. (1977)*
1970	*55.5*	*32.30*	*28.5*	*11.70*	
1971	*62.0*	*38.19*	*34.0*	*11.40*	
1972	*71.0*	*39.15*	*44.0*	*20.15*	
1973	*90.0*	*57.90*	*54.5*	*23.70*	
1974	*65.0*	*33.04*	*31.5*	*12.20*	
1975	*75.7*	*37.37*	*42.3*	*16.30*	
1976	*86.6*	*40.41*	*38.5*	*15.75*	
1977	*90.8*	*42.40*	*34.6*	*13.46*	
1978	*92.3*	*52.28*	*42.5*	*18.28*	
1979	*88.0*	*42.43*	*38.5*	*17.41*	

SOURCES: Snow cover data - satellite images; runoff data - Pakistan Water and Power Development Authority.

RESULTS AND DISCUSSION

As reported in our earlier study (Dey *et al.*, 1983), a simple regression analysis, with regard to average percent snow cover for April and seasonal runoff from April through July for the period 1969-1979, explains 60% of the variation in flow of the Indus River at Besham (Table 2). The analysis was done using the data for 1969-1973 from the earlier study by Rango *et al.* (1977) and the data for 1974-1979 from the present study. The scatter of the plotted points and regression equations defining the best-fit-lines for the above two periods, separately as well as combined, are presented in Fig.2. The regression coefficients for the 1969-1973 and 1974-1979 equations are found to be statistically not different at 0.05 significance level. The apparent shift of the regression lines over the two study periods may be partially attributed to the difference in the resolution of various satellites used in the two studies. Furthermore, the flow measurement may have some amount of inherent error which is not considered here.

In order to improve the Indus model so it can explain more of the variability in flow, the concurrent runoff in the Kabul River, estimated from the simple regression model relating basin snow-cover area to snowmelt runoff, is used as an additional input parameter

TABLE 2 Regression equations showing seasonal runoff as a function of early spring snow cover for the Indus and Kabul basins in different time periods during 1969-1979 (Dey et al., 1983)

Period	*Regression equation* X = *Average % of snow cover* Y = *April-July runoff,* $10^9 m^3$	*r*	*Remark*
Indus River above Besham			
1969-1973	$Y = 0.64X - 3.88$	*0.82*	*Data from Rango et al. (1977)*
1974-1979	$Y = 0.52X - 1.57$	*0.73*	*Present study*
1969-1979	$Y = 0.45X - 6.14$	*0.60*	*Combined data*
Kabul River above Nowshera			
1969-1973	$Y = 0.52X - 3.99$	*0.92*	*Data from Rango et al. (1977)*
1974-1979	$Y = 0.49X - 2.98$	*0.82*	*Present study*
1969-1979	$Y = 0.52X - 4.07$	*0.90*	*Combined data*

along with the original parameter viz. basin snow-covered area. The multiple regression model thus obtained is

$$Y = 2.693712 + 0.26348X_1 + 1.1199X_2 \qquad (r^2 = 0.79)$$

where

Y = Indus runoff April-July ($10^9 m^3$),

X_1 = percent snow cover for April over the Indus basin,

X_2 = Kabul runoff April-July ($10^9 m^3$), estimated from the bivariate regression model in Table 2.

The multiple regression equation explains 79% of the variability in flow as against 60% by the earlier bivariate equation. Moreover, a significant reduction (27%) in the standard error of estimate is caused by the revised model. Figure 3 represents the snowmelt runoff in the Indus River estimated by both the bivariate and the multiple regression models. Seasonal runoff estimated by the multiple regression model lies within 8% of the measured flow, as against 11% in case of the bivariate regression model used earlier. Error in estimation of the 1979 snowmelt runoff by the multiple regression model is about 4% whereas by the bivariate model it is as high as 10%.

The Indus and the Kabul are adjacent Himalayan basins - Kabul being a tributary to the Indus. Both the basins come under a broadly similar environmental setting marked by steep Himalayan slopes and affected by similar rhythms of snowmelt and glacier runoff. The regression equation representing the snow cover-runoff relationship in the Kabul River (Fig.4) is statistically not different (at 0.05 significance level), in terms of the regression equation slope, from the equation for the Indus River Fig.2(c). Concurrent snowmelt runoff in these adjoining Himalayan basins, the Indus and the Kabul, are correlated ($r = 0.7$). For reasons not known in our present limited knowledge about these remote, data-sparse basins, the Kabul basin is characterized by a stronger relationship between basin snow cover and runoff as compared to the Indus basin (Table 2). In view of the facts cited above, the concurrent runoff in the Kabul River is chosen as an additional forecast parameter in the Indus model. Although the results obtained tend to justify the incorporation of the parameter, the physical explanation as to the rationale of it probably needs more than what is suggested above based on the present state of our knowledge about the basin. Until a more elaborate and diversified data-base is obtained, it is not possible to explore further a question like the one at hand.

In such mountainous basin as the Indus with limited physical

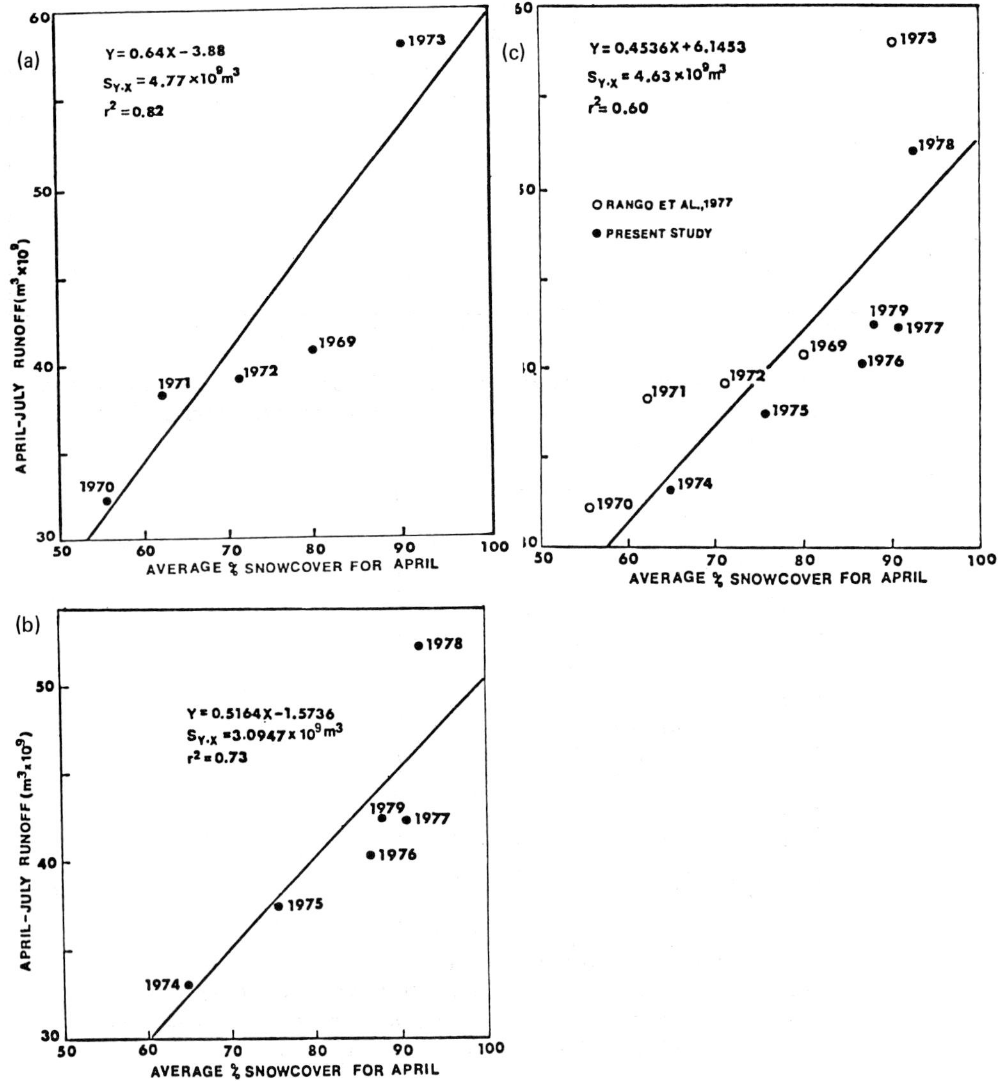

FIG.2 Satellite-derived snow cover estimates vs. measured runoff for the Indus River above Besham, Pakistan: (a) 1969-1973 (Rango et al., 1977); (b) 1974-1979 (Dey et al., 1983); (c) 1969-1979 (Dey et al., 1983).

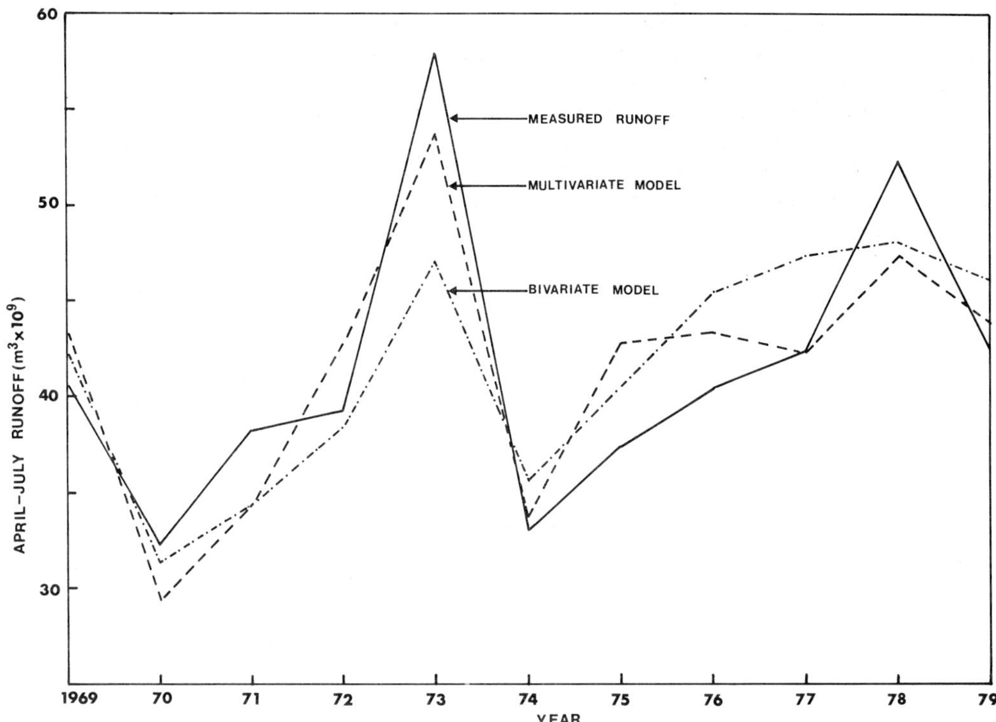

FIG.3 Seasonal snowmelt runoff estimates for the Indus River at Besham during 1969-1979 from different forecasting models.

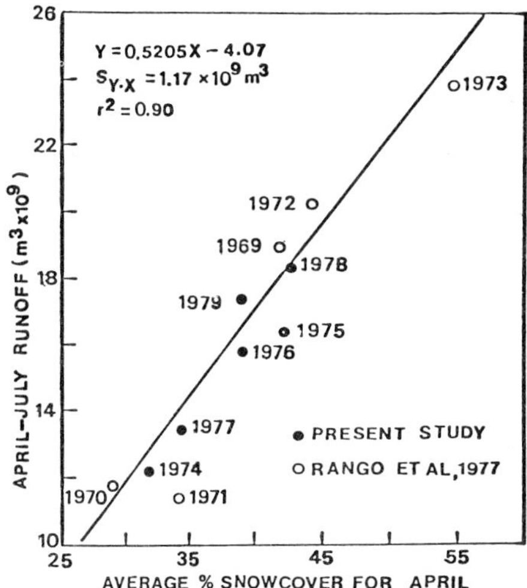

FIG.4 Satellite-derived snow cover estimates vs. measured runoff for the Kabul River above Nowshera, Pakistan, 1969-1979 (Dey et al., 1983).

accessibility and high cost of data acquisition by conventional methods, satellite remote sensing is undoubtedly the most time-saving as well as cost-effective procedure for the collection of snow cover data. Use of data collection platforms (DCPs) for timely and reliable transmission of flow data from widely scattered and remote stations in such basins will ensure improvement in the quality and size of the data base, bringing the data in real time to the user community. The geo-synchronous satellites put up in space by India may provide the much-needed transmission facility for the DCPs in the Indus basin. International cooperation in the areas of resource development and management is not only desirable but highly beneficial, from an economic standpoint, for all concerned.

CONCLUSIONS

The bivariate regression model relating basin snow-covered area in April to subsequent snowmelt runoff from April through July, 1969-1979, explains 60% of the variation in flow of the Indus River at Besham. Incorporating the concurrent runoff in the adjoining Kabul River as an additional input variable, the Indus model was improved. The multiple regression thus obtained explains about 20% more of the variability of the Indus flow as compared to the bivariate model. The standard error of estimate was also reduced by about 27%. Seasonal runoff estimated by the multiple regression model lies within about 8% of the measured flow. Regression coefficients are statistically significant at the 0.05 significance level. The rationale of using concurrent runoff in the adjoining Kabul basin as an additional forecast parameter for the Indus River model stems from the fact that the snowmelt runoff in these two basins, characterized by steep Himalayan slopes and similar snowmelt and glacier runoff regimes, are correlated ($r = 0.70$). Until a more elaborate data base is acquired, remotely sensed snow cover data provide the most valuable input in snowmelt prediction techniques for remote, data-deficient basins like the Indus. Use of cross-correlation of flows in adjoining Himalayan basins may aid in better estimation of snowmelt runoff as demonstrated in this study.

ACKNOWLEDGEMENTS The authors acknowledge with thanks the financial assistance provided by NASA under grant NAG5-224. This paper is a part of the proposed study on snowcover, snowmelt and runoff in the major Himalayan river basins.

REFERENCES

Dey, B., Moore, H. & Gregory, A.F. (1979) Snow cover, snowmelt and runoff in the Mackenzie Basin. In: *Proceedings of Canadian Hydrology Symposium on Cold Climate Hydrology* (Vancouver, British Columbia, May 1979), 449-460. National Research Council of Canada.

Dey, B., Goswami, D.C. & Rango, A. (1983) Utilisation of satellite snow-cover observations for seasonal streamflow estimates in the western Himalayas. *Nordic Hydrol.* 14, 257-266.

Gupta, R.P., Duggal, A.J., Rao, S.N. & Sankar, G. (1982) Snow cover area vs. snowmelt runoff relation and its dependence on geomorphology - a study from the Beas catchment (Himalayas, India). *J. Hydrol.* 58, 325-339.

Hannaford, J.F. & Hall, R.L. (1979) Application of satellite imagery to hydrologic modelling snowmelt runoff in the southern Sierra Nevada. In: *Proceedings of Final Workshop at Sparks Nevada, April 16-17, 1979,* 201-222, NASA Conference Publ. no. 2116.

Howley, M.E., McCuen, R.H. & Rango, A. (1980) Comparison of models for forecasting snowmelt runoff volumes. *Wat. Resour. Bull.* 16 (5), 914-920.

Ramamoorthi, A.S. & Subba Rao, P. (1981) Application of satellite technology for forecasting snowmelt runoff of perennial rivers of India. *Proc. Second Asian Conference on Remote Sensing, Beijing, China.*

Rango, A. & Martinec, J. (1979) Application of a snowmelt-runoff model using Landsat data. *Nordic Hydrol.* 10, 225-238.

Rango, A. & Peterson, R. (eds) (1980) *Operational Application of Satellite Snowcover Observations.* NASA Conference Publ. no. 2216.

Rango, A., Salomonson, V.V. & Foster, J.L. (1975) Employment of satellite snow cover observations for improving seasonal runoff estimate. In: *Operational Applications of Satellite Snow Cover Observations,* 157-174. NASA SP-391, Washington, DC.

Rango, A., Salomonson, V.V. & Foster, J.L. (1977) Seasonal streamflow estimation in the Himalayan region employing meteorological satellite snow cover observations. *Wat. Resour. Res.* 13, 109-112.

Salomonson, V.V. & MacLeod, N.H. (1972) Nimbus hydrological observations over the watersheds of the Niger and Indus Rivers. In: *Fourth Annual Proceedings of Earth Resources Review,* 5.1-5.11. NASA Doc. Msc 05937.

Tarar, R.N. (1982) Water resources investigation in Pakistan with the help of Landsat imagery - snow surveys, 1975-1978. In: *Hydrological Aspects of Alpine and High-Mountain Areas* (Proc. Exeter Symp., July 1982), 177-190. IAHS Publ. no. 138.

Hydrological Applications of Remote Sensing and Remote Data Transmission
(Proceedings of the Hamburg Symposium, August 1983). IAHS Publ. no. 145.

Operational requirements for water resources remote sensing in Canada: now and in the future

B. E. GOODISON
Hydrometeorology Division, Atmospheric Environment Service, 4905 Dufferin Street, Downsview, Ontario, Canada M3H 5T4
J. M. WHITING
Saskatchewan Research Council, 30 Campus Drive, Saskatoon, Saskatchewan, Canada S7N 0X1
K. WIEBE
Inland Waters Directorate, Environment Canada, Ottawa, Ontario, Canada K1A 0E7
J. CIHLAR
Canada Centre for Remote Sensing, Department of Energy, Mines and Resources, Ottawa, Ontario, Canada K1A 0Y7

ABSTRACT Satellites offer the greatest potential for improving the temporal and spatial coverage of hydrometeorological data to meet the real time needs of Canadian water agencies. The current level of application of remotely sensed data, primarily those from meteorological satellites, for snow-cover mapping, surface water temperature determination, rainfall determination, water quality investigation and data retransmission of DCP data, is reviewed. Currently, most effort in meeting operational requirements of water resource agencies is in the DCP field. Development of hydrological applications has depended on the data available to Canadians from existing satellite sensors which were put up for other users. In planning for the Canadian RADARSAT satellite, priorized needs and applications of remote sensing data in hydrology were established including consideration of the economic value of the information, the optical band requirement, the value of SAR data, the timeliness of the data and the processing and delivery requirements. Such a review is required if hydrological needs are to be used effectively in planning future satellite systems.

Besoins opérationnel pour la télédétection intéressant les ressources en eau au Canada
RESUME Les satellites offrent les plus grandes possibilités d'amélioration de la couverture temporelle et spatiale des données hydrométéorologiques pour répondre aux besoins en temps réel des organismes canadiens des ressources en eau. On examine le niveau actuel des applications des données de télédétection, en particulier celles qui proviennent des satellites météorologiques, pour l'établissement de cartes d'enneigement, la détermination de la température de

l'eau de surface, la détermination des hauteurs de précipitations, les études sur la qualité de l'eau et la retransmission des données des plate-formes de collecte de données (PCD). A l'heure actuelle, c'est dans le domaine de la PCD qu'on concentre les efforts visant à répondre aux besoins d'exploitation des organismes s'occupant des ressources en eau. La développement des applications hydrologiques dépend des données accessibles aux Canadiens et provenant des capteurs satellitaires existants lancés pour d'autres utilisateurs. Dans la planification du satellite RADARSAT canadien, on a établi la priorité des besoins et des applications des données de télédétection, en tenant compte de la valeur économique de l'information, des besoins en bande optique, de la valeur des données du radar à ouverture synthétique, de l'opportunité d'obtention des données et des besoins du traitement et de la communication. Un tel examen s'impose, si l'on veut intégrer les besoins hydrologiques dans la planification des systèmes satellitaires.

INTRODUCTION

Next to air, water is the most vital natural resource. As for most atmospheric elements, the temporal and spatial requirements for remote sensing data for hydrology and the timeliness of receipt of these data by the user agency are often more stringent than for the land resource sector.

Due to the areal extent ($9.9 \times 10^6 km^2$) and population distribution of Canada (80% within 150 km of the United States border), remote sensing and data transmission via satellite offer the greatest potential for improving the temporal and spatial coverage of hydrometeorological data to meet the real time data needs of Canadian water agencies (e.g. for flood forecasting, reservoir regulation, navigation, water allocation). Examples of the value of water resources in the Canadian economy are given in Table 1. These costs are based upon the next best alternative for providing similar

TABLE 1 Value of water resources in Canada (1980)

Hydraulic structures - 1980 (design, construction)	*$2 billion*
Flood damage and relief assistance	*$200 million*
Crop insurance payments for complete crop failure due to drought	*$500 million*
Replacement value for hydroelectric	*$11.7 billion (world price)*
Withdrawal of water effect of severe water shortages on thermal power production, manufacturing (e.g. pulp and paper), municipal services, mining, and recreation	*$926 million*

services and goods. These dollar values are significant, but only refer to the estimated worth of water to the economy. Unlike NASA in the United States, which has conducted several Application System Verification and Transfer (ASVT) projects, cost-benefit studies related to remote sensing applications in water resources have generally been lacking in Canada. Such studies are crucial if hydrologists are to have an influence in determining the sensor complement on satellites, such as RADARSAT, or in convincing an international committee that there should be a hydrological satellite, such as HYDROSAT.

This paper will provide an overview of some of the current activities in Canada where remote sensing and data transmission are used in water resources management. It will also review the process used in establishing hydrology requirements for consideration in the Canadian RADARSAT programme.

DATA RETRANSMISSION

The most effective satellite application in the water resource sector, affecting every water agency in Canada, has been data retransmission from data collection platforms (DCPs). DCP networks operated by federal, provincial and private agencies are expanding rapidly, with 14 agencies currently operating more than 200 platforms in largely remote regions of Canada. The establishment of such DCP networks has had the greatest potential impact in leading to improved short term flow forecasts where hourly and three-hourly transmissions offer the timely data required by forecasting agencies. For this reason many agencies feel that DCPs are the only operational tool in the remote sensing field!

The launching of Landsat 1 by the USA in 1972 transported Canada's hydrometric programme into a new era. Real-time data communication from remote sites to network operators and users became economical and reliable. Initial experiments with Landsat 1 demonstrated the feasibility of transmitting hydrometric data via satellite in real time. Subsequent trials with Landsat, ANIK, GOES and ARGOS satellite systems showed conclusively that the GOES system had the highest technical and economic benefit to the Canadian hydrometric programme.

Of the 2700 gauging stations operated by Environment Canada within the national network, 350 can be considered remote, requiring airplane access. An analysis of the cost of operating remote stations indicated that equiping these stations with DCPs would reduce data loss and increase flexibility in the planning of field trips. An overall reduction in the number of annual station visits is estimated to result in a savings of $500 per station per year in operating costs. On the basis of this, resources have been obtained to equip the 350 remote sites with DCPs over a five year period beginning in 1983. The Water Survey of Canada expects to be operating 500 hydrometric DCPs by 1988. These DCPs will be capable of handling other hydrometeorological sensors and other Departmental agencies (such as the Atmospheric Environment Service) are expected to locate additional sensors, such as temperature and precipitation, at selected hydrometric sites.

Most Canadian operational water agencies will be focusing their attention on the use of satellite data retransmission. Standards for sensors, communication and archiving of data are problems which must be addressed. Is there a need for additional DCP receiving stations for data retransmission via GOES? Is there a need for data retransmission facilities on Canadian satellites such as MSAT and RADARSAT? Many feel the answer to these questions is yes.

As an initial effort to meet some of these demands, Environment Canada has outlined the services which it can provide for the acquisition, communication and archiving of environmental data from automatic stations (Environment Canada, 1983). Full implementation of communication and archiving services is yet to be implemented. A plan has been developed and funding requested for the purchase and installation of three Direct Readout Stations compatible with the GOES satellite system. This addition would provide Environment Canada with a fully operational data communication system.

REMOTE SENSING APPLICATIONS

Snow-cover mapping

The first application of satellite data in the water sector was the observation of snow-cover. The Canadian contribution to the World Meteorological Organization's Snow Studies by Satellite Project was initiated in 1974. Snow-cover analyses for four international bodies (Columbia, Souris, Lake-of-the-Woods and Saint John) were carried out by different agencies using NOAA and Landsat imagery. In most cases, the basic technique was optical - electrical image analysis, but some analysis was conducted with digital satellite data. Satellite snow-cover analysis has been continued by the Atmospheric Environment Service (Hydrometeorology Division) for the Saint John basin. A digital processing system using NOAA/TIROS multi-channel data has been developed to determine the areal extent of snow cover in this forested basin (Waterman *et al.*, 1980). The snow-cover map, produced in Toronto, is forwarded via telecopier to the Canada/New Brunswick Saint John River Forecast Centre in Fredericton, New Brunswick, within one data of data acquisition for use in their operational flood forecasting system. The timely acquisition, analysis and transmission of results to the user is critical if the satellite data are to be used effectively in operational water resources management.

From these studies the limitations of satellite data for snow-cover studies were identified. In Canada, Landsat data cannot be used effectively on an operational basis because the 16 or 18 day temporal coverage is inadequate. The probability of cloud-free coverage every 18 days is low and during that time interval the snowpack could disappear entirely. For large basins, such as the Saint John, the increased spatial resolution of Landsat means that passes on four or five successive days are required for coverage of the entire basin and this limits operational application of these data to many snow-cover problems. Cloud cover is a real problem in snow-cover mapping both in obtaining coverage of the basin and in distinguishing between cloud and snow. Daily coverage of target areas by the weather satellites is an advantage in obtaining usable and timely data.

Currently, only the areal extent of snow cover is operationally derived from satellite data, but there is no centralized system for mapping every basin that might be required by user agencies. For each user to implement their own analysis system would require the receipt of satellite data in near real time and the development of an objective interpretation system which is affordable and transferable to "non-specialists".

A major challenge in the remote sensing of snow cover is to develop algorithms to determine snow depth, water equivalent, areal extent and liquid water content using sensors having all-weather capabilities. The most immediate promise in this area is the application of passive and active microwave data to snow-cover problems. As part of the RADARSAT programme, there was a proposed experiment to assess the feasibility of using X and C band SAR data for the determination of snow depth, state of the ground and snowmelt and to determine the effect of land cover, terrain roughness and diurnal and seasonal variations on the measurement capabilities. As well, a major Canada/US cooperative multi-stage remote sensing snow-cover experiment involving 10 agencies was conducted during February 1982 over the Canadian Prairies. The study's objectives were: to assess the utility of passive microwave data for the mapping of Prairie snow cover, particularly in relation to areal extent, depth and water equivalent; to develop the capability of mapping areal snow cover (areal extent, depth, water equivalent) on the Canadian Prairies, integrating ground-based, airborne and satellite data; and, to provide a direct intercomparison of Canadian and American airborne gamma-ray systems for the measurement of snow water equivalent. In addition to the two gamma aircraft, a US Air Force Hercules flew the NASA airborne multifrequency microwave radiometer over the target areas. Satellite data from relevant NOAA (visible and infrared) and NIMBUS-7 (SMMR) passes were recorded. A major success was in obtaining coincident ground, airborne and satellite data on 1400 km of target lines over Saskatchewan!

A more complete description and initial results from this experiment are reported in Carroll *et al.* (1983) and Goodison *et al.* (1984).

Surface water temperatures

The use of surface water temperatures derived from satellite data is another important operational application for water resources management. From 1966 to 1980 the Hydrometeorology Division of the Atmospheric Environment Service monitored temperatures of the Great Lakes using airborne radiation thermometry (ART). Until 1978, surveys were conducted approximately monthly on each of the lakes during the ice-free season, but as the capability to determine water temperatures from satellite data was perfected, the ART programme was terminated in 1980. Airborne line-scanners are still used for smaller lakes where satellite resolution is inadequate for accurate temperature mapping.

Retrieval of Great Lakes and East Coast marine surface temperatures from satellite digital infrared data (SRT) began in

1977. Analyses are based on data from the NOAA polar orbiting environmental satellites. Comparisons with meteorological buoy measurements to date indicate that the RMS error is about 0.6°C. SRT temperatures are averages of, at best, 1 km square surfaces at the satellite sub-point, and represent progressively larger areas outward to the edge of the scan. At present most analyses are derived using data from the 10.5-11.5 μm channel combined with an atmospheric correction routine that requires real time radiosonde data as input (Irbe *et al.*, 1982). Analyses are performed on a regular bi-weekly basis and supplied to users by mail.

Uses of the temperature data include local weather forecasting, forecasting lake effect snowstorms, radiation budget calculations, forecasting freeze-up on the St Lawrence Seaway, coastal climate studies, studies of fish reproduction and fish movements and the assessment of Great Lakes nearshore water quality.

Water quality

In the field of water quality there has been considerable research conducted toward the utilization of multispectral radiance responses recorded by satellite as a means of water quality monitoring over inland lakes. Initially, Landsat digital data were used to estimate sediment levels in the lakes. Chagarlamudi & Schubert (1979) reported correlations greater than 90% between estimated and measured sediment levels, expressed as upwelling irradiance. Not all investigators, however, are as positive about the use of satellite data for water quality measurement.

Bukata *et al.* (1981) concluded that "the remote sensing for water quality parameters from aircraft altitudes presents distinct difficulties to thematic mapping of both chlorophyll-a and suspended minerals to much better accuracy than ±(50-100)% for inland water masses as optically complex as those found in Lake Ontario". They go on to state the "further complexities introduced by atmospheric scattering and absorption would only serve to render such water quality mapping from satellite altitudes even more tenuous". Earlier Bukata *et al.* (1980) has cautioned about the use of operational atmospheric correction algorithms which had been developed for water quality work, particularly those based on the CZCS 670 nm and the 700-800 nm bands.

Some scientists in the water quality field argue that remote sensing has not yet made inroads into quantitative water quality measurements from satellites. As in the case of snow-cover mapping, the 16-18 day cycle of Landsat is not adequate for water quality studies. It appears that there is still much to be done to meet Canadian operational water quality needs.

Precipitation

One application which offers considerable potential for use in operational water management is the determination of rainfall from radar and satellites. Use of radar for rainfall determination has received world-wide attention and will not be discussed in detail in this paper. No Canadian water resource agency is yet using radar data on a fully operational basis for water resources management.

However, Alberta Environment has been working with Alberta Research Council on the development of a data processing system which will convert digital weather radar data into precipitation data for use by the River Forecast Centre in Edmonton. Products which will be available to the flood forecaster include a colour video display of instantaneous precipitation intensity, displays of accumulated precipitation for various time intervals, and tables of precipitation amounts for various time intervals integrated over pre-defined areas such as watersheds. In Quebec, the McGill University and Institut National de la Recherche Scientifique - Eau are continuing their study on the integration of radar data and ground-based rainfall measurements for use in the CEQUEAU hydrological model. The ultimate aims are to increase the accuracy of the model's runoff prediction and to assess its sensitivity to remotely sensed precipitation information. The results are encouraging, but the system is not yet operational.

The integration of radar, satellite and ground-based data is a very logical extension of current remote sensing studies. One example of such an effort is the development of the RAINSAT system by the Atmospheric Environment Service. The system identifies areas of rain using half-hourly data from GOES East and from weather radars near Toronto and Montreal. Data from one radar are used to determine a relationship between the intensity of VIS and thermal infrared radiances and radar rain areas. This relationship is then used to extend the rain analysis throughout the RAINSAT area. The other radar is used to verify the analysis. This system is still under development, but offers an interesting tool to water managers. As for so many remote sensing applications in the water resources sector, the timely receipt and processing of the data will be critical for its ultimate operational application.

ESTABLISHING PRIORITIES FOR REMOTE SENSING APPLICATIONS IN HYDROLOGY

Based on experience gained in the development of the above-noted applications, problems and limitations in using satellite data were identified. The limitations of Landsat data must be remembered: repeat coverage only every 18 days; cloud cover (in combination with the 18-day cycle) limiting operation applications (Peteherych *et al.*, 1983); passes on consecutive days may be necessary to cover the target area: and, acquisition of the data (digital, transparencies) by the user in a near real-time mode. Timely receipt of satellite data in a format directly useable by an agency is also a problem with satellites other than Landsat, particularly for near real-time applications. Implementation of a "delivery system" for satellite data to "outside users" to meet their operational requirements is a need and a challenge for current and future satellite systems.

One of the problems in this context is that operational hydrology has had to use the satellite data, processing and distribution designed largely to meet the needs of other users or economic sectors. As Barrett (1983) argued, the hydrological community as a whole must lobby for the service it requires from earth orbiting satellites.

RADARSAT hydrology mission requirements

Canada is planning the design, construction and launch in 1990 of RADARSAT, a polar orbiting satellite carrying as its primary sensor a synthetic aperture radar (SAR). Goodison *et al.* (1985) provide a review of this proposed satellite system. The Canadian RADARSAT mission is aimed at providing timely satellite data for earth resources application. Although SAR is considered as the primary sensor, other sensors such as an optical (VIR) instrument, a scatterometer or a microwave radiometer are being considered as potential secondary sensors. To assess and ultimately decide upon a sensor complement it was realized that a statement of mission requirements was necessary for the various disciplines that could be served by the satellite. Hydrology, agriculture and forestry requirements were assessed by a renewable land resources study team. These requirements and justifications would then be reviewed along with those determined for geological, oceanographic and sea ice applications.

The determination of requirements for satellite information for use in Canadian hydrology was not as simple as it might seem, because it is necessary to achieve a consensus on the most acceptable compromise of requirements within imposed technical and operational limits. Table 2 summarizes the priorities and the justification established by the study team with respect to C-band SAR and VIR sensors. The VIR sensor was considered to be a thematic mapper type.

Twenty applications were identified. Rainfall determination from satellite data was considered important, but the proposed sensor complement on RADARSAT was not appropriate for this application. The estimated value (high, medium, low) refers to the dollars gained or saved by using the information, assuming that the information could be obtained successfully. The optical VIR bands are those considered to be appropriate for each particular application; the bands are generally listed in the order of decreasing priority. The probability of success refers to the likelihood that the required information can be obtained from the satellite data. For example, high refers to an already proven application or to strong evidence for success already existing; medium refers to experimental or theoretical evidence existing; low means that there is as yet inconclusive evidence or the results of previous studies are not encouraging; and zero means the required information cannot be obtained from such data. Timing considerations, as related to repeat coverage or time of year, refer only to needs over Canadian territory. These of course may be different if data were required for other regions of the earth.

Finally, the type of product required by the user and the delivery time of either data or an analytical product were considered. The user may want raw (image or digital data with radiometric corrections and SAR data probably corrected to a ground projection) or processed data (topographic distortions removed and registered to the UTM projection) or both. The time listed for "delivery to analysis" refers to the maximum length of time between sensing, and data delivery to the analysis while "delivery to use" refers to the maximum length of time between

TABLE 2 Hydrology priorities and justification for satellite information

Application	Estimated Value	Optimal VIR Bands	Probability of Success (No Clouds)			Timing			Processing and Delivery	
			SAR Alone	VIR Alone	SAR + VIR	Repeat Coverage (Days)	Available Window (Canada)	Type	To Analysis (days)	To Use (days)
Snow Distribution (Dry)	H	3,2,4,1	0	H	H	14	Oct-June	P	0.5	0.5
Snow Melt (Wet)	L-H	3,2,4,1	M-H	M-H	H	2	Feb-June	R	0.5	0.5
River and Lake Ice (Transport Breakup)	L-H	3,2,4,1	M	M-H	H	2	Oct-June	R	2.0	3.0
Glacier Melting	L	3,1,2	M	M	H	14	June-Oct	P	7.0	7.0
State of Ground	M	3,1,2	M	L	H	14	Jan-Dec	P	2.0	2.0
Flood Mapping	M	3,1,2	M	H	H	on demand	Jan-Dec	R,P	0.5	0.5
Drainage	M	1,2,3,5	M-H	M-H	H	Once	early summer or early fall	P	60.0	60.0
Soil Moisture	M	1,2,3,7	M-H	L	H	2	April-Dec	R(P)	0.5	0.5
Wetland Classification	M	3,1,2,7	M-H	M-H	H	30	April-Sept	P	60.0	60.0
Crop Irrigation	L	3,1,2	M-H	M	H	2	May-Oct	P	2.0	3.0
Soil Salinity	L-M	1,2,3,7,6	M-H	M	H	60 3/yr 1/5yr	April-May & July	P	60.0	300.0
Water Depth (Lakes, etc.)	L	5,4	0	M	H	1800	open water	P	90.0	90.0
Suspended Sediment Load	L-M	1,2,4,5	0	M	M	15	open water	P	30.0	30.0
Eutrophication	M	7,1,2,4	0	M	H	15	June-Sept	R	7.0	7.0
Thermal Effluents in Water	L	8	0	H	H	15	open water	P	1.0	1.0
Ground Water Recharge/ Discharge Areas	L-M	1,2,3,7,8	L	M	M-H	365	spring June & Sept	P	30.0	30.0
Mapping Shoreline, Reefs, Shoals & Islands	L	5,1,2,6	M	M-H	H	once	all year	P	180.0	180.0
Surface Water Area Monitored	L	1,5,2	H	H	H	on demand	no ice	P	3.0	2.0
Chlorophyll a Concentration	H	0.43-0.45 μm 0.51-0.53 μm 0.54-0.56 μm 0.660-0.671μm 0.671-0.682μm	0	H	H	3	every clear day Apr to Sept	R,P	1.0	2.0
Fresh Water Quality	M-H	1,2,4,5	0	M	M	7	open water	R,P	1.0	1.0
Lake Acidification	M	7,1,2,4	0	M	M	365	June to Aug	R,P	7.0	7.0
Stream Bed Monitoring	M	4,1,3,6,7	0	H	H	600	June to Aug (open water)	P	7.0	21.0

Notes: H is high; M is medium; L is Low; P is processed; R is raw; ( ) both

Band No.	Band Limits (micrometres)
1	0.80 - 0.90
2	0.64 - 0.69
3	1.55 - 1.75
4	0.40 - 0.50
5	0.52 - 0.60
6	2.08 - 2.35
7	"Red edge bands"
8	10.5 - 12.5

Source: RADARSAT, 1982a and 1982b

receiving data for analysis and the delivery of the resource information to the user.

In the determination of requirements, the needs of various regions in Canada were considered and incorporated where possible. A key factor to note in Table 2 is the short processing and delivery times required in most hydrological applications. Whether the system can ever be developed to meet these requirements is yet to be seen.

In terms of priority, it was agreed that snow-cover data - areal extent, water equivalent, depth - rated as the top need in Canadian hydrology where satellite data offered a major potential source for the temporal and spatial coverage required. A review by the Inland Waters Directorate, independent of that of the RADARSAT study team, also identified snowpack information as a major requirement for improved operational forecasting of lake levels in the Great Lakes, and for improved flood forecasting in areas prone to spring runoff flooding.

THE CHALLENGE

Within Canada, a serious effort has been made to identify the current level of remote sensing activity within water resources management and to identify, priorize and justify requirements for satellite data.

The challenge for those of us working in hydrology and hydrometeorology is to develop and assess techniques to meet these needs.

Specifically, the objectives include the need to:

(a) Gain more credibility in the remote sensing community to get HYDROSAT.

(b) Develop and assess techniques which use sensors with all-weather capabilities, i.e. passive and active microwaves, and to gain continued support for our research on these applications.

(c) Conduct research into the application and integration of remote sensing data into hydrological models and of the integration of ground, airborne and satellite data for the determination of components of the hydrological cycle.

(d) Institute a data base management system (including quality control, archiving and delivery) for the timely dissemination to users of data from new sources, such as RADARSAT.

(e) Improve the transfer of technology to hydrology consultants.

The challenge is not only to receive data, but to see its timely distribution to users.

REFERENCES

Barrett, E.C. (1983) Organizational needs for hydrological applications of satellite remote sensing in developing countries. *Hydrol. Sci. J.* 28 (2), 273-281.

Bukata, R.P., Bruton, J.E., Jerome, J.H., Jain, S.C. & Zwick, H.H. (1981) Optical water quality model of Lake Ontario. 2: Determination of chlorophyll-a and suspended mineral concentrations of natural waters from submersible and low altitutde optical sensors. *Appl. Optics* 20 (9), May, 1704-1714.

Bukata, R.P., Jerome, J.H., Bruton, J.E. & Jain, S.C. (1980) Non-zero subsurface irradiance reflectance at 670 nm from Lake Ontario water masses. *Appl. Optics* 19 (15), August, 2487-2488.

Carroll, T.R., Glynn, J.E. & Goodison, B.E. (1983) A comparison of US and Canadian gamma radiation snow water equivalent measurements. *Proc. Western Snow Conference* (51st Annual Meeting, Vancouver, Washington, April 1983), 27-37.

Chagarlamudi, P. & Schubert, J.S. (1979) *Development of an Operational Water Quality Monitoring System Using Landsat Data: Calibration.* Contract Report (no. 15Z78-00193) by the Sibbald Group, for the Freshwater Institute, Fisheries and Environment Canada, Winnipeg, March 1979.

Environment Canada (1983) *Policy on Services for Communication and Archiving of Data from Automatic Stations.* Environment Canada, Atmospheric Environment Service, Downsview, Ontario.

Goodison, B.E., Banga, A. & Halliday, R.A. (1984) Canada-United States Prairie snow cover runoff study. *Can. Wat. Res. J.* 9 (1), 99-107.

Goodison. B.E., Langham, E.J. & Athanassiadis, D. (1985) RADARSAT and MSAT: proposed Canadian satellite systems with hydrological applications. In: *Hydrological Applications of Remote Sensing and Remote Data Transmission* (Proc. Hamburg Symp., August 1983), 75-85. IAHS Publ. no. 145.

Irbe, J.G., Cross, R.K. & Saulesleja, A. (1982) Remote sensing of surface water temperature on the Great Lakes and off the Canadian East Coast. *NAFO Sci. Coun. Studies* 4, 31-39.

Peteherych, S., Goodison, B., Swail, V. & Saulesleja, A. (1983) Clouds: a fundamental limitation to satellite remote sensing in the visible spectral region. *Proc. 8th Canadian Remote Sensing Symp.* (Montreal, P.Q., 3-6 May), 223-228.

RADARSAT (1982a) *RADARSAT Mission Requirements Document.* Report 82-7. Energy, Mines and Resources, Ottawa, Canada.

RADARSAT (1982b) *Optical Sensor for RADARSAT.* Report 82-14. Energy, Mines and Resources, Ottawa, Canada.

Waterman, S.E., Hogg, W.D., Hanssen, A.J. & Polavarapu, V.L. (1980) Computer analysis of TIROS-N/NOAA-6 satellite data for operational snow cover mapping. *Proc. 6th Canadian Remote Sensing Symp.* (Halifax, N.S., 21-23 May), 435-442.

Hydrological Applications of Remote Sensing and Remote Data Transmission
(Proceedings of the Hamburg Symposium, August 1983). IAHS Publ. no. 145.

Study of the impact of man's activity in Middle Asia using remote sensing data

V. A. SUMAROKOVA
*State Hydrological Institute, 2 Linija 23,
199053 Leningrad, USSR*

ABSTRACT Satellite survey of land surfaces from space permits determination of a correlation between changes of landscape elements under the impact of man's activity and changes in river hydrological regimes. Consequences of man's activity in irrigated areas are revealed through: the change in type and density of vegetative cover; smoothing of the land surface, and, division of it into sub-areas occupied by cultivated lands; new components of the hydrographic network; building of dams, roads, bridges and settlements. Basic features for interpreting images of irrigated areas are: the spotty and mosaic character of images; dark phototone on the images in the visible spectrum; presence of objects of regular geometrical shape and straight light-grey (roads) and dark-grey (irrigation system) lines. Examples are given illustrating the dynamics of the area of irrigated lands in the region of the middle reaches of the Syrdarya River and the decrease of the surface area of the Aral Sea. Computations of values of specific water consumption make it possible to estimate approximate volumes of water diverted for irrigation.

Etudes de l'impact de l'activité de l'homme sur les régimes hydrologiques en Asie centrale par la télédétection

RESUME Les relevés consécutifs de la surface terrestre à partir de satellites permettent d'établir les corrélations entre les variations des éléments du paysage sous l'influence des facteurs anthropogèniques et les variations des régimes hydrologiques des fleuves. Dans les zones de développement hydraulique agricole les conséquences de l'activité humaine sont caractérisées par les indices suivants: variation du type et de l'épaisseur de la couverture végétale, aplanissement relatif du sol et subdivision de celui-ci en diverses zones cultivées, apparition de nouvelles dispositions du réseau hydrographique, existence des barrages, de chemins, de ponts et de localités. On peut souligner les caractéristiques principales utiles pour l'interprétation des images des régions agricoles irriguées: l'obscurcissement général du ton des images dans le visible, la structure en mosaïque de l'image, la présence de structure de forme géométrique régulière, des lignes droites gris clair (chemins) et gris foncé (ouvrages irrigations, collecteurs). Sur des exemples concrets on peut voir la dynamique de la structure des terres irriguées dans la région du cours moyen du Syrdarya et celle de la réduction de la surface de la Mer d'Aral. A l'aide de calcul des valeurs de la consommation spécifique de l'eau atteignant selon les régions 700-1400 m^3ha^{-1} il devient possible d'estimer les volumes approximatifs de l'eau prélevée pour l'irrigation.

INTRODUCTION

Among the problems related to the control of the natural environment is the development of methods to monitor changes caused by man's activity. Space surveys contribute much to the solution of this problem. Remote sensing data are used for obtaining information on the radius of the anthropogenic impact, its dynamics, periodicity and time variability. Determination of the magnitude and type of natural environment transformation is made using the analysis of changes in the structure of interrelated landscape features (Vinogradov, 1981). Natural complexes are considerably influenced by water management practices especially in such arid regions as Middle Asia.

Development of the correlation between changes in landscape elements under the influence of man's activity and the change of hydrological characteristics of rivers is one of the most important problems. Irrigation is aimed at the improvement of unfavourable natural conditions by changing and regulating water, heat and salt regimes of the territory to provide high crop yields. Intensive development of irrigation results in increased soil moisture content over large territories, that leads to a decrease in river flow and is accompanied by a change in the character of its intra-annual distribution. Figure 1 shows runoff hydrographs of the River Talas for natural and disturbed hydrological regimes.

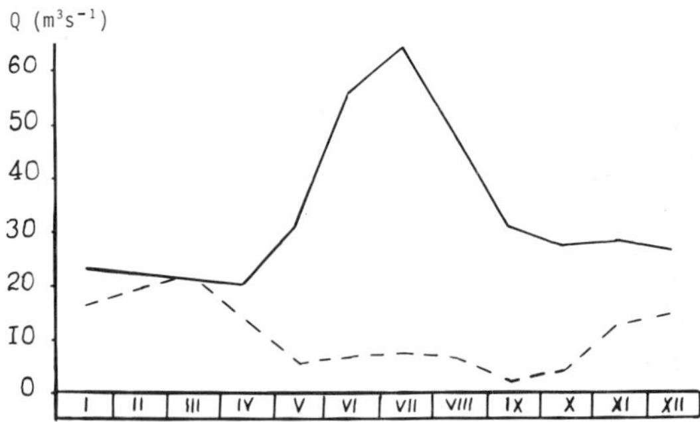

FIG.1 Hydrographs of mean long-term runoff of the River Talas: ——— at the village of Kirovskoye, ------ at the village of Ucharal.

At the upper reaches (the village of Kirovskoye) runoff losses are not large; the hydrograph reflects the spring-summer flood period and the autumn-winter low flow period characteristic of mountain rivers. At the site at the village of Ucharal, 80-90% of runoff is diverted for irrigation and consequently in summer, instead of flood, low flow takes place.

In Fig.2 runoff decreases for the rivers Syrdarya and Amudarya over the entire river length from the headwaters to the mouth are graphically illustrated. Runoff at the middle and lower reaches is

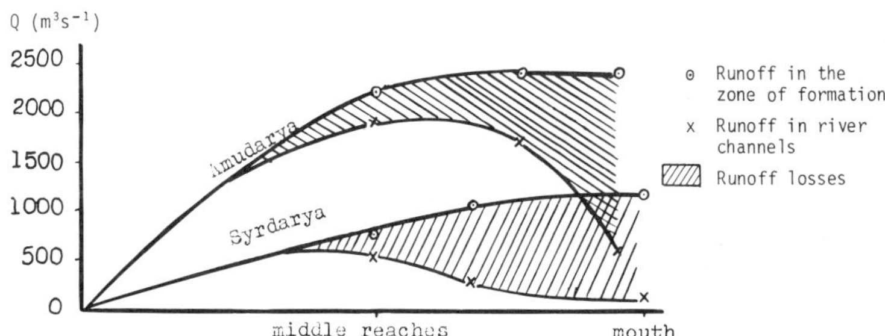

FIG.2 Runoff decreases for the Syrdarya and the Amudarya.

considerably less than the volume of water resources formed within the basins. Runoff losses (hatched parts of the graph) take place mainly because of runoff diversions for irrigation, and partly due to natural reasons, according to Kharchenko *et al* (1980). During individual years of low water content streamflow of Syrdarya doesn't reach the mouth at all. Today in the Aral Sea basin, water consumption for irrigation reaches the total amount of water resources available (Fig.3).

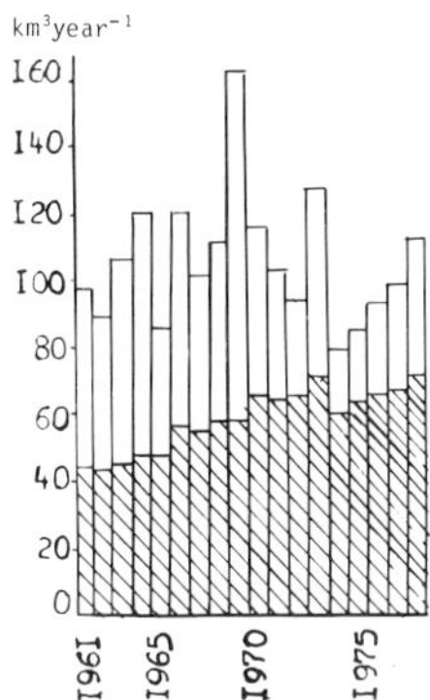

FIG.3 Diagram of the use of water resources of the Aral Sea basin for irrigation (hatched sections - water consumption volumes).

Considerable changes in the hydrological parameters take place together with the transformation of the basin surface characteristics because of irrigation.

The use of remote sensing data for the monitoring of water resources needs the development of indicators of landscape element changes under the influence of man's activity. For irrigated areas such indicators are:

(a) the change of the type and density of vegetative cover;

(b) smoothing of the soil surface within the limits of cultivated lands and division into sections occupied by arable crops;

(c) creation of artificial and transformation of natural hydrographic network;

(d) creation of dams, bridges, roads, settlements, etc.

The above features influence the interpretation of images. They create peculiarities such as the diversity of the phototone colours and mosaic structure of the image within irrigation massives, the

FIG.4 Images of the Middle Asia region made from the satellite "Meteor" in the spectrum range of 0.6-0.7 μm on 26 August 1977 (1 - irrigated areas, 2 - lakes, into which water used for irrigation is discharged).

predominance of objects of regular geometric shape (arable lands), the presence of straight light-grey (roads) and dark-grey (canals, collectors) lines. Depending on the scale or resolution, interpretation of the features of the image vary. On small-scale visible images, regions of irrigation are distinguished only by dark phototone and spotty structure of the pattern (Fig.4). Information of this type is not applicable for quantitative assessments, but it gives a general idea of the structure of the hydrographic network in the basin and mutual position of zones of runoff formation and utilization.

Information on the dynamics of the areas of irrigated lands and water-bodies serve as indirect (additional interpretative features for revealing the scale and trends of water management activity. The dynamics of areas are determined from data of successive space surveys with the corresponding conversion of images into one projection. Space photographs and middle-scale TV imagery allow one to identify gradual increases in the area of irrigated lands, the beginning of new lakes in land depressions on the periphery of irrigated massives (Syrykamysh, Aidar etc.), the disappearance of channels in reaches near the mouth, the decrease of the number of streams and lakes in deltas, in the Aral Sea basin, and as a result of this, the decrease in the surface area of the Aral Sea itself. The change of the position of the Aral Sea shoreline for the period 1960-1979 is illustrated in Fig.5. In the case of stabilized sea regime, information on the change of its area may be used for determining the amount of river water flowing into it.

The dynamics of the areas of irrigated land are exemplified by the Golodnaya steppe, a region situated in the middle reaches of the Syrdarya River (Fig.6).

By comparing areas of irrigated lands obtained from land and satellite surveys, it was found that the coefficient of transition from the area of the extracted contour to the actual area of irrigated lands was, on average, 0.78 for the Middle Asia region under study. The high values from the satellite survey can be explained by the fact that the contours extracted from the image comprised non-irrigated lands within the whole irrigated massif during the given year, areas occupied by villages, land strips along roads and canals.

The estimation of areas of irrigated lands using satellite survey data gives the opportunity to estimate approximately runoff volumes lost through transpiration from arable lands; to do that it is necessary to know specific indices of water consumption. Values of specific water consumption (S) for individual crops, as well as the average for the existing system of sowing were determined by the methodology developed at the State Hydrological Institute. The method starts from data on heat and water balance of meliorated lands with an account of groundwater depth. The results of computation of mean weighted values of S for individual regions are given in Table 1. As a whole, for the Aral Sea basin in 1978, the volume of water consumption for irrigation together with losses for preparative measures and diversions made up 72 km^3, total water resources amounting to 113 km^3.

Another aspect of satellite information is the possibility of marking out areas of formation of backflow from irrigated areas. The account of them is necessary when taking measures on the rational

FIG.5 The change of the surface area of the Aral Sea. ——— the shoreline in 1960; ----- the shoreline on 19 June 1975, photographed from the "Saliut-4"; ..... the shoreline on 26 September 1979 photographed from the satellite "Meteor-29".

use of water resources. Areas of backwater formation are determined starting from the peculiarities of the structure of natural and artificial hydrographic network as well as from the assessment of mutual position of irrigated lands and the river, the source of water for irrigation. In this case, it is efficient to use the method of synthesizing multi-zonal images. Thus, using remote-sensing monitoring of the consequences of man's activity within the basin it becomes possible to estimate the use of water resources during various stages of irrigation within the territory.

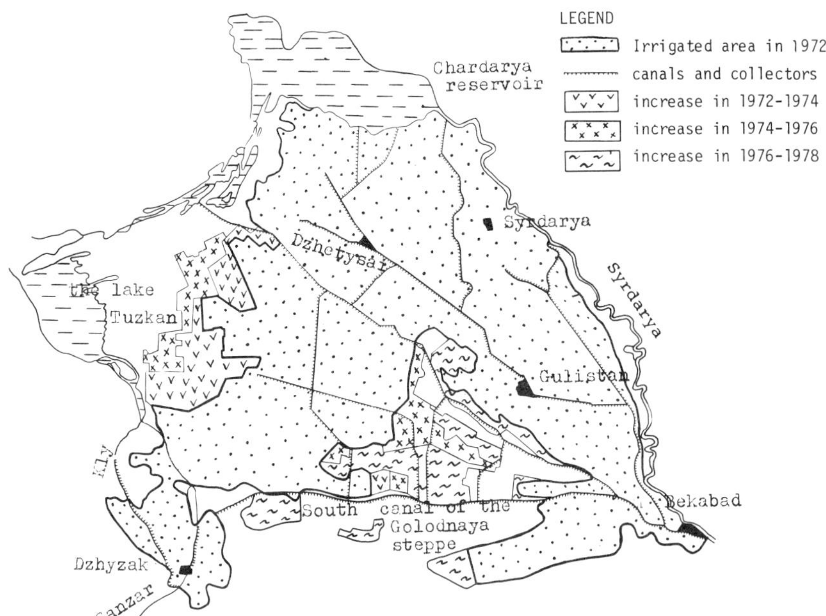

FIG.6 The dynamics of irrigated land area of the Golodnaya steppe for the period 1972-1978.

TABLE 1 Specific water consumption of irrigated massives (m^3ha^{-1})

River basin, region	*S*	*River basin, region*	*S*
(1) Upper reaches of the Amudarya	900	(6) Upper reaches of the Syrdarya	270
(2) Basin of the River Surkhandarya	930	(7) Fergana valley	810
(3) Basin of the River Zeravshan	1470	(8) Golodnaya steppe	710
(4) Middle reaches of the Syrdarya	1260	(9) Middle reaches of the Syrdarya	670
(5) Lower reaches of the Amudarya	1065	(10) Lower reaches of the Syrdarya	850

REFERENCES

Kharchenko, S.I., Sumarokova, V.A. & Tsytsenko, K.V. (1980) Izmenenie vodnykh resursov Aralskogo moria v sviazi s razvitiem oroshenia i perebroskoi chasti stoka Sibirskikh rek (The change of water resources of the Aral Sea caused by irrigation and transfer of a

portion of runoff of some Siberian rivers). In: *Mezhzonalnoe pereraspredelenie vodnykh resursov (Inter-zonal redistribution of water resources)*, Gidrometeoizdat, Leningrad.

Sumarokova, V.A. & Griazev, S.N. (1983) Rol distantsionnykh dannykh v otsenke antropogennykh vozdeistvii na vodnye resursy (The role of remote sensing data in the estimation of anthropogenic impact on water resources). *Trans. GGI.*

Vinogradov, B.V. (1981) *Preobrazovannaya Zemlia (aerokosmicheskie issledovania)* (Transformed Earth (remote-sensing investigations)). Mysl., Moscow.

Hydrological Applications of Remote Sensing and Remote Data Transmission (Proceedings of the Hamburg Symposium, August 1983). IAHS Publ. no. 145.

Estimation of percent imperviousness of urban basins using remote sensing data

SRINIVAS G. RAO
School of Civil Engineering, Georgia Institute of Technology, Atlanta, Georgia 30332, USA
STEPHEN E. DRAPER
US Army Corps of Engineers, Fort Benning, Georgia 31905, USA

ABSTRACT Percent imperviousness is an important parameter in modelling urban rainfall-runoff processes. This parameter is usually determined using manual methods such as the random sampling method or conventional accounting method. In this study, two computerized methods of automatic extraction of percent imperviousness using high altitude remote sensing imagery are developed. These methods include the Laser Image Processing Scanner and the Video-Tape Camera system. Imperviousness is estimated directly in the former method while in the latter it is estimated as a function of the statistics of the responses on the emulsions of the imagery. The methods are applied to four urban basins and the percent imperviousness computed by these methods compare well with those obtained by the normally used manual methods. The study demonstrates that remote sensing imagery can be utilized to estimate accurately the percent imperviousness in less time than the manual methods.

Estimation du pourcentage d'imperméabilité sur les bassins urbains par la télédétection
RESUME Le pourcentage de zones imperméables est un paramètre important dans la mise en modèle des processus précipitations-écoulement dans les bassins urbains. Ce paramètre est déterminé habituellement en utilisant des méthodes manuelles telles que la méthode d'échantillonage au hasard ou la méthode du décompte conventionnelle. Dans cette étude on présente deux méthodes utilisant l'ordinateur qui extraient automatiquement le pourcentage d'imperméabilite à partir de l'imagerie de télédétection à haute altitude. Ces méthodes sont: le "Laser Image Processing Scanner" et le système "Video-Tape Camera". L'imperméabilité est estimée directement dans la première méthode alors que dans la seconde elle est estimée comme une fonction des caractéristiques statistiques des réponses des émulsions de l'imagerie. Les méthodes sont appliquées à quatre bassins versants urbains et les pourcentages d'imperméabilité qu'elles permettent de calculer sont en bon accord avec ceux que l'on obtient par les méthodes manuelles utilisées habituellement. L'étude montre que l'imagerie de télédétection peut être utilisée

pour déterminer avec précision le pourcentage d'imperméabilité en un temps plus court qu'avec les méthodes manuelles.

INTRODUCTION

Urbanization of basins alters the physical characteristics of the basins resulting in changes in the response. A number of hydrological models have been proposed in the past to model the urban rainfall-runoff process. These include empirical models relating runoff to basin and climatic parameters, conceptual models relating to the storage and conveyance characteristics of basins, and simulation models in which various hydrological components are simulated to determine runoff hydrographs from a basin. Regardless of the method used, studies have shown a strong correlation between basin response and the amount of impervious area in the basin. Accurate estimation of percent imperviousness is therefore essential for effective investigation of basin response. Present techniques normally use either detailed manual procedure or random sampling procedure to determine the impervious percentage. These methods involve considerable subjectivity in the analysis procedure and require large analysis time and therefore the results may be inaccurate. The main objective of the present study was to demonstrate the feasibility and accuracy of impervious percentage estimation using remote sensing imagery for modelling urban runoff.

Remote sensing imagery used for urban hydrology applications include the imagery provided by satellite sensors and by cameras in high-altitude aircraft. Satellite imagery detects the electromagnetic signature of a large area, on the order of 104 km^2 and can do so in six separate spectral bands. On the other hand, high altitude imagery detects the signature of small areas of the order of 1 m^2, but normally does so in four overlapping bands. Ambaruck & Simmons (1974) and Salomonson & Rango (1974) reported on the feasibility of using ERTS and SKYLAB satellite data to determine basin physiographic parameters while Jackson & Ragan (1980) developed methodology to use satellite imagery to classify land use by determining the SCS runoff curve numbers. Land uses such as commercial and business districts, industrial districts, five separate classifications of residential use and paved areas were determined.

Colwell (1970) used high-altitude imagery to detect urban features: vegetation, non-vegetation and water as well as the feasibility for separation of nine different land uses. Root & Miller (1971) through field measurements of urban land use, concluded that impervious features could be separated by use of remote sensing data in the blue and green portions of the spectrum. Egbert (1970) suggested that separation might be possible by analysis of ratios between land-use response in the visual and infrared ranges while Centner & Hietner (1971) reported a signature recognition technique using a decision logic network to classify objects based on statistical information from known land uses. Kristoff & Zachary (1974) used the ratio technique to extract terrain features. Scarface & Quirk (1980) reported accurate land-use classification based on the emulsion of colour and colour-infrared photographs. A densitometer was used to digitize the emulsions in very narrow bands in the visible spectrum and allowed 88% correct classification of land use with one of five possible classifications.

In view of the foregoing, the present study deals with automatic extraction of urban imperviousness parameter using high-altitude colour and colour-infrared imagery. This imagery has much better resolution than Landsat imagery and does not require a training model. Two computerized methods are developed to estimate the percent imperviousness and the methods are applied to four urban basins in Connecticut. These results are compared to those obtained from the manual methods.

PERCENT IMPERVIOUSNESS BY MANUAL METHODS

The basins chosen for study are located in and around Hartford, Connecticut. All are contained in the basin of the Park River, which in turn drains into the Connecticut River. The four basins include three tributaries of the South Branch of the Park River; the South Branch provides some 60% of the drainage area of the Park River. The major tributaries are Mill, Piper, and Trout Brooks. The area encompassing the four basins ranges from totally rural on its western edges to highly urban in its southern portions. The drainage areas of the sub-basins vary from about 8 to 78 km^2 and imperviousness varies from 15 to 22%.

TABLE 1 Impervious percentage by manual methods

Basin	*Conventional accounting*	*25% random sampling*	*50% random sampling*
Mill Brook	*0.185*	*0.154*	*0.178*
Piper Brook	*0.215*	*0.235*	*0.210*
Trout Brook	*0.150*	*0.153*	*0.147*
South Branch	*0.201*	*0.206*	*0.255*

Impervious area was defined in the study as any man-made construction feature of impermeable nature. Identification of these features was made using 1:25 000 maps from the Hartford Metropolitan District Commission and by aerial photographs of areas not covered by the maps. The level of detail on the maps allowed accurate determination of the location and extent of the impervious areas. Two methods of manual determination were used. One method involved the conventional accounting method (CAM) and the other involved random sampling method (RSM) wherein the percent imperviousness is computed by using these maps. In the second method both 25 and 50% random sampling was used. The details of these methods are found in Draper (1981) and the results of these methods are summarized in Table 1.

PERCENT IMPERVIOUSNESS USING REMOTE SENSING IMAGERY

Data for development of the automatic extraction of impervious material included two 23 cm aerial photograph transparencies. These imageries were colour and colour-infrared transparencies obtained from imagery taken from an RB-57 aircraft, flying at 18 288m, in August 1971. The imagery was obtained from the EROS Data Center, USGS, Sioux Falls, South Dakota. Less than 5% cloud cover appeared on the photographs. The scale of the scenes is approximately 1:120 000 and each scene covers an area of approximately 285 km^2.

Digitization of the emulsion signatures of the colour and colour-infrared transparencies was necessary for computer analysis. Digitization using spectro-radiometer was found to be inadequate for estimation of imperviousness (Rao & Draper, 1980). In the present study, two systems were used to digitize the land-use signature data on the emulsions of the imagery: the Laser Image Processing Scanner (LIPS) and the Video-Tape Camera System (VTC). The advantage of the first system is its ability to determine signatures in a very narrow spectral band while that of the latter is its ability to analyse basins of larger size. The major difference between the two systems was resolution. The LIPS' resolution was almost twice as great as that of the VTC, depending on the area measured. The LIPS could extract point land use for small basins while the VTC could provide statistics for large basins.

The SDC-800 computer system was used for both the LIPS and VTC methods of digitization and the development of the methods to extract the impervious percentages. The computer assigns to each pixel a grey value from zero to 255, according to the light transmission sensed. Zero is assigned to the pixel passing the most light (i.e. the whitest). Other points receive a value according to their relative passage of light by linear interpolation between the darkest and lightest level. The matrix of pixels may be displayed according to assigned grey levels in the 490 (row) x 384 (column) form.

Laser Image Processing Scanner (LIPS)

This self-contained digitization device consists of an industrial HeNe laser that emits a beam of red light with a wavelength of 6328Å, with a beam diameter of 40 microns. The fixed beam is directed at a moving cylinder upon which the transparency is placed. The cylinder revolves and moves laterally so that the beam can be focused on all points on the image. A photocell is fixed inside the cylinder to measure the intensity of light passing through the transparency. This cell generates a current proportional to the light intensity. This information is digitized and placed on magnetic tape for input to a digital computer. The maximum size of imagery that can be placed on the cylinder is a 40 mm x 40 mm area, thereby constraining the size of basin that can be digitized with sufficient accuracy. With photographs taken from 18 288 m, resolution of approximately 3 m x 3 m can be obtained; the maximum size of basin is, therefore, approximately 7.8 km^2. Two different wavelength responses were obtained by digitizing the point responses from both a colour and a colour-infrared transparency. Comparison was then made of signatures on the cyan forming layer at 6328Å.

The laser system was used for direct classification of each pixel into one of the three general classifications of impervious cover, pervious cover, or water. In order to develop a more accurate algorithm for this purpose, an experimental data base was established by using the responses of known points in areas other than those under analysis. Thirty known land uses of each classification were selected and their densities on a colour and a colour-infrared transparency extracted using the laser system.

Use of the post-1969 Mill Brook basin, with a 6.9 km^2 drainage area, provided a resolution of approximately 1.8 m x 1.8 m. Using the Boolean Logic subprogram, this two-dimensional matrix of land use response provided the basis for the development of an algorithm for classification into one of the three types. An analysis of the averages of responses indicates differences exist in the three land uses. From the colour transparency, the data indicate that, on the average, pervious land use transmits approximately 60% less of the laser light than does impervious land use while water and pervious land use transmit somewhat the same amount of light. From the infra-red transparency, impervious land use transmits 75% less light than does pervious land use while water transmits 50% less light. Individual land uses, however, vary drastically from this pattern.

Egbert (1970) suggested that ratios of different radiation band signatures might distinguish various types of land use. The compatibility of Boolean logic with this theory suggested that such a ratio scheme coupled with analysis of relative light transmission in each transparency might allow identification. Inspection of the data base indicated that natural pervious land uses provided low transmission of light in the 6328Å band while impervious land use provided high transmission. Except for a few cases of fields and grass, pervious land use and water could be separated from impervious land use by the fact that impervious land use signatures in the 6328Å band were largely in the upper half of possible responses while the former were in the lower half. This separation by itself could account for a 91.6% correct identification between pervious land use or water and impervious land use. A Boolean algorithm was developed to separate the three land-use categories. Using the test variables, regeneration of the possible combinations by the algorithm yielded correct separation into the three categories of 92.2%. For those land uses whose signatures were in the upper half, a further separation showed that impervious land uses had a colour to colour-infrared response ratio (C/IR) of greater than 3.5. Use of the responses in the colour and colour-infrared bands enabled correct separation of 91.2% between pervious and impervious land uses. For separation of pervious land use and water, a similar analysis was made for more land uses whose response was in the lower half of possible light transmission. The result was a correct separation between pervious and water of 92.2%.

For prediction purposes, the area surrounding the post-1969 Mill Brook basin was used. This basin was small enough to allow sufficiently large resolution to detect point impervious land use. Analysis was made on the basin itself, five quadrangle map areas in and around the basin and 12 quarter-quadrangle map areas. Results obtained by the algorithm are shown in Table 2. The results determined that 25.0% of the basin contained impervious land use, 2.2% contained

TABLE 2 Comparison of impervious percentage (U) values from LIPS method and manual methods for Mill Brook basin

Map	Conventional accounting	LIPS	Map	Conventional accounting	LIPS
202	19.0%	24.1%	203	17.2%	33.3%
.1	23.4	29.7	.1	20.6	47.6
.2	16.8	21.8	.2	21.6	24.4
.3	30.7	31.8	.3	7.3	32.2
.4	4.9	12.9	.4	19.3	28.0
263	24.3	24.6	264	16.3	27.4
.1	22.5	18.5	.1	4.4	21.8
.2	22.2	20.9	.2	22.1	35.3
.3	21.3	17.8	.3	18.7	16.6
.4	31.2	40.8	.4	19.8	33.2
332			333	13.5	16.8
.1	20.6	16.8	.1	12.7	16.6
			.2	28.1	17.6
.3	18.7	16.6	.3	4.5	6.8
			.4	8.7	9.4

Entire watershed: conventional accounting method U = 18.5%
LIPS method U = 25.0%

Decimal numbers indicate quadrants on map 1 2 / 3 4

water, and the remainder was pervious land use.

The 25% value for the impervious percentage of Mill Brook basin is 6.5% higher than the approximated true value. The error is mostly from new construction features that were not on the city quadrangles or aerial photographs, in identification of a natural surface material (red shale) that may in fact be a natural impervious land use, from areas that are located near public use facilities used for parking, and incorrect identification of pervious land use, mostly sand traps on a local golf course.

Considering the results of the CAM and the LIPS extractions, the average error squared is 1.53. Most of the large value results from the third quadrangle of Map 203 and the first quadrangle of Map 264. If these two quadrangles are not considered, the average error squared is 0.31. Comparison of the results of LIPS and the two RMS's for the entire basin indicates the LIPS technique provided over twice the error of the 50% RSM as compared to the CAM method, while being only slightly larger than the 25% RSM. However, these differences are attributed to the factors discussed above and the assumption that conventional accounting method gave true value of imperviousness.

Video-Tape Camera System

The second digitization system contained a movable scanner mounted over a fixed white light table. The scanner sensed the white light table. The scanner sensed the white light intensity passing through each data point and converted the analog information to digital tape. Three narrow band filters were used to differentiate response of each emulsion. Placed over the lens of the video-tape, these filters allowed measurement of the land-use signature in the blue, green, and red regions of radiation on both the colour and the colour-infrared transparency. Effectively then, the responses in the cyan, magenta, and yellow forming emulsions could be digitized. This means comparison of responses of the blue, green, and red regions could be made. The VTC scans the picture in a 490 (row) x 384 (column) matrix of pixels. Therefore, the resolution is a function of the size of transparency under analysis.

The lack of sufficiently narrow bands when using the video-tape system, coupled with the decreased resolution of the larger areas, obviated exact point land-use mapping. However, the frequency of responses in the various emulsions did appear to correlate with the amount of impervious land use in a particular area. For each of the emulsions and for the combination of emulsions, the statistics of mean, mode, standard deviation and median were collected.

Data were obtained for the quarter-quadrangles in the Mill and Piper Brook areas, for the full map sheets in the Trout Brook area and for both in the separate portion of South Branch. The data contained statistics for 108 quarter-map quadrangles, 24 full map quadrangles, and for the four complete basin areas. Ffty-six of the quarter-quadrangles and 10 of the full map sheets were used in regeneration of the impervious percentages. Regression analysis was used to correlate the statistics of the signature responses of each of the transparencies using the three filters individually and using unfiltered white light to the value of the impervious percentage (U). Both linear and nonlinear regression analysis were performed as indicated below:

$$U = \alpha_0 + \beta_{ij}X_{ij} + \gamma_{ij}Y_{ij} \quad (1)$$

$$U = \alpha_0 + \alpha_1 X_{ij}^{\beta_{ij}} Y_{ij}^{\gamma_{ij}} \quad (2)$$

where x represents parameters from the colour transparency; y represents parameters from the colour-infrared transparency; i-values ranging from 1 to 4 represent the filter all emulsion, yellow, magenta, cyan, used during digitization; and, j-values ranging from 1 to 4 described the statistic mean, standard deviation, mode, and median involved.

Significance level for the regression was set at the 95% level. For both the linear and nonlinear regression, the single parameter providing the highest correlation was the median of responses on the magenta emulsion of the colour-infrared transparency (y_{33}):

$$U = 4.07 \times 10^{-6}\ y_{33} - 89.8 \qquad R = 0.546 \quad (3)$$

$$U = 4.07 \times 10\ \ y_{33} \qquad R = 0.612 \quad (4)$$

The correlation coefficient (R) increased with the parameter inclusion indicated in Table 3. The final results, with all parameters

TABLE 3 Significant parameters, in order of inclusion

Inclusion order	*Emulsion - Statistic*	*Parameter*	*Regression coefficient*
1	*Magenta - Median*	y_{33}	*0.546*
2	*Cyan - Mean*	y_{41}	*0.762*
3	*Yellow - Median*	y_{23}	*0.793*
4	*Yellow - Std.Dev.*	y_{22}	*0.805*
5	*Yellow - Mean*	y_{21}	*0.820*
6	*Yellow - Mode*	y_{24}	*0.827*

significant at the 95% significance level, were as follows:

$$U = 0.809y_{33} - 0.464y_{41} - 1.428y_{23} - 0.439y_{22} + 0.936y_{21} + 0.154y_{24} + 38.6 \qquad R = 0.827 \tag{5}$$

$$U = 612 \frac{y_{33}^{8.183}}{y_{41}^{1.680}\, y_{11}^{0.430}\, y_{23}^{4.297}\, y_{13}^{2.426}} + 3.16 \qquad R = 0.817 \tag{6}$$

The responses of the remaining quarter-quadrangles and full map sheets were then used for prediction. The results are indicated in Table 4. Comparing the correlation of both the regeneration and the prediction, Equation (5) was chosen as being the most accurate and precise.

TABLE 4 Results of VTC method

Eq. No.	*R in regeneration*	*R in prediction*	*Mill Br (U=18.5%)*	*Piper Br (U=21.5%)*	*Trout Br (U=15.0%)*	*S Branch (U=20.1%)*
(3)	*0.546*	*0.437*	*2.0%*	*25.6%*	*15.5%*	*18.8%*
(4)	*0.612*	*0.588*	*8.2%*	*17.5%*	*12.9%*	*14.3%*
(5)	*0.827*	*0.756*	*15.2%*	*20.7%*	*12.8%*	*26.9%*
(6)	*0.817*	*0.700*	*15.2%*	*18.9%*	*12.5%*	*12.2%*
By conventional accounting method			*18.5%*	*21.5%*	*15.0%*	*12.2%*

A comparison of the values of U developed by conventional accounting, random sampling, and by the video-tape analysis is shown in

Table 5. A t-test was made to determine if a significant difference existed between the approximately true value of U and any of the three values estimated by VTC extraction of RSM. As shown in the table, the t-statistics in each of the methods are less than the critical value, indicating that no significant difference existed. The conclusions are that the VTC method is an accurate means for determination of the impervious percentage of a basin.

TABLE 5 Comparison of U values from VTC method and manual methods

Basin	*Concentional accounting*	*Random sampling: 25%*	*50%*	*VTC*
Mill Brook	*18.5%*	*15.4%*	*17.8%*	*15.2%*
Piper Brook	*21.5%*	*23.5%*	*21.0%*	*20.7%*
Trout Brook	*15.0%*	*15.3%*	*14.7%*	*12.8%*
South Branch	*20.1%*	*20.6%*	*25.5%*	*26.9%*
t-statistic		*0.0696*	*-0.660*	*-0.0548*
critical t = 2.950				

CONCLUSION

The study demonstrates that automatic extraction of impervious percentage by using high-altitude remote sensing imagery is feasible. The LIPS method utilized the ratio between land-use responses in different spectral bands, allowing point land use determination. Current technology, however, limits the size of basins that can be so mapped to less than 13 km^2 in area. For larger basins, the VTC method with multiple regression equation in terms of the statistics of densities on the three emulsions of the colour-infrared photograph can be used. Whereas the LIPS method could develop a resolution of less than 3 m x 3 m, the VTC method produced a resolution of over 12 m x 12 m. Effectively, use of either method reduces greatly the time necessary to determine the parameter and eliminates the inaccuracies and subjectivity of analysis involved with the normally used manual methods.

ACKNOWLEDGEMENTS Authors are grateful for the financial support by the US Army Corps of Engineers and Georgia Institute of Technology for the work reported herein.

REFERENCES

Ambaruck, T. & Simmons, J.W. (1974) A study of remote sensing as applied to regional and small watersheds. *Report no. 74W-00175,*

IBM, Inc., Huntsville, Alabama, USA.

Centner, R.M. & Hietner, E.D. (1971) Automatic pattern recognition, *Photogram. Endng.* 37(2), 177-186.

Colwell, J.E. (1970) Multispectral remote sensing of urban features. *Willow Run Laboratories, The University of Michigan, Ann Arbor, Michigan, USA.*

Draper, S.E. (1981) Urban rainfall-runoff modeling using remote sensing imagery. PhD thesis, Georgia Institute of Technology, Atlanta, Georgia, USA.

Egbert, D. (1970) Spectral reflectivity data: a practical acquisition procedure. *CRES Tech. Report 133-21, University of Kansas, Lawrence, Kansas, USA.*

Jackson, T.J. & Ragan, R.M. (1980) Runoff synthesis using Landsat and SCS model. *J. Hydraul. Div.* ASCE 106(HY5), 667-673.

Kristoff, S.J. & Zachary, A.L. (1974) Mapping soil features from multispectral scanner data. *Photogramm. Engng.* 40(12), 1427-1434.

Rao, S.G. & Draper, S.E. (1980) Remote sensing applications to urban hydrology. Paper presented at the AGU Fall Meeting, San Francisco, California, USA.

Root, R.R. & Miller, L.D. (1971) Identification of urban watershed units using remote multispectral sensing. *Environmental Resources Center, Colorado State University, Fort Collins, Colorado, USA.*

Salomonson, V.V. & Rango, A. (1974) ERTS-1 applications in hydrology and water resources. *Ann. Wat. Wks Ass. J.* 66, 168-172.

Scarface, F.L. & Quirk, B.K. (1980) Land-cover classification using digital image processing of aerial imagery. *Photogramm. Engng Remote Sens.* 46(8), 1059-1065.

Hydrological Applications of Remote Sensing and Remote Data Transmission (Proceedings of the Hamburg Symposium, August 1983). IAHS Publ. no. 145.

Landsat image interpretation of sand dune movement in the Yellow River valley

NIU ZHAN
Bureau of Hydrology, Yellow River Conservancy Commission, Ministry of Water Conservancy and Power, Beijing, China

ABSTRACT Based on the view of the land surface displayed by Landsat images, the paper describes the three main passages through which wind-blown sand enters the Yellow River basin and the branches of the channels along which the sand moves further into the interior part of the valley. Analysis has been made on the effect of climatic condition and landform on mobility of sand dunes and the features of dune sand movement have been depicted, which together with particle distribution of sand grains and mineral composition of sandy materials substantiate the hypothesis of aeolian deposition of loess. The forming of the E'erdousi closed basin in the Yellow River valley and the effect of dune sand mobility on sediment of some rivers in north Shaanxi have also been investigated.

Mouvement du sable éolien dans le bassin du Fleuve Jaune: explication par les photos de Landsat
RESUME A partir des images de la surface du sol montrées par les photos de Landsat, le présent article décrit les trois couloirs par lesquels le sable éolien pénètre dans le bassin du Fleuve Jaune et leurs bifurcations menant à l'intérieur du bassin, analyse l'influence des conditions climatique configuration du paysage sur le mouvement du sable éolien, présente l'aspect du mouvement avec la granulométrie des grains de sable et la composition minérale de ces matériaux sableux l'hypothèse de la formation du loess par le vent. Enfin on étudie la formation de la zone endoreïque d'Erdousi dans le bassin du Fleuve Jaune et la relation entre le mouvement des dunes de sable et le régime du transport de sédiments dans les rivières du nord de la province de Chensi.

DEPICTION OF THE ROUTES OF DUNE SAND MOVEMENT FROM LANDSAT PHOTOS

Landsat photos are data gathered through satellite remote sensing, which have found wide application. From the point of view of physics, information is recorded for the respective reflected energy of ground objects in different bands of the spectrum, to be demonstrated in the density of the tones on the photos and images. The range of wavelength of the four spectral bands MSS-4, 5, 6 and 7 is, respectively, 0.5-0.6 μm, 0.6-0.7 μm, 0.7-0.8 μm and 0.8-1.0 μm. These include most of the visible light (wavelengths 0.38-0.71 μm) and extend into the scope of near infrared radiation. By using the multispectral technique, the amount of information gathered is increased and the resolution power in distinguishing ground objects is raised. Geometrically, the images are two-dimensional models of the ground surface, and give a full-field view of land features. Owing to parallax and stereometric effect of the land surface and with the appropriate incidence angle of sunlight, the landform may be reflected in a three-dimensional display of images, to different extents, by making photos at different positions. Hence, the pictures produced by Landsat closely resemble the natural view, ideally represented in the structure of landscape, very close to the habitual feeling of human eyesight.

Images from different spectral bands and different colours of light are combined in the multispectral colour composite technique to display ground objects of different nature as having different densities of tones of colour, so that the resolution power for differentiating different types of ground objects is raised. For example, on the so-called standard false colour composites formed with MSS-4, 5 and 7 with blue, green and red light used in composing, the deserts and the zones of deposition of wind-blown sand are clearly displayed in blue colour, apparently different from vegetative cover which shows red in colour. Therefore it is easy to distinguish areas of mobile sand, oasis and grassland, thus facilitating interpretation of the movement of wind-blown sand.

One particular feature of Landsat photos is the wide scope of image-forming. One image covers an area of 185 x 185 $(km)^2$ in general cases. When the images are attached together to give a full-field view of a certain zone or basin, it looks really magnificent and panoramic, facilitating investigation and planning for large areas.

Apparent features of mobility of wind-blown sand as seen on the Landsat images are blue-coloured mobile sand deposits and broom-like traces of wind erosion. On the mosaic formed by sticking together Landsat images of the Yellow River basin, it is possible to see the three main passages through which the mobile sand enters the Yellow River valley. The first lies between Qinghai south Mt and Ela Mountains. The second is between Qilian and Helan Mountains and the third between Helan and Langshan Mountains. After coming into the Yellow River basin through these passages, the mobile sand moves further into the inner parts of the basin by way of branch passages, divided in accordance with topography. The landform and routes of sand movement as interpreted from Landsat images are shown in Fig.1.

The first route begins while entering Wulan and passing the valley of Shazhuyu River to reach Gonghe and Guinan basin. The last-mentioned is a basin that remains from an ancient lake (Geological Institute, Chinese Academy of Sciences, 1966), manifesting a long and narrow zone in the northwest, broadening gradually in the southeasterly direction. The elevation is about 3000 m, that of surrounding high mountains being 4500 m or higher. The basin contracts gradually in the northwestern direction while gaining in elevation, finally reaching the Gobi desert at Chaidamu basin after passing the mountain pass of Wulan, called Yakou. The Yellow

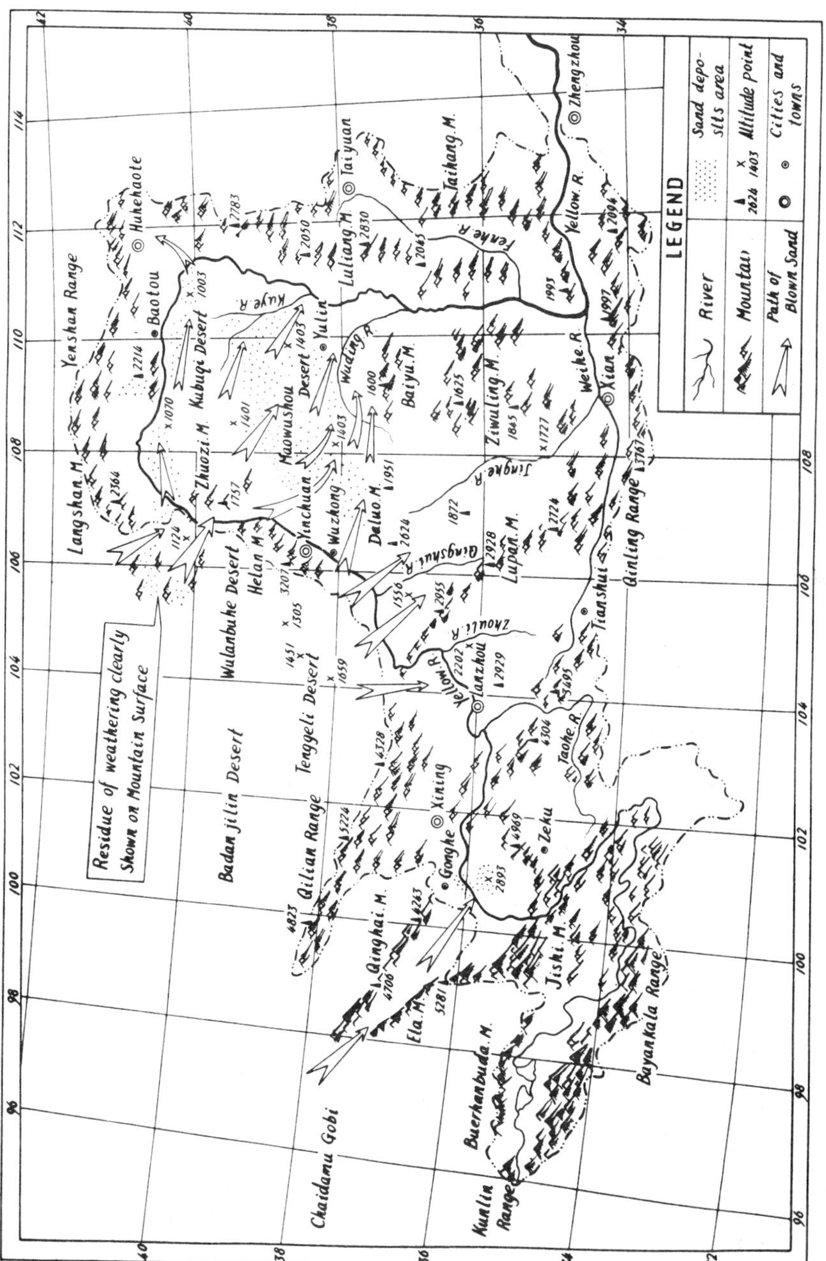

FIG.1 Map of topography and wind-blown sand in the Yellow River drainage basin (taken from Landsat images).

River cuts through the basin at its southeast part slanting in the direction from southwest to northeast. Deposition of thin layers of mobile sand, exhibiting a blue colour in the false colour composite, can be seen along both banks. The Shazhuyu River valley exhibits a light brown colour and traces of windblown and rainfall effects on the landscape. It is, therefore, readily seen that the deposits of mobile sand in this basin are the result of strong winds blowing along this route.

The second route is connected externally to the Tenggeli desert, displaying large patches of smooth and bright blue colour on the Landsat images. In the photos, the country is seen to be open and broad, revealing vast expanses of desert and clearly visible traces of north and northwesterly winds. After entering the Yellow River basin, the wind-blown sand moves into the interior of the basin in three directions. In the southward direction, the sand is pushed forward in a belt bordered at the east by the Liupan Mountains, towards the west Longshan basin in the Zuli River basin. The branch towards the east traverses the Zhongwei Plain somewhere between Daluo Mt and Wuzhong, to reach Baiyu Mt at its northern foot, on the upper reaches of Wuding River. The other branch directed towards the southeast, however, moves upstream along the Qingshui River to extend into the Jinghe River basin after crossing the watershed. The part of the Yellow River basin affected by this route is not a closed and intact (or integrated) basin and where the stream system is developed to an advanced stage, no apparent deposition of dune sand occurs except for a small closed basin on the left bank of the Zhuanglang River to the north of Lanzhou and some accumulation of mobile sand on the upper reaches of the Wuding River, corresponding to the dominant wind direction towards the east. Traces of the phenomenon of wind-blown sand sweeping across the Yellow River further towards the interior may however be seen quite obviously in the reach of Lanzhou to Wuzhong on the Yellow River.

The third route is bordered by the Wulanbuhe desert, and in the northwest is adjacent to a mountainous area of an appreciably weathered residual formation. It can be clearly seen from the Landsat images that in the area between mountains which exhibit black tones, the view of wind erosion brought about by the northerly winds is very distinct and pronounced; tracks of the wind belt reach the Yellow River valley after transversing the Wulanbuhe desert, which proves that dune sand movement has been very intensive here and that, generally speaking, the sand pushes forward in three directions after crossing the Yellow River. One of the branches passes through the wind gap in the narrow Yellow River valley somewhere between the Helan and Zhuozi Mountains, then in a southerly direction up the river to reach Wuzhong, where it merges with the eastern branch of the second route to turn towards the upper reaches of Wuding River, the corresponding belt of wind-borne sand deposits exhibiting crescent shapes in the direction from north towards east. The second branch crosses the more or less level highland round Zhuozi Mt, where the highest elevation is only 1700 m. It rushes toward the watersheds of Wuding and Kuye River after traversing the closed basin in the southeasterly direction; the deposits are formed in a straight and smooth belt from northwest towards southeast, which shows that the direction of the wind path is rather stable in the vast, smooth area. Another path leads from the Wulanbuhe desert eastward towards the completely deserted Kubuqi area and finally to the Tuoketuo region, where it is a long and narrow belt with ground elevation of only 1000 m or so, some 400 m lower than that of the closed basin. Dune sand movement along the Kubuqi path affects areas as far as beyond the Dahei River watershed in Nei Monggol. It should be pointed out that some of the gaps and depressed areas along the Yinshan Mountains let through winds affecting dune sand mobility in the E'erdousi region to a certain extent and the grid-formed dunes spread all over the Kubuqi desert are the result of the interference of dominant westerly and supplementary northerly winds. Also, there are traces of wind sweep by the northerlies in the northern part of Maowusu.

INFLUENCE OF CLIMATE AND LANDFORM ON DUNE SAND MOBILITY

It is a well known fact that the climate in the Yellow River valley in winter is governed by the existence of a stable high pressure area at low temperature in Siberia. In the cold season, the warm and humid air current from the southeast is weakened and the predominant northwesterly flow (Shixun Chen, 1959), which is dry and cold, causes the dune sand movement of the Yellow River basin accompanying the inland cold, dry air current to concentrate in this period. In the warm seasons, however, the oceanic air current of high humidity enters this region, so that the dune sand mobility is appreciably reduced. Complying with the seasonal variation, the wind-borne sand movement exhibits an overall northwest to southeast orientation.

When the air current from the northwest - as a general tendency - approaches the Yellow River valley, the direction of winds changes frequently, as influenced by the topography. The frequency of occurrence of ground surface wind direction (see Fig.2) for the month of January shows that at Lanzhou the northerly occurs more

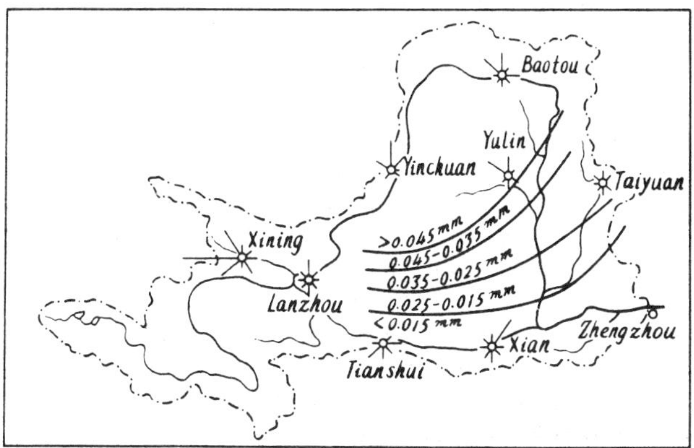

FIG.2 Frequency distribution of wind direction in January. Average grain size of new loess is also shown (after Shixun Chen, 1959; and Dongshen Liu, 1964).

frequently, in accord with the southern branch of the second route of dune sand movement, whereas the predominant north wind at Yinchuan is closely related to one branch of the third route, up the river. The northwesterly wind, which occurs very frequently at Yulin, corresponds well with the southeastern branch of the third route. The prevailing northerly and northwesterly at Baotou have much to do with the gaps in the Yinshan Mts and have their corresponding effect on the forming of grid-shaped dunes scattered round Kubuqi. There is no predominant wind at Taiyuan, which shows that the Lüliang Mts, with their main peak at an elevation of 2800 m or more, hinder the further advance of the air currents from the northwest.

The weather information shows that, as on average between 1951 and 1955, each year there were 60.4 days with dune sand movement at Baotou, 35.2 days at Yinchuan, 44.8 days at Yulin and 48.2 days at Xining, mostly occurring in the spring season, comprising over 50% of those for a whole year. Average wind speed in spring is about 3.0 m s^{-1} (Shixun Chen, 1959) reaching a high of 4.3 m s^{-1} at Dengkou (Zhenda Zhu, 1980) and frequent winds as such bring about the transport of fine sand from afar as well as dislodging sand dust in the locality, so that the process of desert forming tends to be more serious with each passing day and the area of mobile sand is also increasing. It has been seen in some place in north Shaanxi that fine sand grains and dust have been removed by wind action, especially in cemetries and fallow lands, leaving behind small patches of dune sand area with only the coarser sand particles. It can be seen therefore that although there is the effect of sand and silt accumulation borne from remote areas, dislodging of local soils is the main cause of the forming of the Mauwusu sand waste and Kubuqi desert, with remains of re-distributed sand and silt particles segregated from earlier deposits (Zhenda Zhu, 1980). It is readily seen from Landsat images that the dune sand mobility is very complicated in the E'erdousi area, where the dislodging effect of wind in the closed basin is very pronounced. After moving across the level highland around Zhuozi Mt, the winds in the locality have their streamlines diverged and the subsiding air current (similar to the phenomenon of hydraulic jump) will take up more sand and silt particles to carry them further southward to be deposited, or to be re-distributed locally, forming a series of depressions and ridges in the direction of the wind. Thus, the evenness of the land surface is destroyed. As water readily accumulates in the depressed areas, hollows are formed, or the moist soil favouring growth of vegetation is well covered by plants, rendering a mixed landscape of waterlogged areas, dune sands, oasis and flood plain, reflected on the Landsat images in rich blue (waterlogging), bluish green (dune sand), green (wet sandy land), red (vegetation) and brown (flood plain), together with other tones. Generally speaking, geomorphological units of small scale are brought about by wind erosion and rainwash instead of being the direct consequence of tectonic movement caused by internal geological forces. Besides, the shallow lakes and waterlogged areas are generally connected in an alignment which forms a lot of flood plains in the area adjacent to the basin with free efflux, displaying a view that the two are seemingly connected to each other or were once linked together. From this it may be concluded that the E'erdousi closed basin with a difference in elevation of only several tens of metres was formed by the force of the wind.

It may be seen from the Landsat images that the effect of landform and restrictions imposed on dune sand mobility are extremely marked. There is the mountain pass on the first route of wind-borne sand movement, linked to the Zeku basin, which permits free entry of sand carried along the first route to affect districts as far away as the upper reaches of the Tiaohe River and beyond. The main peak of Helan Mts is at an elevation of over 3200 m, whereas the desert lying to the west and the sandy land to the east have elevations of 1400-1500 m. The existence of this natural barrier alters the direction of the air current from the west in entering the Yellow River basin. It serves as a shield to prevent the E'erdousi basin lying at the north of the Yellow River valley from being turned into deserts like those to the west of the mountain range. Sheltered against wind action, well-known fertile fields and good pastures are spread in the area to the east. On the left bank of the Dousitu River on the southeastern side of Zhuozi Mt, dune sand is deposited only at a certain distance from the mountain slopes and exhibits similar crescent shapes. This shows that the area sheltered from winds has boundaries conforming to the position of the mountains. The Liupan Mts forced the second route of dune sand movement to bifurcate when entering the inner part of the Yellow River basin, whereas Luliang Mts stopped the eastward migration of dune sand altogether, being a high and solid barrier of the Fenhe River basin. The fan-shaped basin surrounded by Helan Mts, Langshan, Yinshan and Luliang Mts and Baiyu Mts causes the dune sand to whirl and accumulate while entering the E'erdousi basin. The long and narrow Kubuqi depression serves as a passage for near-surface winds, where sand dusts are readily dislodged and mobile sand deposited. All in all, sizable masses of mountains either hinder the advance of dune sand, or force the sand-laden wind currents to branch, whereas narrow depressed valleys and basins often favour the passage and deposition of dune sand.

Traces of the continuous sweeping by winds from amidst the deserts towards the loess plateau are apparent on the Landsat images. The view of dune sand mobility as displayed by the Landsat images coincides with the aeolian hypothesis, that the loess plateau was formed by wind-blown sand and dusts from central Asia finally being deposited in this locality. It can also be said that the history of the deposition of loess is the history of largescale dune sand movements in the Yellow River basin.

Dune sand mobility brought about the formation of the loess plateau in the history of geological processes and is the main cause of hyper-concentration of sediment in the Yellow River and its tributaries. In short, the loess plateau is not only an intermediate station of sediment delivery by wind and by running water, but that the combined action of the latter speeds up the development of erosion.

SUMMARY

From Landsat images, the overall effect of the accumulated result of dune sand phenomenon is seen in a large extent over a certain period of time. These are otherwise hardly discernible by using conventional pictures or diagrams. It demonstrates the superiority and high potential of the application of remote sensing to the study of the problem of dune sand movement. The mobility of dune sand is, however, a very complicated phenomenon. As regards quantitative measurements, only the area of sand deposits can be obtained from Landsat imagery. There are no other methods in use. Interpretation from Landsat images is still difficult for dune sand movements in small scale and over limited areas because of the lack of sufficient precision and accuracy, whereas sand deposits in valleys and the phenomenon of wind erosion are still to be investigated *in situ*. Efforts are to be exerted by all concerned and from different angles in a comprehensive study of the problem of dune sand.

REFERENCES

Dongsheng Liu (1964) *Loess on the Middle Reaches of the Yellow River*. Science Press.

Geological Institute, Chinese Academy of Sciences (1966) *Problems of Geology in the Quaternary Period*. Science Press.

Obrachev, V.A. (1958) The Problem of Sand and Loess. In: *Selected Works on Geography of Asia*. Science Press.

Shixun Chen (1959) *Climate of China*. Commercial Press.

Zhenda Zhu (1980) *General Outline on Deserts in China*. Science Press.

INTERNATIONAL ASSOCIATION OF HYDROLOGICAL SCIENCES

TECHNIQUES FOR PREDICTION OF RUNOFF FROM GLACIERIZED AREAS

Edited by
Gordon J. Young

149 + ix pages
price $18 (US)
IAHS Publ. no. 149
(published March 1985)
ISBN 0-947571-30-2

The **IAHS** *International Commission on Snow and Ice* **(ICSI)** designed and encouraged the snow and ice programmes of the **UNESCO** sponsored *International Hydrological Decade* **(IHD)** and *International Hydrological Programme* **(IHP).** As a result of the **IHD** and the **IHP** very considerable advances have been made in our understanding of hydrological processes in high mountain areas, and several good integrated data sets are now available for further research analysis.

This new **IAHS** publication has been produced by the **ICSI** Working Group on Prediction of Runoff from Glacierized Areas and edited by Gordon J. Young, the working group chairman. The publication opens with an overview by Gordon Young (Ottawa, Canada) which discusses the worldwide distribution of glacierized areas; how predictive techniques for runoff serve water supply and flood control; and climate and hydrological response. An overview of contemporary techniques then follows by Andrew G. Fountain (Tacoma, USA) & Wendell Tangborn (Seattle, USA). This second overview summarizes current techniques for predicting runoff from glacierized basins with emphasis on techniques for estimating the drainage of water from glaciers. The next section presents case studies as illustrations in an attempt to bring together the current knowledge and practices in hydrological predictive techniques. The wide-ranging case studies include studies of river basins of various sizes and having substantially different climatic regimes, and are separated into case studies for water supply (from Switzerland, Canada, Greenland, USSR, China and Pakistan) and case studies of catastrophic floods (USSR, Nepal, Pakistan and Canada).

ORDERS This **IAHS** publication may be ordered from any of the following addresses:

Office of the Treasurer IAHS, 2000 Florida Avenue NW, Washington, DC 20009, USA

IUGG Publications Office, 39 ter rue Gay Lussac, 75005 Paris, France

IAHS Press, Institute of Hydrology, Wallingford, Oxon OX10 8BB, UK

Please note that unless instructed otherwise the publication will be sent by surface mail and delivery to some destinations outside Europe and North America may take up to six months. Air mail postage is extra. Prepayment is welcomed but not obligatory.

A catalogue of all IAHS titles may also be obtained free of charge from any of the above addresses.